1992
Yearbook
of Science
and the
Future

1992

Yearbook of Science and the Future

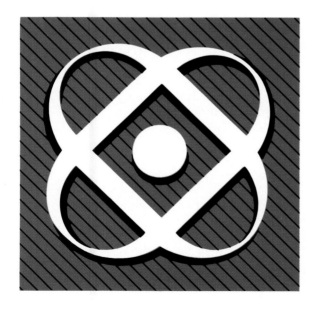

Encyclopædia

Britannica, Inc.

Chicago
Auckland
Geneva
London
Madrid
Manila
Paris
Rome
Seoul
Sydney
Tokyo
Toronto

1992
Yearbook
of Science
and the
Future

The University of Chicago
The Yearbook of Science and the Future is published with the editorial advice of the faculties of the University of Chicago.

Encyclopædia Britannica, Inc.

Editor
David Calhoun

Associate Editor
Charles Cegielski

Editorial Staff
Daphne Daume, Karen Justin,
Arthur Latham, Melinda Shepherd

Creative Director, Art
Cynthia Peterson

Operations Manager, Art
Marsha Mackenzie

Senior Picture Editor
Kathy Nakamura

Picture Editors
Harriett Hiland, April A. Oswald

Layout Artists and Illustrators
Kathryn Diffley, John L. Draves,
John J. Mahoney, Stephanie Motz

Art Production Supervisor
Richard A. Roiniotis

Art Staff
Patricia A. Henle, Margaret Liebezeit,
Diana M. Pitstick

Manager, Copy Department
Anita Wolff

Senior Copy Editors
Julian Ronning, Barbara Whitney

Copy Staff
Lynette Bertsche, Elizabeth A. Blowers,
Madolynn Cronk, Ellen Finkelstein,
David Gottlieb

Manager, Production Control
Mary C. Srodon

Production Control Staff
Marilyn L. Barton, Stephanie A. Green, Lee Anne Wiggins

Manager, Composition/Page Makeup
Melvin Stagner

Coordinator, Composition/Page Makeup
Michael Born, Jr.

Composition/Page Makeup Staff
Eram A. Ahmad, Griselda Cháidez, Duangnetra Debhavalya,
Carol A. Gaines, Vertreasa Hunt, John Krom, Jr.,
Thomas J. Mulligan, Arnell Reed, Gwen E. Rosenberg,
Tammy Tsou, Danette Wetterer

Contents

Encyclopædia Britannica Science Update

The Science Year in Review

A Science Classic

Institutions of Science

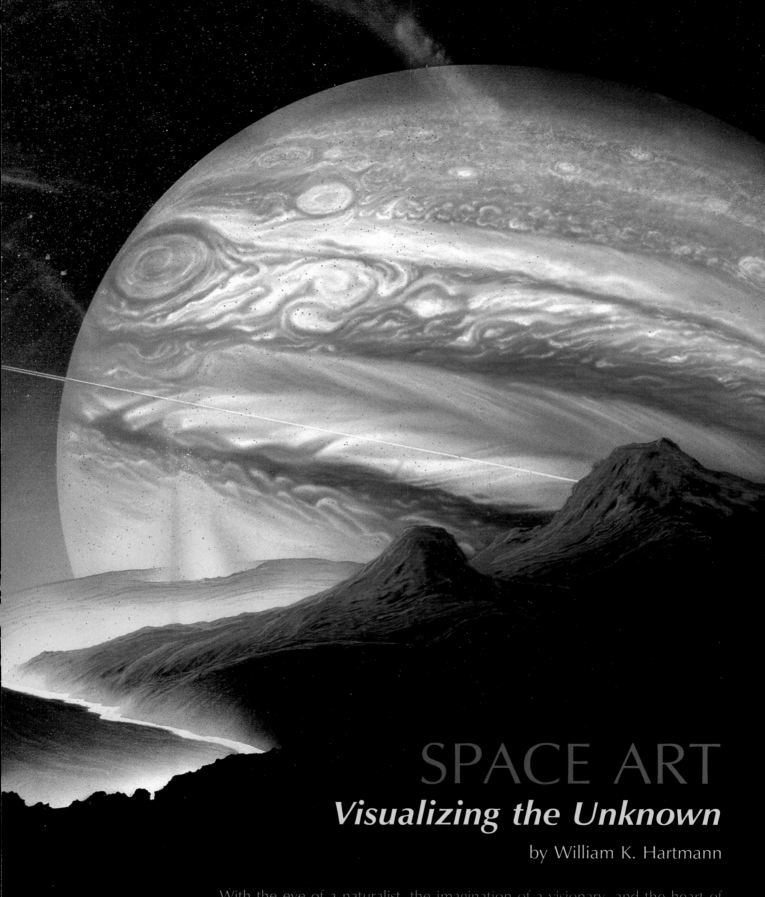

SPACE ART

Visualizing the Unknown

by William K. Hartmann

With the eye of a naturalist, the imagination of a visionary, and the heart of an Apollo astronaut, artists of a special breed are working to bring the grand adventure of cosmic exploration to people everywhere.

WILLIAM K. HARTMANN is an Astronomical Artist and an Astronomer with Science Applications International Corp., Tucson, Arizona. He is lead editor of In the Stream of Stars, a collection of Soviet and American space art.

(Overleaf) Jupiter viewed from the volcanic surface of its moon Io; painting by Kazuaki Iwasaki—Space Art International

Space artists are heirs to the 19th-century artist-naturalist tradition that captured the wonders of the New World on canvas. Thomas Moran's "The Grand Canyon of the Yellowstone" (1872) and other renderings of the Yellowstone region made a powerful impression on the public, helping to create a new national appreciation of the American wilderness.

As Soviet cosmonauts make yearlong sojourns in the *Mir* space station and as the United States launches probes to Jupiter and Venus, the frontier of human exploration continues to expand off the Earth. Unmanned spacecraft from Europe, Japan, and the Soviet Union have sailed past Halley's Comet. As our bodies and our machine-expanded minds move into this new environment, our aesthetic impulses follow.

Or do they lead the way?

Long before the first Sputnik of 1957, a select breed of artists began taking their inspiration from astronomical discoveries of the day. For more than a century now, they have fashioned dramatic but realistic views of scenes far beyond the Earth, where no humans have ever visited. Like artists who have re-created the past worlds of the trilobite and the dinosaur, they have reveled in the challenge of understanding the latest scientific findings, and then—putting facts, figures, photos, and fantasies together—they have imagined scenes that may really exist but have never been seen.

For want of a better name, modern artists of this school have evolved the term *space art* for their work. Space artists are inspired by the human, intellectual adventure of exploring the cosmic environment. They portray vistas of other planets, moons, asteroids, comets, and star systems; events in the past, present, and future of the universe; and subjective visions of human space exploration. Their paintings, whether photographically realistic or more abstract and nonrepresentational, are informed by astronomical knowledge.

National Museum of American Art, Smithsonian Institution, lent by the U.S. Department of the Interior, Office of the Secretary; photo, Art Resource

"Cotopaxi," oil on canvas by Frederic Edwin Church, 1862; 121.9 cm × 215.9 cm; © The Detroit Institute of Arts, Founders Society Purchase, Robert H. Tannahill Foundation, Gibbs-Williams, Dexter M. Ferry, Jr., Merrill, Beatrice W. Rogers, and Richard A. Manoogian Funds

West into space

Paradoxically, this art of the space age has roots in the experience of the American frontier. Art as an expression of human interaction with nature, although unfashionable in modern painting, was the dominant influence in 19th-century American art, as well as during the flowering of Impressionism in Europe. As Barbara Novak chronicled in *Nature and Culture: American Landscape and Painting 1825–1875* (1980), the American landscape movement of the 1800s, with its Luminist and Romantic nature painters such as Frederic Church, Thomas Moran, and Albert Bierstadt, grew from a national feeling that the American wilderness was a vast Garden of Eden, a divine gift spread across the new continent for humans to explore, revere, and use. The prevailing thought was that all three activities were possible at once, if a rational approach to nature prevailed. Many painters made trips to the Western frontier as members of major geographic and scientific survey expeditions. John Kensett went in 1854, Bierstadt in 1859, and Moran in 1871. Church, who had become wealthy from his early paintings, organized his own expeditions to nature's most extraordinary locales, including South American volcanoes, tropical forests, and Arctic seas.

These artists made pictures that acquainted the "folks back home" with the natural wonders of the New World. They were cousins of the scientists; they wanted to see even the most alien handiworks of nature, to know how things looked, and to find out why they are the way they are. Studying the luminous glow of sky and cloud under different conditions, sensing the swell of the prairies, or depicting newly discovered geysers, artists transformed the national view of land from adversarial to

Frederic Church's "Cotopaxi" (1862) acquainted spectators with the exotic locale of an active Ecuadoran volcano. Church organized his own expeditions to South America, the Arctic, and the Near East, seeking the most alien of nature's handiworks as subject matter for his monumental landscapes.

11

Space art began in the late 19th century with strong ties to commercial illustration. By that time, the old, astrological view of the universe beyond Earth had given way to scientific realism: objects in space obeyed known physical laws, while planets and their satellites were geologic bodies similar to the Earth. An illustration from Jules Verne's novel From the Earth to the Moon *(right) depicts the weightlessness that would be experienced by space travelers once outside Earth's gravitational pull. A turn-of-the-century lunar landscape (above), from the fictional* Un mundo desconocido dos años en la Luna *("A World Unknown: Two Years on the Moon"; 1898) by Pierre de Sélènes, details a rugged, cratered surface devoid of atmosphere.*

awe-inspiring. The scale of some of their paintings matched the land's grandeur. For instance, Moran's famous 1872 painting of the Grand Canyon measured 2.1 by 3.7 meters (7 by 12 feet) and received adulation in literary magazines of the day.

Playing a role that is now largely forgotten, artists contributed to the preservation of American natural wonders. Moran's paintings of the Yellowstone region during the expedition of 1871 so enthralled the public that Yellowstone was designated the first U.S. national park by Pres. Ulysses S. Grant a year later. Moran became known as Thomas "Yellowstone" Moran and adopted a monogram designed from the letters TYM.

These artists also encouraged exploration and adventure. Moran used the "Artist's Adventures" column of the popular *Century Magazine* to chronicle his arduous 1892 trip to Devils Tower, Wyoming's tremendous stump of columnar basalt. The article appeared in 1894, and partly as a result, Pres. Theodore Roosevelt made Devils Tower the first U.S. national monument a dozen years later.

Today's space artists are heirs to this artist-naturalist tradition. The frontier, now the cosmos beyond the Earth, still beckons space artists, who use information from today's scientific expeditions—space-probe photos, maps, and telescope data—to summon up views of exotic places on this frontier. They rely on their creativity to make these scenes at once realistic, aesthetic, and dramatic. Furthermore, they can bring the exotic to the "folks back home" and thus inflame a new generation of explorers. Perhaps, like their forebears, they will even inspire a future system of international nature preserves in space.

Rudaux: the first master

Not by accident, astronomical painting evolved during the era of the naturalist painters, as a parallel stream of artistic endeavor. Its beginnings, however, had stronger ties to commercial illustration than fine art. In 1865 Jules Verne's novel *From the Earth to the Moon* carried the first scientifically realistic illustrations of scenes beyond Earth. Verne was in the habit of checking the illustrations for his books for geographic and astronomical authenticity. By that time the old view of planets as ethereal astrological entities had given way to the new concept of the plurality of worlds; planets were Earthlike places having landforms, seasons, and sometimes atmospheres. Charles Darwin's evolutionary ideas raised the possibility that these alien landscapes might have witnessed the appearance of extraterrestrial life. Science-fiction novels from the 1860s onward abounded with early sketches of extraterrestrial scenes.

The first master, and the grandfather, of modern astronomical painting was the Frenchman Lucien Rudaux (1874–1947), an artist, writer, and active amateur astronomer. His portraits of the lunar landscape offer a brilliant example of the way in which his close observations allowed him to imagine lunar scenes correctly. In the pre-Apollo days the Moon's surface was widely perceived to be a mass of jagged pinnacles, yet Rudaux's paintings show the gently rounded lunar mountains as astronauts later photographed them. How did Rudaux manage to get this detail right? In his own small observatory he used a telescope to observe the true profiles of the lunar mountains on the edge of the lunar disk. He then noted correctly that others had been misled by telescopic photographs taken at very low Sun angles, which exaggerated the Moon's apparent roughness by showing long spiky shadows.

With similar attention to accuracy, he calculated how Saturn and its rings would appear if seen from the positions of various moons, whose distances from Saturn were well known. As a final example, after studying Mars telescopically, he painted pinkish dust storms as might be seen by an observer on the Martian surface. As for Mars's daytime sky, Rudaux and other early space artists usually colored it the hue astronomers advised—a dark blue because of the planet's very thin atmosphere, like that

Careful studies through the telescope allowed Lucien Rudaux (top) to imagine planetary scenes with an accuracy of detail that would wait decades for astronauts and interplanetary space probes to confirm. After observing Mars, Rudaux painted the planet with pinkish dust storms (center; from Sur les autres mondes), one of the few early representations of Mars showing pink tones in part of the sky. Telescopic observations of the true profile of the lunar mountains on the edge of the lunar disk moved Rudaux to render gently rounded mountains on the Moon (bottom) rather than the jagged pinnacles envisioned by others.

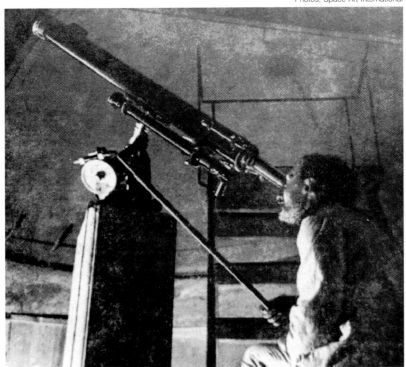

on Earth 30 kilometers (100,000 feet) up. This mistake was repeated by all astronomers, and hence artists, until July 20, 1976, when the Viking 1 lander's cameras first revealed that the sky on Mars is bright and faintly pinkish owing to airborne red dust blown off the Martian surface. Rudaux's prescient dust-storm picture is one of the few early representations of Mars having pink tones in part of the sky.

Rudaux's 1937 book *Sur les autres mondes* ("On Other Worlds") featured masterly illustrations of an incredible variety of space phenomena. He was honored in 1990 with an exhibition of his paintings (along with those of his artist father and grandfather) in the museum of his hometown of Granville, France.

Bonestell: "mathematician with a paintbrush"

Rudaux is called the grandfather of space art because another figure has come to be recognized as its father: Chesley Bonestell (1888–1986). Bonestell's masterwork was the 1949 color-illustrated *The Conquest of Space*, with text by space expert Willy Ley. Perhaps more than any other set of

With such now-classic works as "Exploring the Moon, " from the 1949 book The Conquest of Space, *Chesley Bonestell inspired not only the next generation of space artists but also many youngsters who would later become scientists and engineers involved in astronomy and space exploration during the Apollo era and afterward.*

15

images, this book exemplifies the inspirational aspect of space art, for it encouraged not only a whole new generation of space artists but also a great number of the scientists and technicians in the current space program. Its most famous painting shows a silvery rocket poised on the lunar surface behind astronauts exploring shadowy lava crags. A historic work, it predated actual manned lunar flights by almost 20 years and colored the dreams of youngsters who would later become Apollo engineers and scientists. In 1973 the painting was included along with cave art from Lascaux, France, in a London *Sunday Times Magazine* article covering the 1,000 most influential paintings and sculpture of Western art.

Bonestell also became famous among the generation that led human beings into space for his illustrations of a series of articles by Wernher von Braun and other rocket scientists in *Collier's* magazine in the early 1950s. These influential features showed how it was possible with contemporary engineering to launch satellites into orbit, build a space station, and send astronauts to the Moon. They were a direct antecedent of the Soviet and U.S. programs that put the first artificial satellites into

orbit in the late 1950s. Jules Verne said, "What one person can imagine, another person can do." Bonestell imagined; the engineers did the doing.

How did Bonestell achieve such an impact with his paintings? More so than Rudaux, Bonestell was trained in geometry and drafting. He studied and worked in architecture for years before becoming Hollywood's highest-paid special-effects matte artist in the 1930s and 1940s. He painted backdrops for such famous films as *The Hunchback of Notre Dame* (1939) and *Citizen Kane* (1941). This training gave him the skills needed to make incredibly photo-realist scenes of planets and space vehicles as contemporary astronomers and rocket pioneers believed they would look. Coauthor Ley called Bonestell "a poetical mathematician with a paintbrush." Bonestell bragged to Ley that he could draw from imagination alone the reflection of a chair as seen from a specific angle in a mirror that was tipped from the wall at a different angle.

Bonestell, a boyhood hero of mine, received me in his Carmel, California, home on several occasions. Even at age 90, he would enthusiastically climb to the upstairs studio off his back porch to paint a revised planetary landscape when a new spacecraft photo came in. With a twinkle in his eye, he would offer curmudgeonly criticism of young artists who had the temerity to attempt an extraterrestrial scene. He chuckled malevolently as he noted that Norman Rockwell got the shadow directions wildly

Bonestell's contributions to space art continued into his 90s. The painting above, showing the mining of an asteroid for metals and other raw materials, was done in 1976 when the artist was 88.

17

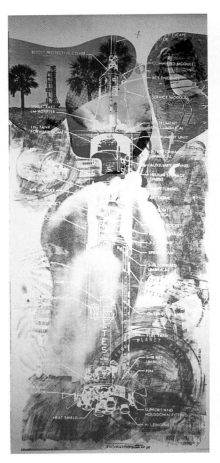

The room-high lithograph "Sky Garden" (above), one of the "Stoned Moon" series by American painter and graphic artist Robert Rauschenberg, was done for NASA's Fine Arts Program. "Soyuz Rendezvous with Salyut 7" (right) embodies the realism characteristic of the work of Andrei Sokolov, who is widely regarded as the dean of Soviet space artists.

wrong in a painting made to celebrate the Apollo Moon landings. (The Earth in the sky was lit from one direction, the foreground lunar landscape from another.)

Though Bonestell's art long was known to space enthusiasts, wider tributes began to come in his last years. A number of Bonestell originals are in the collection of the National Air and Space Museum, Washington, D.C., and are occasionally displayed in its gallery of aviation and space art. Two books of space paintings were dedicated to him in 1981, one by California space artist Don Dixon and the other by Virginia-based space artist Ron Miller and myself. A biography and retrospective collection of his work appeared in *Worlds Beyond: The Art of Chesley Bonestell*, published in 1983 by Miller and space authority and art dealer Frederick

Durant III. A few months before Bonestell died in 1986, an asteroid was named in his honor, much to his satisfaction. Following this lead, and as a result of my own work in asteroid astronomy, I suggested that another be named for Rudaux, an honor bestowed in 1988.

In their footsteps

In recent years Rudaux and Bonestell have had many followers. Arizona artist Robert McCall, for example, has painted giant, dramatic murals of space travel for the Air and Space Museum and the National Aeronautics and Space Administration's (NASA's) Johnson Space Center, Houston, Texas, and has designed several U.S. postage stamps featuring space missions. Space art also flourishes in the Soviet Union, where McCall's closest counterpart is Andrei Sokolov, who knows many cosmonauts, has visited Soviet launch facilities, and has sent sketches into orbit to be annotated and corrected by cosmonauts. Sokolov is recognized for his realistic depictions of Soviet spaceships and space stations and of events during specific missions.

American space artist Robert McCall is known internationally for the range of his illustrations, which include conceptual art for feature films, designs for postage stamps (left) and NASA mission patches, and giant murals for museums and space facilities. A section of a mural on space travel, done by McCall for the National Air and Space Museum, Washington, D.C., is shown above.

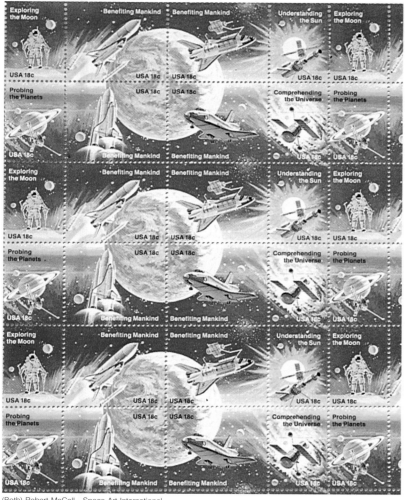

(Both) Robert McCall—Space Art International

Space art continues to find a home in a variety of applications. American artist Carter Emmart is known for work that conceptualizes engineering design studies for future spacecraft and programs. Illustrated above is a Mars base making use of empty cargo landers as living quarters and inflatable, partly pressurized greenhouses for growing food. The painting is one of a series detailing the mounting of a manned mission to Mars. (Opposite page) The astronomical paintings of Chesley Bonestell exhibited in "fine art" style draw interest from young visitors to a planetarium gallery.

In the 1960s NASA began a Fine Arts Program that gives artists small grants and takes them to launches and other important space events; in exchange the artist creates a major piece for NASA's art collection. The early years of the program drew a number of artists well known in other genres, such as Robert Rauschenberg, Jamie Wyeth, and Wilson Hurley. In recent years it has been open to younger artists.

Meanwhile, a band of new artists specializing in space themes have evolved from the experience of growing up in the space age. In 1982 I invited a group of them to a workshop to sketch from nature among the craters and lavas of Hawaii Volcanoes National Park. So successful was this venture that they met again in 1983 in Death Valley, California, and voted to form the International Association for the Astronomical Arts (IAAA). The IAAA has since conducted several painting workshops in exotic geologic terrains, such as volcanic lava fields, deserts, and glaciers, chosen to simulate landscapes on other planets.

In 1987 an IAAA delegation was invited to Moscow to share in the 30th anniversary of the Sputnik I launch, an event that led to a joint program with the Union of Artists of the U.S.S.R., which also promotes space painting. Together, Soviet painters and an IAAA group toured the Marslike outback of Iceland in 1988 and held Soviet-American workshops and exhibitions in Moscow and California in 1989. These activities show that space art has blossomed into a truly planet-wide enterprise and now reflects broad human reactions to space exploration.

Many applications, one passion

In recent decades the applications of space art have continued in several of the directions pioneered by Rudaux and Bonestell: pure art, educational illustration, science-fiction illustration, and special effects. Some practitioners, such as Dennis Davidson in New York and Geoffrey Chandler in California, emphasize the fine-art approach and exhibit their work in galleries. IAAA president Kara Szathmary, of Quebec, teaches physics and paints to show broad metaphoric relationships between science, art, and creativity. California artist Carter Emmart and Washington artist Paul Hudson are noted for paintings that conceptualize various engineering design studies for future spacecraft. Los Angeles artist Rick Sternbach, known for science-fiction covers, more recently has spent time doing special-effects paintings and computer graphics for Carl Sagan's "Cosmos" TV series, the *Star Trek* film and second TV series, and other films.

Yet other artists have developed reputations for their paintings for books and periodicals. San Diego artist Michael Carroll, who works in a planetarium, has written and illustrated a number of magazine articles about astronomy. Miller, California artist Pamela Lee, English artist David Hardy, and others have illustrated both scientific books and books of science fiction. Collections of astronomical paintings have been published in book form by Dixon and by Miller, Lee, and myself. Hardy has edited an international collection of space art, and Sokolov, Miller, Soviet artist Vitalie Myagkov, and I have published *In the Stream of Stars* (1990), a collection of space art resulting from the joint Soviet-IAAA efforts mentioned above. The applications of space art seem limited only by culture and the human imagination.

Behind the applications lie the real reasons that most astronomical artists started painting scenes of space: personal passion for the adventure of cosmic exploration and personal satisfaction in expressing it. It is remarkable that the space art community has come together from extremely diverse roots. Some possess art school education, but others are self-taught. Many started in other fields, including science, but wanted to express something beyond the bounds of their formal training. Some lean toward the traditions of fine art and others toward those of magazine illustration. What unifies them is a desire to show the fantastic settings of other worlds and the effects of space exploration on the human experience.

World building

How do artists manage to visualize the unknown? How do they make realistic depictions of other planetary and stellar environments? First, of course, is their reliance on astronomical information. Astronomers make measurements of the sizes of distant worlds, their colors, their compositional properties, their atmospheres and clouds, and other characteristics.

Courtesy, The Adler Planetarium, Chicago, Ill.; photo, Cathy Melloan

21

Space art records the history of humanity's changing conceptions of the cosmos, as can be seen from a comparison of several paintings of Saturn's moon Titan made over the past half century. In the 1940s, soon after the discovery of an atmosphere for Titan was announced, Chesley Bonestell created a classic image of Saturn poised in a clear blue sky over Titan's surface (right). In the early 1970s, responding to astronomers' evidence for some clouds or haze over Titan, artist Ron Miller painted a sky no longer completely dominated by the ringed gas giant (below). A few years later, new evidence for all-enveloping clouds over Titan elicited a painting from William K. Hartmann having a viewpoint above the moon's cloud deck (opposite page, left). Finally, when the Voyager space probes showed in the early 1980s that Titan's haze completely obscured its surface, Miller offered a conception of an extremely dark and overcast landscape pelted by "snow" flurries of organic compounds (opposite page, right).

Ron Miller—Space Art International

But these data do not directly give a sense of how it actually would feel to visit these worlds. Worse yet, different astronomers specialize in different types of measurements. One publishes on mineralogy of a planet, another on spectra observed through a telescope, another on atmospheric calculation. They may express these measurements in technical jargon, and rarely do they put it all together to imagine how the planet would actually be perceived by a human visitor. This synthesis is the task of the artist, who must bring all the data into one picture. Thus, as a first step, astronomical artists must be interested in astronomy. Most artists in the IAAA, for example, developed a passion for space early on, often as they watched the first manned flights and lunar landings on television in the 1960s and 1970s. Usually they subscribe to such magazines as *Sky and Telescope* and *Astronomy*.

By following astronomical discoveries, artists not only receive inspiration but also record history. To take a specific example, Dutch-American astronomer Gerard P. Kuiper discovered the only instance of a thick atmosphere around a planetary satellite—that of Saturn's moon Titan—in 1944. Immediately, Bonestell realized that an atmosphere, by means of the process known as Rayleigh scattering of blue light, could create a blue sky. He saw a chance for a unique painting (space painters tire of black skies): Saturn, hanging in an ethereal blue sky over the snowfields of Titan. The result became one of Bonestell's most famous works, appearing on the back cover of *The Conquest of Space*. In the early 1970s, however, astronomers found that Titan's atmosphere contained substantial reddish haze or clouds. Artists like Miller and David Egge of St. Paul, Minnesota, responded with new views of the moon's

23

Visits to exotic geologic sites on Earth, often carried out as part of organized workshops, assist space artists in visualizing planetary processes on alien worlds. Sketching the landforms and wind-sculpted dunes at Monument Valley in the U.S. Southwest (above) may help an artist picture a Martian landscape, while studying the crater rim of Kilauea on Hawaii Island (opposite page) may inspire a new view of a extinct volcano on the Moon or of an erupting volcano on Jupiter's satellite Io.

landscape showing Saturn peeking through the clouds. A few years later, new evidence indicated that the clouds were very thick and might pass little light to the surface. Miller responded with a late 1970s painting, a nostalgic look at Titan's surface with a misty Saturn dimly glowing through the thick haze. As the Voyager space probes arrived at Saturn in 1980 and 1981, scientists hoped that at least a few thin spots in the clouds might give views of the surface of Titan (or, conversely, from the artist's point of view, views of Saturn from Titan). Alas, the probes showed that Titan's haze completely blocked the surface. Their measurements indicated a thick nitrogen-methane atmosphere and a gloomy surface possibly pelted with snows and rains of various complex organic compounds. Consequently, new paintings emerged of dark skies, storms, and possible rivers and oceans.

To dismiss the early paintings in this sequence as "wrong" would be a mistake. Rather, they provide a unique, invaluable historical record of humanity's fast-changing conceptualization of Titan. Where else can one get an idea of how a distant moon was perceived in the 1940s or the 1970s and contemplate an aesthetic creative effort at the same time?

Another visualization technique used by space artists, mentioned above, is to become familiar with actual planetary processes by visiting appropriate geologic sites on Earth. An artist who grows up amid the wooded hillsides and river valleys of the U.S. East Coast or England

24

William K. Hartmann

will have a hard time rendering the dusty plains of Mars or the impact craters of the Moon. It is for this reason that the IAAA has organized workshops at such sites as volcanoes, deserts, glaciers, and wind-sculpted landforms. At Meteor Crater, Arizona, for example, an artist can hike and sketch on the rim of an actual crater 1.2 kilometers (0.75 mile) wide that was formed some 20,000 years ago when an asteroid fragment crashed into the American Southwest. It is the same kind of crater that pocks the Moon, Mars, Mercury, and most satellites.

Sitting in the sun in the midst of such a landscape, the artist absorbs qualities of the land that can never be communicated by photos. In drawing a scene, one experiences the sensation that it travels into the eyes, through the brain, down the arm, and out the fingers onto the paper. Human and landscape become part of one another. The rock textures, the way sunlight reflects from the rocks and sands, the colors in the shadows—all begin to enter the consciousness and make one's painting of a moon or planet that much more honest and natural.

To the help in visualization provided by recent astronomical information and by the study of earthly landscapes can be added an acquaintance with esoteric physical effects. One example is the heiligenschein—the luminous glow, appearing on textured surfaces, that surrounds a point 180° away from the Sun, partly because of the disappearance of shadows at this antisolar point. It often can be seen on dewy grass in the morning, surrounding the shadow of the observer's own head like a halo (hence the German term, which means "holy glow"). The microscopic texture of the powdery lunar soil produces a strong heiligenschein, which showed up on astronauts' photos of the Moon's surface. Presumably, powdery surfaces on other airless worlds would do the same.

Other phenomena in this category include different-sized halos around the Sun (produced by atmospheric ice crystals of varying compositions) and sky colors of pink (produced on Mars by reddish, rust-stained air-borne dust), yellowish tan (produced on Venus by light filtering through a perpetual overcast of sulfuric-acid clouds), and blue (produced on the Earth by Rayleigh scattering of light among gas molecules).

Yet another tool of astronomical artists is purely mathematical. Suppose one wants to render a planet as seen from a certain distance in space or from the surface of a moon that orbits at a certain distance. To create this view accurately, one really needs to know how big the planet will look in the sky. For this purpose, one must think of size in terms of angular measure, which is expressed in degrees. For example, a normal (50-mm) lens on a standard single-lens-reflex camera takes a picture about 40° wide. (Telephoto and wide-angle lenses typically cover a range of angular widths, from about 10° to 100° or more.) The Moon's diameter covers an angle of only 0.5° as seen from the Earth and thus takes up a surprisingly tiny $\frac{1}{80}$ of the width of a normal 40° picture, despite the illusion of size it presents to human eyes, especially as it comes up over the horizon.

It is easy to determine how large the Earth looks from the Moon. The Earth's diameter is four times that of the Moon, and an astronaut on

25

The painting by Pamela Lee of an astronaut standing on Jupiter's icy moon Europa (right) incorporates an esoteric physical effect called the heiligenschein, which appears as a luminous glow surrounding the head of the astronaut's shadow reflected in the faceplate. Pink sky color, a phenomenon produced on Mars by reddish airborne dust, was properly incorporated into Swiss artist Ludek Pesek's conceptualization of a Martian landscape (opposite page, top), done after the 1976 Viking Mars landings. In another Pamela Lee work (opposite page, bottom), multiple halos and sun dogs, created by the light from four suns reflecting and refracting through thin ice-crystal clouds, shimmer above the sea on an imaginary oceanic planet.

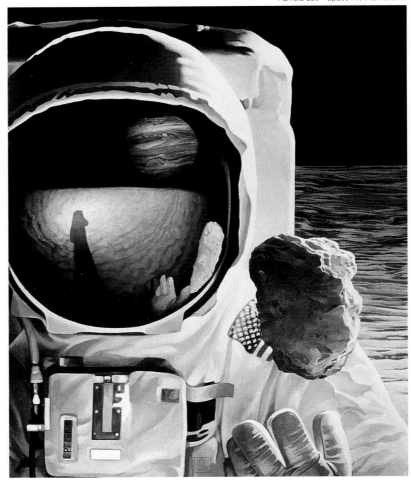

the Moon is as far away from the Earth as we are from the Moon. Thus, the Earth looks four times larger than the Moon looks to us; that is, $4 \times 0.5°$, or $2°$, in diameter.

As for the situation with other planets, some math is involved. If D represents the diameter (in linear measure) of the planet or moon and X represents the distance of the observer from the center of that body, then the angular diameter A, in degrees, of the planet or moon is given approximately by $A = 57.3(D/X)$.

This rule of thumb works well as long as the answer is less than about 30°. For all angles, large or small, the precise formula involves the trigonometric tangent function and is $\tan (A/2) = D/2X$. In other words, the angular diameter of any body in the sky is twice the angle whose tangent is $D/2X$.

With such formulations the artist can choose the angular width of the artwork and then correctly indicate the size of the object in the sky. It is reasonable to ask whether this is a hollow exercise, because the artist can always find an angular picture width such that the sky object fills, say, a fourth of the picture. In some cases, however, such a choice

26

would result in a very wide-angle picture and in others a telephoto view. In subtle ways these constraints in turn would affect foreground objects and lighting angles. The astronomical artist needs to exert firm control over whether the scene is to be perceived as a wide-angle view, a normal view, or a telephoto view and consequently over the appearance of such foreground features as craters or spacecraft, as well as over the appearance of the distant planet or moon that may be present in the sky.

There are other geometric and physical rules that must be observed for realism and scientific accuracy. For example, the horns of a crescent

27

Moon always point away from the Sun (a fact that many comic-strip artists do not know or ignore). Comet tails usually point away from the Sun because they are being blown by gases of the solar wind. Space art thus presents an exciting challenge to understand a vast variety of natural phenomena—and to get them right on canvas.

Straddling the cultural gap

Decades ago British scientist and novelist C.P. Snow wrote of a gap between the "two cultures"—science on the one hand and the arts and humanities on the other—that makes mutual understanding and communication virtually impossible. Space artists bridge this gap or, rather, they see no necessity for it.

Space artists and space scientists are both naturalists, although they ask different kinds of questions. As noted above, scientists are analyzers: they subdivide phenomena until they isolate areas where quantitative measurements can be made. In contrast, space artists are synthesizers: they combine all this accumulated knowledge to create an experience of an alien world—the sights and feelings associated with physically being there.

In some sense, space artists must link the two halves of the brain in order to practice both the analytic functions of the left hemisphere and the spatial perceptiveness and synthesizing functions of the right. Some observers have questioned whether the institutions of science and technology do not focus too much on the analytic functions at the expense of synthesis. At the same time, artists perhaps accept too little input from the logic-oriented talents of the left brain. Hence, the stereotypes of the narrowly focused mad scientist who never perceives the impact of his discoveries on society and of the eccentric artist who is detached from reality and promotes irrational systems of belief. Great creators, like Leonardo da Vinci, have been notable for their ability to combine analysis and synthesis.

Scientists indeed can be remarkably immune to the human side of their discoveries. For example, I once attended a scientific meeting in which a researcher described the newly discovered cloud of sodium vapor around Jupiter's volcanic moon, Io. He expressed his measurement of the yellow glow emanating from the cloud in kilorayleighs, a proper but obscure scientific unit of brightness. Sensing the artistic potential for a view of yellow auroral glows in the sky over Io's volcanic plains, I asked if this value corresponded to a brightness perceivable to the human eye. He had not considered the possibility and did not know. Later we found another researcher who remembered how many kilorayleighs correspond to visible auroras on Earth, allowing us to conclude that Io's yellow glow would probably be bright enough to be seen sometimes by a human visitor on Io. Yet it seemed noteworthy that scientists can spend months measuring the intensity of something and then have no idea what that intensity means as a sensory experience.

On the other hand, mainstream artists often are divorced from the realities revealed by the scientific method. Although this split may be

28

Painting by William K. Hartmann, adapted from nature at Kilauea Volcano, Hawaii

true today, it was not always so. After all, the 19th-century Impressionists were well acquainted with the latest discoveries and theories about light and carefully studied the perception of light themselves. It was only after they had unleashed the power of bright pigments that the dominant movements in 20th-century art moved away from a base in external nature toward a base in internal feeling. Colors and pigments came to be used for their own sake as artists sought to project internal feelings that were detached from constraints imposed by outside "reality." This factor surely contributed to the separation of Snow's two cultures.

Artists inspired by astronomical discoveries reverse the separation by returning to practical questions about the physical universe. For instance, what pigment colors would best match the various spectra measured by astronomers looking at different worlds through telescopes? How does light interact with various planetary rock and soil types? How is light colored by various atmospheres? Although space art remains aesthetically motivated, the work requires more answers from the study of physical phenomena than does much of contemporary art.

Toward an art worthy of its subject
Although one may talk of scientific reality, the proof of the pudding lies in the art. Is there art—a sustainable, creative, aesthetic impulse—in space art? Is there a future for the field?

Delicate yellow auroral glows emanating from sodium vapor appear in the sky of Io in a painting by William K. Hartmann. Although researchers had discovered the existence of the moon's sodium auroras and had expressed their brightness in scientifically proper units of measurement, it remained for a space artist to establish that the glows could sometimes be bright enough to be seen by a human observer.

29

Encouragingly, the subject matter appears virtually limitless. The astronauts' lunar touchdowns and the Viking landings on Mars occurred at rather dull, flat sites, chosen to ensure spacecraft safety. Even the sites reached and photographed by Soviet probes on the Venusian surface were chosen at random, since no maps were available to tell in advance what topography lay below the planet's clouds. Thus, humans have not yet witnessed the most vivid landscapes of the Moon, Mars, Venus, or other worlds. It is as if a few daguerreotypes had been made at random spots on the plains and hills of the Western frontier, and civilization had still to witness the Yellowstones and Yosemites sought out by Moran, Bierstadt, and their kin. But, as Arizona space artist Kim Poor has said, painters can swoop down into craters, volcanoes, and fissures too dangerous for the engineers. And as for the astrophysicists' pulsars, black holes, and binary stars that lie far beyond Pluto, there is no prospect in the forseeable future of photographing them at close range. Only artists can "visit" them.

Here again one can draw a parallel with the American landscape artists of the 19th century. Those people spoke of "the sublime"—a term used during the romantic revolution for scenes that evoked wonder, awe, or even terror. Erupting volcanoes, jagged ice chasms, flaming auroras, and crimson sunsets bearing portents of storms—these were sublime. In today's pasteurized environment the term has all but disappeared and might evoke visions of nothing more exciting than a down comforter. Yet in the late 20th century, anyone struck with awe by the silent explosions of Io, the red smog layers of Titan, or the desolate polar dune fields of Mars must know "the sublime" in the sense sought after by the Beethovens, Shelleys, and Morans of old.

At present the future of space art seems to lie somewhere between fine art and illustration. In emotional approach it is more like the former, but in technical background it is more like the latter. Discussions among its practitioners have revealed some frustration with this state of affairs, particularly in their dealings with the art editors of commercial magazines, many of whom are trained more in design than content. Artists have shared horror stories of their great effort to achieve realism during an assignment, only to be frustrated by an art director's request for a color change to achieve better harmony with something else in the magazine. On the other hand, the growing awareness of astronomical paintings as fine art has translated into more exhibitions for the genre.

As space exploration continues, interest in space art should broaden. There may even come a future when art historians as well as scientists reflect on the work of the painters who documented humanity's early conceptualizations of new worlds. One can hope that, as the first generation to take humanity off the Earth, we also create an art that is worthy of that historic adventure.

See also *1989 Yearbook of Science and the Future* Feature Article: RELIGION, REALITY, AND RELATIVITY: THE SCIENTIFIC TRADITION IN ART.

As David Hardy's whimsical "Self-Portrait on Io" (opposite page) suggests, space artists' successful synthesis of imagination and scientific knowledge allows them to "visit" worlds no human eyes have seen and to bring back the adventure of space exploration to a wide audience. As did their 19th-century forebears, they seek to communicate "the sublime" in nature, be it as near as a multicolored patchwork of land, sea, and sky viewed from low Earth orbit or as distant as a panorama of the universe seen from the edge of the Milky Way (below, by Pamela Lee).

Paintings, Space Art International; (opposite page) David A. Hardy; (above) Pamela Lee

Colors for a Cosmic Canvas

by David H. Clark

In the final decade of the 20th century, astronomers stand on the brink of a new understanding of the heavens as an advanced generation of space observatories extends the portrait of the unseen universe.

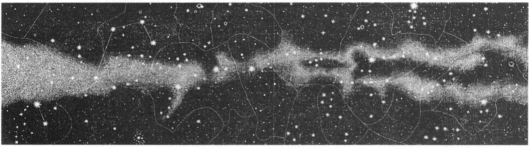

Just as rational investigation changed humankind's early ideas of the cosmos, data from new research are changing current ideas. To ancient Egyptians, the world comprised deities who accounted for the sky, Earth, and air (top left). Later, medieval Europeans saw the universe as a set of concentric spheres centered on hell and moving outward through the Earth, planets, and Sun to the fixed stars (top right). In the 19th century, the Earth belonged to a universe of stars seen in the sky as the Milky Way (above). Today the Milky Way is known to be but one galaxy among billions, as suggested by the map (right) of some two million galaxies, the result of a recent survey covering a small fraction of the observable universe.

DAVID H. CLARK is Deputy Director, Programmes, Science and Engineering Research Council, Swindon, England. His books include Superstars, The Quest for SS433, and The Cosmos from Space.

(Overleaf) Illustration by M. Renee McGinnis

Astronomy is one of the most ancient of sciences. Primitive peoples worshiped celestial objects and assigned them mystical powers, this interest evolving over the millennia from religious regard to rational and systematic investigation. Today astronomical publications record the present understanding of the universe, as in their day did primeval cave paintings. Just as surely as the latter were superseded, so scientists' current ideas of the universe can be expected to change as exciting new space missions unveil a fascinating cosmic vista. While several of these missions concentrate on the Sun and planets, others—the topic of this article—probe beyond the solar system into the depths of the universe.

The scope of present-day astronomical research extends from the origin of the universe, beyond its present turbulent state, to predictions about its ultimate fate. It stretches from the Earth's nearest, and comparatively well-understood, planetary and stellar neighbors to bizarre and enigmatic

34

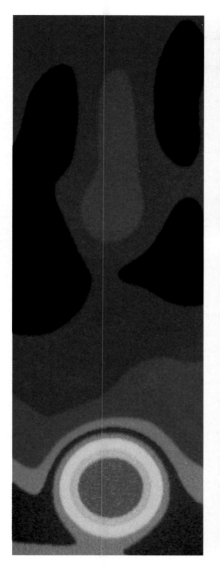

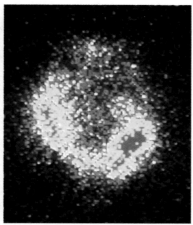

Astronomers study all types of radiation from space in addition to visible light. Radio emissions gathered by ground-based antennas were used recently to image what may be the accretion disk of a black hole at the core of the Milky Way (far left), a region obscured in visible light by dust. The orbiting observatory EXOSAT provided a picture of the supernova remnant Cassiopeia A (left) from the object's X-ray emissions, which do not penetrate the Earth's atmosphere. An infrared view of the familiar Andromeda galaxy (M31; below), from the IRAS satellite, has helped identify areas of new star formation.

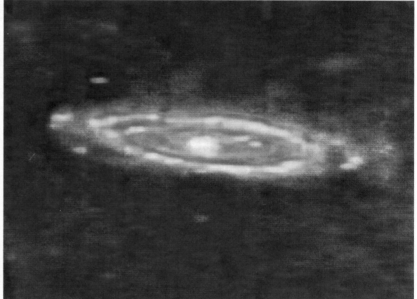

objects at the limits of the observable universe. The language of science has acquired a new colorful vocabulary. Black holes, white dwarfs, and red supergiants are but a few exotic members of the family of stars.

Astronomical researchers find it important to detect and analyze all types of radiation from space, not just the light sensed with the human eye and collected with the most familiar kind of ground-based telescope. Various forms of radiation are produced by the diverse range of celestial objects, each saying something different about the nature of the cosmos. Thus, for example, certain radio waves originate from objects undergoing violent change, X-rays are emitted from particularly hot regions, and infrared radiation comes from comparatively cool regions. Extending the limited scope of the human senses requires the most sophisticated instruments technology is able to devise. Of the various types of radiation from space, only visible light, some infrared radiation, and radio waves

(Opposite page, top left) Copyright British Museum; photo, ET Archive; (top right) detail from Arundel 83, folio 123ᵛ, by permission of the British Library; (center) Sygma; (bottom) S.J. Maddox, W.J. Sutherland, G.P. Efstathious, and J. Loveday, Oxford Astrophysics; (this page, left) F. Yusef-Zadeh; photo, courtesy of NRAO/AUI; (top right) ESA; (bottom right) JPL

can penetrate the Earth's atmosphere to be captured by Earth-bound instruments. (*See* Sidebar below.) Detection of ultraviolet radiation, some infrared radiation, X-rays, and gamma rays from the cosmos requires that instruments be mounted on rockets or spacecraft to lift them above the obscuring blanket of the atmosphere. Observations from space thus allow astronomers to paint a multicolored cosmic canvas of a universe known to be undergoing violent upheaval and change—in stark contrast to the quiescent sky observed since antiquity by men and women looking with unaided vision out into the night.

Celestial cathedrals

Medieval cathedrals are acknowledged to be among the greatest human achievements of their age, pushing nascent crafts to their limits. A 20th-century equivalent is the sophisticated spacecraft exploring the cosmos,

The multicolored universe

Radio waves, infrared radiation, visible light, ultraviolet radiation, X-rays, and gamma rays are all forms of radiant energy called electromagnetic radiation. Historically the various forms were recognized or discovered as separate phenomena before they were seen to be of a similar nature. They all travel through space with the same speed, the speed of light, and differ only in their so-called wavelength, or color. As far as human physiology is concerned, the one special thing about visible light is that it comprises the span of wavelengths from the Sun that most effectively penetrate the Earth's atmosphere. Thus, billions of years of evolution have ensured that it is the form of radiation to which the human eye is sensitive.

The phenomenon whereby white light that is passed through a prism is spread into a rainbow of colors, forming a spectrum, is familiar to all. Spectra can be formed from all forms of electromagnetic radiation, and the nature of the spectra can tell astronomers the composition of the emitting object and the type of tenuous material that the radiation has passed through along its journey through the cosmos to the telescope. The forming and interpretation of spectra, called spectroscopy, is one of the more powerful techniques of astronomy. So, too, are monitoring the intensity of sources of radiation, or photometry; taking pictures of the sky, or imaging; and establishing the position of radiation sources with extreme accuracy, or astrometry.

The electromagnetic spectrum (right) ranges from short-wavelength gamma rays to long-wavelength radio waves and includes the comparatively small region to which the human eye is sensitive. Of the various types of electromagnetic radiation from space, essentially only visible light, some infrared radiation, and radio waves reach the ground. The curve shown with the spectrum specifies the altitude at which atmospheric absorption reduces the intensity of incoming radiation of a given wavelength to half its original value.

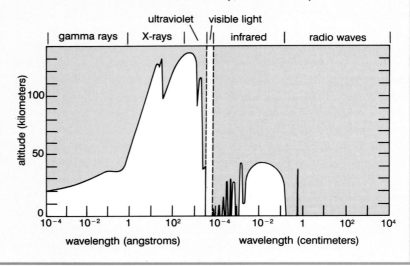

which extend technology to new bounds. The standard bearer for a new generation of scientific spacecraft was to be the Hubble Space Telescope (HST), launched into orbit in April 1990 by the U.S. space shuttle *Discovery*.

The HST, named after Edwin P. Hubble, one of the great observational astronomers of modern times, had been several decades in gestation. The initial challenges were fiscal rather than technical, with U.S. congressional support being hard won and being dependent on European collaboration, which eventually was achieved. The technical challenges that followed included attempting to shape the most accurate optical surface ever made, the precision needed being such that if the 2.4-meter (94-inch) primary mirror for the telescope were scaled to the size of the U.S., no hill or valley would depart more than five centimeters (two inches) from the mean surface. The spacecraft and its instruments took a decade and a half to design and construct, only to see a launch delayed four years by the tragic explosion of the shuttle *Challenger* in early 1986.

The main instrument on the Hubble telescope is the wide-field–planetary camera, designed to produce images of the sky considerably sharper, or better resolved, than could be achieved even with mountaintop-based telescopes, whose images are still distorted by fine-scale atmospheric turbulence. Other instruments on board the HST are optimized for photometry at optical and ultraviolet wavelengths, plus spectroscopy over this same range. The sophisticated guidance system of the spacecraft would also allow astrometry. (For a comprehensive description of the HST's history, construction, mission, and support institute, see *1991 Yearbook of Science and the Future* Feature Article: THE SPACE TELESCOPE SCIENCE INSTITUTE.)

The Hubble Space Telescope (HST), still gripped by the manipulator arm of the space shuttle Discovery, unfurls one of its solar array panels during deployment in April 1990. Orbiting of the 12-ton observatory, which took a decade and a half to design and construct, was delayed four years by the explosion of the shuttle Challenger in 1986.

NASA

37

When the first test images were radioed back from the spacecraft shortly after launch, no one was surprised that they were not as sharp as expected. After all, the telescope would need to be focused and the advanced instrumentation adjusted. As the days of testing passed, however, it became disturbingly evident that sharp images could not be produced. The telescope was displaying spherical aberration, an effect causing sharp images of the stars to be surrounded by circular halos such that overall resolution was barely better than that obtained from the ground. At a price of $1.5 billion, the HST exceeded the combined cost of the world's top 40 ground-based telescopes, and the prospect of the mission doing little better in terms of resolution than any one of them depressed the mission's supporters greatly and provided fresh ammunition for the denigrators of space expenditure.

By late 1990 the source of the spherical aberration had been found to lie in the defective grinding and polishing of the HST's main mirror some 10 years prior to launch. The fault was traced to a device called the reflective null corrector, which had been built to test the shape of the mirror as it was polished to the required figure. Although two cruder test devices had indicated that the mirror possibly was being incorrectly figured, they were ignored in favor of the "certified" reflective null corrector, which was indicating results of exceptional precision. Tragically,

A cutaway diagram of the Hubble telescope's cylindrical body traces the optical path of the instrument. Light entering the aperture first strikes the 2.4-meter (94-inch) primary mirror and is reflected forward to the 32-centimeter (12 1/2-inch) convex secondary mirror. The secondary then redirects the light back through a hole in the primary to a plane of focus in the science instruments section. After the telescope was placed in orbit, it was discovered that an error in grinding the main mirror had produced a curved surface that was slightly too flat near the mirror's edge. As a result, light reflected from the edge region comes to a focus behind the intended image plane.

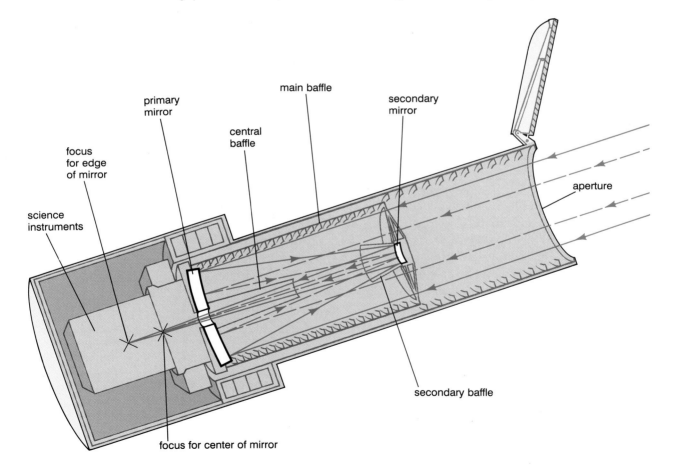

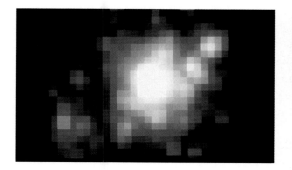

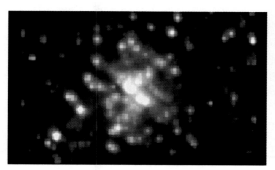

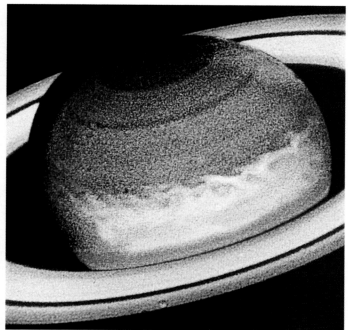

the certified device was flawed, resulting in a mirror precisely ground to the wrong shape. Thus, the most expensive telescope ever built, sent into space on the most costly scientific spacecraft ever launched, did not perform as expected.

In fact, the situation is not as bad as it first appeared. Various image-processing techniques can be used to reduce the effect of spherical aberration, and the telescope's ultraviolet observations will still be of unique value since they are not possible from the ground. The HST is a long-term mission, expected to be operational for 15–20 years, with visits by shuttle astronauts every three or four years to refurbish and replace instruments. It will be possible to insert corrective optics into the existing instruments to compensate for the spherical aberration of the telescope. Furthermore, a replacement wide-field–planetary camera that will achieve near optimum resolution is being built; it will be fitted to the HST on the first refurbishment shuttle flight. One cannot excuse the mirror error, which resulted from sloppy management and inadequate quality control. Ultimately, however, the HST should be able to achieve most of the science expected of it.

In its first months of imperfect operation, the HST has still produced unprecedented scientific results. Since late 1990 its wide-field–planetary camera has tracked an atmospheric storm of extreme ferocity on Saturn. Spectacular images of bright clusters of stars of hitherto unachievable detail have been obtained, including an intriguing glimpse of a "stellar nursery," a cluster of young and forming stars, in the Large Magellanic Cloud, a neighboring galaxy. Ultraviolet spectra have also provided new scientific insights about objects ranging from nearby stars to distant quasars.

Despite its flawed main mirror, the HST, aided by computer image-processing techniques, produced unprecedented, often spectacular results in its first months in orbit. Individual stars in the cluster R136, a stellar nursery in the Large Magellanic Cloud, are blurred together even in an exceptionally good ground-based image (top left), but an image made with the HST's wide-field–planetary camera (bottom left) allows dozens of hot, massive young stars to be distinguished, including some in the bright core of the cluster. In late 1990 the Hubble telescope tracked the progress of a giant storm, dubbed the Great White Spot, across Saturn's equatorial region (above) in the kind of detail previously seen only in images from interplanetary space probes.

(Top left) Meylan/ESO; (bottom left and right) NASA

During the rest of the 20th century and well into the 21st, the Hubble Space Telescope will be seeking answers for many of the most important questions in astronomy. What is the large-scale structure of the universe? How did the universe begin? How do galaxies evolve? What role do violent events play in the evolution of the universe? How will the universe evolve in future? (These questions all fall in the realm of cosmology.) How do the stars and planets form? How do stars evolve, and how do they die? What causes activity on the surfaces of the Sun and other stars? How widespread is life in the universe? (These questions are for the sciences of stellar and planetary evolution.) How are the chemical elements formed? How are the elements that are made in stellar interiors fed to interstellar space to contribute to future generations of stars and planets? What are the roles of supernovas and massive stars in forming the heavy elements? (These problems fall under the heading of nucleogenesis.) After only a short time in orbit, the HST has already gone some way in helping to answer these and other fundamental questions about the cosmos.

Precision—at a price

In August 1989 the European Space Agency's (ESA's) spacecraft Hipparcos was blasted into space atop an Ariane rocket. Elation at an apparently successful launch was short-lived. The spacecraft was destined for a geostationary orbit having an altitude of 36,000 kilometers (22,000 miles), in which the orbital period of an object is identical to the length of the

A dust mote called home

Distances in astronomy can be described in terms of how far a pulse of light travels in a vacuum in one year. One light-year is equivalent to 9,460,000,000,000 (9.46×10^{12}) kilometers, or 5,880,000,000,000 miles. The nearest star to the Sun is at a distance of some four light-years.

Stars are not uniformly scattered throughout space but accumulate in conglomerates called galaxies, each containing billions of stars. Galaxies themselves accumulate into clusters. The Sun is just one of 100 billion stars within our galaxy, the Milky Way. The stars of the Milky Way lie within intertwined spiral arms, with the Sun occupying a rather insignificant location some 30,000 light-years from the galactic center.

If our place within the Milky Way seems insignificant, then the place of our galaxy within the universe is equally so. The part of the universe observable with the newest space instruments contains billions of galaxies, clustering together by the thousands but still spaced from one another by millions of light-years. The most remote galaxies to be observed with the Hubble Space Telescope are on the order of 10 billion (10×10^9) light-years distant. On this scale planet Earth shrinks to a mere speck of cosmic dust.

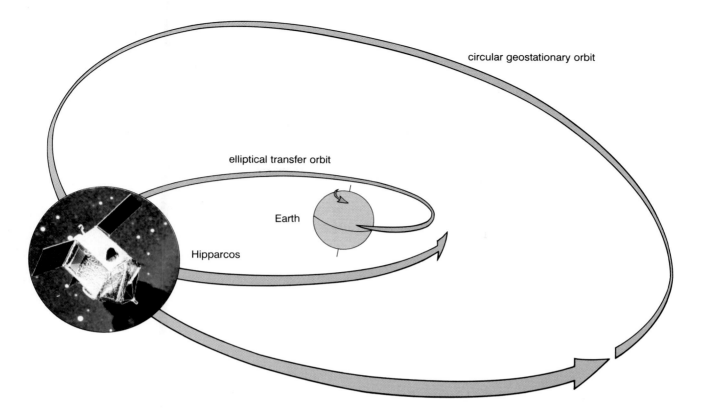

circular geostationary orbit

elliptical transfer orbit

Earth

Hipparcos

day, effectively retaining it in the same spot above the Earth's surface. Ariane first placed Hipparcos into a transfer orbit having a closest point 500 kilometers (310 miles) above the Earth and the most distant point at 36,000 kilometers, from whence a boost rocket on the spacecraft was to place it in the desired orbit. To the chagrin of all those involved with the mission, the boost rocket, which had proved highly reliable on previous missions, failed to operate despite repeated attempts to activate it. As a result, Hipparcos was marooned in its transfer orbit.

The primary objective of the Hipparcos mission was astrometry, in particular, to measure the position of stars with a 10-fold improvement in precision over that achieved from the ground. Such measurements are desirable because they enable astronomers to establish a scale for determining distances in the universe and thence its history.

Distances in the cosmos are determined via a number of overlapping steps, each step depending on the precision of the preceding one. The more important steps in this progression begin with finding the distance to nearby stars using triangulation techniques, described below. The next step is to estimate the distance to certain stars called Cepheids, whose brightness varies periodically in a way that depends on their intrinsic brightness. Astronomers use this property to estimate the distance of more distant clusters of stars and even nearby galaxies in which Cepheids can be identified. Additionally, the brightness of the brightest stars (and also supernovas) in galaxies can be used to estimate the distances to the nearest galaxies. For more distant galaxies, use is made of Edwin

The European Space Agency's satellite Hipparcos has been able to carry out its prime astrometry mission despite being in the wrong orbit. Hipparcos had first been launched into a highly elliptical transfer orbit, which was to be rounded out to a circular geostationary orbit by means of an onboard boost rocket. Failure of the booster, however, marooned the satellite in its elliptical path, forcing ESA to seek extra ground stations in order to keep Hipparcos in the nearly continuous telemetry contact needed for its mission.

(Inset) ESA

41

Hubble's discovery that all galaxies are receding from each other (an observation compatible with a big bang origin for the universe) and that the more distant a galaxy is from the Milky Way the greater is its speed of recession. The speed of recession of a galaxy can be determined—and, hence, its distance estimated—by measuring the galaxy's so-called red shift, the shift of its light toward the red end of the spectrum, which is a consequence of its motion away from the observer.

The critical first step in determining the cosmic distance scale is the use of trigonometric parallax for the nearby stars. This is merely an adaptation of the traditional triangulation techniques used by surveyors to determine the distance to remote objects on the Earth. First, measurements are taken of the relative position of nearby stars with respect to distant background stars. Then new measurements are taken six months later, when the Earth is on the opposite side of its orbit around the Sun, and the difference in the apparent positions is determined. Finally, the diameter of the Earth's orbit is used as the baseline to triangulate the distance to the star.

Because any errors in the first step of determining stellar distances are carried over and amplified in later steps, it is important to get the first

The telescope as a time machine

Looking out into the cosmos is looking not only deep into space but also, because of the finite speed of light, back in time. Thus, the telescope acts as a time machine, observing the nearby stars as they were just a few years or decades ago and the more distant stars within the Milky Way as they were hundreds or thousands of years ago when the light now reaching the Earth left them. The nearby galaxies appear as they were millions of years ago and the more distant galaxies as they were hundreds of millions of years ago. Few cosmic objects exist at this instant in the form they presently appear.

The history of the universe thus is laid out like a cosmic kaleidoscope for astronomers to study stars and galaxies at various stages of their evolution. Observers see nascent stars procreated from giant clouds of interstellar gas, young stars, middle-aged stars, old stars, and dying stars. Quasars, among the most distant objects known, are thought to be young galaxies with a brilliant core, but astronomers also see galaxies in formation, interacting galaxies, and galaxies being torn apart. The unfolding drama of the universe is revealed as stars and galaxies are born and die.

Near and distant subjects for the cosmic canvas include Tycho's supernova remnant (right), whose portrait was made from radio emissions that left the object 7,500 years ago, and a patch of deep space (far right), in which the faintest, reddest objects, thought to be extremely distant galaxies, are imaged in near-infrared light that has taken perhaps 10 billion years to reach the Earth.

(Left) S.P. Reynolds and R.A. Chevalier, photo, courtesy of NRAO/AUI; (right) Lennox Cowie, Institute for Astronomy, University of Hawaii

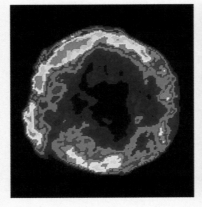 

step as accurate as possible. The precision of Hipparcos depends on a very simple technique. Using two fields of view separated by a fixed (and accurately known) angle of 58° but brought to a common focus, Hipparcos continually scans the sky, measuring precisely the relative positions of selected stars in the two fields as they drift across a fine modulating grid. Once relative positions are determined for some 120,000 preselected stars, then a global solution to ascribe them each a position of hitherto unachieved accuracy can be found. The computational complexity of determining that solution, and providing a stellar map of the heavens of extreme precision, should not be underestimated.

That was the objective of Hipparcos prior to the boost rocket failure. Scientists wondered if it still could be achieved. Two problems had resulted from Hipparcos' remaining trapped in its transfer orbit. First, retaining nearly continuous telemetry contact with the spacecraft for the reception of data now would require three ground stations spaced around the globe, rather than just the single ESA station planned at Odenwald, Germany. Adding ESA's facility in Perth, Australia, and the U.S. National Aeronautics and Space Administration's (NASA's) Goldstone tracking station in California to Odenwald indeed did enable contact to be maintained with Hipparcos for 90% of its highly elliptical orbit. Thus, the first problem was overcome, at the price of involving three ground stations rather than one.

The second problem was potentially more serious. The highly eccentric transfer orbit plunges the spacecraft through the Van Allen radiation belts twice per orbit, exposing sensitive electronics and solar cells on the spacecraft to damage. Careful monitoring has suggested that this problem is not as severe as first thought, and the prospect is good that Hipparcos will be able to complete its prime mission of providing an accurate first stepping stone on the cosmic distance scale.

Rosettes for ROSAT

Arguably the most spectacular and unexpected discoveries from space astronomy have come from the study of X-rays emanating from a wide variety of celestial objects. It is sobering, therefore, to recall that until 1962 X-ray astronomy had been widely thought to hold little promise. The initial detection of a stellar X-ray source (other than the Sun) was a chance discovery from a rocket experiment designed for a completely different purpose. But progress in this nascent astronomical discipline was spectacular, first from rockets and then from a series of highly successful satellite missions culminating with the launch of NASA's Einstein Observatory in 1978. Although there have been small X-ray astronomy missions following Einstein, none has matched it for scientific insight.

To obtain X-ray images of the heavens, one cannot use ordinary telescope mirrors in the regular fashion since X-rays easily pass through them. Fortunately, X-rays can be focused by reflecting them at a very low angle, or grazing incidence. An X-ray telescope thus can be made up of a concentric nest of paraboloid- and hyperboloid-shaped cylinders, which direct the X-rays onto an electronic detector.

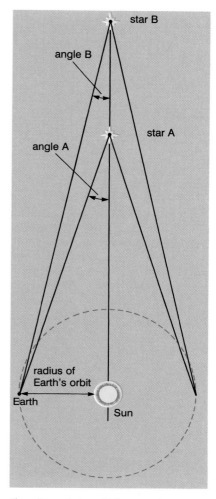

The prime mission of Hipparcos is to make precision measurements of the positions of nearby stars and thus allow astronomers to determine their distances from the Earth more accurately. Pairs of position measurements for each star, taken six months apart when the Earth is on opposite sides of its orbit around the Sun, are used to determine the angle through which the star seems to move with respect to distant background stars. Half of that angle, called the parallax of the star, forms one angle of a right triangle having a leg of known length, the radius of the Earth's orbit. From the parallax and leg, the distance from the Earth to the star can be derived by means of simple trigonometry. In the diagram the star (star A) that has the larger parallax (angle A) will be found to be closer to the Earth.

43

West German engineers lower the ROSAT observatory into a test stand for a prelaunch checkout following the satellite's arrival at Cape Canaveral, Florida. The large square panel at the far right covers the aperture to the grazing-incidence optics of ROSAT's X-ray telescope.

The X-ray images obtained from the Einstein Observatory gave a new view of the universe. Nevertheless, during that mission detailed images were obtained for less than 10% of the sky, and X-ray spectroscopy was accomplished for a limited number of sources. Astronomers were eager to complete an all-sky imaging survey, and the challenge was taken up by West Germany. Planning for a German X-ray mission had started even before the Einstein Observatory went into orbit, but the tantalizingly incomplete, albeit spectacular, vista that it had opened up added impetus to the planning. The main instrument was to be an X-ray telescope with a capability not too dissimilar to that of Einstein, but the scope of the mission was extended when a British consortium of X-ray astronomy groups undertook to produce a wide-field camera (also based on grazing incidence optics) that would complete a survey at extreme ultraviolet (EUV) wavelengths, the radiation lying between the conventional ultraviolet and X-rays. A triumvirate of participating nations was completed when the U.S. offered an advanced electronic detector—a derivative of one of Einstein's imaging detectors—plus a launch.

The mission was christened Röntgensatellit, in memory of pioneering X-ray researcher Wilhelm Röntgen, and abbreviated ROSAT. The spacecraft was designed initially for a space shuttle launch, but the *Challenger* tragedy precipitated rapid (and costly) modifications so that a Delta II rocket could provide the lift into space. Within days of its successful launch in June 1990, ROSAT's systems, X-ray telescope, and EUV camera were found to be operating satisfactorily. Detailed checking and calibration came next, after which ROSAT started a six-month all-sky survey, to be followed by a protracted period of detailed observations of objects discovered during the survey and objects previously known.

The all-sky survey is expected to reveal some 100,000 X-ray–emitting objects. Many of them will prove to be single stars. The tenuous outer

44

Photos, Max-Planck-Institut für Physik und Astrophysik/Institut für Extraterrestrische Physik

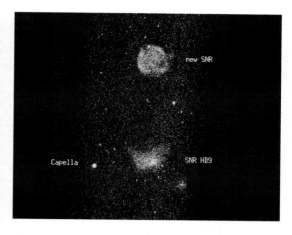

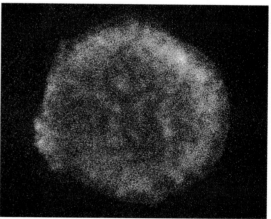

atmosphere of a star, called its corona, is often sufficiently hot (millions of degrees) to emit X-rays. Frequently stars are born in pairs, with the two bodies orbiting each other. During the evolution of such a binary star system, matter may be transferred from one star to the other, being heated in the process to extreme temperatures and emitting X-rays. The mass transfer occurs not directly but via a pancake-shaped mass called the accretion disk that swirls around the receiving star. The expanding debris from supernova explosions also emits X-rays; in fact, an early discovery from ROSAT was a supernova remnant undetected in other forms of radiation. In addition, the centers of certain galaxies are undergoing extreme upheaval, and such active galactic nuclei can be studied in X-rays. Permeating the complete X-ray image of the celestial sphere is a faint background of X-rays originating in the hot interstellar medium and the tenuous gas between the galaxies. X-ray astronomy continues to reveal a universe of intriguing variety and violent upheaval.

Addition of the EUV wide-field camera has brought an intriguing new dimension to the ROSAT mission. Extreme ultraviolet radiation long had been thought to be absorbed strongly within the interstellar medium, offering little possibility of detection. But the joint U.S.-Soviet Apollo-Soyuz mission in 1975 somewhat unexpectedly detected several EUV-

ROSAT's early accomplishments include an X-ray image of the region around the binary star system AR Lac (left) and the discovery of a previously unknown supernova remnant in the constellation Auriga (top right; labeled "new SNR"). A ROSAT image of the remnant of Tycho's supernova of 1572, received through the X-ray telescope by a high-resolution imager, reveals fine details in the expanding shell of matter ejected by the stellar explosion.

45

emitting objects, indicating that in certain directions the interstellar medium is not as obscuring as first believed and holding out the prospect of finding thousands of EUV sources, the majority of them likely to be white dwarf stars. Expectations of a bountiful harvest of discoveries from ROSAT were fulfilled with the detection of several hundred new EUV-emitting objects.

The birth, life, and death of stars

Stars are formed from isolated clouds of gas and dust in the interstellar medium. As a cloud collapses under the action of gravity, its temperature increases to the point at which certain nuclear reactions, known as fusion, can take place. A star is born.

In the newly formed star, hydrogen nuclei are fused together to form helium accompanied by the release of thermonuclear energy. A young star then settles down to relative stability, with its life expectancy dependent on its initial mass. Massive stars shine the most brilliantly but burn up their nuclear fuel reserves rapidly, often within a few tens of millions of years. On the other hand, stars of more modest size like the Sun will live for 10 billion years or longer.

The ultimate fate of a star again depends on mass. For stars some 10–20 times the mass of the Sun, death comes in a spectacular blaze of glory. The accelerating consumption of nuclear fuel leads first to the expansion of the massive star into a red supergiant. Eventually, with all the fuel reserves expended, the central core of the star collapses catastrophically to form a compact stellar remnant called a neutron star; for more massive cores gravitational collapse produces the ultimate state of compaction, a black hole. The collapse of the core is accompanied by an explosive ejection of the star's outer envelope, witnessed as a supernova explosion. For stars of more modest size, when nuclear reserves are expended the star contracts and cools to become a white dwarf. This peaceful form of death is the eventual destiny of 999 of every 1,000 stars.

Interstellar clouds of gas and dust, like the nebula NGC 2264 near the star S Monocerotis (right), are the birthplace of new stars.

(This page) NASA; (opposite page) © Anglo-Australian Telescope Board 1981

Artist's conception shows the Cosmic Background Explorer (COBE) in polar Earth orbit. The gold conical radiation shield protects the satellite's cryogenically chilled infrared- and microwave-receiving instruments from unwanted thermal and radio-frequency energy.

Authenticating the signature of creation

In the beginning, most astronomers and cosmologists believe, was the big bang—the epoch of creation that took place some 15 billion years ago. In the seconds following this event, the universe must have been a dense "soup" of subatomic particles bathed in a primordial fireball of radiation. The temperature was too extreme for the subatomic particles to combine to form atoms. Within a few minutes, however, the expanding celestial soup would have cooled such that protons and neutrons could combine to form nuclei of deuterium (a heavy isotope of hydrogen) and helium. It was to be at least a million years, however, before the universe had cooled enough to allow electrons to combine with the hydrogen and helium nuclei to form true neutral atoms. It was during this "epoch of neutralization" that the universe became abruptly transparent to remnant radiation from the primordial fireball; now the radiation could expand freely, decoupled from the matter in the universe. Today, astronomers detect in the microwave (short-wavelength radio wave) region of the spectrum a mere glimmer of the primordial fireball, cooled to a few degrees of the absolute zero of temperature ($-273°$ C, or $-459°$ F). This cosmic background radiation is the faint signature of creation.

The cosmic background radiation was first detected in 1965 as a feeble hiss of radio static. Extensive observations from the ground and by means of rocket payloads subsequently indicated that the radiation was of a form characteristic of a so-called blackbody—a perfect absorber and emitter of radiation. This particular signature was what was required for support of the big bang hypothesis of creation; any large departures from an ideal radiation field would have been difficult to reconcile. But uncer-

47

tainty in the measurements remained because of errors inherent in the experiments, and the residual doubts were exacerbated by observations that seemed to show an excess of brightness at certain wavelengths.

Was the big bang hypothesis at risk? Some astronomers certainly thought so, and various alternative hypotheses were considered—until a remarkable spacecraft restored respectability to the big bang.

In November 1989 NASA's Cosmic Background Explorer (COBE) was launched, carrying three instruments continually cooled to within two degrees Celsius of absolute zero by the evaporation of liquid helium. One instrument, called the far-infrared absolute spectrophotometer (FIRAS), was designed to check whether the spectrum of the background radiation was actually that of a blackbody; *i.e.*, whether the radiation could really be the remnant of the primordial fireball. The detector on FIRAS is so sensitive that it can measure a hundred-trillionth of a watt (10^{-14} watts), about the power received by a postage stamp in Washington, D.C., from a light bulb in New York City. The second instrument is the differential microwave radiometer (DMR), designed to map the sky at several wavelengths while looking for variations in intensity of the background radiation. The final instrument in the trio is the diffuse infrared background experiment (DIRBE), designed to search for radiation from the primordial galaxies. All three instruments achieve a measurement precision far greater than that of any previous experiment.

After a mere nine minutes of observing, FIRAS obtained a cosmic background radiation measurement fitting that of a blackbody to better than 1% (a precision of 0.1% ultimately should be possible), the inferred temperature being 2.735° C above absolute zero. When the results were presented for the first time at a meeting of the American Astronomical Society at Washington, D.C., in January 1990, the packed lecture theater burst into sustained applause. The big bang hypothesis was back in favor, and COBE had been guaranteed a place in the history of science.

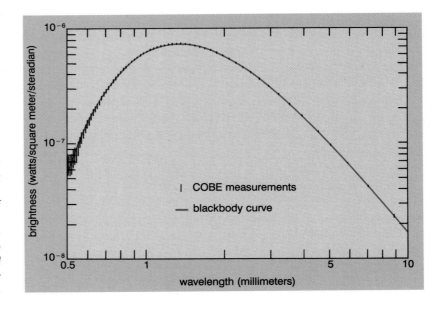

The earliest radiation measurements from COBE's FIRAS instrument elicited a sustained ovation when they were first presented at an astronomical meeting in January 1990. Plotted together with a blackbody curve for a temperature of 2.735° C above absolute zero (right), the measurements fit the curve with a precision better than 1%. Any large departures from the ideal blackbody would have been difficult to reconcile within the big bang hypothesis of cosmic creation.

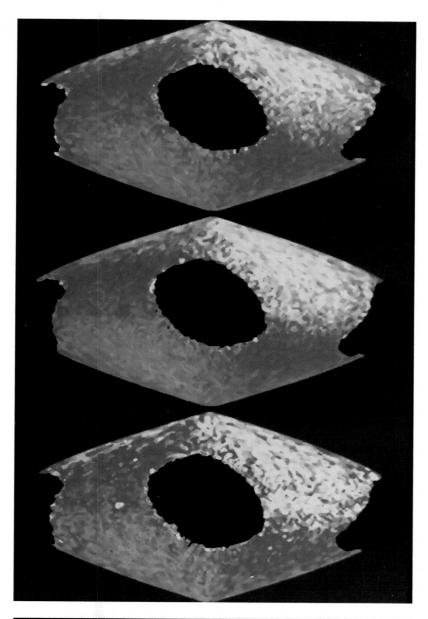

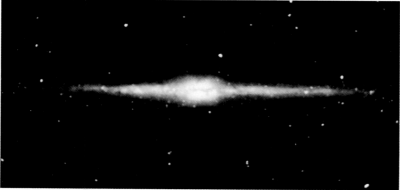

The images at top left are microwave sky maps made by COBE's DMR instrument at three wavelengths (3.3, 5.7, and 9.6 millimeters) and are intended to reveal any differences in intensity of the background radiation in various directions of the sky. The only prominent feature is the well-understood difference due to the Doppler shift resulting from the motion of the solar system with respect to the distant matter in the universe. The lack of other variations is evidence for the extraordinary uniformity of the early universe. COBE's DIRBE instrument provided the first clear picture of the Milky Way Galaxy (left), free of much of the dust that obscures its disk and central bulge in visible light. The solar system lies within the disk and about 30,000 light-years from the center, making the view an edge-on one. The measurements were taken at infrared wavelengths corresponding to the radiation emitted predominantly by stars rather than by dust particles.

Photos, NASA

Not that COBE has left the big bang with an entirely clean bill of health, however. The smoothness, or lack of variations in brightness, of the diffuse background radiation detected by COBE—to better then one part in 30,000—fits awkwardly with the need for a "clumpy" primordial universe in which the first generation of galaxies was formed. Such clumpiness would be expected to be detectable even today in radiation fluctuations at a level of one part in 1,000. The origin of galaxies remains one of the unsolved riddles of cosmology.

Continuing the canvas

The pace of space astronomy set by the HST, ROSAT, COBE, and other recent missions will be maintained at least until the end of the century. Next in line among the major space observatories to contribute is the U.S. Gamma Ray Observatory (GRO), which was launched successfully in April 1991. Gamma rays from the cosmos, enormously important to astronomical studies, are indicative of events of extreme violence. To date, gamma-ray astronomy has been poorly exploited, with some of the more important discoveries being serendipitous. For example, in the 1970s the U.S. put a network of gamma-ray detectors into orbit to search for atmospheric explosions in violation of the Nuclear Test-Ban Treaty. Astronomers were startled to learn that the detectors were recording bursts of gamma rays from outside the solar system—bursts that are now thought to be giant nuclear explosions occurring on the surfaces of neutron stars. Their magnitude is such that each event releases more

NASA's massive Gamma Ray Observatory, lifted into orbit by space shuttle in April 1991, is designed to conduct a full sky survey in a still largely unexplored area of the electromagnetic spectrum. The satellite carries four instruments that together cover the entire known gamma-ray region of the spectrum.

TRW Space and Technology Group

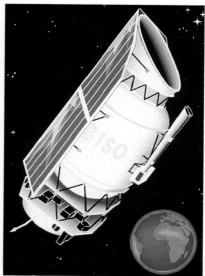

energy in a tenth of a second than the Sun releases in 10 millennia. Gamma-ray astronomy of worthwhile sensitivity requires big instruments; those on GRO weigh some six tons, and the full observatory 15 tons.

Both the U.S., with the Advanced X-Ray Astrophysics Facility (AXAF), and Europe, with the X-Ray Multi Mirror telescope (XMM), have major X-ray missions at an advanced stage of planning; both spacecraft offer a spectroscopic capability not previously achieved for X-ray astronomy satellites such as ROSAT. Spectroscopy in the far ultraviolet is the objective of a U.S.-U.K.-Canadian mission called LYMAN. Spectroscopy in X-rays and the far ultraviolet offer richer astrophysical insight than do any other parts of the spectrum.

In mid-1993 Europe will launch the Infrared Space Observatory, a follow-up to the pioneering infrared survey mission carried out by the Infrared Astronomical Satellite (IRAS) in 1983. (See *1986 Yearbook of Science and the Future* Feature Article: THE COSMOS ACCORDING TO IRAS.) Infrared astronomy studies objects at comparatively modest temperatures (hundreds of degrees), such as planets, gas clouds, newly forming stars, cool stars, and galaxies. Because cool objects are being observed, infrared telescopes and detectors need to be cooled to very low temperatures to avoid contaminating heat radiation from the instruments themselves.

The 1990s promise to be a golden decade for astronomy. Most artists would find it impossible to complete a realistic landscape with only two pigments on the palette. Astronomers had been similarly constrained when restricted to optical and radio astronomy from the ground. Observations from space are adding new colors to the astronomer's palette. By the advent of the new millennium, astronomy will have gone a long way toward completing its multicolored cosmic canvas.

The European Space Agency plans to launch the Infrared Space Observatory (above) in 1993 as a follow-up to the successful IRAS mission of 1983. In the mid-1990s the U.S. Advanced X-Ray Astrophysics Facility (left) may be in orbit, measuring radiation from hot, violent sources of energy, including active galactic nuclei and quasars.

(Left) NASA; (right) ESA

51

BALLOONING
FOR
SCIENCE

by Glenn M. Frye, Jr.

The first vehicle that allowed scientists to probe the upper atmosphere, the balloon continues to be an important research tool for chemists, meteorologists, and astronomers.

On Feb. 24, 1987, a new star appeared in the southern sky, an event awaited by the scientific community for almost four centuries. A cataclysmic stellar explosion, a supernova, had occurred near enough to the Earth to be visible to the naked eye. Even though the star was 160,000 light-years away in the Large Magellanic Cloud, that is nearby in comparison with the distant galaxies that had provided only faint supernovas for observations with modern telescopes.

In addition to observing the visible and radio parts of the electromagnetic spectrum, astrophysicists were eager to try to detect gamma rays because this high-energy radiation is related directly to the nuclear reactions that theorists had predicted were taking place in the supernova. Unfortunately, gamma rays are absorbed in the atmosphere; it is therefore necessary to go to the inconvenience and cost of placing the gamma-ray telescope at the top of the atmosphere. The Gamma Ray Observatory of the U.S. National Aeronautics and Space Administration (NASA), a shuttle-sized satellite, was designed for just such observations, and its original launch date of 1984 would have had it in the right place at the right time. However, a series of delays (including the *Challenger* disaster) kept it on the ground until at least early 1991. Since there were no other satellites in orbit capable of making the desired observation of the supernova, it was necessary to resort to a vehicle that first allowed scientists to probe the upper atmosphere and observe the primary cosmic radiation—the balloon.

GLENN M. FRYE, JR., is Professor of
Physics at Case Western Reserve University,
Cleveland, Ohio.

(Overleaf) Photograph, NASA

The National Scientific Balloon Facility (NSBF), at its location in Palestine, Texas, has conducted 60 to 80 flights per year for scientists since its inception in 1963. For flights that required a different location, NSBF has used many other launching sites in the U.S. as well as in Canada, Central and South America, Sicily, India, and, most importantly, in Australia, where the Alice Springs site met the logistic requirements and was far enough south for a good view of the 1987 supernova (designated SN 1987A).

Because supernovas are transitory, brightening for the first few months and then dimming rapidly, scientists considered it essential to begin observations as soon as possible. Within days NASA had established a special supernova program and expedited the airlift of balloons, helium, and other materials to Australia. Scientists who had gamma-ray telescopes that had been designed for future balloon flights were encouraged to participate.

Supernova 1987A (above), some 160,000 light-years from the Earth, appeared in the skies of the Southern Hemisphere in February 1987. For observation of the supernova's gamma-ray emissions, which do not penetrate the Earth's atmosphere, balloons were quickly launched from the Australian Balloon Launching Station at Alice Springs (right).

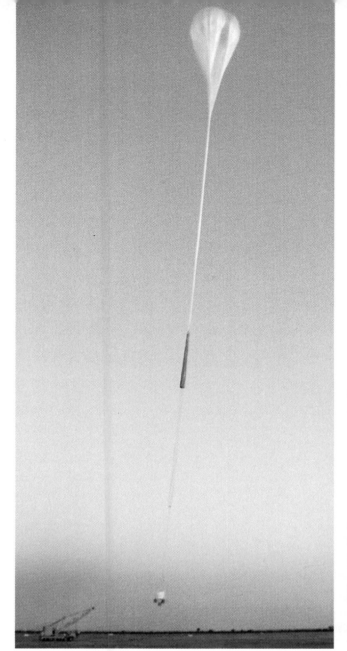

A series of balloon flights in 1987 and 1988, beginning only two months after the supernova explosion, showed conclusively that a large amount of the isotope cobalt-56 (^{56}Co), 7.5% of the mass of the Sun, had been produced in SN 1987A, just as had been predicted by the theoretical models. In the radioactive decay of ^{56}Co to iron-56 (^{56}Fe), two gamma-ray lines are produced at 847 and 1,238 keV. The germanium telescopes showed spectroscopic lines at just those energies. However, the intensity of the gamma rays as a function of time could not be reconciled with the original assumption that the ^{56}Co was distributed in a shell covered by other shells of absorbing material. The gamma rays appeared earlier than predicted, indicating a more complex evolution of the supernova envelope where the ^{56}Co had been mixed into the overlying shells.

The Gamma-Ray Imaging Spectrometer (GRIS) produced detailed measurements of the profiles of gamma-ray lines from the radioactive elements created during Supernova 1987A. (Above) The GRIS is installed on its launch vehicle and (above left) begins to ascend by means of a balloon just after release from the launch vehicle.

Photos, courtesy of Bonnard Teegarden on behalf of the GRIS team, NASA/Goddard Space Flight Center

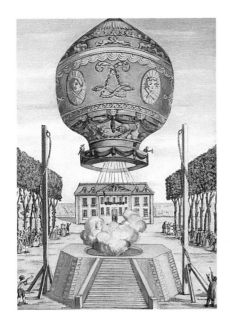

Early balloons

Through the centuries many efforts have been made to emulate the birds and fly through the air. Archimedes' Principle, applied to the atmosphere, suggests one possible method: "The buoyant force on an object is equal to the weight of the air it displaces." Thus, if an object can be designed to have a weight that is less than that of an equal volume of air, there will be a net upward force on the object. The Montgolfier brothers are credited with first achieving flight in public in 1783 with a fabric and paper balloon that was filled with smoke from a fire. They thought that smoke was a separate gas and, since it was seen to rise in the air, that it might lift a balloon. Actually, of course, it was the lower density of the hot air that provided the lift. In the same year, another Frenchman, Jacques Charles, used hydrogen in a sealed, fixed-volume balloon made of silk and on Dec. 1, 1783, achieved a two-hour flight over Paris, landing 43 kilometers (27 miles) away.

Gradual exploration of the lower atmosphere took place during the 19th century. At this time scientists first realized that above 6,000 meters (20,000 feet) supplementary oxygen was needed for the balloonists. Measurements were made of the pressure, temperature, and composition of the atmosphere as a function of altitude. Manned and unmanned flights in the 1930s extended these measurements into the stratosphere to an altitude of about 21,000 meters (70,000 feet). Of particular interest was the discovery that, although the pressure continued to decrease with increasing altitude, at the base of the stratosphere (12,000 meters [40,000 feet]) the temperature stopped decreasing and began to increase. This warming is due to a trace amount of ozone that absorbs the solar ultraviolet radiation. This process is very important biologically, as the ozone layer provides a shield against the harmful ultraviolet radiation from the Sun.

The fabric and paper balloon of the Montgolfier brothers, filled with smoke from a fire, became in June 1783 the first balloon to achieve flight in public (above). It rose to a height of approximately 1,000 meters (3,000 feet) and remained there for about 10 minutes before descending to the ground. Six months later another Frenchman, Jacques Charles, took off from Paris in a hydrogen-filled silk balloon (above right), flew for two hours, and landed 43 kilometers (27 miles) away.

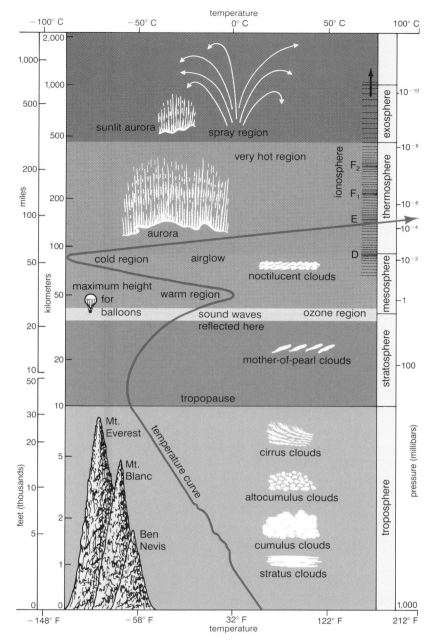

temperature

−100° C   −50° C   0° C   50° C   100° C

2,000

1,000

1,000

500

500

200

200

100

100

50

50

20

10

30

20

10

5

2

5

1

0

miles

kilometers

feet (thousands)

sunlit aurora   spray region

very hot region

aurora

cold region   airglow

noctilucent clouds

maximum height for balloons   warm region

sound waves   ozone region
reflected here

mother-of-pearl clouds

tropopause

Mt. Everest

Mt. Blanc

temperature curve

cirrus clouds

altocumulus clouds

Ben Nevis

cumulus clouds

stratus clouds

exosphere

ionosphere   thermosphere

F$_2$
F$_1$
E
D

mesosphere

stratosphere

troposphere

10^{-10}

10^{-8}

10^{-6}

10^{-4}

10^{-2}

1

100

1,000

pressure (millibars)

−148° F   −58° F   32° F   122° F   212° F

temperature

A profile of the Earth's atmosphere to a height of 2,000 kilometers (1,240 miles) reveals its main layers and their chief characteristics. Balloons have ascended into the stratosphere to a maximum height of approximately 50 kilometers (31 miles).

Adapted from *Exploring the Atmosphere,* by G.M.B. Dobson, Clarendon Press, 1963 © Oxford University Press

After World War II only a few high-altitude manned flights were made, primarily to test life-support systems as an adjunct to the space program. New balloon materials and advances in instrumentation, electronics, and telemetry made it possible to design a variety of experiments that did not require the presence of a human for their operation. Eliminating this requirement made higher altitudes possible because of the weight reduction; it also greatly simplified the operational requirements. The remainder of this article will treat only unmanned balloon flights in the stratosphere.

Present-day models

The basic design of the Montgolfier balloon was the same as is used in the hot-air, recreational balloons that are so popular today, namely the fixed-volume balloon that has an opening at the bottom where a propane burner is used to heat the air. For the last 40 years the workhorse scientific vehicle for flights in the stratosphere has been the zero-pressure polyethylene balloon. For this type of balloon, strips of "dry cleaner-bag material" approximately 0.025 millimeter (0.001 inch) in thickness are heat-welded together to form an approximately spherical, slightly teardrop shape. Just after launch the lifting gas (helium or hydrogen) fills only a small volume at the top of this type of balloon. As the balloon rises, the helium expands until an altitude is reached where the balloon is fully inflated. At this point, if the balloon were sealed, it would continue to rise in the atmosphere. Since polyethylene is only slightly extensible, continued ascension would soon result in a higher internal than external pressure, and the balloon would burst. (This is the fate of the common rubber or meteorologic sealed balloon, which continues to rise until the material is stretched to its yield point.) To alleviate this situation, the bottom of the zero-pressure balloon is left open. Excess helium is vented out of this aperture, and zero pressure differential is maintained at the helium-air interface. The bubble of helium now floats in the air at the altitude where its weight, plus the weight of the balloon and payload, equals the weight of the displaced air. As long as nothing perturbs this equilibrium, the balloon will continue to float at constant altitude, which is ideal for many scientific investigations.

The most important of the many factors that can disturb this equilibrium is the setting of the Sun. During daylight hours, infrared radiation is trapped inside the balloon, producing a greenhouse effect that causes the helium to be warmer than the outside air. After sunset the helium cools and contracts, the lifting force decreases, and the balloon descends. The descent can be countered by dropping ballast. Typically, a ballast drop equal to 10% of the total weight of the balloon plus its payload is required for counteracting sunset. Thus, ballasting is usually practical for at most only two or three nights.

Another factor that limits flight duration is the wind velocity in the stratosphere. During most of the year, velocities at those altitudes are in the 80–160-kilometer per hour (50–100-mile per hour) range. Stratospheric winds (except near the equator) have a much more predictable pattern than do winds in the lower atmosphere. Because of these patterns a stratospheric balloon for most of the year will travel a distance that is equal to the width of the United States in one to three days. If the instruments that have been employed in these flights are to be recovered, as is usually the case, this limits the flight duration to that amount of time. During the spring and fall there is a transition period at which time the wind direction undergoes a 180° reversal. During this "turnaround" winds are light and variable in direction, and flights of longer duration are possible. Consequently, these are busy periods for balloon launchers.

58

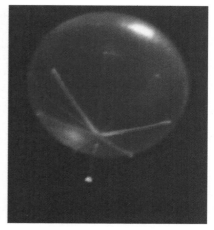

Launch sequence of a zero-pressure high-altitude balloon begins (below) with the balloon being inflated with helium through tubes on either side. The balloon is only partially inflated at launch so that as it rises the helium can expand. The payload is held on the launch vehicle at the right. (Left) The balloon begins to ascend; when it is directly above the launch vehicle, it will be released. (Above) At float altitude, approximately 39,600 meters (130,000 feet), the balloon has a volume of 820,700 cubic meters (29 million cubic feet); the object hanging from the balloon is the scientific payload.

The fabrication of the balloon and its successful launching are both difficult procedures. A 980,000-cubic meter (35 million-cubic foot) balloon, one of the standard sizes in use today, will have a diameter of 138 meters (450 feet), a surface area of 4.8 hectares (12 acres), and 35 kilometers (22 miles) of seams. The polyethylene must be uniform in thickness to avoid a weak spot. The welded seams must be as strong as the polyethylene itself. After fabrication the balloon is carefully folded into a box for shipping to the launch site. The size of the balloon and fragility of the material preclude any testing of the finished product. Thus, quality control is of the essence at every stage of the fabrication. Winzen International in Sulphur Springs, Texas, and Raven Industries of Sioux Falls, South Dakota, the two principal manufacturers, each extrudes its

Polyethylene film for the panels of a high-altitude scientific balloon is extruded from a die at the base of an extrusion tower (right). The material cools as it goes up the tower. Polyethylene panels for a new balloon are laid out on tables that may be as long as 210 meters (700 feet; above). They are cut to a specified curvature and kept in place with weights. Panel material is manually aligned in front of a sealer (above right) that is used to weld the seams of a balloon.

own polyethylene in order to ensure that the necessary standards are met. Each developed its own special type of film, which contains special additives to prevent the balloon material from becoming brittle at the −80° C (−112° F) temperature that can be encountered during ascent.

For some investigations a longer flight duration than just a few days is required. (An advantage of a satellite experiment is the months or years it will be in orbit.) One way to accomplish this is to use a superpressure balloon—a sealed balloon, usually spherical in shape, that is filled with just enough helium so that there is a slight overpressure at float altitude, even at the lowest nighttime temperature. Thus, the balloon will be fully inflated. During the day the heating of the helium will increase the pressure differential, requiring that the balloon film be a very strong material, usually mylar, to withstand the added stress. Because the volume remains constant in this type of design, the balloon floats at the same altitude (or, more accurately, at the same pressure) day and night. Such balloons have been used to trace stratospheric winds, and some have remained aloft for more than a year. However, it has proved difficult to fabricate the large sizes required by many heavy-payload, high-altitude missions.

A superpressure balloon—one that is filled with just enough helium so that there is a slight overpressure at float altitude— is launched to study the atmospheric circulation in the Southern Hemisphere. The balloon fills out at an altitude of 14 kilometers (8.7 miles) and typically remains in flight about four months.

Vincent E. Lally, National Center for Atmospheric Research, Boulder, Colo.

A balloon system developed for the Earthwinds project undergoes a test flight in 1990. In order to achieve long flight duration, it employs the Sky Anchor configuration of a zero-pressure balloon on top, the payload in the middle, and a superpressure balloon on the bottom. The loss of lift by the zero-pressure balloon at sunset is compensated for by increased lift on the superpressure balloon as the system descends to lower altitudes. A three-man crew hoped to circle the Earth nonstop in such a vehicle.

Another method for long-duration flight was developed by Vin Lally of the U.S. National Center for Atmospheric Research, Boulder, Colorado. He pointed out that for certain combinations of balloon size, payload, and flight latitude, the sunset effect would not cause a zero-pressure balloon to descend all the way to the ground but would instead stabilize it at some lower altitude, still in the stratosphere. At the next sunrise the balloon would then ascend again to the original altitude, permitting flight durations of weeks or months. Because the crucial factors affecting such a balloon are the solar radiation and infrared radiation from the Earth, Lally christened it the RACOON (radiation-controlled balloon).

A third scheme, the Sky Anchor, combines the two methods with a configuration of a zero-pressure balloon on top, the payload in the middle, and a superpressure balloon on the bottom. With a proper choice of balloon sizes and superpressure inflation, the loss of lift by the zero-pressure balloon at sunset is compensated for by increased lift on the superpressure as the system descends to lower altitudes. The disadvantages of the Sky Anchor are its cost and the complexity of launch of the two-balloon system.

Observations of the atmosphere

Two main categories dominate the scientific uses of high-altitude balloons: observations of the properties of the atmosphere itself and observations of extraterrestrial radiation that is absorbed by the atmosphere. A third exciting new possibility is the use of balloons to explore other members of the solar system. As of 1991 the latter had been accomplished only on Venus, but several ideas were being studied for a future mission to Mars.

In principle, most high-altitude experiments could be done on either a balloon or an Earth-orbiting satellite. The latter has the advantages of being essentially outside the atmosphere and having a long flight duration. On the other hand, balloon flights are much less expensive, and the flight preparation requires months instead of years. In practice, balloon flights are often the first phase of a scientific investigation in which an instrument is tested and initial data analyzed. If the scientific results of such a flight warrant it, a satellite version may follow. Even after a satellite is launched, balloon experiments often continue to provide complementary observations.

Many experiments, beginning with the early balloon flights and extended to higher altitudes by sounding rockets, have shown that the composition of the Earth's atmosphere—nitrogen 78.1%, oxygen 20.9%, argon 0.9%, carbon dioxide 0.033%, plus smaller amounts of other gases—remains constant up to 100 kilometers (62 miles). There is enough small-scale turbulent motion in the atmosphere to prevent the heavier constituents from settling to the bottom. Water vapor and ozone are exceptions to this uniformity rule. Ozone is produced when molecular oxygen is dissociated by solar ultraviolet photons, and the atomic and molecular oxygen combine to produce ozone. In turn, ozone can be destroyed by the absorption of ultraviolet radiation. The maximum ozone concentration occurs at an altitude of 20 to 30 kilometers (11 to 16 miles). Thousands of observations of ozone above given locations during the past 60 years have shown marked variations with latitude and with the season of the year. More recently it has been realized that many molecules and chemical radicals (for example, OH, NO, NO_2, HNO_3, and HCl), although present in only trace amounts, contribute to the destruction of ozone in a complex series of chemical reactions. The introduction of manufactured chlorofluorocarbons into the atmosphere has the potential to reduce the amount of ozone in the stratosphere and thereby increase the amount of ultraviolet light that reaches the Earth's surface.

A worldwide program observing ozone and the trace molecules involved in its chemical equilibrium was begun during the 1980s using ground-, aircraft-, balloon-, and satellite-based detectors. Although a much more detailed understanding of atmospheric ozone was gained, it was far from complete. Scientists envisioned a long-term goal of developing the ground-based and satellite-based techniques so that they could provide all the needed measurements. For the immediate future, balloon sampling of the stratospheric composition will continue to be essential.

Each day of the year, observations of surface winds are made throughout the world. At many of these stations, meteorologic balloons are flown to obtain data about wind, temperature, and humidity in the lower atmosphere. The coverage is not uniform, being sparser over the oceans and the Southern Hemisphere than over the land in the Northern Hemisphere. Satellite measurements of temperature can be used to infer the wind data, although the results are less accurate than the direct balloon observations. The satellite-approximation method is not effective in the tropics, and so the superpressure balloon has been used to obtain data there. An example is the Tropical Constant-Level Balloon System, which was used in 1987–89 for more than 300 flights in the tropics at 13,500 meters (45,000 feet) near the equator. Data were transmitted up to a satellite. Each flight lasted two months on average, and more than 50,000 wind and temperature measurements were made, which greatly enhanced knowledge of tropical atmospheric circulation. Superpressure flights were also made in the stratosphere above the equator to investigate a little-understood 26-month cycle in which the winds reverse direction.

Planetary exploration

The Soviet satellites Vega 1 and 2, on their way to rendezvous with Halley's Comet, passed near Venus on June 11 and June 15, 1985. Each dropped off a package that included a balloon and a payload weighing one kilogram (2.2 pounds). The first floated at 54 kilometers (29 miles) above the surface 7° north of Venus' equator, and the second was 7° south of the equator. Each yielded information on pressure, temperature, and wind velocity for 46 hours until the batteries expired. Unexpectedly large downdrafts and atmospheric waves were detected in Venus' circulation. Future missions with several balloons aloft at one time would provide a comprehensive picture of that planet's atmosphere.

Jacques Blamont, who first proposed the use of balloons to probe the atmosphere of Venus, suggested the use of a Sky Anchor system to explore the surface of Mars. At night the lift would decrease so that the instrument package would rest on the planet's surface and sample the soil at that location. The next day the sunlight would cause the balloon to ascend to a float altitude of several kilometers and move to a new location. Possibly a deployable spinnaker could be used to navigate to a particular place. Such a system could explore rough terrain much more easily than could a surface rover vehicle.

Extraterrestrial radiation

Balloons have been used for observations at almost every wavelength of the electromagnetic spectrum from the far infrared to high-energy gamma rays. Except for the narrow visible band and some windows in the infrared, the Earth's atmosphere absorbs most of this radiation. However, the 0.5% of the atmosphere remaining at the typical float altitude provides a clear window, absorbing only low-energy X-rays.

One of the most exciting scientific results of 1990 came from the COBE (Cosmic Background Explorer) satellite. The spectral measure-

Weather balloons carry meteorological instruments to altitudes of 30 kilometers (18.6 miles) and above to measure temperature, pressure, humidity, and winds. The balloons are made of rubber and weigh up to one kilogram (2.2 pounds).

National Center for Atmospheric Research/National Science Foundation

64

ment of the cosmic microwave background, from one centimeter to 0.5 millimeter (0.4 to 0.02 inch), corresponds to a blackbody spectrum with a temperature of 2.74 K. (A blackbody absorbs all incident radiation.) This radiation is thought to be the electromagnetic remnant of the primordial cosmic explosion, the so-called big bang. Two decades of balloon experiments preceded COBE, establishing the blackbody shape of the spectrum, though to a lower accuracy, and developing the instrumentation that led to that employed by the satellite. Balloon experiments were expected to continue investigating the spatial distribution of the radiation at the scale of 1°, appreciably better than the 7° angular resolution obtainable by COBE.

Observations in the infrared (IR) part of the spectrum (1–1,000 micrometers; one micrometer = one millionth of a meter) benefit greatly from balloon altitudes because of both the atmospheric absorption and the high background noise level caused by the IR emissivity of the atmosphere. Information about IR is essential for the elucidation of a number of basic problems in astronomy: (1) galactic structure and evolution; (2) the nature of the center of our Galaxy; (3) star formation and evolution in molecular clouds; and (4) the structure of the solar system. During the last 25 years two dozen groups throughout the world have flown a variety of telescopes and detectors that led to many scientific advances and instrumentation improvements. The designs of the highly successful Infrared Astronomy Satellite (IRAS) and the Space Infrared Telescope Facility (SIRTF), planned for the late 1990s, owe much to their balloon ancestors.

The International Ultraviolet Explorer (IUE) satellite has been operating since 1978, providing the bulk of the astronomical ultraviolet data above the atmospheric cutoff. The Hubble Space Telescope has a high-

Artist's drawing shows a Soviet research balloon floating about 54 kilometers (34 miles) above the surface of Venus in 1985. Placed there by a Soviet Vega space probe, the balloon measured pressure, temperature, and wind velocity for 46 hours until the batteries expired.

Mark Maxwell—Space Art International

resolution spectrograph designed for operation in the ultraviolet, which is the least affected of any of the telescope's detectors by the spherical aberration of the primary mirror. Nevertheless, the continuation of an active balloon program will complement the satellite observations in two main areas: high-resolution stellar spectroscopy and wide-field imaging, which bears on a number of important problems in galactic structure.

High-energy electromagnetic radiation above 15 keV (thousand electron volts) penetrates the atmosphere to balloon altitudes and is of particular interest to astrophysics because it is a direct by-product of the high-energy processes taking place in many astronomical phenomena, such as solar flares, the galactic center, supernovas, active galactic nuclei, pulsars, and black holes. A number of landmark observations have been achieved by balloons, including the first solar X-ray flare, the first observation of a flare from a cosmic source, the spatial structure of the Crab Nebula, the long-term variability of Cygnus X-1 (a black hole candidate), and cyclotron X-ray emission from a pulsar. The high-energy part of the spectrum will be only partially covered by upcoming satellite observatories. Future experiments would benefit greatly by long-duration balloon flights. These would improve the statistical precision of the results because many of the sources vary with time.

The boundary between X-rays and gamma rays is rather an arbitrary one, usually placed at 100 keV. A little-understood phenomenon is the gamma-ray burst, a very intense, sharp increase in gamma rays that lasts only a few seconds. Attempts to correlate the bursts with known astronomical objects have, so far, been inconclusive.

All of the gamma-ray detectors that have been flown on satellites were originally developed for balloons. Observations from the Gamma Ray Observatory satellite (GRO), from which long exposures free from the atmospheric background can be made, are expected to produce significant advances in the field. Nevertheless, balloon experiments will still play an important role by utilizing the high-resolution germanium detectors that have recently been developed. The present generation of gamma-ray detectors is plagued by poor angular resolution. On GRO the experiments typically are not able to resolve sources unless they are separated by at least several degrees.

A new method for taking detailed pictures in a part of the spectrum where the conventional optics of mirrors and lenses do not work is illustrative of how it is possible to take advantage of an advance in technology quickly with a balloon flight. This method uses a device called the coded aperture mask. It produces a spatially modulated pattern on the detector that can be decoded to recover the picture. A group at the California Institute of Technology successfully used this method with low-energy gamma rays to map the sky in the region of the Large Magellanic Cloud and show that the gamma rays they detected came from the SN 1987A and not from one of the nearby X-ray sources. Coded aperture masks will in time enhance the performance of satellite gamma-ray telescopes but, given the long time necessary for planning satellite experiments, this will be delayed until well after the year 2000.

Designs of the Space Infrared Telescope Facility (below), planned for the late 1990s, and the highly successful Infrared Astronomy Satellite (bottom) were strongly influenced by the information gained from flights of scientific balloons.

Photos, NASA

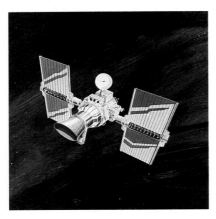

66

In 1911 Victor Hess began a series of balloon flights that resulted in the discovery of cosmic rays, for which he received the Nobel Prize for Physics in 1936. He showed that there is extraterrestrial high-energy radiation that permeates the atmosphere. One of the first achievements of the zero-pressure balloon after World War II was to take particle detectors to an altitude high enough to determine the composition of this radiation, which was 90% protons, 9% helium nuclei, and 1% an assortment of electrons and heavier nuclei ranging from lithium to lead. A few of these particles have an energy of 10^{20} eV, orders of magnitude greater than can be achieved by any particle accelerator on the Earth. A variety of detectors on balloons and satellites have been used to measure the energy spectrum and elemental composition of the individual constituents of this cosmic radiation. One of the experiments planned for the proposed space station is to use a large superconducting magnet for the analysis of cosmic rays, a technique that was well established in a series of balloon experiments. The long exposure time available on the space station would provide improved statistical accuracy in the measurements, particularly for the amount of antimatter present in the cosmic radiation.

Future prospects

Although satellites have taken over and, in many cases, enhanced some of the high-altitude observations that were once performed solely by balloons, there remains a strong need for suborbital flights. In addition to satisfying the specific scientific requirements already described, balloon programs contribute to the training of scientists in space operations. The rapid response time provided by a balloon is better suited to a graduate student's time scale than is a lengthy satellite project. New instrumentation will continue to be flown first on balloons.

The scientific community would benefit greatly if funding for scientific ballooning were increased. There is always a tendency to emphasize the glamorous satellite programs and overlook the contributions made by balloons. Specific improvements in balloon technology that could be developed in the near future with increased funding include flights of up to several weeks with heavy payloads, higher float altitudes, and the capability to launch heavier payloads.

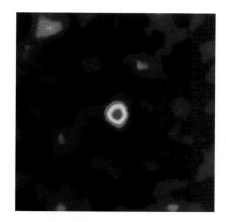

A repeating pattern of hexagonal lead blocks supported on an aluminum base forms the coded aperture mask (above), a device that allows detailed pictures to be taken in parts of the spectrum where the conventional optics of mirrors and lenses are ineffective. This mask was installed in a Gamma-Ray Imaging Platform (GRIP) instrument that was then lifted by a balloon to study emissions from Supernova 1987A. The computer-generated image of the supernova (top), as it appears in its emission of hard X-rays and gamma rays, was obtained from analyses of the GRIP data.

Photos, Stephen M. Schindler, California Institute of Technology, Pasadena

FOR ADDITIONAL READING

Jacques Blamont, "Exploring Venus by Balloon" (*Planetary Report 7*, No. 1, pp. 3–4, 1987); "Exploring Mars by Balloon" (*Planetary Report 7*, No. 3, pp. 8–10, 1987).

Carole S. Briggs, *Research Balloons: Exploring Hidden Worlds* (Lerner Publications Co., 1988).

Tom D. Crouch, *The Eagle Aloft: Two Centuries of the Balloon in America* (Smithsonian Institution Press, 1983).

G.M.B. Dobson, *Exploring the Atmosphere* (Clarendon Press, 1963).

Bruce D. Nordwall, "U.S. Places New Emphasis on High Altitude Balloons," *Aviation Week and Space Technology* (Oct. 23, 1989, p. 34).

SPACE:
A NEW LABORATORY FOR BIOLOGISTS

by George M. Malacinski and Anton W. Neff

Experiments have revealed that animals and plants can survive short-term flights in space. How they will adapt to longer stays in a weightless environment is a question that is stimulating considerable research.

For more than two centuries researchers have been intrigued by the question of the role that the Earth's gravitational force ($1 \times G$) plays in the development, growth, survival, and evolution of animals and plants. They realized early that the best way to test the effect of $1 \times G$ on life on Earth was to perform scientific experiments in the absence of gravity (weightlessness). As early as the late 1700s, newly invented hot-air balloons were employed to hoist a variety of animals to the unheard-of height of 470 meters (1,540 feet) above the Earth. Not surprisingly, all of the test animals survived.

For the next two centuries scientists could only dream about experiments in weightless conditions and had to be satisfied with simulations such as drop towers, high-altitude balloon flights, and low-altitude rocket flights. In the late 1950s, though, the Soviet Sputniks 1 and 2 ushered in a new era. For the first time in human history, true near weightlessness (microgravity) was achieved.

The early orbital missions provided evidence that virtually all organisms manage to survive spaceflight. Attention is now focused on whether animal and plant embryos can develop normally and perhaps even prosper in a weightless environment and what sort of short-term adaptive mechanisms they employ to accomplish this. Eventually, as the duration of spaceflight missions is extended, experiments on evolution in weightless conditions will be possible. Direct experimentation may answer to what extent gravity plays a role in the evolution of biological diversity.

Because of the importance of studies of developmental biology within the broad scope of present-day space biology, it is perhaps worthwhile to define its meaning. Developmental biology is usually defined as the process whereby an organism progresses from its initial unicellular beginning to a more complex and usually multicellular form. In order to generate fully meaningful information, however, the study of develop-

GEORGE M. MALACINSKI is *Professor of Biology and* **ANTON W. NEFF** is *Professor of Anatomy at Indiana University, Bloomington.*

(Opposite page) Illustration by John Mahoney

69

The Long Duration Exposure Facility unmanned spacecraft orbited the Earth from 1984 until it was retrieved by the space shuttle Columbia in 1990. The craft carried 57 experiments to test the effects of a lengthy stay in space on a variety of organisms and other materials.

mental biology in space should encompass an organism's entire life cycle. The designation of the beginning stage of a life cycle is often arbitrary. For animals, fertilization of a mature egg is usually considered to represent the "official" starting point. The production of eggs and sperm is, however, a complex and prolonged process that in itself represents substantial development. Likewise, maturation and aging, since they occur in a regular fashion and are largely regulated by gene expression patterns that are fundamentally similar to those involved in the early development of the embryo, should also be included in a comprehensive developmental life-cycle diagram.

70

Major differences between animal and plant life cycles exist, and so a diagram that attempts to describe both multicellular plant and animal developmental life cycles would be overly simplistic. Plants are, for example, sessile; they do not move. Their seeds are, therefore, highly specialized for dispersal. Having rigid cell walls, individual cells within the plant also do not move. That provides a major constraint on their development. Rigid cell walls do, however, provide substantial structural support. Many plants, therefore, grow to enormous heights in search of sunlight. As will be explained below, developing plants usually display much more dramatic responses to gravity than do animals.

Another feature of plant development that differs dramatically from the typical animal pattern is indeterminant growth. Some plants, such as the famous olive trees of the Middle East and the redwoods of California, grow for centuries. Furthermore, individual plants of a species show much more diversity in size and structure than do individual animals of a single species. Uniformity among animals is possible because they can move; they can find the environment that best suits their structure. Immobile plants cope with their environment by modifying their developmental growth patterns. They respond to environmental fluctuations more slowly than animals—by bending, growing new organs, or spreading to occupy a new space.

Incentives for research

Several considerations have propelled the study of developing organisms to the forefront of contemporary space biology. One of them is the obvious concern for the health and safety of astronauts during long-term spaceflight. Since the earliest manned spaceflights, it has been widely recognized that the microgravity environment has anatomic and physiological effects on astronauts, such as space sickness, bone decalcification, muscle atrophy, and cardiovascular system changes. Those effects can impair astronaut activity and delay recovery after the mission. A thorough analysis of the development of tissues and organs is expected to provide background information for devising strategies to cope with the stresses that astronauts must endure during spaceflight. As flight durations increase, concern for astronaut health will become even more relevant.

A second impetus for studying developmental life cycles in space is the novel environmental challenge that microgravity presents to most embryos. Organisms have been evolving in a $1 \times G$ environment for more than three billion years. Sudden exposure to microgravity presents an enormous perturbation. By carefully analyzing an embryo's response to microgravity, researchers are certain that they will gain significant insights into basic cellular and physiological processes. In this regard microgravity serves as an experimental tool or probe for studying such aspects of development as bone formation and muscle growth. Both of those phenomena are substantially altered during microgravity exposure. Unraveling the causes of microgravity-induced bone demineralization, for example, is expected to shed light on the biochemical and cellular events that comprise normal bone development (at $1 \times G$).

Healthy tomatoes were grown from seeds that were maintained in space for more than 5½ years aboard the Long Duration Exposure Facility. The seeds from space germinated more rapidly than seeds that had remained on the Earth.

NASA

71

After eight days in orbit aboard the space shuttle Columbia, *mung bean seedlings grew much as they would have on the Earth. A few bean roots grew out of the soil in the almost*weightless environment of the spacecraft.*

A third reason to study developmental phenomena in space derives from the natural orientation responses that most plants and some vertebrate eggs exhibit in the Earth's gravitational field. Higher plants invariably send shoots up and roots down (toward gravity). Amphibian eggs display a dramatic, fertilization-induced, orientation to the gravity vector (the force of gravity on a unit mass). Other large vertebrate eggs, including those of birds and reptiles, also orient themselves in the Earth's gravity. Whether those orientations are a necessary feature of early development has long intrigued embryologists.

A fourth incentive for the study of developmental biology of organisms in space comes from the momentum generated by research. Once the relatively straightforward question of whether a wide variety of fully grown or adult organisms can survive exposure to microgravity without catastrophic effects was answered, it became obvious that the effects of microgravity on developmental life cycles, if they exist at all, are very subtle. Because of the apparent fragility of embryos and the intricate, timed cell and tissue movements and interactions that occur during development, attention was directed toward embryos, larvae, and juveniles. It was envisioned that effects of microgravity on those early stages would be amplified during later development.

Finally, substantial theoretical interest in the study of developing organisms in space has emerged. This interest has pointed in two directions. First, concern as to whether humans will ever be able to colonize outer space has caused many biologists to examine developmental life cycles. If humans colonize space, they will take domestic plants and animals with them. This raises the question as to whether the passage of animals and plants through multiple generations will be feasible in a space station. That question will be addressed below. Second, the possibility of studying evolution in action might be feasible with long-duration spaceflight. Evolutionary biology as a discipline consists primarily of descriptive and theoretical approaches. The direct experimentation that is usually impossible for most analyses in evolutionary biology might be overcome (for gravity studies) with long-term spaceflights of organisms that have relatively short generation times.

Test systems

Multicellular organisms are usually considered to represent the most appropriate test systems. Although single-celled organisms such as bacteria and protozoa are prevalent on Earth, they lack many of the complex structures that characterize the individual cells of multicellular organisms. Also, they usually lack the sophisticated functions frequently associated with multicellularity, such as elaborate intercellular communication mechanisms.

In addition, most unicellular organisms are too small for most known gravity effects. Cells that are less than 10 micrometers in diameter (which include bacteria and some protozoa) are not expected to be directly affected by gravity. Gravitational force is considered to be negligible compared with other forces that affect these organisms.

Embryos provide especially good test material for spaceflight. They are ordinarily considered to be relatively fragile and, therefore, likely to display the effects of even subtle defects caused by changes in the gravity vector. They are also simpler and smaller than the full-grown adult forms. They contain fewer types of cells and tissues and lack the sensory perception responses that in adults might permit stress-related effects to interfere with data interpretation.

Development of animals

Six research questions are central to the study of animal development in space. The first asks whether survival in the microgravity of space involves adjustments or adaptations in the individual cells of a multicellular organism. There is no doubt that embryos of most species can survive a spaceflight of limited duration. Several types of embryos have been flown for several days. The amount of development they completed in space depended, of course, on their intrinsic growth rates. One of the most rapidly developing types—the insect embryo—developed from fertilization through the larval stages to the adult stage. Less complete but generally similar results were observed for the embryos of more slowly developing species. For example, frog eggs that were fertilized prior to launch hatched normally, and the hatchlings developed to the tadpole stage; also, pregnant rats gave birth, after spaceflight, to normal pups.

In most cases not all of the embryos in an experiment developed normally or, in several instances, even survived spaceflight, yet the fact that in each experiment several embryos in a batch developed normally

Photos, Anton W. Neff

Newly spawned frog eggs, like those of most amphibians, are darkly pigmented in one hemisphere and lightly pigmented in the other (above). Within minutes after fertilization, they spontaneously rotate in their jelly capsules so that the darkly pigmented hemisphere faces up, away from gravity (above right). Scientists plan to expose such eggs to the microgravity of space to see if they will continue to orient themselves in this way and if subsequent development of the frogs will be adversely affected if they do not.

should be interpreted as evidence that they can withstand microgravity. These results surprised many space biologists. During its early development, the embryo is usually considered to be relatively fragile. Therefore, the effects of exposure to microgravity, even if subtle at the outset, were expected to cascade into major embryonic abnormalities, such as convoluted or absent appendages, defects in specialized organs, or behavioral anomalies. That was clearly not the case.

Whether many, if not all, of the individual cells in embryos or, for that matter, in adults (such as astronauts) perceive microgravity and undergo subtle metabolic changes is a subject of debate. Since both embryos and adults survive spaceflight, the so-called cellular effects of microgravity are either confined to a limited number of cells or compensated for by changes in selected metabolic functions. Nevertheless, alterations in cellular functions have been observed in various types of cells when those cells are cultured as single cells (like microorganisms) during spaceflight. For example, during a seven-day flight human tumor cells multiplied and there was a slight increase in cell size, and over six days Chinese hamster cells multiplied and exhibited slight differences in structure.

A major consideration in the interpretation of the data is the conditions under which the cells were cultured during the microgravity exposure. The experiments were carried out on cells isolated from their natural environment and placed in a highly artificial environment; this in itself might sensitize them to microgravity.

The second basic research question is concerned with whether a wide variety of animals will develop through multiple generations in space. For developmental biologists the ultimate experiment is this "multiple-generations" test. Determining whether an organism can successfully complete its full life cycle in microgravity would clarify many of the aspects of space developmental biology. In addition, successful multiple generations would set the stage for the evolutionary questions and space-colonization issues discussed below. Although the multiple-generations test on *Arabidopsis* is nearing completion (*see* below), similar efforts for animals remain in the planning stages.

Four considerations complicate the animal efforts. First is the need for a spaceflight of relatively long duration, especially if a vertebrate is chosen to be the test organism. The relatively long generation times of a typical vertebrate will probably necessitate the use of an orbiting space station rather than the more convenient space shuttle. Second is the requirement for a habitat that will facilitate breeding. Most vertebrates incorporate courtship routines into their mating scheme. Designing a cage or habitat that will facilitate physiological conditioning, courtship, copulation, development of embryos, postnatal development, growth to adulthood, and a repeat of that process for a second round represents no trivial task. Third is the choice of an appropriate test organism. Aquatic species would probably be the easiest to accommodate in the cramped quarters of a space station, yet mammals would likely provide the most useful information because they share features of fertilization, implantation, and gestation in common with humans. Fourth, for terrestrial organisms, there is the need to cope with the musculoskeletal system's tendency to atrophy in microgravity (see below). Installation of a large centrifuge that maintains the habitat at $1 \times G$ during spaceflight may be the most practical solution, but that would, of course, circumvent the organism's test encounter with weightlessness.

A third basic question asks whether spaceflight-induced changes exhibited by load-bearing bones and antigravity muscles can be prevented. The key events in the evolution of the gravity-loaded musculoskeletal system of present-day vertebrates occurred approximately 400 million years ago as sea animals moved onto land. Since then, all land-dwelling vertebrates have had to cope with the Earth's constant gravitational pull as a one-directional, stable environmental force. Gravity has probably had an influence on the evolution of size and strength. In the absence of weight, the musculoskeletal system undergoes profound changes. Although gravity requirements have not yet been extensively studied during spaceflight, it is expected that for normal embryonic and fetal development of muscular size and bone strength, a $1 \times G$ load is needed. The minimal gravity load that is required for normal bone and muscle development and maintenance should, of course, be established. It may, in fact, be somewhat less than $1 \times G$.

Two ways to deal with the effects of weightlessness have been proposed. The first is to install large centrifuges in the spacecraft to house all animals at approximately $1 \times G$. A second is to develop drugs, medications, or physical therapy routines that will either prevent or reverse deterioration of the musculoskeletal system. Before this second method can be successful, however, considerable further research is necessary. Additional basic information on muscle and bone metabolism must be accumulated. It was recently discovered, for example, that spaceflight decreases the proportion of slow-twitch fibers in many muscles. Spaceflight also suppresses the development of both the bone-forming cells and the matrix that surrounds them. The question arises as to whether (1) individual cells in those tissues "read" their environment and recognize that the load on them has been diminished because of the weightlessness and then respond to this by shrinking; (2) the musculoskeletal system works less in microgravity and then changes its metabolism; or (3) hormones that are released from the brain "spread the word" that less bone and muscle are required, thus reducing size.

Answering this question will be tedious because it is often difficult to distinguish between direct and indirect (stress-related) effects. Many of the spaceflight results on the musculoskeletal system can be achieved on Earth by placing organisms in physical restraints so that parts of the body bear reduced weight. This causes musculoskeletal shrinkage similar to that observed during spaceflight.

Understanding and resolving this problem is of great importance. A successful resolution of the muscle- and bone-loss problem will permit spaceflights of longer duration. Additionally, attempts to colonize space will be much easier if that problem is solved. If it is not, it is highly unlikely that vertebrate embryos will be capable of developing normally through the stages of their life cycles that involve development of the musculoskeletal system. Crippled, deformed, and severely handicapped individuals, from lower vertebrates such as amphibia to higher organisms such as humans, will result.

A related problem that must be addressed concerns the possible effects on vertebrates, including humans, when they return to Earth after experiencing long-term adaptation of their musculoskeletal systems to microgravity. Will they be able to readapt to the $1 \times G$ of Earth? Will there be permanent damage to their musculoskeletal systems? To prevent those possible undesirable outcomes, the installation of a gigantic centrifuge to house vertebrates in the orbiting spacecraft or the provision for centrifuging the entire spacecraft will be necessary. That type of modification of the spacecraft will require the design and construction of extensive equipment at considerable expense. In order for a permanent colony to be developed in space, such a centrifuge will therefore be required as an integral component of a large habitat.

The fourth question deals with the physiological and behavioral changes that short-term adaptation to microgravity comprises. The extent to which animals adapt to microgravity by altering their behavior patterns remains to be discovered. Although collectively a virtual zoo of animals—ranging from jellyfish through insects, frogs, and dogs to humans—has been flown in space, technical constraints have prevented careful study of behavior patterns.

Typically, short-term adaptation is mediated by sensory organs such as the vestibular and visual systems. These highly specialized "information receptors" perceive change in the external environment and use the nervous system to transmit relevant instructions to the appropriate muscle, gland, or other organ. The resulting adjustments in physiological processes or behavioral patterns constitute the short-term responses. The qualitative and quantitative features of these adaptations to microgravity are largely unknown. Just how much adaptation to microgravity is possible will be the subject of future experiments in space. Since the microgravity condition cannot be duplicated on Earth—it can only be

76

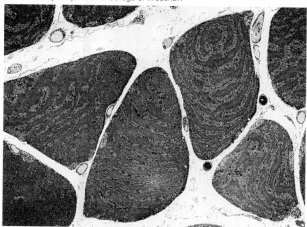 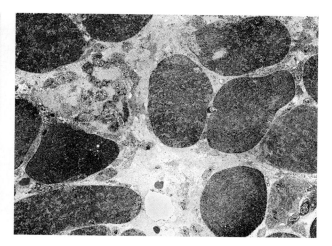

briefly simulated by parabolic aircraft flight, a drop tower, or a clinostat (an instrument that constantly rotates a sample slowly about a horizontal axis)—adaptation studies will require authentic space trials.

The fifth question is concerned with the types of evolutionary changes that will take place in organisms that have an opportunity for long-term adaptations to microgravity. In contrast to short-term adaptation, which comprises mainly behavioral modifications, long-term adaptation involves genetic changes. Predictions of the outcome of evolutionary studies in space will be difficult. A microgravity environment will be so novel, and the ramifications of weightlessness so extensive, that precedents for such sudden and wholesale changes in the environment do not exist. Typically, evolution has involved small and gradual changes in organisms as they evolve to fill increasingly more specialized niches.

One general prediction offered by evolutionary biologists concerns the nature of the changes organisms will exhibit. A metabolic function or structural property of an organism is almost never suddenly discarded. Rather, new functions and structures are added onto the end of a developmental sequence. Present-day organisms, having adapted to an earlier biosphere, reflect the history of that previous environment. Consequently, many of today's land-dwelling vertebrates possess vestigial gills as the evolutionary debris from their ancestors' aquatic environment. Evolution in microgravity can be expected, therefore, to generate new embryos that are more complex than those of today.

Since multicellularity appeared independently in many different lineages during evolution, developmental strategies employed by embryos vary widely. Also, mass extinctions may have eliminated some representative groups. These two considerations further complicate the matter of making accurate predictions concerning the eventual appearance of present-day embryos permitted to evolve at microgravity. Needless to say, developmental biologists will concentrate on studying the evolution of plants and animals that exhibit the following features: small size, so that a whole population can be analyzed; relatively rapid life cycles, so that evolution can be tracked over a reasonably short time frame; and rel-

Electron micrographs reveal the effects of microgravity on the adductor longus (AL) muscles of rats; these muscles have antigravity, postural skeletal functions. Above left are the fibers of an AL muscle of a ground-based control rat. They are packed with highly organized contractile proteins, and many capillaries occupy the connective tissue between the fibers. In a rat exposed to microgravity in a space satellite for 12 1/2 days (above), the fibers have shrunk about 36% compared with those of the ground-based animal. One severely damaged fiber (upper left) is filled with mononuclear cells that have ingested the contractile proteins. In addition, capillaries have degenerated, allowing red blood cells to escape from the muscle.

atively simple habitat requirements. Fruit flies and nematodes (worms) are likely candidates because they are well understood genetically.

Attempts to answer the evolution question will almost certainly generate many surprising discoveries. The joy of discovery that so often motivates scientists awaits those researchers who are willing to invest the time and effort in this endeavor. Truly remarkable evolutionary innovations, adaptive breakthroughs, and losses and gains of functions are all likely to occur.

The sixth basic question concerns the minimal requirements for an ecosystem that can support a colony in space. One of the first considerations is the need to generate an artificial gravitational field in an orbiting space station. This may not be necessary for the cultivation of plants because in the absence of gravity stems and shoots grow toward light. As discussed above, however, it may be necessary for the long-term reproduction, growth, and maintenance of higher organisms such as humans. Logistic questions abound, especially if recycling rather than resupplying is chosen as a strategy for dealing with the oxygen, water, food, and waste-disposal requirements of an orbiting space station. Resupplying a space colony with regular space-shuttle flights would be very costly, so recycling has been proposed as the most reasonable strategy. Both the U.S. and the Soviet Union have, therefore, established Controlled Ecological Life Support System (CELSS) programs. The goals of these programs include designing plant-growth chambers to generate sufficient yields of foodstuffs such as wheat, potatoes, and green vegetables to support astronauts for one or more years. In addition, technologies for processing and recycling wastes are being developed. One major concern, however, is the possibility that plant pathogens such as the bacteria that normally inhabit a spacecraft might infect a CELSS food crop. Resistant varieties of plants will therefore be needed for actual deployment in space. Another concern is the need for animal protein in order to supply astronauts with adequate supplies of essential amino acids and other nutritional requirements. Fish farming in space represents one attractive possibility, and it is being studied. It may even be possible to have a food chain in which waste disposal is connected to vegetable farming, which, in turn, supplies a fish farm with food.

Some researchers are thinking even farther into the future. They propose to develop a CELSS module for use on the Moon's surface. Such a lunar farm would have one distinct advantage; there is some gravity on the Moon. However, a lunar food farm would have to cope with the high radiation levels that bathe the Moon's surface, as well as the extreme vacuum in which the Moon exists.

Gravity effects on plants

Gravitropism, a plant's tendency to grow its shoots upward and away from gravity and its roots downward toward gravity, represents the most dramatic and easily demonstrated "gravity effect" on the development of a living organism. Research during recent years has focused on two major themes—the mechanisms of gravitropism and whether plants can

Plants are grown in a chamber at the Kennedy Space Center as part of the Controlled Ecological Life Support System research. Scientists hope that the knowledge gained from this project will help them design plant-growth chambers that will generate enough foodstuffs such as wheat, potatoes, and green vegetables to support astronauts in space for one or more years.

develop from seed to seed in space. Progress on the former issue has been substantial. The latter issue, the multiple-generations question, which is also on the agenda of many animal developmental biologists, was recently resolved in a definitive fashion for plants.

Plants offer distinct advantages over animals for space developmental biologists: (1) Virtually all higher plants display an unmistakable gravitropic response. (2) Earth-based studies that mimic spaceflight are easily carried out. (3) Plants are relatively easy to cultivate in a spacecraft. Approximately 30 years ago, the first plants were included in the early Soviet and U.S. satellite experiments. As is the case for developing animals, plants grow well in space. Survival is not an issue. Growth patterns and adaptation mechanisms have, therefore, provided the main focus of recent research.

Using a small, fast-growing plant, the Thale-cress, Soviet scientists recently carried out experiments on the Soviet orbital stations in an effort to answer the multiple-generations question. Seeds were planted during the flight. Approximately 10 weeks later the experiment was terminated, and the plants returned to Earth. Although the plants developed more slowly than their Earth-based controls, several of them produced seeds while in space. Those seeds were gathered and planted on the Earth. Many of them developed normally and grew into fruit-bearing plants. The percentage that did so was somewhat less than for the Earth-based plants used as a control group. Nevertheless, successful seed-to-seed growth and development was achieved in microgravity.

Further experiments are being designed to promote the growth and development of multiple generations in space. Seeds that develop in space will be planted in space rather than on the Earth, and their development through successive generations will be monitored. This is the "plant biology" version of the evolutionary adaptation project described above for animals.

A broad range of spaceflight effects on various plant organisms have been reported. In spite of the success with the seed-to-seed experiment, scientists are concerned about the following developmental abnormalities that have been observed: chromosomal aberrations such as breakage and mitotic defects, lower rates of cell division, diminished growth yields, and developmental arrest (frequently at the flowering stage).

The question arises as to whether these difficulties represent direct effects of gravity deprivation or are associated with specific spaceflight trauma such as liftoff stress; temperature fluctuations; water, oxygen, or carbon dioxide imbalances in the growth chambers; and cosmic radiation. Many plants are much more sensitive to their environment than animals because of their inability to adapt to changes quickly. Animals exhibit lightning-quick physiological changes, rapid movement, and instantaneous behavior alterations. Plants respond more slowly, usually by means of novel growth patterns. Perhaps that explains why they display so many abnormalities during spaceflight.

One of the recent Soviet space trials included centrifuges that generated a range of gravitational forces, including $1 \times G$, as a control for the experimental (weightless) group of plants. The result was always clear; plant growth and development occurred with a high frequency at a wide range of gravitational forces.

Originally, specialized cells of plants—statocytes—that contain amyloplasts (small organelles that contain starch granules) were considered to be the prime candidate for a plant cell's gravity-sensing mechanisms. Those organelles are easily displaced physically within the statocyte by gravity. However, a mutant form of a plant that lacks starch granules has recently been identified. It exhibits a somewhat reduced, but nevertheless distinct, gravitropism. Thus, the search for the molecular mechanism of gravitropism continues.

Although the site of the initial recognition event—previously believed to reside in the amyloplast—is now highly uncertain, evidence is mounting that the transfer of the hormone indole-3-acetate acid (IAA) to a new position in the cell and the movement of calcium ions constitute

A potato plant is grown in a controlled environment as part of the Controlled Ecological Life Support System project. Researchers are paying particular attention to the goal of increasing crop yields in microgravity.

the transmission system. Direct evidence for calcium ion movement was recently obtained by means of high-resolution tracking methods. The ions appear to accumulate on the slow-growing side of shoots that bend away from gravity. There they presumably inhibit cell wall extendability. To answer the "molecular mechanism" question conclusively, researchers must perform clear-cut experiments that demonstrate cause-and-effect relationships between each of the components (such as IAA and calcium) that are candidates for important roles.

Conclusion

As numerous space trials undertaken by scientists from the U.S., Europe, and the Soviet Union have clearly demonstrated, both animals and plants survive the rigors of short-term spaceflight. The extent to which animals will adapt to prolonged spaceflight is, however, unknown. Because the size, structure, and functional features of virtually all adult animal tissues and organs are established during the early stages of an organism's life cycle (especially during the formation of the embryo), researchers have focused attention on the features of development at those stages that are likely to display adverse consequences of weightlessness. Bone and muscle development have, for example, received substantial attention. Once those "gravity effects" are understood, scientists might be able to design strategies for coping with them in order to make long-duration spaceflights safer.

For plants, which display an unmistakable response to the Earth's gravity, adaptation to spaceflight is less difficult to accomplish. A successful seed-to-seed experiment, performed by a Soviet team, has been achieved. Attention is now being directed to such issues as increasing crop yields in microgravity and establishing the molecular mechanisms that cells employ to respond to changes in gravity.

Masqueraders
of the Plant World

by Paul Simons

Weeds pretending to be crops, plants shaped like small stones, flowers that look like insects or smell like dead animals—scientists are finding such strange deceptions to be more common than had been thought.

This is a story of false identities, deception, camouflage, and unwitting accomplices. It sounds like a thriller novel, but it is entirely about mimicry in plants, a subject gaining more attention as biologists continue to unravel the complex ways plants and animals interact. Plants often score surprising frauds over the animal kingdom. Their deceits include flowers that attract male insect pollinators with imitations of their female partners, plants camouflaged as stones to escape the attention of predators, and carnivorous traps that lure flower-seeking insects to their deaths. Although the masquerades vary widely, the ultimate aim is the same: to enhance the plant's chances of survival.

Not that plants deliberately trick animals by premeditated malice. Mimicry has evolved mindlessly through natural selection and random genetic mutations over many generations. Some feature that happens to serve as a mimic and that helps the plant survive is a valuable adaptation and so is more likely to be passed on to future generations. For example, if a plant whose flower looks like an insect attracts more pollinators than its neighbors, it is more likely to set seed and produce offspring.

Fraudulent females

Among the flower mimics, many species of orchids are superb imitators. They share the ability to fool a male insect into believing it has met a female partner ready for mating. The orchid flower copies not one but several features of the female—her shape, texture, smell, and color, the light she reflects, and the way she behaves—to make the deception work. If the fraud succeeds, the male tries to copulate with the blossom and during his struggles inadvertently dusts it with pollen he has carried from a previous flowery liaison.

Orchids reproduce particular species of insects so faithfully that they often are named for their models; for example, bee orchids and fly orchids. The best known of this type are members of the genus *Ophrys*, the European and Mediterranean bee orchids. Their flowers have no

PAUL SIMONS is a Producer for BBC Television, a free-lance writer, and a botanist.

(Opposite page) Illustration by Skip Williamson

SKIP WILLIAMSON

Photos, David Thompson—Oxford Scientific Films

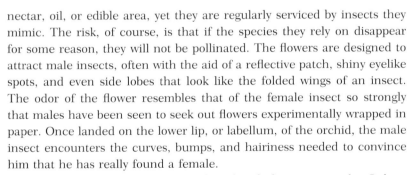

A male horned bee (above) attempts to mate with a flower of the bee orchid Ophrys tenthredinifera, pollinating it in the process. The flower's shape, color, hairiness, and shiny eyelike spots mimic a female bee with outspread wings (above right). Male bees that visit Ophrys lutea *(below), another bee orchid, place themselves upside down on the flower's lower lip, where the raised pattern resembles a female bee in the same orientation—head down and tail up.*

A–Z Botanical Collection

nectar, oil, or edible area, yet they are regularly serviced by insects they mimic. The risk, of course, is that if the species they rely on disappear for some reason, they will not be pollinated. The flowers are designed to attract male insects, often with the aid of a reflective patch, shiny eyelike spots, and even side lobes that look like the folded wings of an insect. The odor of the flower resembles that of the female insect so strongly that males have been seen to seek out flowers experimentally wrapped in paper. Once landed on the lower lip, or labellum, of the orchid, the male insect encounters the curves, bumps, and hairiness needed to convince him that he has really found a female.

One of the most peculiar examples of orchid mimicry is the *Ophrys lutea* of Mediterranean Europe and North Africa. Its blossom has a dark, raised area with two shiny bluish marks in the middle of a bright yellow lip—a form that at first glance looks nothing like the bees that visit it. Yet the male bee always places himself head down on the lip with his posterior facing up toward the flower. The mimicry in this case is that of a female bee resting on a yellow flower, head facing away from the flower.

An exquisite example of orchid foolery is the warty hammer orchid (*Drakaea fitzgeraldii*) of Australia. The lower lip of the flower is modified to look like the small, plump, wingless female *Thynnid* wasp. Even to human eyes the resemblance is nearly perfect: a shiny head; a rounded, slightly hairy body; and an uptilted end to the abdomen. The deception even extends to the scent—a copy of the sex pheromone, or chemical sex attractant, released by the female wasp. The dummy female sits on

the end of a short hinged arm and is free to bob up and down in the wind, hence the name hammer orchid. In perfect line with the arm and its hinge is the column, where the orchid's female and male sex organs are housed. When a male wasp grasps his intended and tries to fly off with her, his momentum carries him and the dummy up and over, pivoting on the end of the hinged arm and bringing his back smartly into contact with the orchid's pollen bags and female surface, which he pollinates with pollen brought from another hammer orchid. It can take only a second for the entire event to happen, during which he has already started to copulate with the lower end of the dummy. Only when he finds his "mate" to be firmly fixed to a plant and a waste of time does he give up and leave.

Even though the orchid's deception works, it is no match for the real female wasp. Given a choice between the flower and the wasp, the male always picks the insect. So, if the deception cannot compete with the real thing, how is pollination achieved in the wild? The hammer orchid's greatest ploy is its timing. It flowers several weeks before the females emerge from their underground pupae yet while the males have already begun roaming around in search of mates. The males are so eager that they are easily hoodwinked by the deception.

Mealtime mirages

For orchids like *Ophrys* insect mimicry works especially well because it attracts pollinators without having to pay them a nectar or pollen

To achieve pollination, the warty hammer orchid (Drakaea fitzgeraldii; top left) perpetrates one of the more bizarre and mechanically elaborate deceptions of the plant kingdom. The flower's lower lip, which resembles a wingless female Thynnid wasp in appearance and scent, is connected to the plant by a short hinged arm. When a male wasp grasps the dummy insect and attempts to leave with it (top right), he and the dummy are flipped up and over to the other portion of the flower (bottom left). There the wasp's back comes down into contact with the orchid's pollen bags and female surface (bottom right), which the wasp pollinates with pollen carried from another flower.

85

J.A.L. Cooke—Oxford Scientific Films

An insect-mimicking blossom of the Australian orchid Cryptostylis leptochila *deceives a male ichneumon wasp into copulating with it.*

reward. The same type of deceit works for other types of nectarless flowers, although they cadge a free pollination by copying not insects but other flowers. Their models do make nectar, and by mimicking them the imitators do not have to expend energy on their own nectar supplies. The copycat flowers mimic such features as color, texture, scent, and shape of the nectar-rich flower species. Furthermore, because they grow alongside the genuine flowers, they seem to be just another good supply of food to the visiting insects, which pollinate the flower mimics but leave empty-handed. The trick works only up to a point, however. For the con to succeed well, the mimic must not grow in such great numbers that the pollinating insects become frustrated and abandon their foraging altogether.

This is the ploy of the orchid known as the narrow helleborine (*Cephalanthera longifolia*), which is found in Europe, northern Africa, and western Asia. Its model, the flower of the rock rose *Cistus salvifolius,* is white with yellow pollen and is visited by pollen-gathering *Halictus* bees. The orchid sports the same colors as *Cistus* but contains no genuine reward; instead, its lower lip carries a cluster of yellow hairs, which the bee mistakes for pollen. The only pollen the insect gets is stuck on its back inside a special pollination bag, which it cannot reach to feed on—a clear case of food in the window, but none on the shelves.

Some flowers apparently mimic the prey of predatory insects to entice them into pollination. In the 1980s scientists discovered a European orchid, *Epipactus consimilis,* whose flowers seem to resemble aphids, or greenfly. The lower lip of the flower oozes a sugary secretion resembling the honeydew excreted by aphids, and its bumps and patterns look like an aphid infestation. These features are enough to fool aphid-eating hover flies, which buzz excitedly around the flowers.

The stench of subterfuge

Other flowers use a much more unsavory fraud to interest pollinators. Such insects as midges, bluebottles, and carrion beetles feed on rotting flesh, feces, and other organic detritus. To match this taste, a variety of flowers have copied the sensory essentials of decaying matter to lure the insects into calling on them.

The narrow helleborine orchid (Cephalanthera longifolia; *right) produces no reward for pollinators. It grows among patches of rock rose* (Cistus salvifolius; *far right), the flowers of which are white and carry yellow pollen that is gathered by* Halictus *bees. While the orchid features the same colors as the rock rose, what looks like pollen to the foraging bee is, in fact, yellow hairs on the orchid's lower lip. To human eyes the mimic and model do not look much alike, but to the bee's senses they are sufficiently similar that the insect pollinates both.*

Photos, Bruce Coleman Limited; (left) Hans Reinhard; (right) Eric Crichton

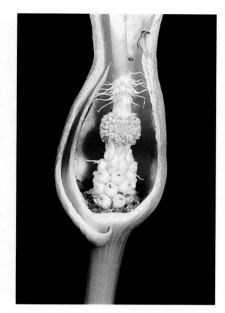

The arum lilies are masters at mimicking detritus, from color and texture to smell. At worst their putrid stink can be so vile that the average human would find it difficult to stand next to the colossal 2.5-meter (8.2-foot) bloom of Devil's tongue (*Amorphophallus titanum*) from the rain forests of Sumatra. Nevertheless, the scent is a powerful attraction to the large *Diamesus* carrion beetles that pollinate the flowers.

The foul odors of many arum lilies come from a pokerlike spadix nestling inside a cornet-shaped sheath, which swells at its base into a round chamber where the real flowers lie. An enormous release of metabolic energy is connected with the sudden production of these overpowering smells. In the European cuckoopint, or lords-and-ladies (*Arum maculatum*), researchers have found that as the plant's sheathed flowers begin to bloom, the upper portion of the spadix heats up 15° C (27° F) above the temperature of the surrounding air, vaporizing volatile chemicals responsible for the putrescent odor. The warmth also helps imitate rotting flesh and, together with the stench, draws carrion flies down past a one-way barrier into the floral chamber, where they pollinate the flowers inside. Only when that task has been achieved does the floral chamber wilt, letting the insects escape. Sadly for many of them the exhaustion of imprisonment is fatal, and insect bodies often pile up inside the chamber base.

The art of mimicry and kidnapping has been refined to its greatest sophistication in an arum lily found only in Sardinia, Corsica, and the Balearic Islands. The species, *Helicodiceros muscivorus*, grows among colonies of gull nests. Not being the most hygienic of animals, the birds collect a variety of trash, including bones, feces, regurgitated seafood, dead chicks, and rotten eggs—a happy hunting ground for blow flies. The challenge for *Helicodiceros* is to imitate this detritus to seduce the flies into pollinating its flowers.

*The foul, carrion-mimicking smell of the European cuckoopint (*Arum maculatum*) comes from a pokerlike spadix that protrudes from a large sheath resembling a flower (above left). When the plant begins to bloom, the upper portion of the spadix heats up, volatizing compounds responsible for the fetid odor. Together the warmth and smell attract flies, which become temporarily trapped in the bowl-shaped chamber at the base of the sheath, where the real flowers lie (above, shown sectioned). Only after the flowers have been pollinated does the trap wither and allow the insects to escape, although not before some of them have died.*

87

(Left) Hans Reinhard—Bruce Coleman Limited; (top right) Kjell B. Sandved; (bottom right) John Cancalosi—Bruce Coleman Limited

Mimicry of decaying matter is a strategy shared by the stinkhorn mushroom Phallus impudicus *(above), the carrion flower* Stapelia marginata *(top right), and the pelican flower* Aristolochia grandiflora *(bottom right). The cap of the stinkhorn is covered with a thick, shiny layer of spore-containing slime, which is eaten by blow flies and other insects attracted to the foul odor. Later, the undigested spores are dispersed in the insects' feces. The carrion flower's stench draws blow flies, which lay their eggs in the flower while pollinating it. The pelican flower is pollinated by small flies when they become trapped temporarily at the bottom of the giant, heart-shaped blossom.*

The floral sheath looks like a large ruddy-colored dinner plate standing on edge and flared out at the base into a flat platform. The plate is streaked with pale veins and is covered on its upper surface with dark red hairs. The spadix protruding from the center releases a stench with the power of a rotting sheep carcass.

The plant comes into flower when the gulls are nesting, but because competition from the real putrescence is simply too weak, the female flies flock to the *Helicodiceros* inflorescence instead. Once they have landed on the floral sheath, they look for a place to lay their eggs. Finding no obvious crevice, however, they pass down into the orifice leading to the floral chamber at the base of the spadix. It is just such damp, dark, fetid apertures that the flies would find in the eye socket of an animal carcass. Once inside the chamber the blow flies cannot escape past an array of inwardly pointing hairs, but the high humidity and smell excites them into laying their eggs as well as inadvertently collecting or brushing off pollen. Eventually the trap withers, allowing the flies to depart.

Fleur fatale

Plant mimics can be decidedly deadly. Carnivorous plants deliberately entice prey into death traps to consume them. Some of the more successful meat eaters are the pitcher plants (species of *Sarracenia*) of North American wetlands. To human eyes the pitchers of *Sarracenia* look like cornet-shaped green leaves with red veins, but recent research has shown that insects see the pitcher trap differently because their vision extends into the ultraviolet range of light, which is invisible to humans. Using a camera fitted with an ultraviolet filter, Danny Joel at the University of Haifa, Israel, and Barrie Juniper at the University of Oxford revealed how in ultraviolet light the traps show up brightly against the surrounding vegetation and their red veins stand out even more sharply, like the nectar guides of flower petals. Thus, it seems that insects are fooled into seeing the traps as flowers.

The deception goes further still. The rim of the pitcher makes drops of nectar, but once the insect has landed and tasted the offering, it becomes intoxicated with a powerful narcotic, slowly loses its footing, and slides down inside the trap to its death in a bath of digestive juices.

Fungal foolery

Species of fungi practice mimicry, and one recently discovered case may help save millions of dollars in damage to a valuable fruit crop. Blueberries are plagued by a disease called mummy berry, which is caused by the fungus *Monilinia*. Infection by the fungus induces leaf and shoot damage and, most costly of all, mummifies the berries into hard, white, inedible kernels, causing more than $100 million in annual losses worldwide. It had been thought that the disease spreads from one bush to another by spores blown in the wind, but no one had ever found the spores airborne. Recently this puzzle led mycologist Lekh Batra and entomologist Suzanne Batra of the U.S. Department of Agriculture, Beltsville, Maryland, to look at the diseased blueberry bushes more carefully. What they found took them completely by surprise: visiting flies and bees licked the fungal spores off diseased blueberry leaves as if they were feeding on flowers.

(Below left) Courtesy, Chicago Botanic Garden; photo, Charles Cegielski; (below right) from "Ultraviolet Patterns in the Traps of Carnivorous Plants," D.M. Joel, B.E. Juniper, and A. Dafni, *New Phytologist*, vol. 101, pp. 585–593, 1985, © 1985 The New Phytologist

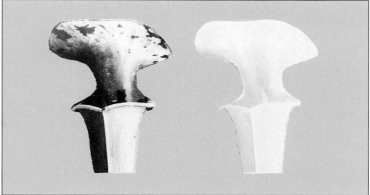

The pitcher traps of the carnivorous Sarracenia *pitcher plants are not flowers but specialized tubular leaves. Insects are lured into the traps by a sweet-smelling, intoxicating nectar secreted on the pitcher rim (left, S. rubra shown) or the inner surface of the hood. Recent research has shown that, as do many flowers, the pitcher traps in ultraviolet (UV) light display conspicuous patterns, to which insects presumably are attracted. Above left and right, a pitcher of* S. flava *photographed in UV and visible light are compared. Pools of secreted nectar stand out in the UV photo as dark spots on the hood's inner surface.*

Photos, Suzanne W.T. and Lekh R. Batra, U.S. Department of Agriculture, Beltsville, Md.

Inedible white kernels among blueberries (top) are the result of mummy berry disease, which is caused by the fungus Monilinia. (Above) A bee, fooled into regarding an infected blueberry leaf as a flower, picks up fungal spores while licking sugary secretions from the lesions; it will then carry the spores to real flowers, producing mummy berries. To complete the cycle, the fungus overwinters in mummy berries that have dropped to the ground. In early spring small mushroomlike cups appear (top right), whose spores infect emerging blueberry leaves.

It seemed a wild guess at the time, but it appeared as if the fungus was fooling the insects. Yet there were no obvious signs of mimicry. The infected leaves developed brown spots ringed by a blue-violet border, whereas the blueberry flowers are white and fringed with green sepals. Under the ultraviolet light that insects see, however, both the fungal lesions and the flowers showed like bright stars against a dark background. The scientists also found the sugars sucrose, glucose, and fructose on the lesions, the same sweeteners that blueberry flowers make in their nectar. To heighten the floral deception, the fungus gave off the same distinctive tealike smell as the flowers, a perfume that passing bees and flies found irresistible. While the insects fed on the "nectar," they collected fungal spores, which they then carried to healthy flowers—unwitting accomplices to the spread of a disease.

Fungi can even dupe large, intelligent mammals. It has long been known that sow pigs are driven frantic by the scent of truffles and dig vigorously for them, thus apparently helping spread their spores. No one knew why sows were so besotted with the subterranean fungus until it was found in the early 1980s that truffles synthesize a steroid that is chemically identical to a strong sex pheromone made by boars. Interestingly, the same substance is made in human testes and secreted in sweat. Psychological tests on men and women volunteers exposed to the steroid showed that both sexes rated photos of women more highly for beauty than did unexposed volunteers. Such an effect might partly explain why people find truffles a delicacy.

In addition to being mimics, fungi can serve as the models of imitators. In the late 19th century the esteemed botanist Arcangeli described a pollination strategy so "unbelievable" that his friends feared for his sanity. The little arum lily known as the mousetail plant, *Arisarium proboscideum*, attracts small flying insects into its floral chamber, where

90

A trained pig (left) helps locate underground truffles in Périgord, France. The natural affinity of female pigs for truffles may well be explained by the finding that the fungus synthesizes a steroid chemically identical to a strong sex attractant made by boars. The flower of the tropical orchid Masdevallia bella (below) attracts fungus-visiting insects with a fan-shaped central projection that has fleshy, mushroomlike gills and high humidity.

they are confronted by a spongy, off-white spadix uncannily similar to the *Boletus* mushroom. Arcangeli claimed that female fungus gnats, which normally breed in decaying mushrooms, were tricked by the mousetail plant into believing that they had found a safe mushroom on which to lay their eggs. More recently, botanists confirmed Arcangeli's suspicions, showing that the gnats do pollinate the flowers inside the floral chamber at the base of the spadix.

Fungus imitation is not uncommon among other species of flowers. Such plants tend to live close to the woodland floor, where one expects fungi to grow, and their flowers copy the colors of fungi—usually dark purple or brown with pale or translucent patterns. The flower's structure often accentuates the mimicry, which is sufficiently realistic to mislead fungus gnats into pollinating the flower. In the tropical *Masdevallia* orchids, for example, the prominent central part of the flower is shaped like a fan and features a number of fleshy, mushroomlike gills. The flowers even give off large amounts of water to the air, imitating the humidity of a mushroom.

Put-ons for protection

Self-protection is a powerful driving force in the evolution of plant mimicry. Several species of passion-flower (genus *Passiflora*) trick female butterflies into laying their eggs on other plants, so avoiding damage from their caterpillars. The deception relies on the fussy behavior of the female butterfly, which first feels her way over the stem to check for the presence of eggs from other females. If she discovers eggs, she flies off to find a fresh site. The passion-flower has exploited this behavior by growing its own dummy eggs—small nodules the same shape, size, and texture as butterfly eggs and deceptive enough to persuade the butterfly to leave.

91

Small nodules on the leaf stems of some species of passion-flower serve as butterfly-egg mimics, tricking female butterflies into laying their eggs elsewhere.

Though only distantly related to cultivated rice (left), the barnyard grass Echinochloa phyllopogon (center) mimics its appearance so closely that the two are almost indistinguishable. By contrast, E. crus-galli (right), a close relative of the mimic, is easily recognized by its color.

For some species the evolution of mimicry for protection is intimately tied to a long association of the plants with human beings. Thousands of years of farming have inadvertently selected weeds that look or behave so much like their crop-plant equivalents that farmers cannot get rid of many of them. Since plants were first domesticated, farmers have been removing weeds from their crops by hand. Even as the war between farmer and weeds has escalated with modern herbicides and better seed-cleaning techniques, the weeds have persisted. Often an imitator is so closely related to the crop plant that they cross-pollinate, yielding hybrids that are even more faithful replicas of the crop. The vicious cycle of inter-breeding can continue indefinitely, producing better and better copycats.

Such is the case for a species of wild rice (*Oryza rufipogon*), which has evolved so closely to cultivated rice (*O. sativa*) by hybridizing with it that the hybrids can no longer exist outside of rice fields. For the farmer the hybrids are the worst of everything. They retain the features that make wild rice inedible: small grains and hard husks that are difficult to mill. On the other hand, they have inherited all the features of cultivated rice that make them look like crops, and so their camouflage grows ever more successful.

Plant geneticists in India tried to rid the rice fields of the weedy rice by breeding a cultivated rice plant having purple leaves. That way the crop would stand out from the weed, letting the farmer pick off the weeds by hand more easily. Unfortunately, the weedy rice hybridized with the purple rice crop, and through the selective force of hand weeding, purple-leaved weeds became established.

Nevertheless, there is a strange irony to this evolution, because taken to its logical conclusion the hybrids of crop plants and weeds will become so similar to cultivated rice that they, too, could become a crop. After all, what is a crop other than a useful plant, and a weed a useless one? Oats and rye probably originated as weeds during wheat farming, thanks to the similarity between their seed and that of wheat. The mimicry helped the weeds survive winnowing, the ancient method of removing weed seeds by letting the wind blow them off together with the husks from the heavier grain. As weed seeds evolved with the same weight, density, and appearance as the wheat grain, they survived winnowing and became sown the next season as if they were a crop.

Not all weed mimicry, however, relies on a close genetic relationship with the crop. In the early 1980s Spencer C.H. Barrett at the University of Toronto made a detailed study of barnyard grasses (species of *Echinochloa*), which infest a wide variety of crops including corn, cotton, and fruit trees as well as rice. Unlike the wild rice weeds, barnyard grasses are too distantly related to rice to hybridize with it. Instead they "experiment" by producing a wide spectrum of genetic species and varieties having different appearances, some of which by sheer law of statistics look like cultivated rice plants. Indeed, one particular species, *E. phyllopogon*, is such a striking copycat that it can be distinguished from rice only by its lack of a tiny flap of tissue that is present in rice at the top of each leaf sheath. Even when the mimic produces seed, its fraud

Certain species of African succulent plants are masters at mimicking their backgrounds. Anacampseros buderiana (top left) looks like bird droppings. Even in bloom Pleiospilos simulans (top right) succeeds in passing for pieces of broken granite. Lithops lesliei (bottom) lies almost flush with the ground, its shape and color giving it the appearance of pebbles.

is still intact, for its grain looks like the rice grain yet is a completely useless food. With such camouflage barnyard grasses have infiltrated rice supplies worldwide and become a serious menace; no amount of mechanized or chemical weed control has eradicated them thus far. They have spread from Asia to many of the major rice-growing regions of the world, including California, where one species contaminated seed supplies that were sent to Australia in the 1930s. Today the weed is scattered throughout the rice-growing areas of New South Wales.

The art of camouflage in plants is taken to its most beguiling in the succulent *Lithops* genus of plants from the South African Mesembryan-themum family. Like the weeds mentioned above, *Lithops* plants use camouflage for survival, but rather than mimicking other plants, they pretend to be stones. The entire plant blends into its background of stony waste, its flat-topped surface lying almost flush with the ground and its shape and color resembling pebbles in shades of gray, brown, red, and beige. The plants are virtually impossible to spot, particularly during the dry season, when they shrivel. Other mimic succulents of this family include *Pleiospilos,* rough and speckled like pieces of greenish granite, and whitish, warty *Titanopsis,* which imitates limestone. The unrelated succulent *Anacampseros,* also found in Africa, resembles bird droppings.

93

The way that stone mimicry evolved probably dates back to the days when large numbers of mammals and ground-foraging birds roamed the plains of Africa. Grazing on low-growing vegetation, the animals might have devoured anything remotely plantlike in appearance, particularly during the dry season, when many plants wilt and die. Consequently, a plant that blends in with its background is likely to avoid being eaten. In support of this idea it is interesting that *Lithops* flowers only briefly during the wet season, when there is plenty of other food to occupy grazing animals.

Chemical chicanery

Research exploring the complexities of plant-animal interactions is uncovering ever more examples of plants that mimic important biological compounds of predators to defend themselves. For example, scientists have revealed how some plants subvert the hormone system of leaf-eating insects. Insects reach sexual maturity only after passing through a series of larval stages punctuated by molts. Molting is controlled by a balance between two hormones known as ecdysone and juvenile hormone. An upset to this balance sabotages the insect's development and often causes lethal abnormalities.

Chemical mimicry came to light in 1964 when entomologist Karel Slama moved from Czechoslovakia to the U.S., taking with him his favorite insects, colorful heteropterans (members of the true bug order) called fire bugs, or pyrrhocorids. After their relocation the bugs began to suffer a mysterious ailment: those that had molted normally in Prague remained immature in Cambridge, Massachusetts, and refused to molt further. The problem was found to lie in the newspapers carpeting their boxes. Whereas *The Times* of London had allowed them to molt properly, the *New York Times* retarded their development. Painstaking chemical detective work eventually pinpointed a substance in U.S. newsprint that occurred naturally in the balsam fir tree (*Abies balsamea*) from which the paper was made. The substance, which was called juvabione, delayed the insects' development by mimicking their juvenile hormone.

In the wild, fire bugs are unlikely to be threatened by American newspapers, but Yock C. Toong of the Universiti Sains Malaysia, Penang, and two colleagues from the Zoecon Research Institute, Palo Alto, California, in 1988 reported discovering a rich supply of another type of juvenile hormone in a plant called grasshopper's cyperus (*Cyperus iria*), a Malaysian relative of the sedge. Grasshoppers raised on a diet of cyperus experienced a range of defects attributable to hormonal upsets, including twisted wings, altered wing patterns, and infertility. The cyperus leaves were found to contain 1,000 times more juvenile hormone than the comparable weight of an average insect. Although the plant clearly benefits by fighting off herbivores, scientists hope that its chemical defense could be the basis of a new type of insecticide or that perhaps the appropriate genes could be engineered into crop plants to make them pest resistant.

Plants can mimic animal chemistry other than that of insects. Certain species of clover, for example, reduce the fertility of sheep by making a

94

Grasshopper's cyperus (Cyperus iria; bottom), a Malaysian plant, defends itself against herbivorous insects with a copy of a juvenile hormone, a compound important in regulating insect development and reproduction. In laboratory experiments grasshoppers raised on a diet of cyperus exhibited a range of defects attributable to excess juvenile hormone, including abnormal wings (left, bottom row). A control group of grasshoppers fed a diet of wheat seedlings showed normal development (left, top row).

substance that mimics female sex hormones known as estrogens. Even human reproduction can be affected by plant mimics, although the phenomenon has been turned to use for birth control. The earliest estrogen oral contraceptives were made from yam tubers, which had long been exploited as a form of birth control by South American Indians. Plant estrogens may also explain why women in The Netherlands who had eaten tulip bulbs during the famine in World War II suffered a range of menstrual abnormalities, including failure to ovulate. In effect, they may well have been taking oral contraceptives. Although it is tempting to speculate that plants have evolved the ability to make estrogens as a defense against plant-eating mammals, the chemicals may have several functions, all yet to be clarified.

More to unmask

Mimicry in plants encompasses a wide range of deceptions for a number of different purposes. Yet they all evolved from the interplay of random genetic mutations and the selective pressures of the environment in which the plants live, whether it be the pressure to find insect pollinators, to avoid predation or human interference, or to supplement their diets. In the past these strange adaptations attracted little attention, in part at least because plants were studied mainly in relation to their physical environment. While nectarless blooms that copy the appearance of nectar-producing species had been noted as early as the late 1700s, it was not until ecology took its place as a distinct science in the 20th century that scientists began to concentrate on the range of relationships—from mutually beneficial to inimical—between plant species and their biological neighbors. No doubt more examples of plant mimicry wait to be discovered, particularly in tropical ecosystems where the high species density has made the coevolution of many kinds of plants and animals inevitable. No doubt, too, some of these finds will prove to be important contributions to science and to have valuable applications in agriculture, medicine, and other fields.

In Australia several varieties of subterranean clover (Trifolium subterraneum) reduce the fertility of sheep that graze on them. The plants have been found to contain a compound whose biological effects mimic those of female sex hormones known as estrogens.

Stephen Dalton—Oxford Scientific Films

With the relatively recent emergence of ecology as a distinct discipline has come the realization that plant mimicry is more widespread than had been thought.
As biologists continue to focus on the interactions of plants and other species in the environment—particularly in tropical forests with their high species densities—many more plant masqueraders will reveal their true faces to science.

FOR ADDITIONAL READING

Spencer C.H. Barrett, "Mimicry in Plants," *Scientific American* (September 1987, pp. 76–83).

Suzanne W.T. Batra, "Deceit and Corruption in the Blueberry Patch," *Natural History* (August 1987, pp. 56–59).

D.D. Edwards, "A Leafy Home for One Insect Hormone," *Science News* (May 21, 1988, p. 326).

Thomas H. Maugh II, "The Scent Makes Sense," *Science* (March 5, 1982, p. 1224).

Bastiaan J.D. Meeuse, "The Voodoo Lily," *Scientific American* (July 1966, pp. 80–88).

Michael Proctor and Peter Yeo, *The Pollination of Flowers,* chapters 7, 10, and 12 (Collins, 1973).

Wolfgang Wickler, *Mimicry in Plants and Animals* (McGraw-Hill, 1968).

Invader from the South:
The Africanized "Killer" Bee

by Mark L. Winston

Since 1956, when several swarms escaped into the wild in Brazil, Africanized honeybees have multiplied to form millions of colonies and have moved steadily northward to the border of the United States and Mexico.

U.S.
BORDER

Nest of a colony of wild Africanized honeybees in Brazil is in a garden (above). Unlike bees in temperate zones, which almost always build nests inside cavities to protect themselves against the cold winters, the tropical Africanized bees often suspend their nests from tree branches, overhanging rocks, or buildings. At an apiary in Mexico (below right), a sign warns beekeepers to exercise caution when working with the easily disturbed Africanized bees.

MARK WINSTON is a Professor in the Department of Biological Sciences, Simon Fraser University, Burnaby, British Columbia. He spent many years in South America studying the Africanized honeybee and is the author of a forthcoming book on that subject, Killer Bees: The African Honey Bee in the Americas *(Harvard University Press).*

(Overleaf) Illustration by Ron Villani

The introduction of African honeybees to South America in 1956 has resulted in one of the most astounding success stories in the history of introduced species. These bees have spread at almost unprecedented speed, with populations growing rapidly to high densities throughout their range. Furthermore, the Africanized honeybees, the name most commonly used to refer to them in the Americas, have had an enormous impact on beekeeping and the public and have generated countless radio, newspaper, and television stories. Indeed, this bee has become such a significant media star that it has been granted its own nickname, the "killer bee."

By late 1990 these bees had spread throughout most of South America and all of Central America, and in October they first entered the United States from Mexico. Predictions of their impact are serious and include disruptions of both beekeeping and the production of bee-pollinated crops. The threat from these bees was recognized soon after their introduction, and it stimulated an enormous amount of research into their biology and potential management and control. What has emerged from these studies is a picture of a bee ideally preadapted to its new habitat and impervious to any barrier to its spread that has been proposed or attempted. This article will describe some of the reasons behind the unparalleled success of this unusual insect, discuss its impact in Latin America, and present predictions concerning what can be expected when the bee colonizes the southern United States.

Spread through Latin America

The key to understanding the success of Africanized honeybees is to recognize that they evolved in the tropics and thrive much better in tropical habitats than do their temperate-evolved cousins, the European honeybees. Honeybees (*Apis mellifera*) are not native to either North or South America but evolved in Africa and Europe. The bees from these two regions are the same species but developed different characteristics

Agricultural Research Service, USDA

Africanized honeybee (left) is physically almost indistinguishable from the domestic U.S. honeybee (right), which is descended from European ancestors. The Africanized bee, however, is more easily disturbed than its European counterpart and is, therefore, more likely to attack anything perceived as a threat.

to survive in their respective tropical and temperate habitats. All of the honeybees in North America were imported from Europe, and until the mid-1950s the bees in South and Central America also had a European origin. While European bees are good honey producers in the temperate climates of North America, they do not do well in tropical Latin America. African honeybees, on the other hand, had a good reputation for honey production in the tropics, although they were also known to be rather aggressive.

In 1956 a Brazilian geneticist imported some South African queen bees to Brazil with the intent of crossing the aggressive but tropically productive African bees with the gentler but less productive European variety. The objective of this experiment, of course, was to produce a better honeybee for Brazilian beekeepers to use. However, at least 26 swarms of pure African bees escaped into the wild before the crossbreeding could be accomplished, and other African queens were bred and distributed to Brazilian beekeepers; some of their offspring also escaped into the wild. These bees formed the nucleus of a feral honeybee population, which has since spread at rates of 325 to 485 kilometers (200 to 300 miles) per year. Further, these bees achieved enormous densities; it was estimated that in 1990 there were between 50 million and 100 million feral honeybee colonies in Latin America.

The phenomenal success of these bees is interesting in itself, but they also have had a tremendous impact on beekeeping. The queens from managed colonies have been mating with the feral Africanized bees, and these queens return to their colonies with Africanized characteristics. As is discussed below, the African bees did not live up to their reputation, and many of the same characteristics that proved so successful in the wild are highly undesirable for bee management.

101

Nest of Africanized honeybees on a beauty parlor in Mexico (right) demonstrates the wide diversity of sites that such bees will use for their nests; other locations include old tires and empty oil drums. A scientist from the U.S. Department of Agriculture analyzes parts of an Africanized honeybee (below). Scientists hoped that learning more about these bees would help them deal effectively with the swarms that were expected to invade the U.S.

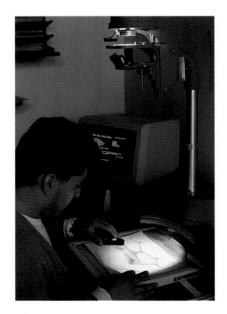

Characteristics of Africanized bees

The underlying reasons for differences between temperate and tropical honeybees are based in differences of climate, resource distribution, and predator abundance in their respective habitats. In temperate regions, cold winter conditions have selected for bees that construct large, honey-laden colonies to provide energy for winter survival. In contrast, winter has a different meaning for tropical honeybees. Temperature differences between seasons are minimal, and it is rainfall that determines seasonality because of its effects on flowering and nectar and pollen production. Tropical bees construct small nests and are quick to abandon them if floral resources diminish. Also, the overwhelming number of predators in tropical habitats relative to temperate regions has had considerable impact on tropical bees, particularly in the evolution of exaggerated defensive behavior. Interestingly, the spreading Africanized bees have remained virtually identical in their physical and behavioral traits to the bees originally introduced from Africa, indicating just how superbly pre-adapted these bees were to their new Latin-American habitat.

The most obvious difference between temperate and tropical honeybees is in their nest design. Temperate bees almost always build nests inside cavities to provide protection from cold winter conditions and are rarely observed by people. In contrast, tropical bees construct small nests and often build them outside cavities, suspending them from tree branches, overhanging rocks, or buildings. The diversity of nest sites that the Africanized bee will use is astounding; investigators have found nests in sewer manholes, old tires, rusting cars, empty oil drums, air-conditioning ducts, and many other unusual sites. Indeed, these bees are everywhere in Latin America, as they are in Africa, and are conspicuous aspects of the tropical landscape. The small size of the nests has considerable survival value for the tropical honeybees because they are easily defended from the intense predation by ants and mammals that is

102

A swarm of wild Africanized honeybees in Guatemala is captured and placed in a hive for use by a beekeeper.

typical of tropical habitats. Also, if a predator succeeds in destroying a nest, much less is lost by a small colony, which can then leave the site and begin a new nest elsewhere.

A second, striking difference between temperate and tropical honeybees is the higher reproductive rate of the latter. Honeybees reproduce by swarming or colony division, in which the old queen leaves the nest with a majority of the workers and establishes a new nest. Left behind are developing queens, which, when they emerge, may also swarm with smaller groups of workers; these are called afterswarms. Finally, one of the new queens in the old nest will kill the other young queens and reestablish the original colony. Unusual aspects of the Africanized bees are how frequently they swarm relative to European bees and the high number of afterswarms they produce each time they go through a swarming cycle.

The temperate-evolved European bees generally swarm only once a year and produce an average of one or one and a half afterswarms. This low swarming rate makes sense in a temperate climate, where much of a colony's energy needs to be applied to nest construction and honey production in order to survive the winter. Tropical-evolved bees have no such restriction on their reproductive rate and so can invest more energy into swarming. Africanized bee colonies will swarm three or even four times a year, producing averages of two or more afterswarms each time. Thus, a single Africanized colony can produce between 10 and 15 swarms a year; at this rate it is not surprising that feral Africanized nests quickly reach high population densities.

The high swarming rate characteristic of Africanized bees is largely responsible for the success of these bees in the wild, but it also has been one of the major management problems associated with them. In order to produce surplus honey, beekeepers must prevent swarming, thereby causing colonies to grow to abnormally high populations. The extra bees

103

Beekeeper uses a smoker to calm a swarm of Africanized bees (above). Smoke diminishes the bees' aggressiveness. A small plastic bottle with a sensor inside is hung near the entrance to a hive of Africanized honeybees (above right). The device records the number of times the bees will strike the bottle as they try to sting it. An early prototype of the device recorded up to 24 strikes per second for Africanized honeybees; domestic U.S. bees encountering the same device struck it about four times per second.

in colonies that have been prevented from swarming are available to collect nectar from flowers, thereby producing copious yields of honey. However, it has proved difficult for beekeepers with Africanized bees to prevent swarming, and so honey yields in their colonies have been severely reduced.

High rates of reproductive swarming are not the only problem facing beekeepers with Africanized bees; these bees also have a high probability of absconding, the abandoning of a nest by a colony that forms a swarm and reestablishes itself elsewhere. These absconding swarms differ from reproductive swarms in that no adult individuals are left behind when the swarm emerges, and so the original colony is no longer active. Unfortunately, this is not a rare occurrence with Africanized bees. An average of 30%, and up to 100%, of colonies in an apiary will abandon their hives each year.

There are two reasons for absconding, predator attack and poor resources. Attacks by ants, birds, wasps, anteaters, and even humans will cause any bees to abandon their nests. However, Africanized bees also abscond during the dearth season, which is usually the rainy season in Latin America. During this time flowering is patchy, and so a colony in an area without flowers may benefit by leaving the nest and searching elsewhere for better resources. European bees, which evolved in a climate where absconding would be highly detrimental, will dwindle and die rather than abscond during a tropical dearth season. Absconding by Africanized bees is highly adaptive in the wild but presents a major

104

problem for beekeepers. Obviously, honey production will be difficult if all the bees abandon the nest! When the high absconding rates of Africanized bees are coupled with high swarming rates, it is quite apparent why beekeeping has suffered in Latin America since the arrival of Africanized bees.

The defensive behavior of Africanized bees has received the most attention, and there is no doubt that these bees cause many more stinging problems than European bees. The sting of a single Africanized bee is essentially the same as a sting from any honeybee. When a bee stings, barbs on the stinger anchor it into the flesh, and the bee pulls away and dies, leaving the throbbing stinger behind to inject venom and give off alarm odors that alert other bees to attack. Honeybees are unusual among stinging insects in sacrificing their defenders, presumably because additional venom is injected when the stinger is left in the victim. The venom of Africanized bees does not differ from that of European bees, but the bees themselves are much more sensitive to disturbance and, therefore, more likely to attack and pursue anything perceived as a threat to their nests.

What is remarkable about Africanized bees is that under some circumstances some colonies are capable of sudden, large-scale attacks induced by only minimal disturbances. While there certainly are European bees that will sting readily and Africanized bees that are relatively gentle, the average Africanized colony is considerably feistier than most European colonies. Furthermore, the extreme attacks that can occur with Africanized bees are almost unknown among the European variety. Sometimes just walking near a nest will elicit a massive response by Africanized bees, with thousands of workers flying out to sting the walker within seconds. Under these circumstances there have been many livestock fatalities and some human deaths as well. It is difficult to get accurate statistics on the frequency of this type of attack, but it is known that about 350 Venezuelans were killed between 1975 and 1988 in this type of incident. While these attacks are uncommon, they are spectacular enough to earn the bee its moniker.

Fortunately, stinging problems tend to subside after Africanized bees have been present in a locality for a number of years. There is a familiarization period after the bees' arrival during which the public learns to avoid their colonies; in Latin America children rarely throw stones at beehives anymore. In North America, where there are better communications and access to medical facilities, excessive stinging incidents seem unlikely to be as common or as serious as in Latin America. Nevertheless, there will always be the potential for these bees to explode in spectacular stinging incidents.

The defensive behavior of Africanized bees is another trait that, in addition to causing beekeeping problems, has ideally preadapted them for a feral existence in tropical America. The high rate of predator attacks in Africa favored the development of rapid and effective colony defenses and was adaptive in the high-predation environment of Latin America. These defensive traits have given colonies a successful battery

Roadside apiaries in Mexico (top) are poorly located for Africanized honeybees; the traffic noise will disturb the bees, causing them to swarm and sting. A properly situated apiary, also in Mexico, is in a secluded area behind high vegetation (above).

of weapons with which to survive in the tropics. Unfortunately, the bees do not distinguish between beekeepers and predators.

Impact and management of Africanized bees

The notable success of Africanized bees in the tropics has caused serious problems for beekeepers. The high swarming and absconding rates typical of these bees, coupled with their extreme defensive behavior, make them difficult to manage. Furthermore, owing to mating between managed queens and wild Africanized drones, most beekeepers' colonies quickly become Africanized after these bees arrive in a new area. At this point most commercial and hobby beekeepers abandon their hives.

The experience of Venezuelan beekeepers has been typical of the problems that these bees can cause. The Africanized bees arrived in Venezuela in 1976, and their impact was dramatic. The nation's annual honey production fell from about 1,300 to 78 metric tons, and fewer than 10% of the beekeepers were able to maintain their colonies. Even the few beekeepers who persisted had to reduce severely the numbers of their colonies. In Panama the number of beekeepers was reduced by half, and they were managing fewer than 40% of the colonies that were in production before the Africanized bees arrived. Even worse, the honey harvest dropped to only 19% of its previous level, and a country that had exported honey was no longer producing even enough for domestic consumption. These statistics are typical of virtually every country that has had to deal with Africanized bees. In recent years the beekeeping industries throughout Latin America have bounced back slowly as they have learned to cope with these bees, but even today most countries have not fully recovered from the initial impact of Africanized bees.

106

In October 1990 the first swarm of Africanized bees reached the United States, crossing the Rio Grande from Mexico to southern Texas. The swarm was lured into a trap that was baited with an attractant lure. After they were identified as Africanized, the bees were killed.

Though the Africanized bees originated in the tropics, they should be able to survive throughout the southern United States. There will, however, be a limit to their northern spread. For example, the spreading front of Africanized bees has stopped in northern Argentina and has not progressed farther south into more temperate regions for almost 10 years. However, if the bees have a similar climatic range in the United States, they can still survive in Texas, Louisiana, Alabama, Florida, Georgia, Arizona, New Mexico, and most of California.

Can these bees be stopped? A major effort to do exactly that was proposed and implemented in Mexico in the late 1980s. Called the Bee Regulated Zone, it comprised a barrier involving thousands of European colonies and also large-scale destruction of feral Africanized nests. The expectation of this program was to genetically dilute most of the Africanized bees and physically destroy whatever swarms or feral colonies remained. However, this proved to be a fruitless endeavor; the number of wild Africanized colonies overwhelmed the project. These bees spread

Map reveals the spread of the Africanized honeybee in the Western Hemisphere since its introduction into Brazil in 1956. The projected spread northward into the United States is also shown. The cold winters in the central and northern U.S. are expected to stop the bees, just as they have checked their southward spread in Argentina. The Andes Mountains have stopped the bees from spreading into western South America.

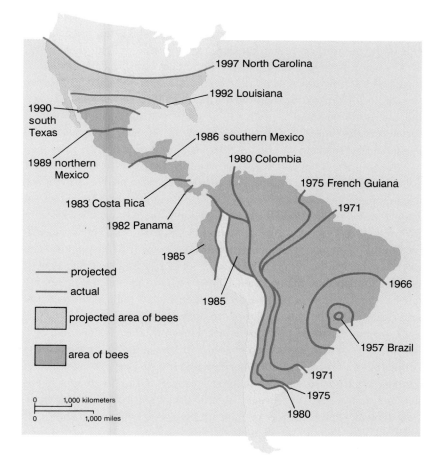

1997 North Carolina
1992 Louisiana
1990 south Texas
1989 northern Mexico
1986 southern Mexico
1980 Colombia
1975 French Guiana
1971
1983 Costa Rica
1982 Panama
1985
1966
1985
1957 Brazil
1971
1975
1980

—— projected
—— actual
☐ projected area of bees
☐ area of bees

0   1,000 kilometers
0   1,000 miles

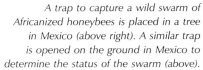

A trap to capture a wild swarm of Africanized honeybees is placed in a tree in Mexico (above right). A similar trap is opened on the ground in Mexico to determine the status of the swarm (above).

too fast, at too high densities, and were too successful in the wild for any type of barrier to slow or stop their spread. It is also difficult to conceive of a scheme to stop them, because honeybees are basically beneficial insects. Thus, any program to intervene in the feral population has to be specific to Africanized bees and leave the European bees alone. To date, there is no disease, pest, pesticide, or other control agent known that can accomplish this task. Therefore, people in the U.S. must accept the inevitability of the bees' arrival and learn how to deal with their presence.

The most detailed predictions from the U.S. Department of Agriculture concerning the potential impact of Africanized bees on beekeeping are frightening, with estimates ranging from $26 million to $58 million in annual losses (in 1984 dollars). Even the most conservative estimate of $26 million represents a 20% reduction in revenue, based on an annual total value of honey, wax, queens, and bulk bees of $122 million. The main impact will be reduced production of honey and beeswax, caused by the elimination of many colonies and reduced yields in the remaining ones. Other sources of income loss include loss of pollination fees and fewer sales of queens and bulk bees to beekeepers.

As serious as these predictions are, however, these effects on bee-keeping may be trivial when compared with the potential impact on the pollination and production of bee-pollinated crops. The U.S. agricultural systems involve vast acreages of single-cropped, pesticide-treated fields, in which native bees are virtually absent. Crops that require bee pollination depend almost entirely on moving honeybee colonies to the fields during bloom. More than two million colonies are rented by growers each year, and beekeepers receive anywhere from $15 to $40 per colony; thus,

108

An Africanized queen bee (above left) is marked with a dot of paint so that a beekeeper can determine if there has been any natural change of queens between requeening episodes. A drone (above) is marked to reveal the distance it travels during mating flights.

growers across the U.S. pay beekeepers about $40 million to $50 million annually for colony rentals. This figure is dwarfed by the estimated value of pollination to the crops, which was estimated at $9.3 billion in 1985. Some of the major crops that require pollination include almonds, apples, melons, plums, prunes, avocados, and blueberries.

The situation is not all grim, however. With proper management these bees can be controlled and stinging problems minimized. The following simple procedures have facilitated management for beekeepers in Latin America and will be useful in the United States as well:

Apiary locations: Backyard beekeeping and beekeeping near people and livestock are not possible with Africanized bees. Apiary locations need to be isolated and remote, at least 200 to 300 meters (655 to 985 feet) from roads, houses, and cultivated fields. These sites should be located behind high vegetation in order to prevent disturbed bees from spreading through the nearby countryside.

Personal protective equipment: Beekeepers used to work their European bees in shorts and sandals, with no head covering or sometimes with a simple mesh veil. With Africanized bees that attire could be fatal. Beekeepers need bee-tight clothing, such as a complete suit with a zippered veil that leaves no holes for bees to enter. A proper outfit includes an additional layer or two of thick clothing underneath the suit, thick leather gloves, and high, heavy boots. This outfit can be excruciatingly hot in warm weather, but the alternative is to receive hundreds or thousands of stings. A sting kit containing injectable epinephrine is highly desirable in case someone receives a life-threatening number of stings.

109

Beekeepers working with the comparatively gentle European honeybees require little protective clothing.

Management procedures: Working in pairs is important, with one person continuously applying smoke to a colony in order to pacify the bees while the other person manages the bees. Inspections and manipulations should be kept to a minimum, and colonies maintained at smaller sizes than with European bees in order to reduce stinging and facilitate rapid management.

Queen rearing: The selection, rearing, and distribution of usable queens is the single most important technique for dealing with Africanized bees. Workers in colonies get their characteristics from their queens, and changing the queen from an Africanized to a European type will allow the colony to change over to the more manageable bees over a period of one to two months. Colonies should be requeened annually and queens marked with a dot of paint so that a beekeeper can tell if there has been any natural change of queens between requeening episodes. It may be difficult to rear pure European queens in Africanized zones, and so those queens may have to be reared in the northern United States, Canada, or on offshore islands.

Hobby and sideline beekeepers: A higher level of beekeeper training will be necessary than is currently practiced, especially for beekeepers who may operate within the limits of a city. Courses in beekeeping and some form of licensing should be mandatory, and apiary locations will need to be inspected and approved for safety. These procedures may appear restrictive but are necessary since only one incident may be sufficient to ban beekeeping in an area entirely.

Public health and education: An important aspect of an Africanized-bee-control program involves public health and education. Awareness of the potential danger from Africanized colonies has

110

Beekeepers, familiar with European honeybees, must be trained to work with the more easily disturbed and aggressive Africanized variety.

proved to be a real deterrent in approaching wild or managed colonies and has proved successful at reducing human fatalities.

Future outlook

Finally, another aspect of the Africanized bees' success is that they may have a serious ecological impact on native bees and plants in the tropics. Bees and the plants that they pollinate are a rich component of tropical forest ecosystems, and the advent of a successful competitor for the nectar and pollen that all bees require, and for the nesting sites used by other social bees, may be having considerable effects on those native communities. Particularly vulnerable to this competition may be the stingless bees, which are unusual in not having a stinger, although they are far from defenseless; they have evolved powerful bites that often inject venom and are as effective as the stings of the other bees. These bees nest in similar-sized cavities and forage on many of the same flowers as honeybees and could diminish as the Africanized bees build in population. Also, changes in bee diversity could affect the tropical plants that require the pollinating visits of specific bee species, although these changes may take decades or even centuries to become apparent.

Thus, while the remarkable adaptations that have made Africanized bees such a success are marveled at, there is also serious concern about their impact. While their reputation as "killers" has been exaggerated, they do have the potential for occasional outbursts of stinging. More serious, however, is their potential for disrupting beekeeping and agricultural communities and the unpredictable effects they may have on native plants and animals. The management program described above will go a long way toward minimizing their impact, but people must nevertheless learn to adjust to a new, successful, and highly adaptable organism in their midst.

BIOTECHNOLOGY FOR THE '90s

by Jeffrey L. Fox

The recent, ongoing development of an awesome array of tools centered on the molecular basis of life has brought new excitement to the biological and chemical sciences. Present and future beneficiaries range from basic research and medicine to agriculture and the environment.

No one is quite sure how to define *biotechnology*. Furthermore, opinions differ as to whether it qualifies as an industry or merely as a set of techniques in service to several industrial and research sectors. Nonetheless, the term has become part of the vocabulary of the 1990s, and its continued use reflects some degree of the power of this new field—with its dazzling assortment of laboratory techniques, manufacturing processes, and products. To grasp recent accomplishments and future directions in biotechnology, one must survey some of the techniques being used as well as some of the realms for which new products are being developed. The range is wide, extending from laboratory investigations and human medicine to agriculture and the cleanup of massive oil spills.

Biotechnology has its roots in recombinant DNA research—or, more broadly speaking, genetic engineering—which has evolved at a startling pace from a series of discoveries and successes beginning in the 1970s. Genetic engineering has given mankind the means to modify the genetic makeup of existing organisms and even to generate totally new organisms by directly manipulating molecules of deoxyribonucleic acid (DNA), the carrier of genetic information. During the 1980s much of genetic engineering centered on inserting genes from one organism into the cells of another, thereby endowing the recipient with the traits expressed by the transferred genes. On the practical side, the benefits have been enormous. To cite but one example, pharmaceutical companies now routinely engage in industrial-scale culturing of bacteria that have been given the human-derived gene for making the insulin molecule, and large vats of these microbial factories serve as the source of insulin for thousands of diabetics around the world. On the theoretical side, genetic engineering has advanced the understanding of many aspects of genetic function, organization, and control, thus fertilizing the field of biotechnology for the burst of new developments and offshoots that has followed and that will be pursued throughout the 1990s.

Protein engineering

Sometime during the 1980s a group of researchers, refusing to become complacent with the progress being made in genetic engineering, co-

JEFFREY L. FOX is Current Topics and Features Editor, ASM News, published by the American Society for Microbiology, Washington, D.C. He is also a Contributing Editor to Bio/Technology magazine.

(Opposite page) Pharmaceutical technician checks a large vat used to ferment microorganisms that have been genetically engineered to make a key protein of the hepatitis B virus. After the protein is extracted from the fermentation mixture, it will form the basis for a vaccine against hepatitis B. Photograph by © Hank Morgan—Science Source/Photo Researchers

112

Proteins are assembled from amino acid building blocks that are linked end to end in a linear chain. An individual amino acid (below) consists of a central carbon atom, designated the alpha (α) carbon, to which are attached an amino group (NH₂), a carboxyl group (COOH), and a side chain that distinguishes one type of amino acid from another. In a protein the amino acids are held together by strong peptide bonds that connect the carboxyl carbon atom of one amino acid to the amino nitrogen atom of the next (below right). Interactions among the protein's amino acid units induce various segments of the chain to twist and fold, mainly around axes of the nonpeptide bonds in the chain (arrows), forming characteristic structures identifiable as helices, sheets, and turns. The interactions also cause the entire molecule to fold up into an overall final shape. Since the shape that a protein assumes strongly contributes to determining its specific function, researchers engaged in protein engineering are interested in understanding protein folding as fully as possible. To help visualize folding of the protein thioredoxin (opposite page), computer graphics are used to model some of the steps by which the protein goes from an unstable open chain to a final globular shape (left to right, top to bottom). Each sphere in the model represents an atom in the chain: light blue, carbon; dark blue, nitrogen; red, oxygen; and yellow, sulfur.

alesced to form a new specialty called protein engineering. Their aim was to combine many of the new tools of biotechnology and make a concerted effort to understand the inner workings of proteins, design new ones, and eventually custom build them at will. Although these dreams are yet to be realized fully, the researchers who share them have progressed steadily toward understanding how proteins function and thus how to modify them with greater confidence and purpose than ever before.

Proteins are complex organic molecules made by and crucial to all living organisms. They are synthesized within an organism's cells according to coded instructions carried in genes. Each protein is assembled from amino acid units, often hundreds of them, linked end to end in a linear chain by peptide bonds. Interactions among the amino acid units cause the chain to twist and fold into a characteristic three-dimensional shape that may be interlinked by additional covalent and other weaker bonds. Both the shape that a protein assumes and the amino acids that make it up define the protein's specific function. Sometimes small nonprotein molecules—for example, sugars, fatty molecules, or metal-containing groups—are attached to a protein, distinguishing it further in shape and function. Proteins can be divided into two main categories, structural proteins and biologically active proteins, although some proteins span both categories. Examples of structural proteins are the collagen of bone, tendons, and skin and the keratin of hair and nails. Major biologically active proteins include enzymes, hormones, and antibodies.

By definition, protein engineering is an expensive undertaking, requiring researchers with expertise in diverse specialty areas, including genetic engineering, protein chemistry, structural analysis based on X-ray crystallography and nuclear magnetic resonance spectroscopy, protein purification, and production scaleup. Assembling such experts and equipping laboratories so that they can efficiently conduct experiments are not easy tasks, nor can they be done for a bargain.

Site-directed mutagenesis was the genetic engineering breakthrough that gave impetus to protein engineering. Originally developed by Michael

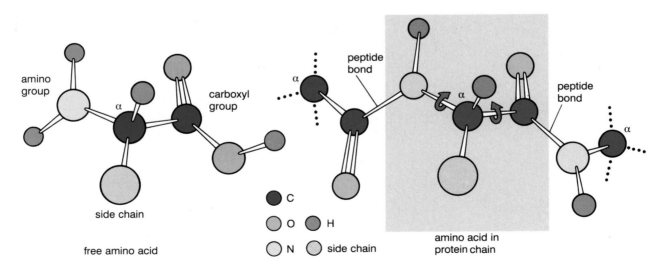

Frederic M. Richards and Paul E. Vogt, Yale University

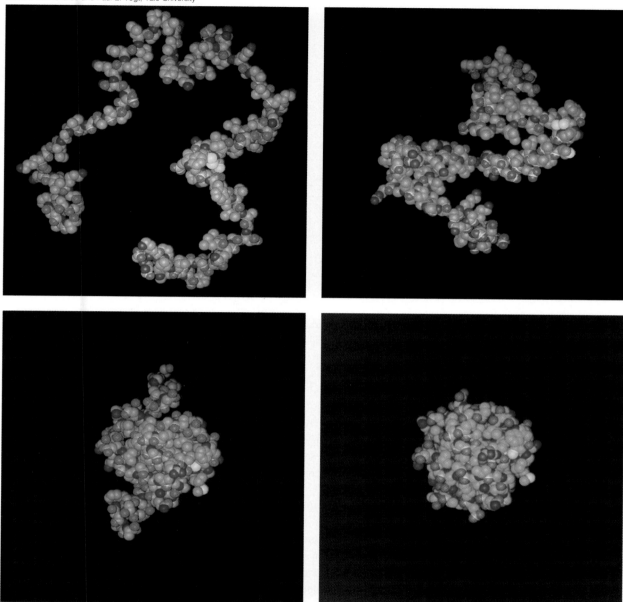

Smith and colleagues at the University of British Columbia, the technique enables a researcher to change designated amino acids virtually any-where within a large, complex protein molecule. This capability makes it possible to study protein structure in great depth and thus to build an understanding of how each component amino acid of a protein contributes to the folding and bending of the molecule and to the way in which it carries out its biochemical functions. The information needed to predict how the sequence of amino acids in a protein determines its full three-dimensional structure is gradually being gathered, analyzed, and tested.

Two of the major structural features that determine how a complex protein will begin to fold up on itself, the alpha helix and beta sheet,

115

(Left) William C. Ripka, Corvas, Inc.; using software by the Polygen Corporation (Quanta) and Biosym Inc. (Insight)

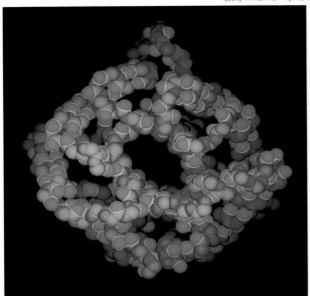 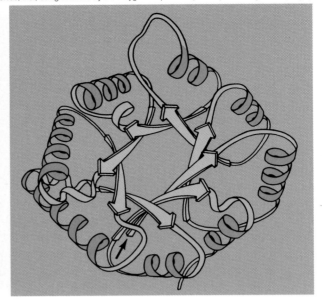

The computer graphic above represents the three-dimensional structure of the enzyme triose phosphate isomerase, as revealed by X-ray crystallographic studies. Only the carbon, nitrogen, and oxygen atoms of the 247-amino-acid backbone (i.e., no side chains) are shown. In the corresponding schematic of the enzyme (above right) are identified the locations of two major structural features adopted by segments of the chain—alpha helices (yellow coils) and beta sheets (blue arrows)—as well as of various turns and loops that, taken all together, define the protein's shape. The basic alpha helix and beta features, separately or in combination, make up a large part of the structure of many proteins. They are now understood well enough for them to be introduced into designs of new proteins.

are now well understood. Thus, they can be introduced confidently into human-designed protein molecules based on analytically determined principles. Even more impressive, proteins that can carry out relatively simple functions, parallel to functions that might be found in living cells, also have been designed and made entirely from scratch, either through direct chemical assembly or by means of a microorganism engineered with a totally synthetic gene. Such accomplishments fall short of designating the structure of a fully functional protein, making it in industrial quantities, and selling the purified product at a profit. Nonetheless, some key interim steps on the way to this ambitious goal are being taken.

Catalytic antibodies

Antibodies and enzymes both belong to classes of proteins that can recognize and bind with high specificity to other molecules. Decades of convention, however, have set the two classes apart because traditionally only enzymes were believed to act as catalysts—*i.e.*, by binding with their target molecules, or substrates, they speed the rate of specific biochemical reactions without being permanently changed by them. On the other hand, the targeting ability of antibodies comes into play in their biological search-and-destroy role as part of the immune system, whereby they patrol the body for foreign substances, which they distinguish from the body's own components and then help eliminate. Recently several research groups began developing the means to give catalytic properties to antibody molecules, making them more like enzymes. Moreover, several naturally occurring antibodies, which may play a role in particular autoimmune processes (abnormal immune responses of the body against its own components), were found to possess hitherto unrecognized catalytic properties. Some investigators have begun referring to catalytic antibodies by the name abzymes, short for "antibody enzymes."

116

Pioneering research on catalytic antibodies has been conducted since the late 1980s principally in three laboratories—under the direction of Richard Massey at Igen, Rockville, Maryland; under the direction of Richard Lerner at Scripps Clinic, La Jolla, California; and under the direction of Peter Schultz at the University of California at Berkeley. Early success in imparting catalytic properties to several antibody proteins has hinged on making them recognize the so-called transition states that substrate molecules assume during biochemical reactions catalyzed by enzymes. Ordinarily, antibodies recognize and bind molecules that are in the ground state, meaning in the configuration they ordinarily assume when dissolved in a liquid, either in living cells or in test tubes. By contrast, enzymes carry out their catalytic functions by binding reactant molecules that are in various short-lived transition, or activated, states as they are being converted into end products. So specific is an enzyme's recognition of these transition states that it can clearly distinguish their configurations from those of the ground states of either reactants or products.

The first documented reaction catalyzed by antibodies was the hydrolysis (a type of decomposition reaction) of relatively simple ester molecules. Since then, more than a dozen different kinds of reactions have been carried out by such antibodies. Prospects for future successes are good. A particularly challenging type of antibody-catalyzed reaction under study is one involving cleavage, or cutting, of proteins at specific peptide bonds. The commercial interest in protein-cleaving antibodies is high, since they could be valuable in basic research or the manufacture of therapeutic proteins or even in direct therapeutic applications; *e.g.*, as clot dissolvers. Surprisingly, perhaps the best model for antibodies with this ability consists of molecules found naturally among a small group of people, particularly joggers, suffering from an unusual form of

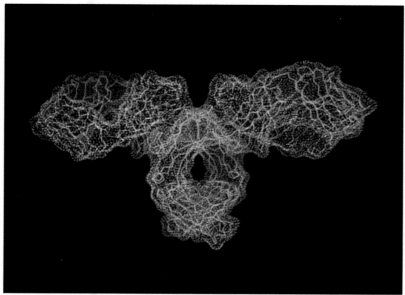

Computer graphic and photography by Arthur J. Olson, Scripps Clinic, La Jolla, Calif.

A typical antibody molecule, as represented by the computer-generated image at left, is a Y-shaped protein made of four smaller protein (polypeptide) chains—two heavy chains that form the stem and part of each arm of the Y and two light chains that make up the rest of the arms. At the tip of each arm, a heavy and light chain fold together to create an antigen-binding site, the part of the antibody molecule that recognizes and binds with its specific substrate, or target molecule. In making antibodies that have catalytic properties, the key requirement is that their binding sites recognize the transition states assumed by molecules participating in a reaction as the molecules are converted into end products.

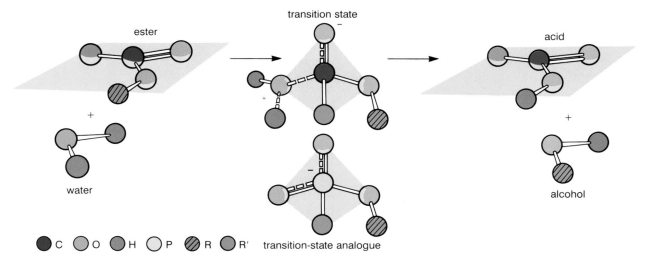

ester   transition state   acid

water

●C ○O ◐H ○P ⊘R ◔R'   transition-state analogue

alcohol

To make catalytic antibodies, researchers have looked for stable molecules whose geometry and electrical characteristics are analogous to those of the fleeting transition states of the reactions to be catalyzed. In the ester hydrolysis reaction diagrammed above, an ester and a molecule of water combine to form a transition state that is distinct (tetrahedral and electrically polarized) from either the reactants or the acid and alcohol products (planar and uncharged). The longer lived analogue shown, in which a phosphorus atom replaces the central carbon atom in the transition state, approximates the geometry and charge distribution of its model. Once a suitable analogue has been identified, it can be linked to a carrier protein and injected into a laboratory animal, inducing the animal's immune system to make antibodies that bind specifically to the transition-state configuration. After a functional catalytic antibody has been raised and isolated, various techniques can then be used to produce it in quantity and even to modify its structure to enhance its catalytic ability.

autoimmunity. These individuals develop antibodies against vasoactive intestinal peptide (VIP), a hormonelike protein molecule found in several tissues of the body, including the airways. Some of the antibodies not only recognize and bind VIP but also apparently cut it at a specific peptide bond. Whether catalytic antibodies play roles in other autoimmune diseases remains to be determined.

In addition to making antibodies of pure protein with enzymelike activity, researchers are chemically modifying them to enhance their catalytic ability. For example, adding sulfur-containing side chains to the antibody protein near its so-called active site can significantly elevate the modified molecule's overall catalytic efficiency. Adding other chemical entities, such as metal ions, also may have similar effects. Although all these manipulations seem a cumbersome way of building catalysts that so far are nowhere near as fast-acting as natural enzymes, there is a practical rationale. The repertoire of enzymes is, in a sense, already set by nature, whereas the antibody repertoire is open-ended. Thus, although natural enzymes catalyze a wide assortment of biochemical reactions, it may not be possible to find the right natural enzyme, if it indeed exists, for a particular reaction of interest. By contrast, the fact that the human immune system seems capable of making literally millions of different antibodies that can recognize virtually any molecular shape imaginable is a very encouraging sign for biotechnologists. Thus, if a chemist or biologist needs a catalyst for an unusual reaction, it may eventually prove most efficient to make that catalyst as an antibody.

Of great potential benefit to catalytic antibody research would be techniques that make the synthesis of antibodies more of a routine undertaking than it now is. Although far from perfected, a strategy is being developed for drastically simplifying antibody production. The approach involves harnessing bacterial cells to manufacture assortments of antibody molecules. Currently, antibody molecules for research and various applications—called monoclonal antibodies—are made either in intact living animals, such as mice or rabbits, or in cells from such mammalian

118

species that can be grown, with considerable difficulty, in the laboratory. Bacterial cells, on the other hand, can be cultured cheaply and easily in large quantities. The challenge is to induce bacteria, which ordinarily do not manufacture antibody molecules, to do so at will. Furthermore, such bacteria should be able to make the full spectrum of antibody molecules that can be induced in mammalian species. Richard Lerner and colleagues at Scripps have been making significant progress toward meeting these challenges, and more of the story surely will unfold in the next few years.

Catalytic RNA molecules

The 1989 Nobel Prize for Chemistry was presented to Sidney Altman of Yale University and Thomas R. Cech of the University of Colorado, who discovered independently that some ribonucleic acid (RNA) molecules can act as catalysts. The notion of catalytic RNA molecules, dubbed ribozymes, further helped in overturning the widely held belief among biologists and biochemists that enzymes are the only natural catalysts to be found in living systems.

Both RNA and DNA consist of long sequences of molecular units called nucleotide bases that jut from a linear backbone structure of alternating sugar and phosphate groups. The precise sequence of the bases constitutes the genetic code, the specific information that the cell uses to assemble amino acids in their proper sequence into specific proteins. A gene is a segment of DNA or RNA that carries the code for synthesizing a specific protein or a subunit of one. An entire DNA or RNA molecule is made of many such genes strung end to end, although there may also be present, both between genes and within individual genes, considerable stretches of nucleotide bases called intervening sequences, or introns, which do not code for proteins. In all living cells, DNA functions as the storage medium for the instructions for protein synthesis, while RNA serves in several capacities, including as a messenger for transporting the genetic code in DNA to the sites of protein synthesis elsewhere in the cell.

A molecule of RNA, like that of DNA, consists of a chain of building blocks called nucleotides. Each nucleotide includes a sugar molecule and a phosphate group, which link end to end with those of adjacent nucleotides to form the RNA's backbone. Each nucleotide also carries one of four molecular units called bases— adenine (A), guanine (G), cytosine (C), or uracil (U) in the case of RNA—whose specific sequence forms the genetic code. When RNA is first transcribed from DNA, it may contain stretches of nucleotide sequences, called introns, that do not appear in the final functional form of the molecule. In the example below, which illustrates part of a molecule of messenger RNA, the intron must be spliced out— i.e., cut out of the molecule and the cut ends joined together—before the RNA can direct the synthesis of the protein for which it codes. Although in many cases the mechanism of RNA splicing is still unclear, it was discovered beginning in the early 1980s that certain RNA molecules can splice out their own introns. More recently RNA molecules have been found that act as true catalysts in the manner of enzymes, cutting and splicing other RNA molecules while remaining unchanged themselves.

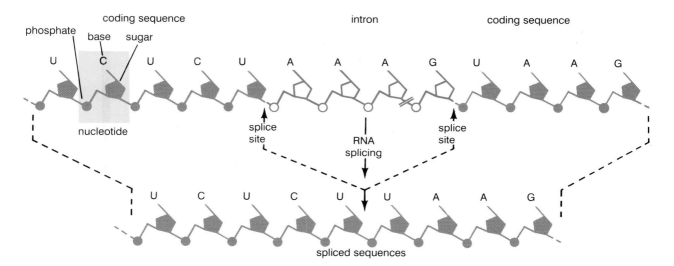

As early as 1982, Cech presented evidence that an intron in a particular RNA molecule had some of the properties of an enzyme, enabling it to break and reform the bonds holding the RNA backbone together. Unlike a true catalyst, however, this RNA molecule did not emerge from the reaction unchanged, for it cut away its intron and then spliced itself back together. Nonetheless, like an enzyme, the RNA molecule could by itself adopt a three-dimensional conformation that contained an active site able to recognize and bind to particular structures and to perform highly specific chemical reactions on them. More recently, true RNA-directed catalysis was found to occur in nature. Altman and colleagues showed that the RNA portion of a complex molecular structure containing both RNA and protein cleaves certain other RNA molecules. Moreover, under some circumstances the RNA molecule studied by Cech—and several other forms of RNA molecules—also can act as true catalysts. By 1990 at least seven types of RNA-catalyzed enzymelike reactions and more than 100 ribozymes had been identified.

Ribozymes may well see wide practical applications before the end of the decade. For instance, the fact that they cleave at very specific

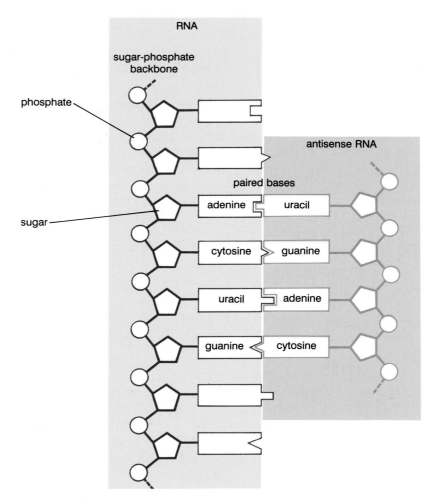

The nucleotide bases of both DNA and RNA molecules can bind chemically to each other in a complementary way known as base pairing. Base pairing is the phenomenon that allows two strands of DNA molecules to link into the double helix and allows the sequence of bases in DNA that code for a particular protein to be transcribed faithfully into the sequence of bases in messenger RNA that will instruct cellular protein synthesis. A recently developed technique for preventing specified genetic instructions from being transcribed or expressed as protein, called antisense technology, involves making small molecules of DNA or RNA whose base sequence is complementary to, and thus binds with, a DNA or RNA target sequence—effectively shutting off its activity. The diagram at right illustrates the case for RNA, whose four bases always pair such that adenine binds with uracil and cytosine with guanine. The sequence of bases in the antisense RNA has been tailored to match up with a specific target sequence in an RNA molecule and so block expression of the functional protein. The term antisense *relates to the fact that such a sequence runs counter to the "sense" direction of its target, the direction along the molecule in which the genetic code is read.*

base sequences may enable researchers to use them routinely to cut RNA molecules containing those sequences and then to splice them with greater control than now is possible. In fact, their discovery already has led to the development of a new biotechnological tool, called gene shears, for selectively cleaving RNA. Moreover, the capacity of particular ribozymes to cleave other species of RNA may make them useful as drugs for destroying viruses that use RNA rather than DNA to carry their genetic code. For example, several approaches toward combating the human immunodeficiency virus (HIV), the RNA-based retrovirus responsible for AIDS (acquired immune deficiency syndrome), take aim at its RNA. One approach involves use of catalytic RNA molecules to digest certain RNA segments of the virus. A second approach—often referred to as the antisense strategy—relies on administering RNA molecules intended to block the biological activity of HIV.

Antisense technology is itself a new tool of biotechnology with promising applications in research, medical therapy, and agriculture. It involves making small molecules of RNA or DNA, called oligomers, whose sequence of bases is tailored to bind to specific base sequences in the genes of living cells and viruses, effectively turning those genes off. In the case of HIV, a properly prepared antisense RNA oligomer can wreck the replication cycle of HIV in infected host cells by binding to a target RNA segment of the virus and interfering with its activity. Both sequence-specific and sequence-nonspecific effects have been observed in laboratory tests, meaning that sometimes the oligomer does not even need to be targeted to a specific RNA sequence to disrupt HIV activity. Because most small molecules of RNA are short-lived, a variety of chemically modified versions of RNA oligomers are being made and tested for their longevity, binding capacity, and antiviral and other biological activities.

Ribozyme-based antiviral agents may offer advantages over antisense RNA for interfering with HIV replication because they not only bind but also cleave their target RNA molecules. If ribozymes indeed can act catalytically to destroy HIV, then low concentrations delivered to infected cells may be enough to rid them of viruses. Some researchers suggest that delivering the gene for the ribozyme might be all that is needed; the cell's own machinery will then transcribe the gene into catalytic RNA.

Computer-aided drug design

Although computers cannot substitute for the traditional way of searching for and testing new drugs, they help to cut corners and give new insights into the arduous task of designing antiviral agents. When it comes to disease, viruses usually have the upper hand. Except for vaccines to prevent a few viral diseases and for the handful of presently effective drugs, the search for clinically useful antiviral agents usually has proved frustrating. Recently, however, optimism has returned, in part because of a computer-aided strategy for drug design. The developers of that strategy are building their hopes on the effective use of a variety of techniques, including high-powered computation, theoretical chemistry, X-ray crystallography, and molecular biology.

Antisense technology was used experimentally to produce unusual pigmentation patterns in what are normally uniformly colored petunia flowers. Employing genetic engineering techniques, researchers injected petunia cells with a small piece of DNA having a base sequence chosen to yield a specific antisense RNA when transcribed in the cell. The target of the antisense sequence was a messenger RNA molecule that codes for an enzyme involved in the synthesis of flower-cell pigment. The enzyme was inhibited in some cells, resulting in the color variations.

121

(Top) T.J. O'Donnell and James P. Snyder of Searle, Skokie, Ill.; (bottom) Sterling Research Group

Detailed X-ray crystallographic studies have allowed scientists to build a computer model (top) of the outer coat, or capsid, of a picornavirus, a type whose members include some of the viruses responsible for common colds. The interlocking tile-shaped components represent the different proteins that form the capsid, which protects the virus' RNA-based genes inside. One of the proteins, called VP1, has been found to possess a cavity into which antiviral drugs can diffuse, thereby preventing the capsid from opening up and releasing its genes during the process of infection. Aided by powerful computers, researchers have been able to visualize the binding interactions between drug molecules and the VP1 cavity and to modify those molecules on the computer screen in order to produce compounds that appear to bind even more effectively. A computer graphic (bottom) depicts a potential drug molecule within the VP1 cavity of the cold-causing human rhinovirus type 14. Unfilled spaces indicate places that could be occupied by structural modifications to the drug, which should result in a more potent antiviral agent.

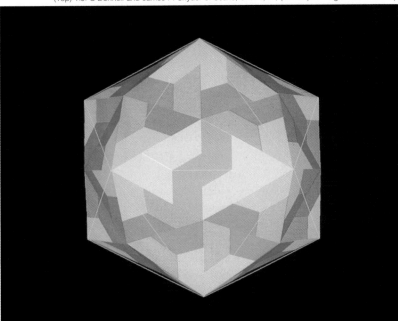

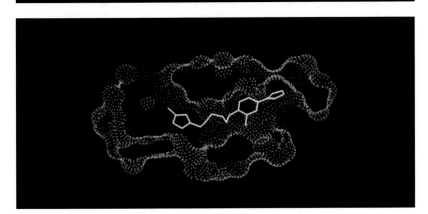

By displaying the detailed molecular structures of disease-causing viruses in atomic detail on the graphics monitors of powerful computers, researchers can make preliminary tests on virtually innumerable drug structures for their ability to target vulnerable sites in viruses. Ideally, much of the time-consuming and expensive work that traditionally has been part of preliminary drug development—the search for new substances, the screening for properties and biological effects, laboratory testing, and the syntheses of variant molecular structures and their screening and testing—can be reduced or eliminated. Instead, out of thousands of compounds imaginable, only a few pass the computerized assay to move into the laboratory for further assessment.

Some researchers believe that computational approaches offer much more than does tinkering with compounds known to have antiviral activity. Thus, instead of determining the biological activity of several closely related compounds and then simply making small changes in their struc-

T.J. O'Donnell and James P. Snyder of Searle, Skokie, Ill.

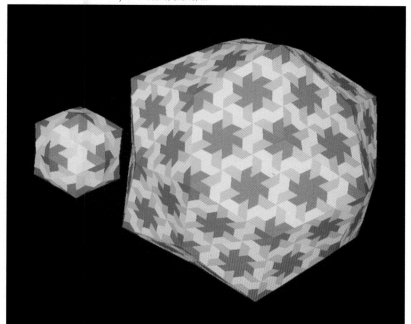

The recent gains from computational approaches to understanding picornaviruses are being applied to the study of HIV, the virus that causes AIDS. As a basis for designing drugs that might interact with the proteins of the HIV capsid, scientists have constructed a computer model of the larger HIV particle (left) that relies on information used to model the capsid structure of the smaller picornavirus (far left).

tures, drug designers aided by computers can conceivably make use of the wealth of biological and chemical data available about a virus and its quirks to develop entirely new antiviral molecules.

Michael Rossman and colleagues of Purdue University, West Lafayette, Indiana, and collaborators at other academic institutions and in industry have been studying several viruses including some that cause colds. To date, their most noted success with computer-assisted design of drugs was in developing one such agent that has appeared so effective against the cold virus that it has entered clinical trials. In the 1980s Rossman and co-workers solved the X-ray crystallographic structure of rhinovirus type 14, one of a family of viruses that cause colds. The members of this family possess genes in the form of a long single strand of RNA. Surrounding the RNA is a protective outer shell, or capsid, made of four proteins that assemble into an icosahedron—a roughly spherical geometric solid having 12 vertices and 20 triangular faces.

Rossman's collaborators from the pharmaceutical industry, the Sterling Research Group, Rensselaer, New York, already had developed by traditional means a family of agents that prevent such viruses from infecting cells grown in the laboratory. By studying a series of those agents, the research group learned how they interact with the proteins that make up the capsid of the rhinovirus. Three of the proteins, called VP1, VP2, and VP3, wrap themselves into barrel-shaped structures, producing cavities within the proteins. The antiviral drugs diffuse into the cavity, called a beta-barrel, of VP1, which alters slightly the way in which this protein interacts with the other capsid proteins. In effect, the drugs overstabilize the capsid proteins, preventing the virus particle from opening up and releasing its genes into the cell in the process of infection. Using high-

123

powered computer graphics, the Purdue and Sterling researchers were able to modify the drug molecules to produce variant compounds that bind more effectively inside the beta-barrel—at least on the computer screen.

These preliminary assessments were further analyzed on a Cray supercomputer to calculate more completely the dynamics of drug binding. A summary of the results from a 100,000-step calculation, which takes several hours on even the fastest supercomputer, was assembled by means of a graphics program into an animated video. From similar calculations with several drugs, the researchers discerned some of the forces acting between the drugs and viral protein that overstabilize the capsid and render the virus harmless. The information generated in such simulations also makes it possible to compare how well various drugs bind to the virus and to correlate this information with the activity that each drug shows in tests on the laboratory bench. From such analysis, medicinal chemists can learn which parts of a drug molecule are not critical to binding, so they can then modify those regions to improve properties, such as solubility and transportability into different tissues, that are also needed to produce a useful drug. In 1991 several new candidate drugs produced in this way were being tested for their effectiveness against the cold-causing rhinoviruses.

Gene therapy and other medical issues

During the 1980s, biotechnology surely proved that it could provide novel diagnostic methods as well as new treatments for human and animal diseases. Human-derived forms of insulin for diabetes, growth hormone for dwarfism and other growth disorders, interferons for certain kinds of cancer and viral infections, tissue plasminogen activator for heart attacks and blood clots, and erythropoietin for chronic anemia are among the more prominent examples of new therapeutic products now available through the power of genetic engineering. As other biotechnology-based pharmaceuticals come along, new technical questions about them continue to be posed. In general, however, the manufacturers and regulators who review the products before they are marketed have been working out ways to address those problems.

Late in 1990, for example, officials of the U.S. Food and Drug Administration (FDA) began pondering the difficult issue of microheterogeneity—namely, slight differences in structure between ostensibly similar biotechnology-based drug products. One concern is that administering slightly different versions of a therapeutic product might trigger an unwanted allergic response. Other worries are that different versions of a product could produce different side effects or that they might vary in efficacy. Although policies for addressing the issue were still forthcoming, FDA officials presumably will develop guidelines for determining when slight differences between products can be ignored or when they should be taken into account.

Meanwhile, thanks to biotechnology, human medicine crossed another frontier in 1990 when researchers at the U.S. National Institutes of

124

Health (NIH), Bethesda, Maryland, received approval and began the first attempts to conduct gene therapy in individual patients. The medical procedure in question is an experimental treatment for some cases of severe combined immunodeficiency disease (SCID), an extremely rare disorder that affects about 40 children worldwide each year. In almost half of the SCID patients studied, the gene for an enzyme, adenosine deaminase (ADA), is defective. The resulting enzyme defect, called ADA deficiency, renders an individual's immune system ineffectual, leading to extreme susceptibility to infections.

The gene therapy approach to treating ADA deficiency was developed by NIH researchers R. Michael Blaese, W. French Anderson, and their collaborators. It involves inserting functional genes for ADA, by means of a genetically engineered carrier virus, into white blood cells taken from the afflicted patient. The cells are then cultured and injected back into the patient at intervals of several weeks. (Earlier in 1990, before the gene therapy procedure was approved, another biotechnology-based treatment for patients with ADA deficiency came into use. That treatment entails administering a purified version of ADA that is chemically bound to the polymer polyethylene glycol in order to prolong the enzyme's lifetime in the body.)

This first gene therapy test corresponds to a phase I clinical trial, which, as defined by the FDA, evaluates the safety of a potential new therapy and determines toxic dosage levels. Testing how well an experimental treatment actually works is called a phase II trial, which must meet more stringent criteria. In a strict sense, because the first recipients of the treatment are helping to evaluate its safety, calling the initial trial gene therapy is somewhat misleading. Moreover, although early results have been encouraging, the initial trial is too small and otherwise too rudimentary to prove readily whether the therapeutic approach will work. Nevertheless, it could well be the prelude to a massive change in medical practice in the years ahead.

Research to identify and understand the molecular underpinnings of human genetic diseases is accelerating at a breathtaking rate. Formerly intractable diseases such as cystic fibrosis (CF), neurofibromatosis, Duchenne muscular dystrophy (DMD), Huntington's disease, and many others not only dominate medical news but are becoming part of the everyday medical vocabulary. Several key advances in technology, the growth and impetus behind the U.S.-sponsored Human Genome Initiative to map and determine the base sequence of all the genes in the human cell, and a general push to identify important landmarks along human chromosomes are some of the forces driving a rapid buildup of knowledge and awareness. In the short run, new technologies could lead to simplified procedures and possibly test kits for diagnosing certain genetic diseases. Further ahead, they could bring new treatments and therapies for diseases traditionally considered incurable or untreatable.

Currently most developments are focused on diagnosis. Much of the increase in genetic testing aims at informing pregnant women and their families of the likelihood that their unborn children will develop particu-

125

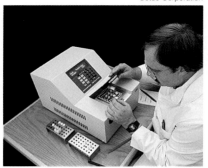

Laboratory machines that automate the polymerase chain reaction (PCR) provide scientists with a simple, rapid means of repeatedly copying specific DNA sequences until millions of identical molecules are available for studies. Each copying cycle of the PCR involves three steps, as diagrammed below. First, the starting material, which is in the form of a double-stranded DNA fragment, is heated to about 95° C (203° F), causing the strands to separate, or denature. This process exposes the individual nucleotide bases on each strand, which serves as a template during the next step. Cooling the reaction mixture to 55° C (131° F) initiates the second step, during which two synthetic "primers"—short DNA molecules representing known sequences that flank both sides of the target region— anneal (bind by base pairing) to their complementary sequences on the DNA template strands. Finally, in the third step, which is initiated by raising the temperature to 72° C (162° F), the two bound primers are elongated by the action of the enzyme DNA polymerase, which sequentially adds on free nucleotide building blocks that are present in the reaction mixture to build new DNA strands that are complementary to the template strands. The net effect of one cycle is the duplication of one DNA fragment, producing two copies. At the end of a cycle, the temperature is shifted back to the first value to start a new cycle. Each cycle doubles the number of DNA fragments gained from the previous cycle.

lar genetic diseases. One new technology being pursued obtains and analyzes fetal cells from maternal blood, thus avoiding invasive procedures that might damage a developing fetus. Eventually, the technique may enable physicians to screen pregnant women routinely and efficiently to determine a whole battery of genetic indicators present in fetal cells.

Powerful amplification procedures for producing selected DNA in quantity are being adapted to make this application feasible. For example, the polymerase chain reaction (PCR), a technique developed initially by researchers at Cetus Corp., Emeryville, California, can double and redouble small, specific segments of DNA quickly and with great accuracy until millions of identical copies exist. Thus, by means of the PCR, even a single gene from one fetal cell can be amplified until enough exists to perform all the genetic tests desired. The PCR is finding wide use in many areas of basic and applied research.

Similarly, elucidating the molecular nature of many specific genetic disorders in order to improve diagnoses and further medical research is occurring at breakneck speed. For instance, in late 1989 the FDA approved an antibody-based diagnostic kit for DMD, and a limited clinical trial involving a cell-replacement therapeutic strategy to combat the disease began early in 1990. An inherited disorder, DMD affects young children, almost exclusively boys, leading to severe muscle degeneration and, frequently, death. Using some of the new methods of biotechnology, researchers in the late 1980s pinpointed the cause of the disease as a defective or missing gene that carries the instructions for making dystrophin, a protein constituent of muscle. The therapeutic approach involves introducing myoblasts, a form of muscle cell, from tissue-matched donors who have normal dystrophin genes into the tissues of individuals with DMD.

polymerase chain reaction

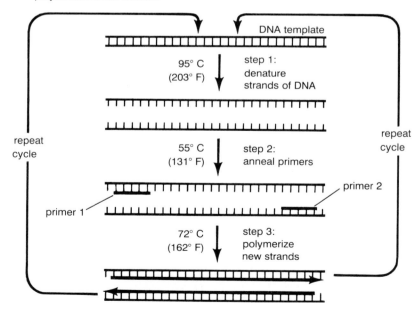

case A				case B				case C			
mother	child	a. father	c. + a.f.	mother	child	a. father	c. + a.f.	mother	child	a. father	c. + a.f.

When a sample of a organism's genetic material is digested with selected DNA-cleaving enzymes, the lengths of the cleaved fragments sort into patterns that are highly individual and are known to be transmitted to offspring in much the same way as conventional genetic traits. Production and analysis of the patterns, a technique known as DNA profiling or DNA fingerprinting, has been applied increasingly in forensic science to provide evidence in rape and murder cases and to help decide paternity disputes. At a double-murder trial (above), the judge and attorneys listen to an expert defense witness as she interprets DNA fingerprints taken from bloodstains, the victims, and the defendant. The DNA fingerprints at left, part of an autoradiogram produced on photographic film by radioactively labeled fragments of digested DNA, compare fragment-length patterns (the vertical lanes of dark bands) from the mother, the child, and an alleged father (plus a mixture of DNA from child and alleged father) in each of three paternity cases. In cases A and C the alleged father cannot be excluded as the biological father because a band from his DNA matches one from the child's; in fact, inheritance of all bands in the child can be accounted for as coming from him or the mother.

Some 30,000 Americans have CF, making it, at least among Caucasians of northern European descent, the most common fatal genetic disorder. Roughly one Caucasian in 20 is a carrier, and one Caucasian in 2,000 live births develops the disease. CF, which affects production of mucus and leads to frequent lung infections and other complications, often causes death by early adulthood. Not all victims of CF have the same exact genetic abnormality, but about 70% do. The remainder possess one of nearly 50 less common mutations. Although the breadth of causative defects continues to puzzle geneticists and complicates diagnosis, several companies have offered CF diagnostic testing services.

In mid-1990 two research groups, one led by Francis Collins of the University of Michigan and the other by Ray White of the Howard Hughes Medical Institute at the University of Utah, announced their discovery of the genetic defect responsible for causing yet another genetic disease, neurofibromatosis. Affecting one in 3,000–4,000 people worldwide, the disease causes a variety of symptoms ranging from unusual pigmentation and disfigurement to abnormal development, proliferating tumors of the central nervous system, and death.

Not all genetic testing coming out of biotechnological research aims at detecting or treating diseases. Some is being exploited in forensic analysis—for gathering evidence in rape and murder cases or for determining relatedness among a group of individuals, as in questions of paternity. Common to many of the recent discoveries in medical genetics as well as to these new advances in forensic science is an underlying technology that looks at patterns in the lengths of enzymatically digested samples of DNA. The patterns, known as restriction fragment length polymorphisms, are highly individual and are inherited in much the same way as eye color and other conventional genetic traits. The Office of Technology Assessment of the U.S. Congress published a study in 1990 concluding that such DNA-based forensic tests are "valid and reliable when properly performed." The main approach, called DNA profiling or DNA fingerprinting, which was initially developed by Alec Jeffreys of the University of Leicester, England, was introduced into U.S. criminal proceedings in 1986. By 1990 it had been used throughout the U.S. in several thousand criminal investigations and in even more paternity disputes. Several private companies and many state and local law-enforcement agencies in the U.S. have begun using or are planning to use such tests.

Biotechnology in the open environment
Although the use of biotechnology to develop products and procedures for the laboratory, the diagnostic clinic, and medical therapy is well accepted, the release into the open environment of organisms and substances created or altered by biotechnology remains a controversial matter. Government officials, representatives of environmental and public interest groups, and researchers at academic institutions and at biotechnology companies all have a stake in the debate over the wisdom and safety of deliberately unleashing organisms that possess abilities not found in their natural counterparts. As a further complication, the issue along with other regulatory matters affecting biotechnological products is regarded as being of international concern, particularly among the countries of the European Communities.

In simple terms, the question comes down to deciding if or when a product of biotechnology can be tested or used safely in the open environment. Virtually all decisions to test genetically modified organisms in the environment have been made on a case-by-case basis, although some classes of engineered organisms, such as certain types of plants or those organisms that carry innocuous marker genes for tracking purposes, are now generally considered safe to release.

The issue continues to affect biotechnology's use in agriculture and aquaculture, in dealing with environmental problems and wildlife issues, and, to a lesser extent, in the food industry. To cite some recent cases, the FDA in early 1990 approved the commercial use in the U.S. of a genetically engineered, microbially synthesized protein, an enzyme called renin, in cheese making. Toward the end of the year, Calgene, an agricultural biotechnology company based in Davis, California, voluntarily submitted applications to the FDA, asking it to review the safety of

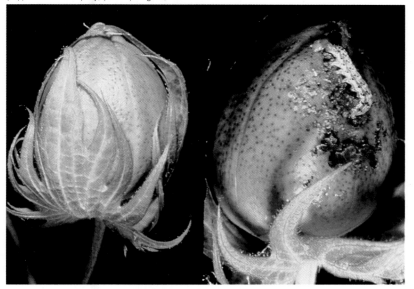

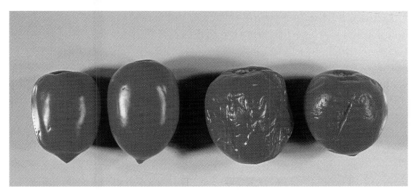

Improved varieties of cotton and tomato are among biotechnologically altered crop plants that have undergone recent field trials in the open environment in preparation for commercial release. The insect-resistant cotton boll (top left) is from a plant genetically engineered to carry the gene for Bt toxin, whereas the caterpillar-infested boll (top right) is from a commercially available plant used as a control. Tomatoes that are still firm three weeks after harvest (bottom left) were given an antisense gene sequence designed to block the RNA that codes for an enzyme involved in tissue softening. By contrast, normal control tomatoes of the same age (bottom right) are soft and have begun to rot.

tomatoes given genes for resistance to certain antibiotics. Although the genes in themselves are not of agricultural value, the review is a prelude to that of other plants engineered to contain genes for natural pesticides, resistance to weed killers, immunity to fungal diseases, or other agriculturally beneficial characteristics.

Just how the FDA will review the safety of genetically altered food, food additives, and their sources recently became a matter of heightened interest. In 1990 it was disclosed that commercial lots of the amino acid L-tryptophan, which some people consume in large amounts as a food supplement or for alleged therapeutic effects, possibly contained contaminants responsible for thousands of cases of a puzzling malady, eosinophilia-myalgia syndrome (EMS). Victims of EMS showed a complex of inflammatory and autoimmune responses that affected the skin, muscles, nerves, blood vessels, lungs, and heart; more than two dozen deaths were reported. Although investigations into the cause of the outbreak were continuing, by the end of 1990 epidemiologists were confident in associating the EMS cases in the U.S. with consumption of some lots of L-tryptophan containing several exotic contaminants. Although those

129

lots may have been produced by genetically engineered microorganisms, it was not known whether genetic engineering itself, changes in the product-purification procedures, or some other factors were the source of the contaminants. As of early 1991 the association of human disease with contaminants in possibly genetically engineered tryptophan not only remained unproved but also was exceptional amid the many products and processes dependent on biotechnology.

For several recent, carefully watched environmental tests of biotechnology-based products, early indications are that they are safe. For example, large-scale agricultural testing began on an engineered version of a natural insecticide known as Bt toxin because it derives from the bacterium *Bacillus thuringiensis*. Bt toxin itself has been in widespread commercial use for many years. The newer version encapsulates the insecticidal protein in killed bacterial cells as a way of prolonging its activity during field use. Other organisms, including such crop plants as corn, are being engineered to carry versions of the toxin in their living tissues. In 1990 cotton given Bt toxin genes underwent field trials in the U.S. in which it showed substantial resistance to caterpillar pests.

Engineered vaccines whose means of delivery are live viruses also are being developed and tested in the open environment. One, the development of which has been dogged by controversy, entered field trials in mid-1990. The vaccine in question is designed to protect wild raccoons against rabies, which has been growing to epidemic proportions in the middle and eastern U.S. It consists of a live vaccinia virus, which had been used against smallpox until the disease was eradicated in 1977, that has been engineered to make a key glycoprotein (a sugar-protein molecule) from the unrelated rabies virus. When treated with this vaccine in laboratory experiments, raccoons and other animals mount an immune response against the glycoprotein, and that response protects them against later infection by rabies virus.

After extensive review for safety at the federal, state, and local levels, the developers of the rabies vaccine, a research team from the Wistar Institute, Philadelphia, received permission to test it on a small island off the coast of Virginia. The test included extensive monitoring of other wild species in that environment as well as precautions to keep human intruders away from the test site. According to preliminary findings, the vaccine, which was administered orally to the raccoons via edible bait, did no harm to the environment. A similar test was being planned for a rural area in Pennsylvania.

Bioremediation

Bioremediation, a branch of biotechnology concerned with reversing environmental degradation, gained considerable momentum in the early 1990s. The most visible impetus behind the increased interest was its apparent success in contributing to the cleanup of crude oil spilled by the tanker *Exxon Valdez* in March 1989 along Prince William Sound, Alaska. Although much of the cleanup consisted of brute-force mopping efforts, teams of workers also sprayed special fertilizers along 110 kilometers (70 miles) of rugged, oil-contaminated shoreline to enlist the aid of indigenous microbes. The fertilizers supplied nitrogen and phosphorus nutrients to oil-degrading bacteria, thereby accelerating their growth rates and the consequent disappearance of the contaminants. Microbes subsequently have been sprayed on oil slicks left from other tanker spills.

The Alaskan mishap and others are being extensively studied as researchers try to find other ways to enhance natural bioremediation processes. Bioremediation works, most experts in this field of research now are saying. Each site and event, however, seem to dictate different approaches. Eventually, researchers expect to combine genes from different microorganisms to advance bioremediation plans. Thus far, and fortunately, the existing microbes have proved adept—albeit sometimes with encouragement—at many of the cleanup tasks, even those involving complex synthetic environmental contaminants such as polychlorinated biphenyls and polychlorinated phenols.

Future outlook

In the past decade and a half, applications of research having its origins in genetics and molecular biology have virtually exploded on the scene—to benefit agriculture, medicine, chemistry, and many other fields. Scientific disciplines that once were much more compartmentalized are now merging in the pursuit and exploitation of biotechnological tools. Researchers from diverse fields are bringing their wide range of training and experience to bear on common goals, creating a new, pervasive excitement in the chemical and life sciences.

Where will these efforts lead during the 1990s and beyond? Scientists envision designing proteins with exquisitely specific functions to disrupt crucial biochemical reactions in disease-causing bacteria and cancer cells, to function as memory elements in organically based computers, to make better laundry detergents and stronger plastics, to serve as the building blocks of synthetic muscle fibers that contract and relax on demand, or to enable bacteria to scavenge valuable metals from the sea or remove toxic pollutants from wastewater. Custom-made catalytic antibodies may ease the tasks of chemists who are looking for routes to molecules not yet possible or practical to make; employed as antiviral agents, such antibodies may seek out specific capsid proteins of infectious viruses, bind to them, and then catalyze their disruption. Already the use of DNA profiling, the PCR, or their combination in diagnosing disease, retrieving intact DNA from mummified humans and fossil plant tissue, assessing genetic diversity in animal populations, identifying poached elephant tusks, and determining the gender of sea turtles hints of the wealth of applications to come. Combinations of biotechnological techniques are helping unlock the secrets of making natural materials—including spider and silkworm silks, biological adhesives, the mineral-protein skeletons of marine animals, and human tooth enamel—that are valued for their unique characteristics.

With the human imagination fired and the scientific means at hand, more marvels seem ready to happen.

A cleanup worker monitors the mixing of sludge from a petrochemical waste dump in Texas with microorganisms able to degrade the waste. Demonstration of the effectiveness of bioremediation at this site and elsewhere has encouraged researchers in their search for ways to exploit and enhance natural biodegradation processes for combating environmental pollution.

131

CLUSTERS

Strange Bits of Matter

by Michael D. Morse

Finite clusters of strongly interacting metal
or semiconductor atoms display chemical and
physical properties that are quite different
from those of either the bulk solid phase or
the isolated atom, providing insight into the
interactions between atoms and opening the door
to the synthesis of interesting new materials.

A crystalline solid, such as a piece of nickel, copper, or iron, consists of a series of basic building blocks called unit cells, which are replicated again and again as one traverses the crystal until one finally reaches the surface of the material. Deep inside the material, an atom is held in place by interactions with the other atoms of its unit cell and the atoms of neighboring unit cells. Near the surface of the crystal, however, these forces are not as symmetrical as they are deep within the material because the neighboring atoms are missing on one side. As a result, it is common for crystal surfaces to adopt an arrangement of the atoms that may be quite different from that which is present deep within the material, giving what is termed a "reconstruction" of the single crystal surface. As one subdivides a material into smaller and smaller pieces, the fraction of atoms that is influenced by a surface increases until all (or nearly all) of the atoms occupy surface positions. Such small pieces of matter, consisting of roughly 100 atoms or less, may possess geometric structures and chemical and physical properties that are dramatically different from those found in the corresponding bulk solids. As a result, these clusters of atoms provide a new arena for probing the interactions between atoms and offer new hope for the synthesis of unusual new materials.

Only recently have scientists been able to systematically prepare and investigate small metal and semiconductor clusters. As one might expect, many questions concerning these unusual systems remain only partially answered, and these form the basis for continuing research. For example, scientists would like to find answers to the following: How large must a cluster be before it takes on the structure and properties of the bulk solid material? How do the atoms of the solid rearrange themselves when they are formed into a cluster of finite size, and what considerations govern this rearrangement? As a cluster grows in size by sequential addition

MICHAEL D. MORSE is an Associate Professor of Chemistry at the University of Utah, Salt Lake City.

(Overleaf) Illustration by Kathryn Diffley

of atoms, does its structure smoothly convert to the crystal structure of the bulk solid, or are there sudden rearrangements that occur at certain specific sizes? Do the smallest clusters have definite structures, or are their atoms in a state of flux, constantly moving as if the material were a liquid? If the clusters do have a definite structure, at what temperature do they melt, and how does this compare with the bulk melting point? How small can a metal cluster be and still retain electrical conductivity? Do small clusters exhibit chemical behavior that differs from that of the bulk material, and can this potentially unique chemistry be put to use in any way?

This last point touches on the potential technological uses of metal and semiconductor clusters. The possibilities are numerous. Many industrial processes, for example, are catalyzed by transition metals, but, unfortunately, it is often the expensive metals that must be used. A widespread example is the use of platinum and rhodium metals in catalytic converters, which are used to remove carbon monoxide and nitrogen oxides from automobile exhaust. The metal catalytically required for this process is rhodium, which is even rarer than platinum and in 1991 cost approximately $1,400 per ounce. Obviously, it would be advantageous to replace rhodium with a less expensive material, and it is conceivable that small clusters of a less expensive metal might possess the required catalytic activity.

Such considerations account for much of the interest in small metal clusters. It is also quite likely that small metal and semiconductor clusters can be used to prepare thin films with unusual optical, electronic, and magnetic properties, and these will likely be useful in enhancing the performance of products such as magnetic data storage devices, diode lasers, photodetectors, electronic devices, and superconductors. In addition to the purely scientific questions of the previous paragraphs, the potential technological applications described above have contributed to the great interest in this field.

A historical perspective

In their initial encounters with clusters, early scientists often had little or no idea that they were dealing with a small cluster of metal or semiconductor atoms. For example, one of the first observations of a cluster was the discovery by William Huggins in 1881 of an emission of violet light at a wavelength of 4050 Å, emanating from a comet. Although Huggins claimed that "the spectrum of this light shows the presence in the comet of carbon, possibly in combination with hydrogen," it was not correctly identified as fluorescence from the triatomic carbon cluster, C_3, until 1951.

Similarly, an understanding of the technological importance of clusters was lacking during the initial development of photography, which relies on the catalytic properties of silver clusters for its success. The active material in photographic plates is an emulsion of tiny crystallites of a silver halide, such as silver bromide (AgBr). When a photon of light is absorbed by one of these crystallites, it detaches an electron from a Br⁻ ion; the mobile electron then drifts from site to site through the crystal. Eventually the electron locates a stable site, perhaps at a defect, where it attaches to an Ag⁺ ion to form a neutral silver atom. Absorption of a second photon may cause this process to be repeated, resulting in the reduction of another Ag⁺ ion to a silver atom. The key to photography lies in the fact that eventually a catalytically active site is generated in this way, and this site is able to accelerate the reduction of AgBr to Ag metal when the crystallite is placed in a developing solution. The developing solution is quite capable of reducing both exposed and unexposed crystallites to silver metal, but the tremendous difference in rate allows the exposed and unexposed crystallites to be distinguished. The photographic image is then preserved, since crystallites that were exposed to a sufficient amount of light have generated the catalytically active species and have been developed by reduction to silver metal. The resulting grains of metallic silver appear black, causing a negative image to be produced in which bright portions of the object are encoded as dark portions of the image (Figure 1).

For years it was thought that the catalytically active species responsible for storing the developable latent image was a cluster of silver atoms, formed when the mobile electrons settled into a single defect site. In 1987 this was finally proved by Ludger Wöste, who deposited size-selected silver clusters on unexposed AgBr emulsions. Wöste determined that the smallest cluster capable of catalyzing the reduction of the AgBr crystallite was Ag₄. The use of Ag₄ clusters in the photographic process

Figure 1. Steps in the exposure to light of a grain of silver bromide (AgBr), the active material in photographic plates, are shown in the diagram below. In (a) the grain has not been exposed to light and consists of Ag⁺ and Br⁻ ions. In (b) a photon of light has been absorbed and has detached an electron from a Br⁻ ion; the electron is now in a mobile state. In (c) the electron has attached itself to an Ag⁺ ion to form a neutral silver atom. When this process is repeated, it results in a cluster of silver atoms, (d).

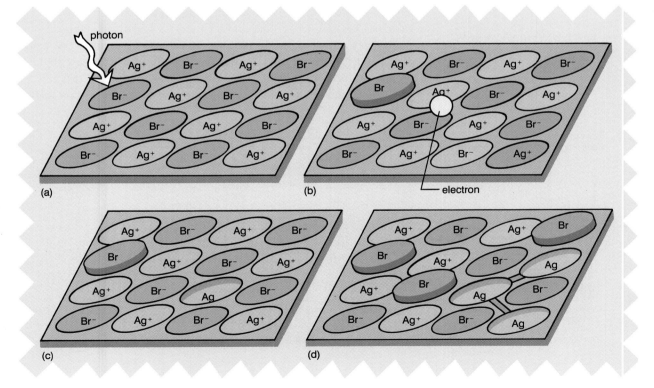

constitutes the oldest and most widespread application of metal clusters in technology and was developed with no understanding whatever that clusters were involved. Now that we are aware of the potential of new chemistry associated with metal and semiconductor clusters, it may be hoped that future applications of these materials will be less haphazard.

Alkali metal clusters and the electronic shell structure model

During the 1950s and 1960s there was a great renaissance in physical chemistry. Chemists used molecular beams to investigate the dynamics of chemical reactions in much the same way that physicists use particle accelerators to study the dynamics of nuclear collisions. This period was known as "the alkali age" because molecular beams of the low-boiling-point alkali metals could be easily generated, and these reactive atoms could easily be induced to react with a collision partner. As a result, the chemical dynamics of the reactions of alkali metals (lithium, sodium, potassium, rubidium, and cesium) were more extensively studied than those of any other type of molecule. At higher temperatures and source pressures, the beams emitted by these high-temperature oven sources contained substantial numbers of alkali metal clusters, and these naturally became the first of the metal clusters to be experimentally studied.

In some of the earliest experiments, the composition of the cluster beam was investigated by detecting the clusters in a mass spectrometer. Regardless of whether the clusters under investigation were composed of sodium or potassium atoms, a distinctive pattern of abundances was observed, with clusters containing 2, 8, 20, 40, 58, and 92 atoms showing up strongly in the mass spectrum, especially as compared with the clusters with 3, 9, 21, 41, 59, and 93 atoms, respectively (Figure 2).

This remarkable pattern of cluster abundances demanded an explanation, but it seemed unlikely that the pattern of abundances could be traced to a set of particularly stable geometric structures. After all, the alkali metals in their solid form are among the softest metals known,

Figure 2. A beam of sodium molecules produced from a high-temperature oven source contains clusters of atoms, as revealed by a mass spectrometer. The graph shows the abundance of each cluster as a function of the cluster size. A distinctive pattern of cluster abundances can be observed, with clusters containing 2, 8, 20, 40, 58, and 92 atoms showing up strongly in the mass spectrum, especially in comparison with clusters of 3, 9, 21, 41, 59, and 93 atoms.

Adapted from "Physics of Metal Clusters," M.L. Cohen, M.Y. Chou, W.D. Knight, and W.A. de Heer, *The Journal of Physical Chemistry*, vol. 91, no. 12, pp. 3141–49, © 1987 American Chemical Society

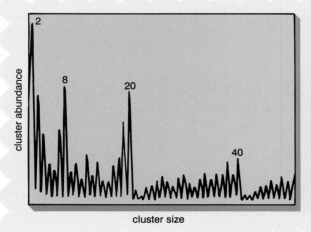
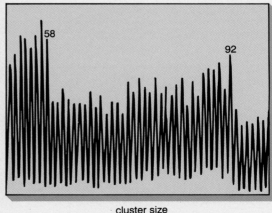

having the consistency of room-temperature butter. Why should the stability of the small clusters be strongly dependent on geometric structure when the solid materials are so easily deformed?

If this effect was not geometric in nature, perhaps it had something to do with the electronic nature of the metals. In 1984 this problem was solved by Walter D. Knight and his co-workers at the University of California at Berkeley. The simplest model of the electronic structure of bulk solid metals assumes that each metal atom releases its valence electrons so that they are no longer bound to a particular atom but are free to move about the crystal lattice. If the same model were applied to the alkali clusters, a given Na_n cluster would, for example, consist of n positively charged Na^+ ions and n electrons freely moving about within the cluster. Knight and his co-workers recognized that a cluster that is roughly spherical would require that these freely moving conduction electrons be placed in orbitals quite similar to the 1s, 2s, 2p, etc., orbitals of the atoms but would extend over the entire cluster. In a flash of insight they realized that alkali clusters placing their conduction electrons in closed shells would be especially stable and thus would tend to be more abundant in the molecular beam experiments.

This is precisely analogous to the rare gases, which are chemically very stable because all of the electrons are placed in filled shells. In the atoms, orbitals are filled in the order 1s, 2s, 2p, 3s, 3p, 4s, 3d, 4p, 5s, 4d, 5p, 6s, 4f, 5d, 6p, 7s, and 5f, leading to shell closings at the atoms with 2(He), 4(Be), 10(Ne), 12(Mg), 18(Ar), 20(Ca), 30(Zn), 36(Kr), 38(Sr), 48(Cd), 54(Xe), 56(Ba), 70(Yb), 80(Hg), 86(Rn), 88(Ra), and 102(No) electrons, respectively. Of course, some of these elements are more stable than others, with the rare gases (elements 2, 10, 18, 36, 54, and 86) by far the most stable. The abundant alkali clusters did not correspond well with these highly stable atoms, however, indicating that the order of the orbital filling in the clusters differs from that obtained in the atoms. In fact, it should come as no surprise that the electron orbitals fill in a different order in the alkali clusters, since in the clusters the electrons move under the influence of a large number of +1 ion cores, while in the atoms they move under the influence of a single positively charged nucleus. Knight and his colleagues, assuming that the valence electrons in the cluster are completely free to move within the cluster but are pulled back toward the cluster if they go beyond a certain distance from its center, were able to predict the precise number of valence electrons associated with the closing of a shell. The result, given in Figure 3, predicts major shell closings at 2, 8, 20, 40, 58, and 92 electrons, just where the stable clusters are experimentally observed. This was a major step forward in cluster science: a simple theory had been developed to explain some otherwise puzzling observations.

Clusters of refractory materials: surprises among the carbon clusters

Clusters of materials that boil at very high temperatures are much more difficult to generate than are the alkali metal clusters. A general approach

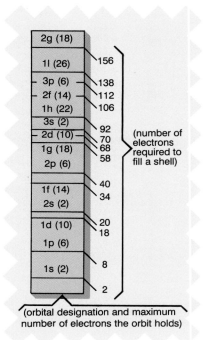

Figure 3. The predicted energy levels of an electron free to move within a metal cluster but without enough energy to leave the cluster reveal large gaps between the 1s and 1p (sometimes denoted as 2p) orbitals and between the 1p and 1d orbitals. These lead to stable n = 2 and n = 8 clusters, respectively, as observed in the mass spectrometer experiment. Similar gaps following the 2s, 2p, and 1h levels lead to stable n = 20, n = 40, and n = 92 clusters, respectively, as are also observed.

Adapted from "Physics of Metal Clusters," M.L. Cohen, M.Y. Chou, W.D. Knight, and W.A. de Heer, *The Journal of Physical Chemistry*, vol. 91, no. 12, pp. 3141–49, © 1987 American Chemical Society

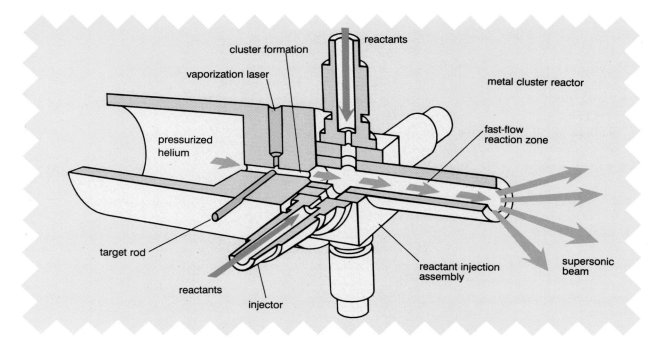

Metal cluster reactor was developed to generate clusters of materials that boil at very high temperatures, such as tungsten and carbon. A high-intensity laser vaporizes a target rod of the desired material to form a plasma. Pulses of an inert gas such as helium carry the plasma along a short, narrow channel, where the plasma cools and forms metal clusters. The cluster-gas mixture then enters a fast-flow reaction tube, into which a reactant such as molecular hydrogen or carbon monoxide is injected. Finally, the mixture exits the tube into a vacuum, forming a pulsed molecular beam.

Adapted from information obtained from R.E. Smalley, Department of Chemistry, Rice University, Houston, Texas

to the production of these species was developed concurrently in 1981 in the laboratories of Richard E. Smalley of Rice University, Houston, Texas, and Vladimir E. Bondybey of AT&T Bell Laboratories, Murray Hill, New Jersey. The method employed a pulsed high-intensity laser to vaporize the material, thereby avoiding the need to heat a substantial portion of the apparatus to high temperatures. By flowing an inert gas, such as helium, over the target surface during the laser pulse, the vaporized atoms could be entrained in the carrier gas and expanded into a vacuum to form a pulsed molecular beam. With this method even materials as refractory as tungsten (boiling point of 5,933 K) or carbon (5,100 K) can be readily vaporized, despite the fact that no known material can withstand these temperatures without melting. Moreover, it was readily found that clusters could be formed and that the extent of clustering could be controlled by varying the length of time that the vaporized material spent in the high-pressure zone prior to expansion into vacuum. Following this discovery the number of workers actively engaged in cluster research expanded rapidly, since many new species that were previously unknown could be studied.

The carbon clusters form an interesting case in point. Would clusters of carbon atoms form structures similar to the diamond lattice, which is the stable high-pressure form of carbon, or would the structures be more like graphite, which consists of planes composed of hexagonal rings of carbon atoms? Alternatively, would small clusters of carbon atoms adopt an entirely new geometry?

Theoretical calculations of small carbon (C) clusters (up to 10 atoms) had suggested that linear structures would be favored. Using various spectroscopic methods, researchers showed that the C_n clusters with

138

$n = 3\text{--}10$ are linear. Evidence now suggests that clusters in the size range from 11 to 31 atoms form rings, although this is not yet conclusive. The most interesting experimental results, however, reveal that under strongly clustering conditions the dominant molecular species in a carbon cluster beam is C_{60}, with C_{70} and, to a lesser extent, C_{50} also showing significantly greater abundance than other clusters in the same size range (Figure 4). As in the alkali metals, these "magic numbers" are the key to understanding the structure of the carbon clusters.

The discovery of C_{60} as a dominant cluster produced in the laser vaporization of carbon was made in 1985 by Smalley and co-workers; this result has since been reproduced by many laboratories that used other methods of vaporizing carbon. In fact, C_{60} has since been shown to be present in soot-producing flames in rather large quantities. The fundamental and difficult question, however, concerns its structure. Why should a cluster of 60 carbon atoms be so stable compared with a cluster of 58 or 62 atoms? In pondering this question, Smalley became convinced that C_{60} must possess a very stable geometric structure. The key to forming a stable geometric structure is to tie up all of the valence electrons in chemical bonds, and this can happen only if the cluster forms a closed surface. With this in mind, Smalley began examining the regular polyhedrons known from solid geometry. He was led to the work of Buckminster Fuller, inventor of the geodesic dome, and rediscovered the highly symmetrical structure known as the truncated icosahedron (Figure 5). This is more familiar as a soccer ball that has 60 vertices (one for each carbon atom in C_{60}). Each carbon atom is chemically bonded to three other carbon atoms, with one bond forming an edge in two hexagons and two bonds forming edges of a pentagon and a hexagon. The structure has a total of 12 pentagons and 20 hexagons on its surface and has an appealingly high degree of symmetry. In fact, all carbon atoms are symmetrically equivalent, taking part in two hexagonal and one pentagonal ring. Of course, this structure was only a hypothesis, but it was an intriguing one. In honor of Buckminster Fuller, Smalley and his co-workers named this proposed structure "buckminsterfullerene."

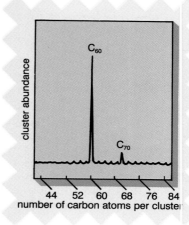

Figure 4. Mass spectra of carbon clusters ranging in size from 42 to 86 atoms were obtained under conditions that led to strong clustering. The striking abundance of the C_{60} and C_{70} clusters suggests that they have uniquely stable structures.

Adapted from "C_{60}: Buckminsterfullerene," H.W. Kroto, et al., reprinted by permission of Nature, vol. 318, no. 6042, pp. 162–163, Nov. 14, 1985, © Macmillan Magazines Ltd.

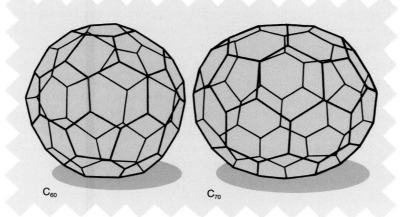

Figure 5. The structure proposed for the abundant carbon cluster C_{60} is a truncated icosahedron (far left), resembling a soccer ball, while that for C_{70} (left) is somewhat more elongated. Because these clusters are unusually stable, they form a closed surface.

Wolfgang Krätschmer and Konstantin Fostiropoulos, Max-Planck-Institut für Kernphysik,
Heidelberg, Germany; Lowell D. Lamb and Donald R. Huffman, University of Arizona, Tucson

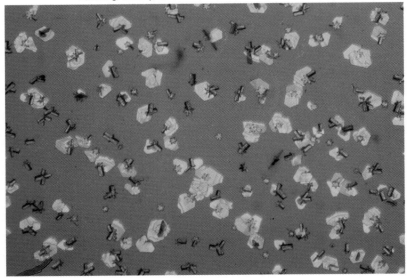

Reflected-light micrograph reveals crystals of solid C_{60}. Formed in such shapes as rods and flakes, the crystals are produced by evaporation of graphite electrodes in an atmosphere of pressurized helium. The resulting graphite carbon soot is dispersed in benzene, where the material giving rise to the spectral features attributed to C_{60} dissolves to produce a wine-red or brown liquid. The liquid is then separated from the soot, and the benzene is evaporated to produce the crystals.

Another observation was that clusters in the range above 32 atoms tended strongly to have only an even number of atoms. In examining the polyhedrons containing only five- and six-membered rings (the least strained rings for carbon-based molecules), Smalley and his co-workers discovered that fully closed surfaces could be constructed by using 12 pentagons and any number of hexagons, and they proposed these structures for the other carbon clusters in the size range above about 40 atoms. They further proposed the name "fullerenes" for these closed structures. The structure composed of 12 pentagons and n hexagons is formed from $2n + 20$ carbon atoms, leading to the requirement of an even number of atoms to achieve a completely closed surface with no "dangling bonds."

Of course, structures with a number of carbon atoms other than 60 must have a lower intrinsic symmetry than buckminsterfullerene. In particular, clusters with 58 or fewer atoms must have two adjacent pentagons, leading to a buildup of strain in a portion of the molecule, which then becomes reactive. It turns out that the smallest cluster that can avoid having three adjacent pentagons is C_{50}, and the smallest that can avoid having more than three adjacent pentagons is C_{32}. The presence of both even- and odd-numbered carbon clusters in the size range below 32 atoms suggests that these species do not form the closed surfaces suggested for the fullerenes but are instead much less stable rings of carbon atoms. Apparently the strain involved in having more than three adjacent pentagonal rings is too severe and prevents the molecule from closing in on itself. The stable C_{70} molecule, which shows up prominently in the mass spectrum of Figure 4, was suggested to be similar to C_{60} but possessed an extra belt of 10 atoms around its equator, making it roughly spheroidal in structure, as is also shown in Figure 5.

Although attempts to test these ideas were made in the late 1980s, they remained speculative and controversial until the late summer of

140

1990, when Donald R. Huffman, Wolfgang Krätschmer, and co-workers determined that C_{60} was not a reactive, unstable molecule that could be contained only in a high-vacuum molecular beam apparatus. By using an electrical current to heat a thin carbon rod to a high temperature in a reduced atmosphere of helium, they formed a pure carbon soot, and from this both C_{60} and C_{70} could be extracted. This method produced C_{60} and C_{70} in about 14% combined yield. Moreover, traditional separation methods were successful in separating the mixtures, allowing C_{60} and C_{70} to be obtained in 99% purity or better. More recently, C_{84} was extracted from the graphitic soot as well, and other, larger carbon clusters may be also present.

This discovery set off a great rush of studies aimed at proving the proposed structures, now that pure C_{60} and C_{70} were available in gram quantities. It also opened a new frontier in chemistry, since the buckminsterfullerene model of C_{60} had been shown to have an exceptional number of resonance structures, in which double and single bonds may be drawn in a multitude of ways. (A resonance structure is any of two or more possible structures of the same compound that have identical geometry but different arrangements of their paired electrons.) For historical reasons molecules that have this property are said to be aromatic, and they react in a way that is quite different from other organic molecules. In this regard C_{60} is reminiscent of benzene, which is the prototype of aromatic molecules. Benzene has only two resonance structures, however, while buckminsterfullerene has 12,500 different ways in which the double and single bonds may be drawn. Furthermore, it is quite common in organic chemistry to investigate a basic class of molecules by attaching various side groups, or substituents, and determining their influence on the chemistry. The observation that it is possible to create molecular beams containing C_{60} and other fullerenes with firmly attached metal atoms, which appear to be inside the carbon cluster—reported

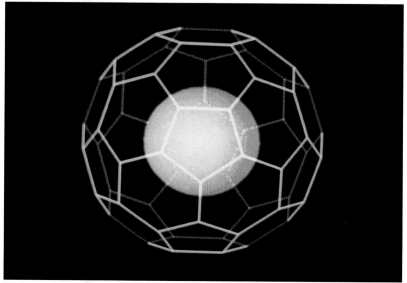

R.E. Smalley, Department of Chemistry, Rice University, Houston, Texas

Computer-generated image reveals a potassium ion inside a C_{60} cage. Rice University chemist Richard Smalley envisions "shrink wrapping" metal ions inside the central cavities of these carbon cages, thereby permitting reactive or radioactive materials to be encapsulated for specialized storage.

by Smalley and his co-workers in 1985—suggests an entirely new way of forming chemical derivatives of these carbon groups. These may be termed "metallofullerenes." It may even be possible to create salts such as $C_{60}K^+C_{60}^-$, in which one fullerene has been modified to be an excellent electron donor by encapsulating an electropositive metal (such as potassium) in its interior.

The possible compounds that may be made from these materials have barely been explored, and their technological uses have hardly been considered. One possibility of considerable interest would be to react C_{60} with a mild source of fluorine to make the perfluorinated hydrocarbon $C_{60}F_{60}$, which would have the chemical stability of Teflon (a highly inert, polymeric fluorocarbon) but which would be spherical in structure. The result might well be an excellent, exceptionally stable, high-temperature lubricant, consisting of ball bearings on a molecular scale.

Reactivity of metal clusters: the potential for new catalysts

The transition metal catalysts commonly used to clean up automobile exhaust, to refine petroleum, and to hydrogenate carbon-carbon double bonds typically involve rare and expensive metals such as platinum, rhenium, rhodium, and palladium. The possibility of using transition metal clusters either to create new catalysts or to help understand the ones that are being used has been a major driving force in the cluster field and has led to industrial participation by firms such as Exxon Research and Engineering Co. In some surprising results dating back to the mid-1980s, Andrew Kaldor and colleagues at Exxon, S.J. Riley and co-workers at Argonne (Illinois) National Laboratory, and Smalley and colleagues at Rice University determined that metal clusters exhibit reaction rates with certain reactant molecules that vary tremendously as a function of cluster size. In the case of iron clusters reacting with H_2, for example, Riley and co-workers found that Fe_{23} is approximately 2,000 times more reactive with H_2 than is Fe_{17}. This remarkable result was quite enticing, since it provided direct evidence that clusters of different size do exhibit different chemistry. This suggests that it may be possible to use cluster size to fine-tune a chemical catalyst, making it either more efficient or more selective in the reactions that it induces.

In 1988 Kaldor and co-workers at Exxon and Michael Morse and colleagues at the University of Utah concurrently used chemical reactivity as a probe of niobium clusters, showing that certain clusters seem to have two different forms that react at dramatically different rates. In both cases these were interpreted as geometric isomers, demonstrating rather conclusively that Nb_9, Nb_{11}, and Nb_{12} have more than one form and, therefore, do have definite geometrical structures. (An isomer is one of two or more chemical substances having the same elementary percentage composition and molecular weight but differing in structure and, therefore, in properties.) This was by no means a foregone conclusion, since it had been thought possible that many metal clusters might be fluxional, having no definite geometry but being rather liquidlike in character. The existence of structural isomers rules out this possibility, at least for

142

the species in which it is observed. Such structural isomerism has now been identified in Ta_{12} and Nb_{12}^+ and among many silicon cluster ions. Eventually, no doubt, such discoveries will help scientists understand the structure and bonding among these fascinating new materials.

Metal and semiconductor clusters and the future

The field of metal and semiconductor clusters, barely 10 years old, is already providing important new insights into the nature of the chemical bond in metallic and semiconducting systems. It has led to the discovery of a new form of carbon that is stable at room temperature and pressure almost indefinitely, and this in turn may well lead to a new branch of organic chemistry. Through the observation of electronic shell structure in the alkali metal clusters, it has led to a better understanding of the motion of the conduction electrons in the alkali metals. It has shown that finite clusters of transition metal atoms possess a different reaction chemistry than that of the bulk material and that this chemistry is dramatically dependent on cluster size. It has also enabled an explanation of the mechanism of photography to be placed on solid footing.

This is an impressive list of accomplishments for such a new branch of chemistry, and it is only a partial list. The future undoubtedly holds many new and exciting possibilities, both for fundamental scientific knowledge and for technological uses of the materials made possible by cluster research.

FOR ADDITIONAL READING

M.L. Cohen, M.Y. Chou, W.D. Knight, and W.A. de Heer, "Physics of Metal Clusters," *Journal of Physical Chemistry,* 91 (June 4, 1987, pp. 3141–49).

R.F. Curl and R.E. Smalley, "Probing C_{60}," *Science,* 242 (Nov. 18, 1988, pp. 1017–22).

W.A. de Heer, W.D. Knight, M.Y. Chou, and M.L. Cohen, "Electronic Shell Structure and Metal Clusters," *Solid State Physics* (1987, pp. 94ff).

Michael A. Duncan and Dennis H. Rouvray, "Microclusters," *Scientific American* (December 1989, pp. 110–115).

T.H. James, ed., *The Theory of the Photographic Process* (Macmillan, 1977).

W. Krätschmer, Lowell D. Lamb, K. Fostiropoulos, and Donald R. Huffman, "Solid C_{60}: A New Form of Carbon," *Nature* (Sept. 27, 1990, pp. 354–358).

H.W. Kroto, J.R. Heath, S.C. O'Brien, R.F. Curl, and R.E. Smalley, "C_{60}: Buckminsterfullerene," *Nature* (Nov. 14, 1985, pp. 162–163).

M.D. Morse, "Clusters of Transition Metal Atoms," *Chemical Reviews* (December 1986, pp. 1049–1109).

PERSONAL COMPUTING IN THE INFORMATION AGE

by William H. Gates

With more than 115 million users in 1990, up from 1.3 million 10 years earlier, the personal computer is now on the threshold of becoming a powerful multimedia information manager.

In 1681 an Italian merchant named Giambattista Sardi struck a deal to bring a shipment of Russian cowhides from Amsterdam to his home city of Livorno. He hoped to turn a decent profit, since the hides were selling in Livorno for twice the price they commanded in Amsterdam. Sardi's shipment of hides arrived, but he lost his shirt; hides imported directly from Russia arrived at the same time, flooding the Italian market, and driving the price below Sardi's cost. To make matters worse, Sardi's hides were of poor quality, so the deal was almost a complete loss.

Sardi knew about the price difference between Amsterdam and Livorno, but he did not know that shiploads of hides from Russia were already at sea, en route to his market, and he had no way to check the quality of his own shipment. Sardi lost money because he lacked information. His story has been the rule, rather than the exception, throughout history. Around the world, from tribal times until very recently, information has been a scarce resource—slowly created, slowly improved, slowly exchanged. For most of human history the biggest information problem has been the lack of it. Now times have changed, however. We no longer lack information; we lack control of the immense quantities of information that now inundate us.

Oversupply of information

Too much information can be as big a problem as too little. Today, we are reached at home by more than 100 cable television channels, rented videotapes, compact discs, local and national newspapers, a vast array of periodicals, and direct mail—an average of more than 19.5 kilograms (43 pounds) per person per year in the United States. At work we are subject to the relent-

WILLIAM H. GATES *is Chairman and Chief Executive Officer of Microsoft Corp., Redmond, Washington.*

Illustrations by John Craig

less output of laser printers, facsimile transmitters, copiers, electronic mail, voice mail, paper mail, cellular phones, thousands of business and professional journals (more than 10,000 in medicine alone), and the occasional corporate video. This list is intimidating, but there is more: in-flight telephones, billboards, on-line information services, radio, multiple sets of yellow pages, our entire educational system, and our old friends—books. We still find time, in the United States alone, to purchase, if not read, 1.5 billion books each year.

We can lay part of the blame for this deluge of data on the advances in semiconductor technology during the past 25 years. The data bases that make the direct-mail business profitable are maintained by computers, and books and magazines are published cost-effectively by means of electronic typesetting. In fact, virtually every information technology, from communications satellites to videocassette recorders, depends on silicon chips. Thanks to them, you will probably be offered, in your lifetime, more information via junk mail than an educated contemporary of Isaac Newton's could find in a lifetime of assiduous scholarship.

Fortunately, one technology based on semiconductor chips has the potential to help us digest the data deluge: the personal computer of the 1990s. Among the many information technologies filling up offices and homes, only one—personal computing—is not only a conduit but a controller. Personal computers (PCs) already give their more than 115 million users unique power to manage information, and this power will increase dramatically during the next few years. Two new sets of features will make personal computers better information managers in the near future: multimedia features and context features.

Multimedia features

We perceive the world through all our senses, and we do a particularly good job of receiving information through our eyes and our ears. Our brains, moreover, are capable of processing different kinds of information in different ways. We are good at comprehending spoken and written language, watching and making sense of the way objects behave in space and time, recognizing and manipulating symbols, appreciating works of art, reading charts and diagrams, understanding visualizations of concepts, and interpreting simplified representations of reality, such as maps. If we consider each of these different ways of delivering information as a different medium, it is clear that we are all great multimedia thinkers. If each piece of information were offered to us in the medium most comprehensible to us, our multimedia thinking ability could even help us cope with the information overload. Beethoven's *Ninth Symphony*, for example, is most readily enjoyed if it is delivered in audio form; an explanation of how an octopus swims is best understood if it includes the opportunity to view the creature swimming. These two examples illustrate the two main benefits of using the best medium for each piece of information: comprehension and engagement.

Listening to Beethoven's *Ninth* and watching the octopus swim are good examples of learning through a medium that is well matched to

Total Worldwide Installed Base of Personal Computers

Year	Number of PCs
1980	1,284,900
1981	2,905,300
1982	7,600,100
1983	17,923,900
1984	31,186,000
1985	43,711,000
1986	54,810,000
1987	65,335,000
1988	75,805,000
1989	94,191,000
1990	115,318,000

0   30   60   90   120
millions

Source: *Dataquest Incorporated* (July 1990).

146

the information it conveys. When the subject matter is broader, the match becomes more complicated. What is the "best" medium by which to understand the impact on American society of the automobile? Text? Maps? Charts? A book can offer those. For sound and motion there is videotape, but the text and detailed graphics found in print would be lost. Personal computers of the near future will offer a unique breadth of media—the best of print, the best of video—and one more very important feature: interactivity.

Interactivity is personal computing at its most essential. In your quest to learn more about the impact of the automobile, you should be able to turn to a map in a computer-based article about your state that would show in animation where new roads were built year by year. You could run the article forward and backward, stop it in any year, and ask for a chart showing the number of cars sold that year. You could change the chart to add car sales for the previous five years and then change it again to also show income per family for each of those years. You could go back to the map and ask it to show you population density in each county, year by year, as well as annual road building. The human brain is good at recognizing patterns, and perhaps you would see interesting patterns in the relationships among population, income, cars sold, and roads built as you watched the maps and charts change year by year.

This same PC-based multimedia article could also offer you a representative selection of images of makes and models of cars from different years, perhaps show you video clips of early television commercials for cars, and maybe let you hear from Henry Ford. The computer could also offer you working models of different cars if you were interested in automotive engineering. You could, for example, select a Porsche 959 and operate its engine. You could change the ratio of fuel to air and then see and hear the changes in engine speed, torque, fuel efficiency, and exhaust emissions. If you were more interested in how cars are built, you could operate a model of the factory and zoom in on steps in the manufacturing process.

As you can see from these examples, multimedia computing is making some powerful promises: to deliver each piece of information in its best medium, to provide access to information in all media in one place, and to allow users to interact with each piece of information. There are more promises to come.

Context features

Every piece of information has, at any given time, a context. Its context is its setting: What other information is with it? What is it connected to, associated with, part of? If you could be considered a piece of information, your contexts would include your family, your friends, places you have lived, places you have been, classes you have taken, books you have read, organizations to which you have belonged, your favorite foods, and important relationships of all kinds in your life. All this information added up would paint an interesting picture of you, even if no specific information about you was in it!

You, in turn, are part of the context for other people, and you share contexts with others: the same history class, the same track team, the same family, the same employer, the same color eyes, the same favorite foods. If you are a piece of information that someone is trying to find without knowing your name, exactly where you live, or what you look like, that person can still find you if he or she has ways of learning about your context. You are probably not the only person in the world who does any one thing that you do, but you are one of a very few, at most, who do most of the things you do. Similarly, each piece of information has context.

For example, consider a short essay about dairy cows. The context for information about cows includes associations of one kind or another with places (Where were cows first domesticated for milk? Where are they found today?), with time periods (When were cows first domesticated for milk? When did dairy farming establish itself in each of the major areas where it exists today?), and with numerous categories of the sort that you find in card catalogs (agriculture, food, mammals, and so forth). The context for a cow essay would also include information pieces about the people who had made important contributions to dairy farming and information pieces that shared some element of content with this piece (used some of the same words or the same pictures, for example).

In general, the context for each piece of information is all other pieces of information with which it has something in common. We use context all the time to deal with information; we find specific facts by sorting through groups of facts with similar contexts, we understand things by learning about their context (you understand a lot about fish when you learn that their context is water), and we learn by branching out, through context, from familiar things to new ones. If you know what a car is, you can understand what a truck is by knowing what it has in common with a car and what is different.

Discovering context information can be a tedious process—exactly the sort of process that computers do very well and very quickly. Imagine, for example, that you wanted to know the names of any women born in Michigan who had ever won medals in the Olympic Games. If one or more such women exist, their context would include groups such as "all women," "everyone born in Michigan," and "all Olympic medalists." It would be tedious to find and examine each group to see if anyone was in all three, but a computer could do this very quickly. Computers are potentially very good at finding things and pointing out relationships among pieces of information. Work is under way to create software that will be very good at helping you to find what you need, even when you are not exactly sure what you are looking for. Your PC will be able to take whatever clues you can give it, examine very large amounts of information quickly, and return some proposed answers to you. On the basis of what it gives you, you can provide more guidance and get more answers and then repeat this process until you have what you need. This special skill of personal computers will make them powerful tools to help people make sense of the information that inundates them at work, at home, and at school.

Microprocessors and memory

It is easy enough to say that personal computers with these new context features will be able to help us find the information we need and, with their new multimedia features, be able to help us understand it. Improvements in hardware and software will be required for making this vision a reality, however. The core technology in a personal computer is the microprocessor. Each of these small (usually 6.5 square centimeters [one square inch] or even less) silicon chips is packed with hundreds of thousands or, nowadays, more than a million tiny transistors. With each year that passes, these chips become faster and more powerful. During the 1990s there will be at least another hundredfold improvement in their performance.

The features discussed above, both multimedia and context, require considerable speed and power, and so it is fortunate that these improvements in microprocessors are coming quickly. Writing the software to take advantage of this added capacity will be a major challenge, but the software industry is working closely with the microprocessor designers to ensure that the software and the hardware are developed to take full advantage of each other.

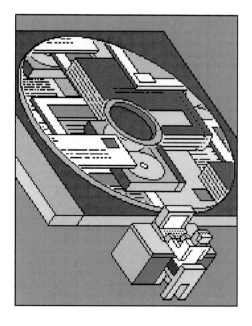

Information in computers is in the form of digital data, and it can be saved by means of different technologies. The most commonly used memory technologies today are magnetic—primarily floppy disks and hard disks. In 1980 the amount of information available to the user was limited to what could be held and distributed on floppy disks (about 7,500 words of text per disk at first). The invention of hard disks increased the amount of information that could be held in each machine (by about 30 times at first, now by as much as 1,000 times), but information is not easily distributed on hard disks.

Three technologies are now increasing the amount of information that can be stored, as well as easing the problem of distributing large amounts of information easily and inexpensively. One of these uses compact discs (CDs), already widely used to distribute music. This adaptation of CD technology is called CD-ROM, which stands for "compact disc-read only memory." "Read only" means that the information on the disc can be read but that information cannot be changed, added, or deleted. One CD-ROM disc can hold more than 600 megabytes of information (24,000 pages of text, or 8,000 quarter-screen full-color images, or 72 minutes of music), and it costs less than $2 to manufacture. A newer technology, called magneto-optical storage, offers the same high capacity as CD-ROM but permits erasing and recording. As the cost of magneto-optical storage falls, it may someday replace CD-ROM, hard disk, and floppy disk technologies. The third technology is networking, connecting computers to one another so that they can exchange information. Networking permits users to search for information elsewhere in their organization or anywhere in the world. As it becomes more common and easier to use, networking will greatly expand the value of the PC as an information manager.

Presentation

We see the real world around us in a wide field of vision, in three dimensions, in very fine detail, in full color, and in motion. We hear it in similar detail and fidelity. For computers to communicate well about this real world, they must be able to present information with acceptable fineness and fidelity of audiovisual detail, acceptable color, and acceptable motion, all at an acceptable size and for an acceptable price. Rapid progress has been made during the past five years to improve the presentation of visual detail and color. By 1991 an acceptable standard, called VGA+, was becoming common at relatively low prices. The handling of detail (resolution) and color will improve until both reach the level of development where further improvements are imperceptible.

Until recently, progress appeared slower on the technologies required for permitting personal computers to present gracefully information that changed rapidly over time—audio and video. However, one key technology and one key technique are now enabling rapid progress. The technology is a category of chips called digital signal processors (DSP). These chips can manipulate audio and video information very quickly and can take over this job from the computer's main microprocessor. The technique is

called compression, reducing the amount of memory required for storing information. Audio and video use very large amounts of memory, and so compression is essential if information in these media is to be stored in significant quantities on CD-ROM discs, transmitted over networks, or even moved around quickly within the computer. Compression can be achieved in a number of ways, and rapid progress has been made on several methods, both with hardware and with software. Compression ratios of up to 10:1 (reducing the amount of memory required by a given unit of information by 90%) are beginning to be achieved in information products for PCs scheduled to be released in the next year or two. Ratios of 100:1 are a goal that may be achieved by the middle of the decade.

The graphical user interface and datacentric model

The basic process of using a personal computer is to enter instructions by hand, see the results on a screen, and then enter more instructions. This process is repeated until the user is satisfied with what he or she has found or created. For many users the manual instructions are in the form of strokes on a keyboard, and the results are seen as letters and numbers on the screen. A useful variation of this process allows the user to enter manual instructions by moving a hand-sized object called a "mouse" around on a screen-shaped section of his or her desk, which moves a pointer around on the screen itself. The pointer can be used to select parts of what the user wants to see on the screen (words, pictures, or small symbols called icons that represent larger pieces of information). Once a certain piece of information has been selected, the pointer can be used again to select what is to be done with it (move it or copy it, for example).

This process resembles those one might use to manipulate physical objects in such small parts of the real world as the top of a desk. The entire idea is called a graphical user interface (GUI), and it is a much easier way for most people to control the ways in which their computers manipulate information. It has become widely accepted during the past few years. The original GUI was developed to help people manage the relatively small amounts of information that they created themselves with their computers. It is now being extended to accommodate the very large quantities of information that computers will soon be able to manage, and it will have to be extended to allow users to take advantage of the multimedia and context features discussed above. For example, the discussion of context features described the problem of how one might learn the names of women born in Michigan who had won Olympic medals. An extension to GUI that might solve this would have to provide a simple way to select Michigan (point to it on a map?), a simple way to limit the results to women, and a simple way to indicate that one was interested in the winning of Olympic medals.

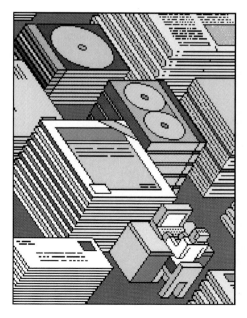

Until recently personal computers—and therefore their users—could not conveniently perform more than one process at a time. Accordingly, the usual way to use a computer was to begin by selecting a program that performed a single process—word processing, for example—and then choose a particular piece of information created by that process—a word-processing document. It is more likely, however, that people would prefer to approach information by subject matter rather than by the computer program that is required for displaying it. That is, if a person is interested in space travel, then he or she is interested in whatever a computer can offer on that subject and does not really care whether the computer needs to use a word processor, some sort of picture-displaying software, audio-playing software, animation-generating software, or all the above. Fortunately, PCs are now becoming capable of keeping up with our natural inclinations to work and think this way. This model of how computers should support our information-finding needs is sometimes called the "datacentric" model, in which the information, not the process of displaying it, is paramount. The shift to this model is not unlike the shift that occurred when astronomers came to understand that the Sun, not the Earth, was truly at the center of the immediate cosmos. It will take a lot of software development to fully support this model, but it is necessary if PCs are to help tame the data dragons that lie ahead.

Future prospects

Today's personal computers support simple working models of small pieces of the real world. With a spreadsheet, for example, it is possible to build a financial model of a business and then try out different assumptions about revenues and costs to determine the consequences. Computer games are also models that simulate small, unusual universes in which you can try things you would not try in real life: operating laser weaponry, flying into black holes, swinging on ropes over pits full of reptiles and rodents, and so forth. In the future, PCs will be able to model much more complex, much more realistic worlds and will allow us to learn by trial and error much more usefully. Software already exists that allows users to operate simplified models of the world's great cities and play rounds on the world's great golf courses, and this is just the beginning. With the added features that have been discussed above, much more engaging and informative simulations can be expected in the years ahead.

Today's PCs communicate via text and graphics on a screen. The PCs of the next few years will add audio and video capabilities. The generation after that may offer very vivid experiences, called "virtual reality." In virtual reality users participate directly in the world created by the computer, a world that addresses many of their senses simultaneously and responds to their actions. Combined with the simulation capabilities discussed above, this suggests that computers of the future could probably immerse users in extended and realistic experiences that they would otherwise never have.

Personal computers today recognize instructions if they are entered from a keyboard or if a mouse is used. In the coming decade computers can be expected to recognize much more complex instructions that will be written in everyday language and be able to read handwriting and understand speech.

Computers need be no bigger than the minimum size required for communicating with their users. They need to be able to give and receive information, and their size should be determined by such considerations as the acuity of the user's vision and the size of his or her fingertips. The trend is already toward smaller computers, and during the 1990s small computers will be able to support all the information-management features discussed in this article.

In conclusion, the personal computer, now only about 15 years old, is on the threshold of becoming much more useful to millions of people throughout the world as it evolves into a powerful information-management tool. There is much work to be done to fulfill this vision, but that work is proceeding rapidly, and it seems certain that the 1990s will see personal computing help build a world in which information is at our fingertips in ways never before imagined.

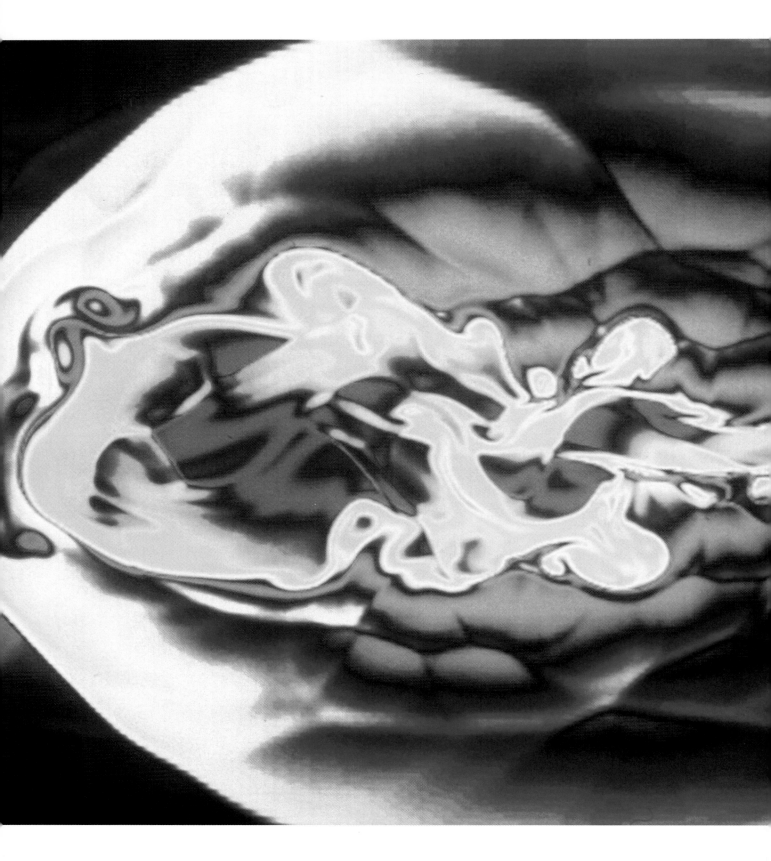

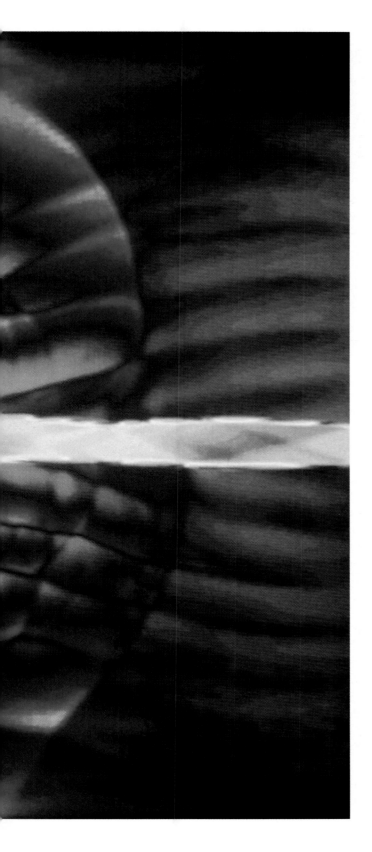

How *Supercomputers* Are Transforming *Science*

by Larry L. Smarr

The world's fastest computers have opened the way to an approach to scientific investigation radically different from theory, observation, and experimentation. Called computational science, it allows researchers to gather data and test theories on detailed simulations of physical reality.

Computers have emerged as universal devices for aiding scientific inquiry. They are used to control laboratory experiments, to help write scientific papers, to solve equations, and to store data. In recent years, however, one particular kind of computer, the supercomputer, has been achieving something much more profound; it has been transforming the basic methods of scientific inquiry themselves.

The term *supercomputer* arose in the past two decades to designate the fastest, largest-memory machines made at a given time. This definition is a relative one, with a changing subject. The supercomputers of just a few years ago have become normal computers, while new devices have arisen to take their place at the top of the technology. In 1990, to rate as a supercomputer, a machine needed to have about one billion bytes of directly addressable memory. (A byte is a unit of information consisting of eight bits; a bit is a binary digit, either a one or a zero.) Furthermore, it had to be capable of sustaining computations in excess of a billion floating-point operations—that is, additions, subtractions, multiplications, or divisions of decimal numbers—per second. Data had to be able to stream in and out of the computer at about one billion bits per second. The hard-disk storage directly coupled to the supercomputer typically had 50 billion to 100 billion bytes of capacity. In comparison, a typical desktop personal computer had a few million bytes of memory, computed a few million numbers per second, had a hard disk with 50 million to 100 million bytes of

LARRY L. SMARR is Director of the National Center for Supercomputing Applications at the University of Illinois at Urbana-Champaign. He is also Professor in the university's Departments of Physics and Astronomy.

(Pages 154–155) In a supercomputer simulation performed at the National Center for Supercomputing Applications (NCSA), a supersonic jet of matter enters from the right of the image, becomes unstable, and breaks up. By studying such representations of reality, scientists can gain insights into physical phenomena that could never be seen in a laboratory; for example, enormous cosmic jets of matter known to be spewing from the cores of some galaxies. Michael Norman, Phillip Hardee, and David Clarke; visualization with Donna Cox, NCSA

storage, and might be connected to a communications network having a transmission rate of about one million bits per second. A supercomputer, then, had roughly 100–1,000 times more capacity in each of the primary measures for computers than the machines familiar to the public.

Nevertheless, personal computers are not without their advantages. They are used by only one person at a time, come with their own monitors and keyboards, and run very user-friendly software that responds almost instantly. By contrast, a single supercomputer typically is accessed by hundreds or even thousands of scientists, has no monitor or keyboard, and runs very complex software that may require hours of execution time to produce results. Not surprisingly, while a personal computer costs less than $10,000, a supercomputer may cost as much as $30 million.

A modern machine room at a supercomputer center contains millions of dollars' worth of state-of-the-art computing equipment. For instance, the photo above shows the facilities of the National Center for Supercomputing Applications (NCSA) at the University of Illinois at Urbana-Champaign. In addition to the cylindrical supercomputers themselves, from Cray Research, Inc., Chippewa Falls, Wisconsin, are box-shaped units whose purpose is storing user data. Numerous hard-disk drives, holding several billion bytes each, stand on the floor. The mass-storage system contains close to a million user files with several trillion bytes of user data. A slower mainframe computer acts as a traffic cop, moving data to and from the supercomputers.

Birth and growth of computational science

Given their high capital cost and the large team of people required for operating supercomputers and their computational environment, it was natural that the U.S. government was the exclusive purchaser of such machines for three decades. Out of World War II came the need for the fastest possible digital computers to aid in nuclear weapons design, code breaking, and other tasks of national security. During the 1950s, '60s, and '70s, the federal government encouraged leading computer manufacturers to create increasingly powerful machines to meet its needs as well as to stimulate technological advances in the industry. The nuclear weapons laboratories, such as Lawrence Livermore (California) National Laboratory and Los Alamos (New Mexico) National Laboratory, continually upgraded these computers, first from IBM, Armonk, New York, then from Control Data Corp., Minneapolis, Minnesota, and, in the '70s and '80s, from Cray Research.

From the efforts of the large teams of scientists, engineers, and programmers who worked on the earlier generations of supercomputers to model the extreme complexity of the physics and engineering of nuclear devices, a methodology arose that is now termed computational science and engineering. This approach to science differs from the traditional ones of theory and experimentation and theory and observation, which can be traced back three centuries to Isaac Newton and Galileo, respectively.

(Opposite page) Cylindrical Cray Research supercomputers that have directly addressable memory totaling in the billions of bytes constitute the heart of NCSA's production supercomputing facilities. Maniac I (below), an early "supercomputer," carried out nuclear weapons simulations and assisted in a variety of scientific studies at Los Alamos (New Mexico) Scientific Laboratory (now Los Alamos National Laboratory) from 1952 to 1957. To perform its calculations the machine depended on vacuum tubes powered by a roomful of batteries. Its memory, which was contained in the suitcaselike boxes on top, was 1,024 bits (128 bytes).

Los Alamos National Laboratory

Theoretical science provides a successful conceptual framework for comprehending and predicting how nature acts as it does. The physical sciences, for example, exploit mathematical equations that are called the "laws of physics." Familiar examples are Maxwell's equations, which describe electromagnetism; Navier-Stokes equations, which describe viscous fluid flow and are the basic equations of aerodynamics; and Einstein's equations of general relativity, which relate the curvature of space and time to the gravitational field. Such mathematical expressions have been discovered to embody the regularities of natural phenomena that experimental or observational techniques have determined.

Unfortunately, the mathematical methods of theoretical science, such as calculus, can solve the basic equations of physics only for extremely simplified cases. It is an easy matter, for example, to predict the course of a single collision between two spherical billiard balls moving in two-dimensional space in an isolated environment. On the other hand, predicting the course of the collisions of myriad objects having different shapes, sizes, and velocities, occupying many positions in three-dimensional space, being acted on by various outside influences, and interacting for a comparatively long time—in other words, trying to model mathematically the likes of an exploding bomb or an exploding star—requires computations involving millions of numbers, a feat hopelessly beyond human capabilities and lifetimes.

The eminent mathematician John von Neumann recognized, during and after World War II, that the technology of digital computers could change this situation dramatically. He argued that the traditional mathematical techniques of theory were not powerful enough for the complex solutions of the laws of physics, solutions representing all the physical variables that one sees operating in nature. Furthermore, experimental techniques were inadequate when the objects one desired to study were too small, too far away, too hot, or otherwise inaccessible. In these situations digital electronic computers could be used to compute realistically complex solutions to the laws of physics and then to interrogate these solutions by changing some of the variables, as if one were performing actual experiments on physical reality.

Gradually the computational science and engineering approach spread from national security to other projects of national importance. Computational modeling in support of the effort to create a controlled hydrogen fusion reactor was first performed in the 1950s by supercomputers borrowed part-time from other projects, but in 1974 a supercomputer center to help with the plasma physics and engineering simulations necessary for fusion reactor research was set up at Lawrence Livermore. In 1960 creation of the National Center for Atmospheric Research, Boulder, Colorado, made supercomputers available to the weather forecasting, climate modeling, and atmospheric science communities. The Geophysical Fluid Dynamics Laboratory, located in Princeton, New Jersey, started providing similar supercomputer access to earth scientists.

U.S. industry began to recognize the advantages of supercomputers in the late 1970s. Because of their high price, the first industries to purchase them were, predictably, those with extremely high capitalization; namely, the petroleum and automobile industries. Throughout the 1980s, however, their use spread rapidly to the aerospace, energy, chemical, electronics, and pharmaceutical industries. In addition, a few commercial service bureaus purchased supercomputers in order to provide commercial access. By the end of the decade, more than 200 supercomputers were serving corporations.

Until the early 1980s academic researchers had been resigned to traveling to federal laboratories or to foreign centers for access to supercomputers. By 1984 three schools, the University of Minnesota at Minneapolis-St. Paul, Colorado State University, and Purdue University, West Lafayette, Indiana, had acquired their own machines. The U.S. National Science Foundation, responding to the demand for wider access by academic researchers, began allowing limited use of these universities' computers, as well as of three others in industry, on a national basis. A national competition was held in 1985 among institutions wishing to act as host for facilities that would provide easy access for peer-reviewed researchers to leading-edge computational resources, including supercomputers. The effort resulted ultimately in the creation of five national centers: the San Diego Supercomputer Center, operated by General Atomics, San Diego, California; the National Center for Supercomputing Applications, located at the University of Illinois at Urbana-Champaign; the Pittsburgh Supercomputing Center, located at Carnegie-Mellon University, Pittsburgh, Pennsylvania; the John von Neumann National Supercomputer Center, located in Princeton (later closed); and the Cornell National Supercomputer Facility, located at Cornell University, Ithaca, New York.

By the early 1990s, in addition to the U.S. national centers, there were similar centers in Europe, Japan, and a number of Pacific Rim countries. As realization of the utility of supercomputers has spread, nearly 50 universities worldwide also have acquired such systems.

Changing computer architectures

Accompanying the rapid spread of supercomputers have been rapid changes in their architecture; that is, the way their subcomponents are combined. Until the early 1970s supercomputer designers increased the speed of their machines by improving the microelectronics of the computers' single central processing unit, or processor. Despite the improvements, such processors still operated on individual numbers, termed scalars, in much the same fashion as one enters numbers into an electronic calculator; thus, the computers were referred to as scalar uniprocessors. At that time U.S. electronics engineer Seymour Cray, the preeminent supercomputer designer of recent decades, successfully incorporated an improvement called vector processing. His Cray-1 supercomputer was able to fetch long rows of related numbers, called vectors, from memory at one time and operate on them together. For certain kinds of data, processing speeds as high as 10 times that of scalar processing were made routine.

The 1980s saw the growth of multiprocessor computers. Such machines as the Cray X-MP and Cray Y-MP from Cray Research are supercomputers that each contain several vector processors—up to four in the X-MP and up to eight in the Y-MP. These multiple processors work in parallel; they can either run different jobs at the same time or work on parts of a single job simultaneously, thus reducing processing time still more. Parallel vector multiprocessors are currently the standard architecture of supercomputers.

The recent remarkable speed gains in microprocessors, *i.e.*, complete central processing units on integrated circuit chips, are bringing about a new class of supercomputers called massively parallel. Rather than pushing technology to create a special superfast vector processor and then coupling a few of them into a vector multiprocessor supercomputer, the massively parallel approach relies on the mass market for ordinary microprocessors (used in everything from automobiles to personal computers to toasters) to drive down the price and increase the speed of general-design chips. To build a supercomputer, one then links hundreds to thousands of such chips together with a high-efficiency network. In the early 1990s supercomputers built on this architecture were offered by Thinking Machines Corp., Cambridge, Massachusetts, and Intel Corp., Beaverton, Oregon, and several others were expected to be forthcoming.

As the worldwide demand for microelectronics components continues to increase, the cost per component of massively parallel supercomputers should decrease exponentially. By the end of the 20th century, price drops should enable the creation of massively parallel supercomputers capable of executing 10 trillion floating-point operations per second, 10,000 times the speed of 1990 supercomputers. In comparison, those same 1990 supercomputers are only about a factor of 20 faster than their 1980 counterparts. The 1990s will see an enormous acceleration in supercomputing power at the same time it sees an enormous increase in the number and range of supercomputer applications.

Linking humans and supercomputers

In spite of their profound differences, supercomputers and personal computers can intercommunicate and work together. This capability, plus the creation and expansion of national networks, is making it possible for researchers to tap the power of supercomputers remotely from desktop computers in their own offices and labs.

National networks started as leased telephone lines between supercomputer centers but have been moving rapidly to a fiber-optic base. In the U.S. this network, called the Internet, is a set of campus, state, regional, commercial, and federal agency networks linked to each other by a common telecommunications protocol. By the early 1990s the Internet had encompassed all research universities and many four-year colleges, federal agencies and laboratories, and computer vendors and was beginning to link junior colleges as well as some grade schools and high schools. It was estimated that more than a million users, working on hundreds of thousands of desktop computers, communicated over the Internet.

160

A Connection Machine built by Thinking Machines Corp. and installed at NCSA in 1989 exemplifies a new class of computers distinguished by massively parallel architecture. The machine can link up to 64,000 microprocessor chips in a high-efficiency network and have up to eight gigabytes (billion bytes) of memory.

In the days before the marriage of personal computers to supercomputers, the standard output from a supercomputer comprised huge stacks of pages of numbers or microfiche of hundreds of line graphs or charts. Typically an investigator searched through these stacks looking for patterns, even though finding correlations in large arrays of numbers is an arduous, time-consuming task and not particularly suited to the way people normally assimilate information. A few pioneering researchers worked to visualize this data graphically, but the task required fairly large computers and specialized high-resolution graphics output devices. Since the mid-1980s, however, this situation has changed rapidly. Because of the rapid spread of and improvements in personal computers and their more expensive and faster counterparts, the scientific workstations, graphic representation of supercomputer output has become the norm rather than the exception.

A single color image on a desktop computer represents hundreds of thousands to millions of individual numbers. Because a comparatively large amount of memory is available on desktop computers today, one can even run animations directly on the screen. This capability, called scientific visualization, is radically altering the relationship between hu-

161

mans and the supercomputer. It is now a common interpretation that by solving the laws of physics, chemistry, or engineering, the supercomputer numerically creates a "virtual reality," which can be observed and probed just as is done with physical reality. One can perform "numerical experiments" on virtual reality and then compare the results with actual laboratory tests or use the results to predict what is likely to happen in situations that cannot be tested directly. For instance, the numbers representing velocity values in calculations that describe a flowing fluid can be transformed into an animation of the way particles would be moved around by that fluid. By watching the animation, researchers can gain the same kind of insight into the nature of the physical phenomenon that they would by watching real flows—say, the movement of volcanic dust through the atmosphere, the spread of plankton by ocean currents, or the distribution of ions and electrons in a jet of matter spewing from the center of a galaxy.

In many cases supercomputer simulations can substitute for traditional laboratory studies that would take much longer and cost much more to carry out. In addition, supercomputers linked directly to laboratory instruments or observational devices can process or image data derived from actual measurements with speeds heretofore unthinkable.

New technologies and skills directed toward improving computer-human interaction are emerging that will blur the distinction between virtual and physical reality. Experimental headsets that present stereo images of computer graphics on tiny television screens in front of each eye enable the user to work in, literally, a new dimension of virtual reality. Similarly, tactile feedback is being explored. In the near future a new form of supercomputer-based scientific investigation may well arise in which "infonauts" don headgear and gloves to climb or fly around computed spaces filled, for example, with virtual molecules or neutron stars. Already a new vocation of visualization specialist has arisen. These experts in the technology and methodology of computer graphics, computer art, computer games, film, video, and communication theory have become indispensable members of the so-called renaissance teams of supercomputer specialists who attack frontier problems in computational science and engineering.

The rapidly increasing speed and connectivity of networks will contribute in at least two ways to altering how humans work with supercomputers. First, because the speed of the network between computers is becoming almost as fast as the speed of the network inside a computer, one will be able to use more than one supercomputer at the same time. For instance, a researcher at a desktop machine in Boston may run one part of a program on a vector multiprocessor supercomputer in California and another part on a massively parallel supercomputer in Illinois while data files stream in from a mass-storage computer in Colorado and real-time graphics emerge from a graphics supercomputer belonging to the user's own institution. Second, in order for all these tasks to be done productively, new software will make it seem as if they were occurring on one computer. All the intermediate steps that have to be done by

Under evaluation by NASA, a "workstation" comprising stereoscopic video-display goggles and sensor-fitted gloves allows the wearer to interact more fully with the "virtual reality" created by numerical simulations. In the future it may become routine for researchers to link several of their senses with the "cyberspace" created by a supercomputer in order, for example, to tour a model of an orbiting space station, tug at the chemical bonds holding a molecule together, test an experimental surgical procedure on a virtual patient, or hover over the surface of a neutron star.

NASA

162

hand today will become automatic. In this sense the national network of computers will appear to be one giant "metacomputer" that is as easy to use as today's most user-friendly personal machines.

Matter most fundamental

Virtually every topic of research in science and engineering during the last decade has been touched by supercomputers. In the early 1990s more than 10,000 academic researchers used a remote supercomputer sometime during the course of a year. Reasons ranged from faster job turnaround to the ability to attack computational problems of a complexity otherwise impossible to solve.

The submicroscopic world of particle physics is the largest consumer of supercomputing time in all of basic research. The fundamental theory of the strong interaction, called quantum chromodynamics, describes how particles known as quarks and gluons interact to make up the hadrons, which include the proton and neutron as well as hundreds of more exotic particles. Because of the way the gluons bind the quarks in this theory, it is quite difficult to solve the equations without the powerful number-handling ability of computers. A major goal in this field is to be able to compute from first principles such details as the masses of elementary particles and why specific numbers of them should exist. Not only is this work important for theoretically understanding the experimental results from particle accelerators, it also is crucial for studying the very early universe, when all matter was so hot and tightly compacted that it existed as a sea of quarks and gluons.

The second largest consumer of supercomputing time is the study of bulk matter, which can exist in the solid, liquid, gaseous, or plasma phase. Because the electrons of atoms and their interaction with each

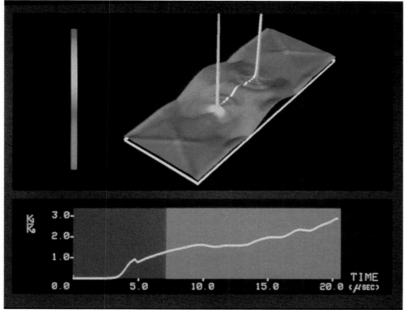

H.M. Koh, H.S. Lee, and R.B. Haber

Next to particle physics the largest consumer of supercomputing time in basic research is the study of bulk matter and its properties; e.g., electrical conductivity, freezing and melting behavior, elasticity, and brittleness. The supercomputer-generated image at left is part of an animated video sequence simulating the wave patterns that appear in a brittle material being cracked at a speed of a kilometer (0.6 mile) per second. Color represents strain energy, with dark blue lowest and red highest. The surface height is a measure of the kinetic energy density and reveals the pattern of stress waves moving through the material. Among other information, the display at the bottom shows the elapsed time, in millionths of a second, since the start of the crack event.

other and with their atomic nuclei are responsible for the chemical and physical properties of matter—for example, combustion, phase transitions such as freezing and melting, and electrical and heat conduction—researchers can use supercomputers to solve the equations of quantum mechanics to study the behavior of materials.

Solid-state physicists are using supercomputers to gain fundamental understanding about the origin of bulk material properties like superconductivity, hardness, elasticity, brittleness, and thermal characteristics. In addition, one can compute surface properties of materials and their interactions with other surfaces on a molecular basis, such as occurs in lubrication or catalysis. For instance, animated scientific visualizations of a supercomputer simulation at NCSA by Larry Ray and Rich Ellson, researchers at Eastman Kodak Co., Rochester, New York, have allowed them to watch hydrogen atoms migrating across a laser-cleaned platinum surface, something impossible to see in real life.

In chemical studies of small molecules, supercomputers working with equations of quantum chemistry can compute precise energy values for electron bonding within individual molecules or for bonding or interactions between molecules. David Dixon, a researcher at the Du Pont Co., Wilmington, Delaware, used his company's supercomputer to design potential replacement molecules for the industrially valuable chlorofluorocarbons (CFCs). The replacements have properties that make them attractive as refrigeration agents but are much less harmful to the Earth's protective ozone layer than CFCs.

In the 1990s supercomputers will be used to create a new generation of materials whose structures are simulated on an atom-by-atom basis. Coupled with the use of recently developed laboratory instruments—such as the scanning tunneling microscope—that enable scientists to see and manipulate materials on an atomic scale, this research will produce "materials by design" having desirable properties that greatly exceed those of materials now known. Eventually, the accumulated knowledge and skills may lead to the building of microscopic machines with molecular-sized components, a still largely theoretical field called nanotechnology. (See *1990 Yearbook of Science and the Future* Feature Article: MACHINES OF INNER SPACE.)

Molecules of biological importance

For modeling large molecules such as the biologically important proteins, computations can be based on classical physics (*e.g.*, Newton's laws of motion) while quantum effects are typically ignored. This kind of simplification is possible because the large number of atoms (hundreds to thousands) in these giant molecules causes the effects of individual electrons to "wash out." Such computations allow one to investigate how the complex shapes of large molecules oscillate and deform as they interact with each other. For example, a recent NCSA visualization of a supercomputer computation performed by Paul Bash and his colleagues of Harvard University and the Massachusetts Institute of Technology, Cambridge, portrayed proteins diffusing through a solution of water

(Opposite page) A supercomputer reveals what no microscope can: the migration of hydrogen atoms across a platinum surface (top) during a simulated heat-induced diffusion experiment. In images generated from first-principles molecular orbital theory, the structural geometry of a widely used chlorofluorocarbon, CFC-12 (bottom left), is compared with a potential replacement molecule, HFC-134a (bottom right). In the color coding used, atoms of carbon are black, fluorine green, chlorine yellow, and hydrogen white. Chlorine content and high stability, two characteristics that make CFC-12 a threat to the Earth's stratospheric ozone layer, are eliminated in HFC-134a, which decomposes in the lower atmosphere before it can reach higher elevations.

(Opposite page, top) Lawrence A. Ray, Richard N. Ellson, Christopher Heckman, and Marc Olano of Eastman Kodak Co.; Donna Cox, NCSA; (bottom) photos, David A. Dixon of Du Pont and Pat Capobianco of Cray Research

164

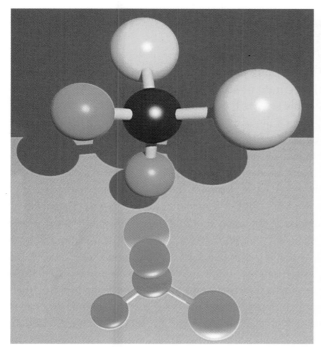

molecules. More ambitious supercomputing calculations have begun to model the fundamental processes of life, such as the transport of ions and molecules across cell membranes, antibody recognition, photosynthesis, and metabolic cycles.

As decoding of the genetic makeup of living organisms proceeds, scientists will gather information on the linear sequence of amino acids that form the backbone of tens of thousands of potentially critical proteins. Unfortunately, supercomputers today are not nearly fast enough to compute the folding of a given chain of amino acids into the final shape that determines the structure and function of the protein. This may be because the mathematical models currently used to represent the process are not well adapted to computation. Protein folding is an intense field of research, and it is likely that breakthroughs will occur in the 1990s.

For many biomolecules, data on three-dimensional structure can be gathered through such laboratory techniques as X-ray crystallography and nuclear magnetic resonance. Transforming the data into comprehensible information is computationally intensive, particularly for supermolecular structures such as viruses. For instance, the atomic structure of a rhinovirus responsible for the common cold was obtained by Michael Rossmann and colleagues using massive amounts of time on Purdue University's supercomputer system. Given a molecule's structure, one can compute and image the binding of that molecule with another. This ability has a direct bearing on medical research, as it is allowing investigators to watch how drug molecules interact with DNA, enzymes and other proteins, and molecular components of viruses, bacteria, and other disease agents. The computer-aided design of biologically active substances will provide a rational (rather than trial-and-error) approach of immeasurable promise for the biological and medical fields. (*See* Feature Article: BIOTECHNOLOGY FOR THE '90s.)

Supercomputers in engineering

Perhaps the most immediate practical applications of supercomputers lie in the field of engineering, the study of man-made machines. In addition to benefiting materials sciences and chemistry, which underlie engineering, the supercomputer is ideal for studying the macroscopic properties of engineering materials. Computing the heat flow and solidification in the casting of a metal or plastic part, for instance, can point out flow instabilities that might weaken the hardened part. Recently University of Illinois computer artist Donna Cox and computer scientist Ray Idaszak teamed up with Kodak's Rich Ellson to visualize highly viscous flow such as occurs in plastic injection molding. Injection-molding processes produce billions of plastic components each year. Thus, avoiding defects before the products reach the public is of crucial importance.

Supercomputers are used routinely to compute the temperatures, pressures, and velocities in a gas, whether for optimizing the air flow in a duct cooling system for a building or for studying the hypersonic flight of a U.S. space shuttle through the atmosphere. In the latter case, to validate the computer model, actual pressure measurements from sensors on the

Supercomputers are finding growing use in modeling biologically important proteins and their interactions with other molecules. Enzymes, for example, are large proteins that act on select molecules, called substrates, catalyzing their conversion to specific products. In the image below, part of an animated video sequence, the catalytically active site of the enzyme triose phosphate isomerase (top shape) is shown interacting with its substrate, dihydroxyacetone phosphate (bottom shape).

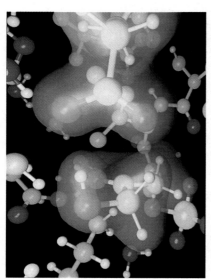

Paul Bash, Martin Field, and Martin Karplus of Harvard University; Robert Davenport and Gregory A. Petsko of MIT; visualization by NCSA

166

Lawrence A. Ray and Richard N. Ellson of Eastman Kodak Co.; Donna Cox and Ray Idaszak of the NCSA

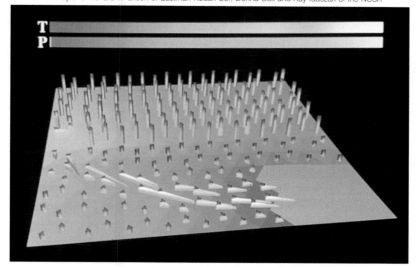

In the field of engineering, numerical modeling on a supercomputer has allowed researchers to "watch" an injection molding process. The image at left simulates a late stage in the flow of molten plastic into a steel mold, which is twice as high in the back as in the front. The state of each modeled point in the flow is represented by a "glyph" rising from the bottom surface. Compact glyphs indicate little or no flow. Elongated glyphs that resemble pinball flippers indicate more pronounced flow, showing both the direction of the flow and a vertical profile of flow speed. The color on the glyphs gives the vertical profile of temperature (T) in the injected plastic, while the color on the plane denotes the pressure (P) in the mold at that point. The simulation reveals an undesirable "shear-thinning" instability, which can be avoided by changing the relative heights of the two sides of the mold.

surface of a shuttle in flight were compared with pressures derived from a computation of the airflow over the body of a shuttle performed at the National Aerodynamic Simulator Facility at NASA's Ames Research Center, Mountain View, California. The comparison yielded remarkable agreement, raising confidence in the predictive value of the model.

The other extreme of computational engineering focuses on the design and properties of large assemblages. In this case the supercomputer has proved indispensable for accurately modeling the many forces and interactions among the large numbers of subcomponents. One can simulate the response of an integrated circuit containing hundreds of thousands of components, the reaction rates and yields of a large chemical plant, the stresses and strains in a multiton earth-moving machine, the flight characteristics of an airliner, or the flexing modes of the girders in a proposed space station design.

Earth, environment, and human society

Perhaps the most demanding applications of supercomputers in the 1990s will be in the earth and environmental sciences. As global consciousness about the effect of human activities on the biosphere has increased, so have the demands of society for scientists to make valid predictions about pollution, acid rain, and global warming. Currently the data base accumulated from satellite-, air-, ground-, and sea-based observations totals hundreds of millions of megabytes. By the end of the decade new Earth-observation satellites will be incrementing that data base at a million megabytes per day.

Recently the U.S., Europe, and Japan launched ambitious national and international programs to bring together interdisciplinary teams of scientists to create enormously intricate supercomputer models of the Earth. The models will be necessary for integration and assimilation of the vast quantities of experimental data. Comparisons of the models with the past behavior of the Earth's climate will serve to calibrate and validate

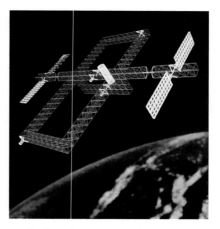

Application of computational engineering to the study of large assemblages has allowed investigators to simulate proposed space station designs like the one above and evaluate the flexing modes in their structural girders.

Charbel Farhat, University of Colorado, Boulder; photo, Thinking Machines Corporation

167

portions of the models. By the 21st century, scientists should possess accurate and robust predictive capabilities in models on supercomputers running some 10,000 times faster than today's best machines, linked by fiber-optic networks and fed continuously by global detectors.

The complex interaction between the Sun, Earth's atmosphere, the oceans, the solid crust, and the collection of living organisms is just beginning to be unraveled. Today's supercomputer climate models, primarily atmospheric, only now are being coupled to models of the Earth's oceans. It is becoming increasingly apparent, however, that life plays a prominent role in both climate and weather. For instance, the amount of forest cover in the Amazon rain forest has been shown to influence the amount of rainfall experienced in Africa.

Progress is being made at both ends of the modeling scale. The researchers who simulate the global climate exploit every increase in computer power to push their representations of the atmosphere and oceans to new levels of spatial and temporal resolution while gradually integrating more and more local physical, chemical, and biological processes. Models of the component processes, in turn, are being developed by scientists who study such phenomena as the life cycle of thunderstorms, regional air pollution, acid rain, groundwater contamination, ecological dynamics, and ocean currents.

Models of individual processes are quite useful in their own right and are perhaps more easily verified and calibrated than global, long-term climate models. For instance, Robert Wilhelmson, an atmospheric scientist at the University of Illinois, recently collaborated with John Anderson and Jerry Straka of the Space Science and Engineering Center at the University of Wisconsin to compare observations of real storms by advanced Doppler weather radar systems with supercomputer simulations of severe storm birth and evolution. Forecasters will ultimately be able to match real storms in progress with computer models to make

Contributing to climate studies, a supercomputer visualization of a future Earth summarizes the numerical output from a global warming simulation by researchers at the National Center for Atmospheric Research, Boulder, Colorado. The time is 12 years after the level of atmospheric carbon dioxide (a major "greenhouse gas") has doubled; red areas are greater than 5° C (9° F) warmer than normal, and blue areas are greater than 5° C cooler.

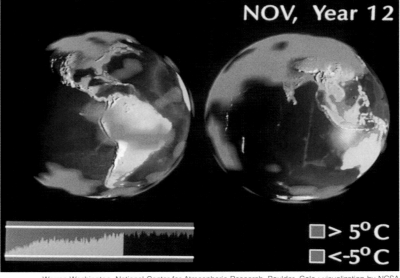

Warren Washington, National Center for Atmospheric Research, Boulder, Colo.; visualization by NCSA

(Top) Robert Wilhelmson, University of Illinois; visualization by NCSA;
(bottom) Gregory R. McRae and Armistead G. Russell of Carnegie-Mellon University/Pittsburgh Supercomputing Center

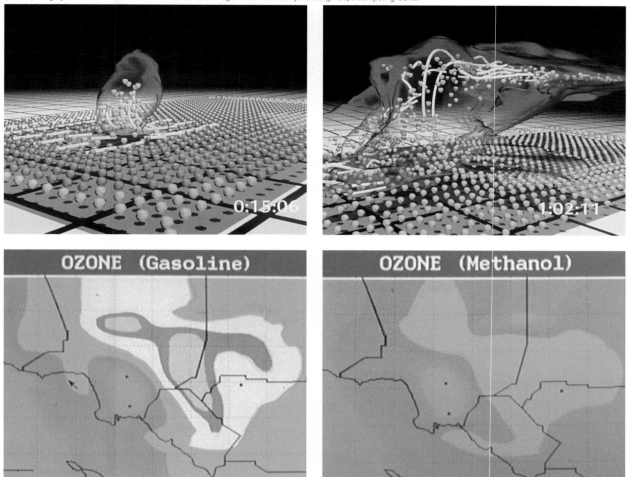

better predictions about a storm's behavior, severity, and capability of inflicting damage.

Nowhere more than in studies of climate and the environment have supercomputer applications become closely tied to social policy and political issues. The results of supercomputer models have been increasingly cited in local, regional, and national debates over such issues as alternative energy sources, chemicals responsible for atmospheric ozone depletion, effects of supersonic aircraft fleets, and the environmental effects of economic development plans. One such model was employed in a study, by Gregory McRae of Carnegie-Mellon University, of the pollution of the Los Angeles basin. Scientific visualizations of the region contrasted the amount of ground-level ozone produced by today's fleets of gasoline-fueled cars with the amount expected from a hypothetical fleet fueled by methanol. The model predicted that switching to methanol-fueled cars, whose emissions showed less ozone-forming potential, could dramatically cut peak ozone levels in the area. The necessary computations, performed at the Pittsburgh Supercomputing Center, coupled the chemistry of air pollution (some 50 separate chemical reactions were computed at each

The evolution of a severe storm is visualized in two images (top pair) from a sequence based on a numerically modeled storm. To track the airflow within the transparent envelope representing the cloud mass, the simulation releases weightless spheres lying near ground level. Spheres colored orange are rising, while blue ones are sinking. Yellow streamers attached to some spheres show the path of air during the previous 8.3 minutes. Visualizations of ground-level ozone pollution in the Los Angeles basin (bottom pair) compare the effect of a fleet of gasoline-powered cars with that expected from a hypothetical methanol-fueled fleet. Colors range from blue (low ozone levels) to purple (highest levels). The model predicts a dramatic drop in peak ozone levels following the switch to methanol-fueled cars.

spatial point) with the atmospheric motions over realistic topography and source distribution (both fixed points such as power plants and mobile sources such as the freeway system).

Not surprisingly, the world's economic, social, and political systems themselves are being modeled numerically. Supercomputers are used daily to compute fluctuating international exchange rates, world trade flows, and investment portfolios—all critical aspects of the global marketplace. As nations worldwide move toward market economies and democratic governments, information on all aspects of population, income distribution, natural resources, manufacturing capabilities, and financial flows are becoming available, thus enabling human socioeconomic systems to be modeled in their full complexity. As these are integrated with past data bases of human activity, researchers should develop a much better understanding of the patterns and dynamics of social organization, which one hopes will aid in wiser use of the Earth's limited resources.

For investigators whose time horizons reach beyond the several million years of human history to the several billion years of the Earth's history, supercomputers have become valuable tools for studying the changing character of the planet's interior and the effect life has had on its atmosphere. The complex convective flow in the Earth's mantle has been modeled for the study of such tectonic activities as the spreading of continental plates, hot spots of rising magma, and earthquake generation. The transformation of the atmosphere by photosynthetic organisms from one devoid of oxygen to one capable of supporting oxygen-metabolizing life forms is being investigated computationally.

Near and distant space

Surrounding the Earth is a magnetosphere, a region of trapped charged particles that is dominated by the planet's magnetic field. The magneto-

Supercomputer model of the dynamic flow taking place in the Earth's mantle depicts the slow churning of silicate rock in vast convection cells. The model suggests that the present pattern of hot upwelling regions (red) and cold sinking regions (blue) is closely related to the influence and past location of Pangaea, the supercontinent that included all the present-day continents as a single landmass about 200 million years ago.

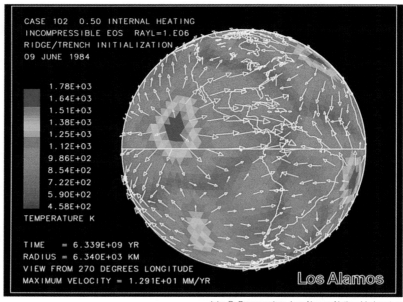

John R. Baumgardner, Los Alamos National Laboratory

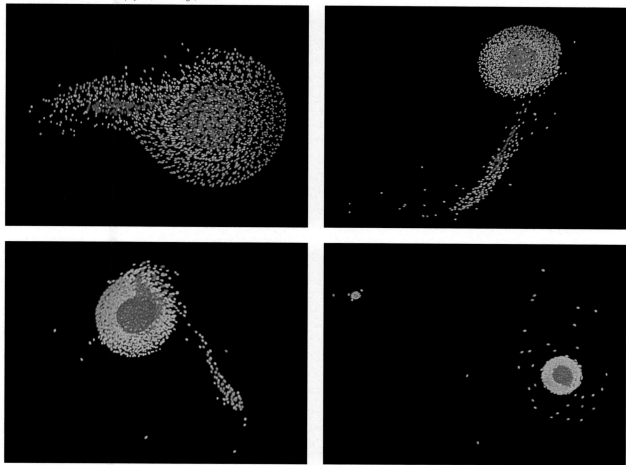

sphere and its interaction with the flux of particles from the Sun known as the solar wind form a highly complex plasma system whose coupling of magnetic fields and charged particles on many scales of time and length stresses the most advanced supercomputers of today. An active field of research, as a result of the extraordinary Voyager space-probe missions to the giant outer planets, is that of comparative magnetospheres, in which the observational results from the flybys serve as input for supercomputer modeling of the planets' magnetospheres. Supercomputers have long been used to model the birth of the solar system itself, including the phases of the collapse of the solar nebula and the accretion of the debris left orbiting the proto-Sun into the rocky inner planets and the gaseous outer planets. During the first billion years of the solar system, an enormous number of collisions occurred between this debris and the forming planets. Supercomputer simulations of these collisions are beginning to provide detailed scenarios for the formation of the moons, rings, or both that are associated with all the planets except Mercury and Venus.

Among the oldest beneficiaries of computation science have been astronomy and astrophysics. Since the 1950s supercomputers have probed the evolution of stars. The 1960s saw the beginnings of explosive super-

The formation of the Moon from the postulated collision of the proto-Earth with a large object is visualized in a sequence of images derived from a numerical model of the interaction. Orange particles represent material making up the lighter, rocky outer layers of the objects, and blue particles their heavy iron cores. (From left to right, top to bottom) An object having a mass about a fifth that of the proto-Earth comes in from the right and strikes the upper hemisphere. Material from both objects is drawn out into a long arc, the near end of which (including iron from the colliding body) falls back on the proto-Earth. Material in the far end of the arc coalesces into a substantial body, which then loses more mass to the proto-Earth. The mass loss boosts the new body, now with a mass about 85% that of the Moon, into a stable orbit around the proto-Earth.

171

nova models derived from computer programs used at U.S. nuclear weapons laboratories. In the next decade dynamical computations broadened to include black holes, neutron stars, the interstellar medium, and colliding galaxies. Observations made from aperture synthesis arrays of radio telescopes began to require supercomputers in the 1980s, and cosmological models of the distribution of matter in the early universe became a major supercomputer modeling field. In the 1990s results from advanced Earth-orbiting space observatories (such as the Hubble Space Telescope) and a new generation of large ground-based telescopes will be coupled into the international computer network and delivered to astronomers' desktop computers. Supercomputers will be critical components of the information processing system required for turning the data streams from all these modern sensors into astronomical images. (*See* Feature Article: Colors for a Cosmic Canvas.)

Because most astronomical objects are at too great a distance from Earth to be resolved in detail, the virtual reality provided by the images from supercomputer models often is the only real way of exploring these systems. In that sense supercomputers are creating numerical astrophysical laboratories for studying the details of the fragmentation of expanding supernova shells, the final plunge of matter into black holes, the creation and propagation of gigantic cosmic jets of gas, and the collisions of black holes, neutron stars, and galaxies. Furthermore, the supercomputer can be used as a time machine, allowing humans to experience the birth and death of astronomical objects that in physical reality take millions to billions of years to evolve. Cosmologists can build very young universes containing different amounts and types of elementary particles and then

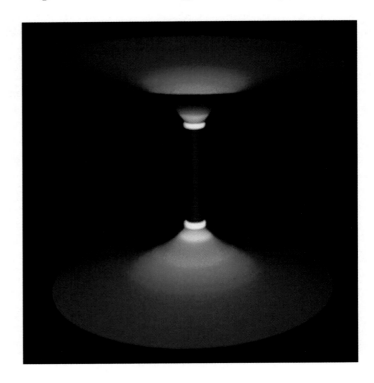

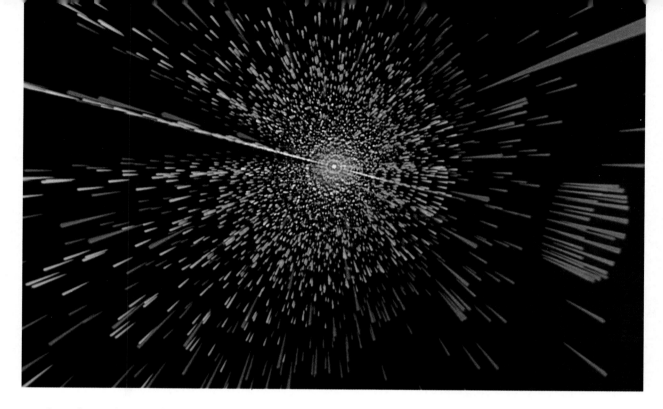

run them forward in time to see whether they acquire the observed large-scale structure of the real universe.

The future

Because supercomputers are defined as the fastest computers available at a given date, they will likely exist as long as people have need of computers. As described above, however, the 1990s will see a great explosion of computer architectures—a "golden age" driven by the microelectronics revolution. Technology now stands in the middle of a period, decades long, marked by continual exponential growth in the speed and memory capacity of microelectronic components. Most experts agree that the dominant supercomputer architecture of the next decade will be massively parallel. To use such a supercomputer effectively, one must break up a given task into many subtasks, assigning each to a separate processor. The major software challenge is the rewriting of applications in this new paradigm and the efficient communication and resynchronization of the subtasks to form a coherent whole.

Meanwhile, supercomputers of the '90s will become woven into a fiber-optic supernetwork connecting virtually all components of the research, development, and education system of the U.S. Collaboration technologies will fuse today's individual technologies of telephone, facsimile, video, computer graphics, telecommunications, and computing. Large-screen, high-definition digital video panels will provide realistic windows into this vast information space in which, for many purposes, distance will have been eliminated. Worldwide real-time video conferences in which human and computer contributions to the discussion are totally intermixed will be routine. How this technological revolution will drive the inevitable social and economic revolution, one can only speculate.

173

BATS: FRAGILE MASTERS OF THE NIGHT

by Paul B. Robertson and Merlin D. Tuttle

Although fascinating for their navigational abilities and for being the only mammals capable of flight, bats have been perennial victims of "bad press." Ironically, many species are now threatened with extinction just as their ecological and economic importance is becoming appreciated.

Bats are among the most fascinating and valuable groups of animals with whom human beings share the Earth. This is the sentiment of biologists as well as of growing numbers of the general public who have come to know something of their intriguing lives. In many Eastern cultures bats are ancient and modern symbols for a variety of positive values. To the surprise of many Westerners, they are considered delicacies on some Pacific islands and in various regions of tropical Asia and Africa. More significantly, bats play an important, often key, role in many of the world's ecosystems.

Nevertheless, many people fear and loathe bats, often actively promoting their destruction. The sharply conflicting feelings evoked by these animals are due primarily to numerous myths and misconceptions, which persist even in the face of overwhelming scientific evidence to the contrary. Public misconceptions are fanned by the Dracula myth, a fictional theme that has been popular in books and movies for nearly a century. Fortunately, the falsehoods are slowly yielding to evidence confirming the ecological and economic importance of bats and the minimal threat that they pose to human health.

Contrary to myth, bats are intelligent, clean, gentle, and likable. All bats have eyes, and some can see extraordinarily well. They do not become entangled in the hair on people's heads, and they pose less of a threat to human health than do many household pets. Like other mammals, bats can contract rabies, but even in the few that do (less than ½ of 1%), aggression is rare. The odds of being attacked by a sick bat are extremely remote and, in fact, much lower than those of being killed by a dog or a bee sting. Aggressive behavior is exceedingly rare for any bat. The once common belief that bats are especially dangerous, asymptomatic carriers of rabies and important reservoirs for rabies epidemics in other wild animals has been scientifically discredited. Despite the widespread fear of contracting rabies, fewer than 20 people in the U.S. and Canada combined are believed to have died of any disease transmitted by bats in the last four decades. People who simply do not handle bats have nothing to fear.

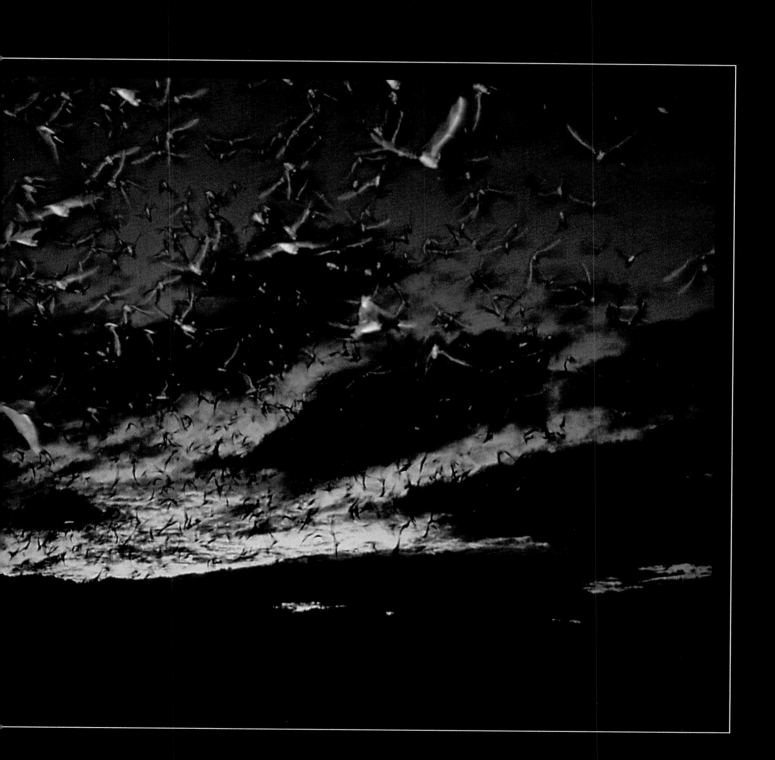

From the collection
of the Palace Museum, Beijing; photo, Wan-go Weng

In a Chinese woven textile design, six stylized bats—symbolizing luck and happiness—form an inner ring surrounded by four dragons.

Misconceptions about bats have been perpetuated in popular Western fiction. The vampire Dracula (below, portrayed by Bela Lugosi) often took the form of a bat. A human captured by batlike Martians (right) is depicted on the cover of a 1908 science-fiction novel.

Despite their documented value and the recent, positive shift in public attitudes, bats are threatened by a variety of human activities. It is particularly ironic that many species and populations are teetering on the edge of extinction just as people are beginning to appreciate them.

Species diversity

Grouped in the order Chiroptera, nearly 1,000 species of bats inhabit the world today, with most still poorly known to science. Making up almost a quarter of all species of mammals, they range in size from the tiny bumblebee bat of Thailand—the world's smallest mammal, weighing less than a U.S. penny—to the largest species—a giant flying fox from Java that possesses a nearly 1.8-meter wingspan. (A meter is about 3.3 feet.) Among mammals only the rodent order exceeds bats in number of living species.

The oldest bat fossil, dated at around 55 million years, has a form and structure remarkably similar to those of modern species. Early in their history, bats evolved into two distinct lineages. The megachiropterans, which are commonly known as flying foxes, consist of approximately 200 species distributed throughout the Old World tropics. Encompassing most of the world's largest bats, megachiropterans are exclusively fruit and nectar feeders and often live in large tree colonies called camps. Their large eyes and foxlike muzzles make them particularly appealing. The microchiropterans comprise about 760 species, most of which are insectivorous. The name is a bit deceiving, as some microchiropterans

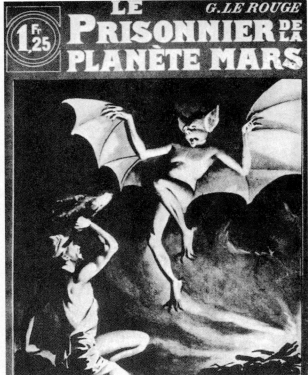

(Left) Culver Pictures; (right) photograph by Christine Haycock from the collection of Sam Moskowitz

Merlin D. Tuttle, Bat Conservation International

Trained to rehabilitate orphaned or injured flying foxes, three Australian "bat mums" proudly display their temporary charges over tea. That bats are clean, gentle, and likable is becoming more widely appreciated as growing numbers of the general public learn about the intriguing lives of these animals and their importance in the world's ecosystems.

can be as large as a crow, surpassing the smaller species of flying foxes in size.

The evolutionary relationship between the megachiropterans and microchiropterans is controversial, with scientists divided over the issue of whether the groups evolved from a common ancestor or from separate mammalian lineages. Recently the debate heated considerably after it was reported that flying foxes and primates share a unique brain structure not found in microchiropterans. Almost everyone agrees that the microchiropterans evolved from mammalian insectivores, a group whose living members are shrews and moles, the same animals that gave rise to primates. Resolution of the precise evolutionary relationship among the two bat groups, insectivores, and primates will require further studies.

The bodies of bats

Although many animals glide, bats and birds are the only vertebrates that possess powered flight. The early evolution and success of both groups are closely linked to the tremendous abundance of flying insects. Bats are highly specialized nocturnal foragers, and they have held dominion over the night skies for millions of years. Apparently because the hind limbs of bats have specialized for clinging to vertical surfaces, their options for feeding and moving about have become more limited than those of birds. Bats also have been less successful than birds at inhabiting high elevations, probably because of the large heat loss they can suffer from the exposure of bare wing surface to cool night temperatures.

The unique wing of bats is the structure most obviously related to their aerial success. Their order name, Chiroptera, comes from the Greek meaning "hand-wing," a particularly accurate descriptive term, as their wings contain the same bones found in human hands and arms although with quite different proportions. The finger bones are greatly elongated and firmly held within a delicate skin membrane. When the arm is extended the fingers spread, and this movement tightens the membrane

PAUL B. ROBERTSON is Associate Professor of Biology and Program Director for Environmental Studies at Trinity University, San Antonio, Texas. He also serves as Director of Special Projects for Bat Conservation International, Austin, Texas.
MERLIN D. TUTTLE, Founder and Executive Director of Bat Conservation International, has devoted the past 30 years to studying and conserving bat species around the world.

(Pages 174–175) Wrinkle-lipped bats (Tadarida plicata) emerge at dusk from a cave in Thailand. Photograph, © Alastair Shay—Oxford Scientific Films

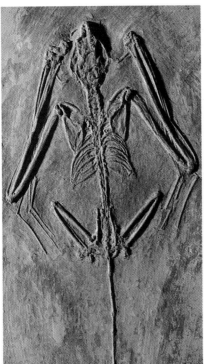

*Sizes of bats range from the bumblebee bat
(top left; Craseonycteris thonglongyai) of
Thailand, the world's smallest mammal, to
the larger flying foxes, the largest species of
which has a wingspan of nearly 1.8 meters
(6 feet). Shown (top right) is Lyle's flying
fox (Pteropus lylei), also from Thailand. The
fossil bat Icaronycteris index (above) dates
from the early Eocene Epoch, about 55
million years ago.*

and forms the wing. The thumb, which is not inside the wing membrane, usually persists as a small, clawed finger on the leading edge of the wing; in many species it is used for roosting and climbing. Frequently there is also a membrane connecting the hind limbs. This skin, the uropatagium, aids in aerodynamics and sometimes in the snaring and handling of prey.

Like the wings of birds, the shape of bat wings varies greatly depending on the flight characteristics of the species. Some bats flutter like butterflies, some hover like hummingbirds, and others fly like falcons. Because bats are often in rapid pursuit of tiny, darting insects, their flight usually appears more erratic than that of birds. The fact that many bats literally grab their prey from the air in a wing tip accentuates their acrobatic movements.

Bats living in cold climates often have angora-like fur on their bodies, while one species, the naked bat of Southeast Asia, is hairless, just as its name implies. Many have a colorful pelage (hairy covering) ranging from bright orange to snow white, while some have unique facial and body markings that put them among the world's most attractive mammals.

Echolocation

The characteristic for which bats are best known is their use of echoes of high-frequency sound waves (ultrasound) to navigate, capture prey, and communicate—an adaptation also found in whales and dolphins. This ability, called echolocation or biosonar, enables them to thread their way through complicated cave passages, detect obstacles as fine as a human hair, and capture tiny insects, all without benefit of light. Bat echolocation is far more sophisticated than comparable electronic systems developed by humans.

In bats, ultrasounds are produced in air that is caused to vibrate rapidly as it passes through the larynx, or voice box—the same way that humans vocalize. Depending on the species, sound pulses are emitted through either the nose or the mouth. In general, bats emit sound waves that

178

The nearly 1,000 species of bats exhibit a great diversity of body form, facial features, and coloration. Clockwise from top left: Indian fruit bat (Pteropus giganteus); naked-backed bat (Pteronotus gymnonotus), from Costa Rica; tent-making bat (Uroderma bilobatum), from Costa Rica; Peter's epauletted fruit bat (Epomophorus crypturus), from Botswana; ghost bat (Macroderma gigas), from Australia; mastiff bat (Eumops perotis), from North and South America; and hoary bat (Lasiurus cinereus), from North America.

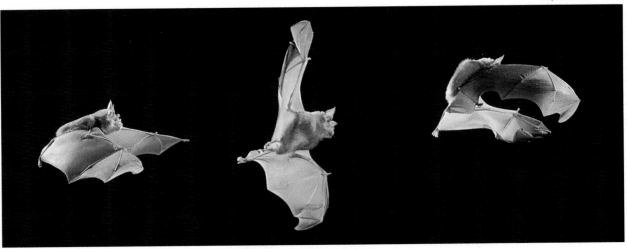

Photo sequence shows a greater horseshoe bat (Rhinolophus ferrumequinum) pursuing a moth. Bats and birds share the ability of powered flight, and the early evolution and success of both groups are linked to the great availability of flying insects.

range from 25,000 to 75,000 vibrations per second, but the frequencies may reach 200,000. These frequency levels are above the normal human hearing range of 20–20,000 vibrations per second.

Bats echolocate by sending out short pulses of ultrasound and then interpreting the echoes. The time difference between sound emission and the echo return yields the target distance. Variation in echo loudness from one ear to the other indicates direction, while variation in its frequency conveys information about the shape and texture of objects. The effective range is about 3–5 meters but may exceed 10 meters if the target is large. For many bat species the rate at which the sound pulse is emitted is also a component of the information-gathering process. When an insectivorous species detects an insect, the pulse rate increases from about 5–20 pulses per second to as high as 200.

Echolocating species use constant-frequency (CF) calls, frequency-modulated (FM) calls, or both, depending on the information needed in various circumstances. CF calls, whose tones do not rise or fall, are characterized by comparatively long pulses, usually lasting 10 milliseconds (a hundredth of a second), whereas FM calls are much shorter and sweep down from higher to lower tones. The particular type of call that a species uses depends on the structure of the habitat in which the bat forages and the type of prey information required. Bats that hunt above the canopy or over large rivers produce simple FM calls, which provide information on target location and range. Species that hunt within forests use complex FM calls, which yield high-resolution echoes carrying a great deal of information about the surrounding environment. CF calls are characteristic of species that forage in clearings within forests and are tailored for locating insect prey against a complex backdrop. Often bat species categorized as CF callers employ FM calls as part of their repertoire.

The call of an individual bat is highly personalized. This feature has obvious benefits when bats are hunting in groups, navigating through a cave filled with thousands of other like-minded individuals, or trying to find their baby among thousands, or even millions, on a cave ceiling.

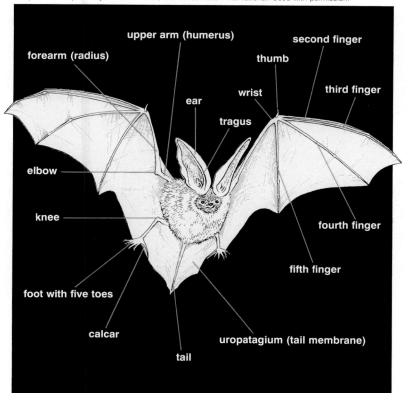

Major structural features of a bat, including its unique "hand-wings," are shown in the diagram (left). Illustrated is the spotted bat (Euderma maculatum), a microchiropteran, of the southwestern U.S. The second through fifth finger bones of each hand are greatly elongated and lie firmly within a delicate membrane of bare skin. The clawed thumb, always free of the wing membrane, is used for walking, climbing, and handling food. In many species of bats another membrane, the uropatagium, connects the hind limbs and tail. The outer ear is usually large and is often funnel-shaped, and it may have a conspicuous flap of skin, called the tragus, at its base. (Below) High-speed flash photography reveals the ability of the echolocation system of a bat (the false vampire, Megaderma lyra) to guide the animal in total darkness through an opening between fine wires.

Echolocation is one reason that bats exhibit some of the most fascinating faces in the animal world. The more unusual ones have spear-shaped nose flaps (some almost half as long as their bodies), facial flaps, and greatly exaggerated and unusually shaped ears. It has been demonstrated that at least some of these facial features increase the efficiency of sound transmission or reception.

With the exception of a few cave-roosting species, flying foxes do not echolocate. Instead, they use their excellent night vision for navigation and their highly developed sense of smell to find ripening fruit and nectar-bearing flowers. Just as one might predict, fruit- and nectar-feeding microchiropterans have relatively simple echolocating abilities and rely heavily on their vision and smell.

Not all sounds produced by bats or used by them fall into the ultrasound range. Most make at least some sounds within the upper range of human hearing, and a few, such as the western mastiff, regularly make calls that can be heard 100 meters or more. In addition, some species use their exceptional hearing to find prey by using the prey's own calls. In the early 1980s an unusual predator-prey relationship involving bats and frogs was found in the rain forests of Panama. Frog-eating bats focus on the mating calls of male frogs of certain species, and the frogs counter by drastically altering their call behavior. Jacqueline Belwood of the University of Florida showed the existence of a similar relationship for several Panamanian bat species and their insect prey, species of katydids.

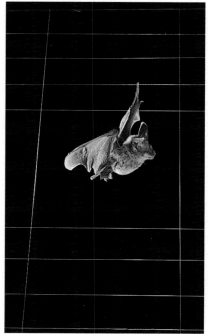

Stephen Dalton—NHPA

181

Courtship rituals of some bat species are complex, spectacular affairs. The male (right), a Gambian epauletted bat (Epomophorus gambianus), has extended his tufts of white shoulder hair while simultaneously calling to the female and beating his half-furled wings. The pouches in which the tufts are normally retracted are believed to contain glands that secrete attractive odors (sex pheromones), which the shoulder hairs and flapping wings disperse into the air.

Behavior and reproduction

The diversity of bat appearance is matched by a tremendous range of behavior. Some species are solitary, some live in small or medium-sized colonies, and others are highly social. For example, the Mexican free-tailed bat of the southwestern U.S. and northern Mexico is a highly colonial species. It forms huge, mostly female, maternity colonies numbering tens of millions each in about a dozen caves in the northern part of its range. In late spring each female gives birth to a single young, which is weaned by midsummer. In the fall the females, some adult males, and the young migrate south into Mexico, where they join nonmigratory males. Even there the two sexes often segregate into separate colonies.

Many temperate species migrate seasonally, some moving to hibernation sites such as caves or mines, others to regions where insects are abundant even during the winter months. Tropical species are reported to travel up and down mountain slopes to take advantage of altitudinal fluctuations in food abundance that accompany the annual wet and dry seasons. It is thought that in the deserts of the southwestern U.S. the long-tongued bat tracks the bidirectional, north-south, seasonal flowering sequence of a variety of giant cacti and agaves.

The courtship displays of some species are spectacular. Males may use sexually attractive odors, mating calls, and "dances" to attract mates. In some species, mating appears quite affectionate, involving prolonged soft whining, mutual licking, and grooming, while others seem to mate with little recognizable courtship. The red bat, a species that occurs in the U.S., mates in flight.

Mating habits vary greatly among species. Bats that hibernate tend to mate in the fall, and they appear to be totally promiscuous, with most members of the colony breeding simultaneously. At the other end of the spectrum, certain tropical and semitropical species are monogamous,

182

(Top) A.N.T./NHPA;
(bottom) Merlin D. Tuttle, Bat Conservation International

sometimes apparently mating for life and sharing parental duties. Male African hammer-headed bats prefer to gather in groups at select sites, called leks, where they sing and engage in communal courtship displays. Females fly from one displaying male to another until they have made a choice. Male Jamaican fruit-eating bats do not bother to court. Instead, they compete among themselves for control of tree hollows and other sites that are attractive to females for rearing young. The male sac-winged bat guards feeding grounds, permitting females to use them only if they join his harem. Although the social behavior of most species is as yet unknown, the distinct color patterns, head crests, epaulets, and odor-producing glands present in many unstudied species suggest that a wide assortment of courtship and other behaviors remain to be described.

For their size, bats have a surprisingly small number of young each year, usually only a single offspring per female in most species. A handful of tropical species may have two litters in a year. There are a few species, mostly solitary ones, that give birth to as many as five young at a time. The young feed from a pair of nipples located on the female's chest in a position similar to that of humans. In some species the young are left in the roost at all times, while in others the females carry young between roosts and even on feeding flights.

Detailed, long-term studies of survival rates for both young and adults have been made for only a few, mostly temperate, species. It is known that individuals of even small species regularly live longer than 10 years, and there are some records of more than 30 years. For one of the better known species, the gray bat of eastern North America, mortality rates for infants and juveniles can be very high during some breeding seasons. Although mortality rates for adults average much lower, the loss of entire colonies has been recorded for both natural and human-related causes. Bats are eaten by a wide variety of predators, including birds, snakes, raccoons, lizards, and even spiders, jaguars, and bullfrogs. Whether predation has an appreciable effect on the long-term population level of any bat species is not known.

The lack of adequate population data for most bat species is one of the more serious problems in developing effective conservation plans for individual species. Experience with other, more thoroughly studied mammals indicates that social species with low reproductive rates are highly sensitive to even small increases in mortality rates.

Foraging behavior

Different species of bats have favorite foraging sites to which they often travel in mass, and it is not uncommon to see a group of bats, from a few to thousands, feeding at night near an electric light or over a stream or pond. Despite such group feeding, each bat's foraging behavior seems quite independent of the others', and most of the time this is probably an accurate interpretation. It has been established, however, that at least a few species, such as Kuhl's pipistrelle in East Africa, hunt in packs, altering their densities and moving between foraging sites in a manner that increases each individual's success.

(Top) A mass of newborn and adult Schreiber's bent-winged bats (Miniopterus schreibersii) cling to the roof of a nursery cave in Australia. A mother Gambian epauletted bat and her nearly grown young (above) represent the birth ratio for most species: one offspring per female per year.

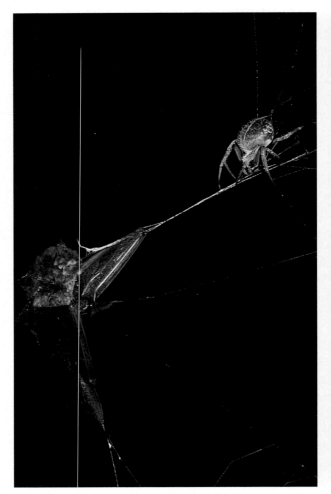 

Bats fall victim to an assortment of predators, including large spiders and snakes. With few exceptions, however, they are not regular food fare for any predator, and the effect of predation on long-term population levels remains to be learned.

Altruism is not a trait that most people associate with bats, but work during the 1980s by Gerald Wilkinson of the University of Maryland, College Park, demonstrates that altruism may be more common than might be expected. He found, in what seems a rather ironic twist, that vampire bats share food with colony members who fail to obtain a sufficient blood meal and that female vampires will adopt orphaned young of the species. In a subsequent study of North American little brown bats, Wilkinson showed that lactating females will help feed the young of unrelated colony mates.

Habitats and roosts

Bats live in almost every conceivable habitat except for the most extreme desert and polar regions. Generally they are much more abundant in the tropics than in temperate regions; while there is only a single species in Alaska, 30 live in Europe, 40 in the United States, and more than 200 in Brazil. In tropical rain forests it is not unusual to find 60 or more species in a given area, whereas it would be difficult to find more than 6 species at any single locality in most temperate regions.

184

Although people often associate bats with caves, bats actually occupy a great variety of roosts—in tree hollows, under old bark, in foliage and unfurling leaves, in holes in the ground, and in rock crevices, among other places. Some tropical species construct tents by biting a patterned series of holes in large leaves such as those of palms and banana plants. A few species are fond of human structures, occupying such places as attics, walls, barns, bridges, and old mines. In fact, several temperate species are now more commonly found in artificial structures than in their original roosts, a situation that may be due to the elimination of their natural homes.

Cave life

In both temperate and tropical regions, caves provide homes for many bat species, and several to a dozen or more species can be found in a single particularly suitable cave. Not all caves are acceptable, however, because bats have very specific temperature, moisture, and safety requirements, three qualities that vary greatly among caves and even among different regions of a single cave. Consequently, bats occupy only a small propor-

Bats choose a variety of daytime roosts, each species having particular favorites. (Top left) A southern yellow bat (Lasiurus ega), whose range includes the U.S. Southwest, emerges at nightfall from under the dead fronds of a palm tree. The attic of a Welsh country house (top right) affords a haven for long-eared bats (Plecotus auritus). Common flying foxes (above left; Pteropus vampyrus) in Borneo sleep away the daylight hours while hanging from tree branches. Big brown bats (Eptesicus fuscus) huddle behind a shutter in Connecticut (above).

Caves are the roosts people most often associate with bats, and indeed they are used by numerous bat species for hibernation, nurseries, migratory stopovers, and other purposes. Large roundleaf horseshoe bats (above right; Hipposideros larvatus) occupy a limestone cavern at Taman Negara National Park, Malaysia. Mines offer cavelike qualities attractive to bats, as in the case of the moisture-coated Natterer's bat (above; Myotis nattereri) hibernating in a disused mine in Wales.

tion of available caves, and the ones they do use may be occupied only during certain times of the year. The Mexican free-tail's use of caves in the southwestern U.S. only during the summer is a good example.

Colonies of several temperate-zone species, such as the endangered gray bat of the southeastern U.S., may use several caves on a seasonal basis and for different purposes. They have migratory stopover caves as well as nursery, bachelor, and hibernation caves. Bats often migrate hundreds of kilometers to reach these unique roosts and may die if even one or two are disturbed too frequently. The special quality of many hibernation caves is their large rooms positioned so that they trap and store cold air. Such a system provides cool and stable temperatures. In addition, difficult access often affords protection against predators—but, unfortunately, not against people who may not yet appreciate the importance of bats or the extent to which they can be harmed by ill-timed human visits.

Repeated human disturbance is a primary cause of population decline in cave-dwelling species. Some harm is caused by deliberate acts of vandalism, but most comes from a lack of awareness of the damage that can be done to a bat colony by what seem to be only minor disturbances. One person entering a hibernation cave even briefly can cause thousands of bats to awaken and waste 10–30 days' worth of their fat reserve, a supply that must last until spring. Repeated entry into caves containing maternity colonies not only causes high mortality rates among young but also may induce a colony to abandon the cave altogether. Bats are extremely loyal to the caves where they were born and where they hibernate and, because of their special environmental requirements, most

186

have few alternative sites. Fortunately, many caves are used by bats for only a portion of the year, and in most cases the needs of both bats and people who like to explore caves can be accommodated without great harm to either. Professional cave explorers are becoming more involved in trying to save bats, but many people need to be educated about the animals' value, requirements, and sensitivity to disturbance.

Life in tropical forests

Bats have been successful in temperate habitats, sometimes spectacularly so, but it is in tropical forests and woodlands that they reach their zenith of diversity and abundance. In the tropics bats live in a wider variety of roost types than in temperate regions, and their diets are more diverse. While a large proportion of tropical species eat insects, the tropics are also home to most of the Earth's fruit and nectar feeders as well as most of the carnivores. The last-mentioned type ranges from species that use enlarged hind feet and claws to gaff fish from ponds to species that prey on frogs, lizards, birds, and other vertebrates. Even though insectivores dominate in number of species, many of the most abundant tropical species are fruit and nectar feeders.

Without question, the vampire bat is one of the world's most notorious animals. Actually there are three species of vampires, one quite common and two rare; all are found only in tropical Latin America. Both of the rare species feed exclusively on birds, while the common vampire bat prefers the blood of mammals, including that of humans. Vampires do not attack—in fact, quite the contrary. They sneak up on their prey, make a small, painless incision, and lap the blood as it flows from the wound, aided by an anticoagulant in their saliva. Their threat is not the amount of blood that they take. They seldom consume so much as to injure their prey, but they sometimes transmit fatal diseases to livestock or leave open wounds that are subject to infection and parasites.

Stephen Dalton—Oxford Scientific Films

A common vampire bat (Desmodus rotundus) feeds on blood from a resting sow after making a small, painless cut with its razor-sharp teeth. In areas of Latin America where overpopulations of vampires exist because of the presence of livestock, poorly mounted vampire-eradication campaigns often kill millions of beneficial bat species and disrupt the ecosystem.

The world's tropical forests are home to most of the carnivorous bats. A fishing bat (above; Noctilio leporinus), from Central and South America, rakes its enlarged, clawed hind limbs over the surface of a stream, having been guided by its echolocation system to some ripple or other disturbance in the quiet water. (Opposite page, left) Two false vampire bats, from India, make a meal of a captured mouse.

In another of those ironic twists so characteristic of the relationship between humans and nature, the unique anticoagulant from the saliva of vampire bats may someday be used to prevent heart attacks and strokes in humans. The chemical, a plasminogen, may replace drugs currently being used because it has none of their toxic side effects.

Before the advent of livestock operations, even common vampire bats were relatively rare, as they are today in places where the original forest is still intact. Where overpopulations exist because of the presence of livestock, their numbers sometimes must be controlled. Unfortunately, vampire eradication campaigns often are counterproductive because poorly trained personnel and ranchers wage war on all bat species. Millions of highly beneficial bats often are killed, sometimes without substantial impact on vampire populations. Vampire bats form small colonies that live in a wide variety of inconspicuous roosts. In one campaign in South America, more than 8,000 caves were poisoned or dynamited. Untold thousands of beneficial bats were destroyed and, quite possibly, the surrounding ecosystem degraded for several decades or permanently. Fortunately, control measures specific to vampires are now available, but financial and educational limitations have restricted their effective use in many countries.

Bats play an essential role in the reforestation and maintenance of many tropical forests because they disperse huge quantities of seeds.

A Wahlberg's epauletted bat (above; Epomophorus wahlbergi) eats a fig, the undigested seeds of which it will expel later during flight. Flying foxes consume enormous quantities of fruit in tropical forests and by means of seed dispersal play an essential role in forest maintenance and reforestation.

Some bats specialize in feeding on the fruits of colonizing plant species, while others disperse seeds from mature forest species, such as the monkey pot tree. The rate at which bats digest fruit is amazingly rapid, often as little as 15 minutes from consumption to defecation, and some consume two to three times their body weight in fruit each evening. A recent study showed that seeds dropped by bats account for as much as 95% of forest regrowth on cleared land in West Africa. Similar importance has been documented for several study sites in Latin America. In Costa Rica it was found that a single Seba's short-tailed fruit bat is capable of dispersing up to 60,000 seeds in a single night.

In tropical forests and savannas the seeds of most shrubs and trees are dispersed by bats, birds, and primates. Because bats are less cautious

189

Photos, Merlin D. Tuttle, Bat Conservation International

The night-blooming flower of the African baobab tree (above) is highly dependent on bats for pollination. Without bats, such as the Egyptian fruit bat (Rousettus aegyptiacus) shown, the tree could die out, triggering a chain of extinctions of other plants and animals that rely on the baobab for food and shelter. (Right) Its face dusted with pollen from another flower, a lesser long-nosed bat (Leptonycteris curasoae) is about to thrust its head into the blossom of a saguaro cactus, a bat-dependent plant of the southwestern U.S. and Mexico. (Opposite page) Two ways that bats demonstrate their economic value are in their enormous consumption of insects and in their pollination of the wild counterparts of important food crops. A pallid bat (top; Antrozous pallidus) carries a katydid that it snatched from the ground, while a greater short-nosed fruit bat (bottom; Cynopterus sphinx) laps nectar from a wild banana plant.

than birds about flying over large open areas, they accomplish a major part of the early reseeding of clearings. As the forest regenerates, birds begin to use young saplings for perches, beneath which they deposit seeds. In the final stage primates join the bats and birds in dispersing seeds, and it is this trio that primarily maintains tropical forests.

Bats as keystone species

Bats often are vital to plants that have great ecological value. For example, the famous baobab tree of East Africa is so important as food and shelter for other animals and plants that it has been called the "tree of life." Yet it is itself highly dependent on bats for pollination. Its flowers open only at night, and their reproductive parts hang down in such a manner that only bats are likely to come in contact with them. Without its bat pollinators, the baobab could die out, triggering a chain of linked extinctions throughout an entire ecosystem. Bats play a similar role in other ecosystems, and they and other animals that perform such vital services have been called keystone species.

In another example, the flowers of tequila- and fiber-producing agaves and of the giant saguaro, cardon, and organ-pipe cacti of the southwestern U.S. and Mexico open during the nighttime hours, relying heavily on long-tongued bats for their pollination. In the absence of bat pollinators, the level of successful seed production by the agaves is reduced to one three-thousandth of normal, and several species of cacti are also highly dependent. Loss of their bat pollinators—two bat species recently recognized as endangered—could seriously threaten these desert ecosystems.

190

Such relationships are widespread, and many others probably have yet to be discovered.

Ecological and economic value

Bats are the main consumers of night-flying insects worldwide. Of all bat species 75% feed on insects; in temperate areas the number is close to 95%. A single gray bat may eat 3,000 insects in an evening's foray, and a large colony of free-tailed bats may capture up to a quarter million kilograms (a half million pounds) of insects in a single night. Bats consume moths, flies, beetles, mosquitoes, and other insects in great quantities, often taking whichever type is most abundant at a given time. Some of North America's most widespread species are capable of capturing as many as 600 mosquitoes in a single hour when the insects are plentiful.

As discussed above, bats are essential pollinators and dispersers of seeds for numerous plants—not only those vital to the survival of rain forests but also the wild counterparts of food crops worth millions of dollars annually. The wild varieties of fruit, nut, and spice crops like bananas, avocados, dates, figs, breadfruit, peaches, mangoes, carob, cloves, and cashews are highly bat dependent. Other valuable commodities from such plants range from fibers for rope to fine timber for furniture, balsa wood for hobbies, and even tequila. Although many of these crops no longer require bats for their commercial production, their wild relatives could die out without substantial populations of bats to service their night-blooming flowers or disperse their seeds. Since ancestral species of commercial forms are the only sources of new genetic material available

191

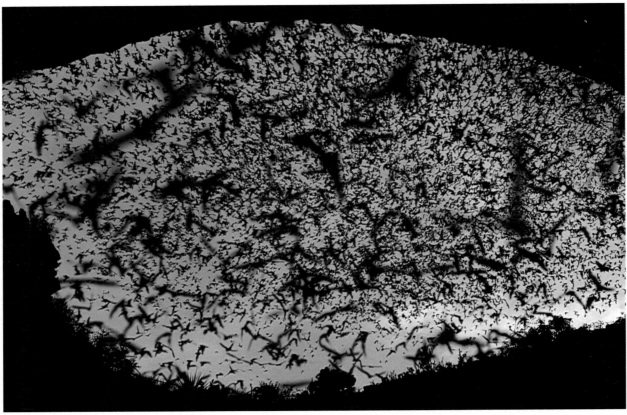

Mexican free-tailed bats (Tadarida brasiliensis) *leave Carlsbad Caverns, New Mexico, for a summer night of foraging for insects. Once numbering nine million, the population at Carlsbad has been reduced to fewer than a half million—just one sign of the urgent need for people to recognize the value of bats and their conservation requirements.*

to combat diseases and to establish new varieties, their loss could have serious long-term consequences for agriculture worldwide.

Other plant products of great economic importance are harvested from semiwild trees that continue to rely on bats. In West Africa the iroko tree, which produces an annual timber harvest worth many millions of dollars, is believed to rely solely on bats for seed dispersal. The prized durian fruit of Southeast Asia requires bats for pollination and sells for an estimated $120 million annually. The long-term success of the many extractive reserves now being planned and established may well depend on the health and protection of local bat populations.

An urgent need for conservation

Despite their crucial roles in the maintenance of healthy environments and human economies, bats rank among the most persecuted and scientifically neglected animals. People continue to fear and needlessly kill them, and even conservationists often remain unaware of their value and plight.

In Europe population declines as high as 90% have been reported during the last 30 years, and some species already have disappeared from areas where they were once abundant. In the U.S. nearly 40% of bat species either are federally listed as endangered or are official candidates for such status. The now-endangered gray bat was once present in vast

192

numbers, and the Indiana bat of the central and eastern U.S. has declined by an alarming 55% just since 1980. The Mexican free-tailed bat, still the most abundant bat of the U.S. Southwest, is also in trouble. At Carlsbad Caverns, New Mexico, it has declined from almost nine million to fewer than a half million, and at Eagle Creek Cave, Arizona, from 30 million to 30,000, a 99.9% decrease, since the 1960s.

In Latin America misguided vampire-bat control undoubtedly eliminates millions of beneficial bats each year, and in the Old World tropics unregulated commercial and subsistence harvesting for human food already has led to the extinction of some species, with many more seriously threatened. Tropical fruit growers often consider bats to be serious crop pests and conduct intensive control programs in many areas. In at least some cases it has been established that bats do extremely minor damage to crops because they feed only on fruit too ripe for commercial harvest. In fact, bats may provide an important service to growers by removing fruits that would otherwise serve as food for injurious insects such as the Mediterranean fruit fly. Human disturbance and killing are among the most serious threats to bats, though many also die from habitat loss, especially when caves and tropical forests are destroyed.

The potential for environmental degradation is enormous if these trends continue. Saving the last few bats from extinction is not enough, since vast numbers often are required for keeping insect populations in balance and for servicing the many plants that rely on bat visitation for their survival. The single Eagle Creek Cave colony once consumed hundreds of thousands of kilograms of insects each night. Their loss has vastly increased reliance on the chemical insecticides that already threaten human health and the health of the ecosystems on which people depend.

As a result of the research and publicity efforts of conservation organizations and dedicated bat biologists around the world, the value and conservation needs of bats are becoming increasingly recognized. Still, the future of these animals—and the quality of human life—remains at stake.

FOR ADDITIONAL READING

Roger W. Barbour and Wayne H. Davis, *Bats of America* (University Press of Kentucky, 1969).

M. Brock Fenton, *Just Bats* (University of Toronto Press, 1983).

John E. Hill and James D. Smith, *Bats: A Natural History* (University of Texas Press, 1984).

Gerhard Neuweiler, "Foraging Ecology and Audition in Echolocating Bats," *Trends in Ecology & Evolution* (October 1989, pp. 160–166).

Wilfried Schober, *The Lives of Bats* (Arco Publishing, Inc., 1984).

Merlin D. Tuttle, *America's Neighborhood Bats* (University of Texas Press, 1988).

Merlin D. Tuttle, *Bats: Gentle Friends, Essential Allies* (available from Bat Conservation International, P.O. Box 162603, Austin, Texas, 78716).

Gerald S. Wilkinson, "Food Sharing in Vampire Bats," *Scientific American* (February 1990, pp. 76–82).

Endangered gray bats (Myotis grisescens) hibernate in a cave in Tennessee. Because of the bats' specific environmental requirements, nearly all of the species overwinter in just nine caves. The loss of suitable cave sites through human intrusion and vandalism is thought to be the major reason for the severe decline of gray bat populations.

Merlin D. Tuttle, Bat Conservation International

PRESERVATION A PIECE AT A TIME

The Captive Breeding and Reintroduction of Wildlife

by Patricia J. West

Propagating wild animals in captivity and restoring them to their native habitats buys precious time for species on the brink of extinction. Despite many success stories, the practice remains controversial even among conservationists.

Since the "Cambrian explosion" some 570 million years ago, when living organisms underwent rapid diversification of forms, millions of species of plants and animals have evolved and eventually become extinct. In fact, more than 99% of the species that have ever existed are now gone, many vanishing during mass extinctions that occurred about every 26 million years. These catastrophic events, which possibly were caused by celestial events or massive volcanic activity, represent the loss of millions of species, primarily animals, in a relatively short time.

The world is once again witnessing a devastating loss of wildlife and plants. Some scientists now believe that well over 100 species become extinct each year; others estimate over one species per day. Experts predict that by the end of the century the Earth may be losing as many as 100 per day. Although such losses may have occurred during other periods in the past, this extinction event is different in that it is due entirely to human beings and is occurring orders of magnitude faster. Most catastrophic or rapid extinctions probably took thousands to hundreds of thousands of years. Today they are occurring within decades.

Without a doubt it is humans that are responsible for the massive and continuing loss of wildlife—largely because of the increase in human populations all over the world. The scope of such growth is hard to imagine, yet for most less developed nations the population doubles every 40 years or less. Such expansion puts a tremendous strain on the Earth's natural resources. Unfortunately, as humans

forge the world to suit their needs, nature is inevitably altered or destroyed.

Human beings are part of the web of life. Consequently, it is for more than commercial purposes—it is ultimately for the purpose of ensuring self-preservation—that humans need to maintain a rich and diverse collection of species. Today more so than ever, plants and animals, including those not yet discovered or studied, are being counted upon as sources for new foods and medicines, potentially useful genetic traits, and fundamental biological knowledge. Each loss of a species makes the reservoir of nature that can be tapped for improving life, health, and the chances for survival that much poorer.

Rapid destruction of the world's wildlife has created an urgency to find ways to assist thousands of species of animals threatened with extinction. Many new techniques and programs were developed by scientists during the past two decades. Zoos, previously mere exhibitors of animals, began to play an active role in conservation. Zoo researchers began to study the reproductive processes of wild animals and to use this knowledge to enhance the reproductive potential of wildlife species in captivity.

Captive propagation, or breeding, of wild animals is one conservation technique that came of age in the 1960s and 1970s. By breeding animals,

PATRICIA J. WEST is an Environmental Information Specialist for Westinghouse Savannah River Co., Aiken, South Carolina, and a free-lance science writer.

(Overleaf) Illustration by Stephanie Motz

196

specialists have been able to increase the numbers of individuals within captive populations, giving them a chance they may not have had in the wild. A closely related technique is reintroduction, or the restoration of a species to its native habitat. Reintroduction is an important follow-on to captive breeding programs, as it seeks to reestablish animals in the wild with the hope that they will be able to once again exist on their own. Essentially the technique buys time for disappearing wildlife species.

Programs of captive breeding and reintroduction have met both with success, as with the peregrine falcon, and with failure, as with the now extinct dusky seaside sparrow. The fate of most targeted species is yet to be decided. Supporters and critics have taken strong stands about the value of captive breeding. And, because of the complexity of animal species and their predicaments, a universal solution does not seem likely.

Endangered species

In the United States, attempts to protect wildlife from human activities include such legislation as the federal Endangered Species Act of 1973. This act is intended to prevent the extinction of plants and animals not only in the U.S. but also in the open sea and in other nations.

Presently about 600 species of plants and animals are federally listed as endangered or threatened in the U.S. and more than 1,100 internationally; approximately 50 species are added each year. These numbers do not accurately reflect the many species that would benefit from such designation but instead reflect the limited manpower and funding of the U.S. Fish and Wildlife Service, which is responsible for the listings. In fact, more than 4,000 species in the U.S. alone are candidates for threatened or endangered status.

The ultimate goal of the endangered species program is delisting, or recovery, but to date few species have recovered to the point that they no longer require protection. In some cases the solution has been straightforward. For example, scientists attributed the startling decline of the brown pelican in the southeastern U.S. to poisoning resulting from the use of the pesticide DDT. Once DDT was banned, pelican numbers increased, and the species was removed from the endangered species list in 1985. Other species, including the American bison, Arabian oryx, and American beaver, were affected by overhunting. These animals have been stabilized or have recovered as a result of stricter game laws. Identifying the cause of the decline of a species, however, is not always this easy. Often by the time the cause has been found, too few individuals remain, making recovery difficult.

Elements for success

Use of technology is sometimes deemed necessary for the preservation of a species. The variety of conservation techniques that have been developed ranges from the translocation of animals between existing populations to artificial insemination.

Captive breeding of wild animals for reintroduction has been employed extensively over the past two decades for a wide variety of animals,

To date, captive breeding and reintroduction programs have had their successes and failures. Prominent among the former has been the 20-year effort to reverse the decline of the peregrine falcon (opposite page) in the eastern U.S. and other parts of the world. By contrast, despite years of work by wildlife specialists, the dusky seaside sparrow (below) became extinct in 1987, a victim of DDT spraying and alteration of its Florida salt marsh habitat.

P.W. Sykes, Jr.—VIREO

197

Zoological Society of San Diego; photos, Ron Garrison

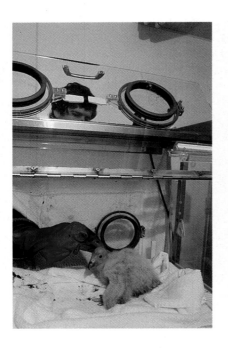

A California condor chick (above) hatched in captivity at the San Diego (California) Wild Animal Park is fed by means of a condor-head hand puppet so that it will retain a healthy wariness of humans and thus later be able to be released to the wild. Two captive California condors (right) engage in courtship behavior prior to breeding. In 1986, in a last-ditch attempt to save the species, wildlife biologists captured the last three remaining wild condors to supplement zoo breeding stock. Four years later, as a result of successful breeding efforts, the captive population comprised about 40 birds.

including butterflies, fish, reptiles, birds, and mammals. The technique has been called on to supplement diminishing wild populations or to repopulate areas where a species has been entirely eradicated.

In many cases such programs provide the only hope for the preservation of a species. In all cases it is considered a last resort. For example, when the numbers of wild California condors plummeted to three individuals in 1986, wildlife biologists captured them to supplement zoo stock for a breeding program. These final-hour attempts to save species do not always work, a reason why many scientists prefer to intervene earlier by translocating animals between populations, to a formerly occupied habitat, or even to a new habitat. The value of translocation was recently demonstrated for several potentially endangered fish species in Sri Lanka. By moving four species of rain-forest fish into another stream system, a new habitat, scientists were able to establish self-perpetuating populations within four years, thereby avoiding the complexities and high costs associated with such techniques as captive breeding. Most conservation biologists, however, are careful to point out that translocating species to new habitats can be dangerous. Some new introductions, either deliberate or inadvertent, are notorious for the effects they have had on the native species. Translocation, therefore, must be performed only after a habitat and its natural inhabitants have been carefully studied.

One of the major challenges of captive breeding programs is maintaining genetic diversity. Genetic diversity, or variation, is thought to be essential to the viability of species because it acts as a buffer against environmental perturbations. For example, if an ecosystem is altered, a species whose genes can give rise to a greater variety of traits is more likely than a genetically more uniform species to have individuals in the population that are able to adjust and survive.

Inbreeding is one of the chief problems associated with managing endangered wildlife populations. Because endangered populations are small and fragmented, potential mates are often related, and the chances of inbreeding increase. Years of breeding among a limited number of individuals or among related individuals can induce inbreeding depression, thereby reducing vigor, fertility, and birth weight and increasing birth defects. Such problems may be especially significant for captive-bred species; the loss of genetic diversity through inbreeding may make it more difficult for the species to survive in captivity or later in the wild. For this reason, as a general rule of thumb, most conservation geneticists believe that a minimum of 150 to 200 animals is necessary for the short-term maintenance of a species in captivity.

Knowing the total biology of the species to be bred and released is also critical to such efforts. Scientists must completely understand the reproductive patterns, feeding behavior, and other characteristics of the animals they are dealing with. Unfortunately, a lack of understanding of a species' biology can result in limited breeding success. Such is the case with the whooping crane, an endangered wading bird of North America. Although the cranes have been bred successfully in captivity, an experimental wild population started in 1975 in Idaho has not yielded a single egg. Biologists involved with the project have yet to learn why the birds have not attempted to breed.

Yet another requirement for captive breeding programs is an adequate amount of resources for proper maintenance of the species in captivity. Zoos, aquariums, and universities must have space that is both large enough for raising animals and suited to the needs of the species. For example, according to Howard Hunt, curator of herpetology at Zoo Atlanta (Georgia), one pair of Morelet's crocodiles from tropical America

Five six-month-old Morelet's crocodiles and a yearling stay close to their mother's tail in a breeding enclosure at Zoo Atlanta in Atlanta, Georgia. One breeding pair of the tropical reptiles requires about 110 square meters (1,200 square feet) of space, half of it being pond—a major commitment of resources for the species to be maintained properly in captivity.

199

Education about endangered species recovery has become increasingly important to wildlife reintroduction efforts. Children at a conservation summit (top) make the acquaintance of a great horned owl. On a beach at Boca Raton, Florida, visitors are brought to watch a loggerhead turtle laying eggs (top right). A sign at Blackwater National Wildlife Refuge, Maryland (above), reminds motorists of the potential effects of their casual behavior on a fragile environment.

requires a 6 × 18-meter (20 × 60-foot) enclosure, half of it being pond. From 1975 to 1978, 93 of the endangered crocodiles captive bred at Zoo Atlanta were released by Mexican wildlife officials. Thus, for some species a major commitment is required by facilities engaged in breeding efforts in order for an effective program to be maintained.

Adequate funding is also necessary to provide the best care for the animals and to conduct appropriate and sufficient research to make the program a success. Unfortunately, both space restrictions and financial limitations are the rule. One reason is that such programs usually rely on public support or private donations and consequently are frequently understaffed and underfunded.

Reintroduction of animals into the wild likewise requires that a number of important steps be taken. One is preparation of the animals for life in the wild, whereby the animals are taught such behavioral skills as obtaining their own food, avoiding predation, breeding, and caring for young. This can be undertaken prior to release or upon release. For example, before small numbers of red wolves were reintroduced to their original habitat in North Carolina in 1987 and 1988, they were systematically taught to hunt by being exposed first to road-killed animal carcasses and then to live prey. Much more intensive preparation was given to chimpanzees destined to be released in West Africa in the 1970s and '80s. While living continually with the animals, researchers personally taught them such skills as nest building, avoidance of poisonous scorpions, the use of sticks to dig for termites, and appropriate chimpanzee social etiquette.

Habitat is another critical consideration. The habitat desired for release must be protected, managed, and in some cases restored. Most scientists recognize that protected, healthy habitat is the key to successful reintroduction programs.

200

Experts with the U.S. Fish and Wildlife Service fit a red wolf with a radio tracking collar prior to the animal's reintroduction to the Alligator River National Wildlife Refuge in eastern North Carolina. Before their release, the captive-bred wolves had to be taught essential behavioral and survival skills, including hunting their own prey.

After captive-bred animals are released, long-term monitoring must be instituted. This task often involves the attachment of radiotelemetry equipment to individual animals so their movements and progress can be observed. Data gathered during monitoring programs allow scientists to assess the survival rates of a released population. Such information is useful in future reintroduction programs.

Educating communities—including teachers, students, and elected officials—about endangered species and their habitats has become an increasingly important part of successful reintroduction programs. Scientists are now realizing that education programs can raise financial support for reintroduction efforts as well as public awareness about the importance of endangered species recovery. By focusing attention on conservation issues, scientists are able to improve the chances of survival for ecosystems and their inhabitants.

Finally, captive breeding and reintroduction programs must be well planned. When they are not, the resulting delays in the undertaking of a recovery program can be devastating. For example, in the case of the black-footed ferret of Wyoming, researchers as early as 1983 recommended removing animals from the wild for breeding and reintroduction. Declines in the population were noted again in 1984 and 1985, yet the organizations charged with managing ferrets did little to come to their rescue until most were lost. When the remaining animals were captured in late 1986, barely more than a dozen were left. In such cases, species suffer because valuable time and valuable reproductive vigor are lost.

Some projects in progress

A review of the status of the fish of North America alone indicates a need to address the problem of disappearing fish species in the U.S., Canada, and Mexico. As of 1990, 364 fish species were considered rare

201

Arizona's Boyce Thompson Arboretum (above), a former habitat of the endangered Gila topminnow (below), is one of a variety of sites that recently were cleared of predatory mosquito fish and restocked with captive-bred topminnows. The topminnow program has been so successful that the U.S. Fish and Wildlife Service is considering downgrading the status of the species to threatened.

in North America, over 90 of which were endangered. One of them is the Gila topminnow, a small live-bearer found in the Sonoran Desert of the U.S. Southwest and Mexico. Captive breeding and reintroduction programs for the Gila topminnow have been so successful that the U.S. Fish and Wildlife Service is considering downgrading the species from endangered to threatened.

Prior to 1940 the Gila topminnow was among the most common fish in southern Arizona. It subsequently was threatened by predation by the introduced mosquito fish and by a loss of shallow-water habitats. By 1977 natural populations existed at only 13 sites. In 1981, to aid in the recovery of the species, a program was begun that included captive breeding of the fish at a hatchery in New Mexico. The original breeding stock was taken from a natural population at Monkey Spring, Arizona. From 1982 to 1986 the Gila topminnow was introduced at 191 U.S. sites. The criteria necessary for downlisting the species to threatened status were met in 1985 and have since been exceeded. Although the chances for long-term survival of the introduced populations are not certain (mosquito fish and loss of habitat are an ever present problem), the recovery program has ensured that the species is out of immediate danger. Further studies will determine if continued intervention is necessary.

Attempts to breed reptiles in captivity and release them to the wild have been comparatively successful in recent years. The Kemp's ridley sea turtle is considered by some to be one such example. The Kemp's ridley inhabits the Gulf of Mexico and is the most endangered species of sea turtle. The discovery that the numbers of nesting females had been reduced from more than 30,000 in the 1940s to only a few hundred by ·the 1970s led to the establishment of a U.S.-Mexico Kemp's ridley recovery program in 1978. Disruption of nesting beaches and the incidental capture of sea turtles in commercial shrimp nets were found to be leading to their demise in the wild.

202

Recovery of the Kemp's ridley involves many aspects at several locations in both Mexico and the U.S. A "head-start" program has been cited as one of the more important tools used in the effort. Head-starting involves gathering eggs on nesting beaches, incubating and hatching, imprinting on the beach, and then raising in captivity for 9–11 months. In the imprinting process, the hatchlings are exposed for a short time to what would have been their natal beach so that they will return there as adults to nest. The turtles are tagged and released when they are the size of a dinner plate, a size at which they are less susceptible to predators that eat hatchlings.

Since the recovery program began, more than 14,000 Kemp's ridley turtles have been head-started, tagged, and released. Although survival of head-started ridleys has been documented, it is not known whether their survival rates are equal to that of their wild counterparts. Gauging the success of their nesting in the wild has also been difficult. As of 1989 none of the released turtles has been reported to have nested. It is not known whether this is because the animals still may be too young to breed.

Attempts to preserve a species of tortoise, the angonoka, have been started, although no individuals have yet been reintroduced into the wild. The angonoka is a large tortoise found in a patchy habitat around the Bay of Baly in northwestern Madagascar. Extremely rare and secretive, it is considered by the International Union for the Conservation of Nature and Natural Resources (IUCN) to be one of the most endangered reptiles in the world. At first angonokas were menaced by commercial exploitation that occurred around the turn of the century when the tortoises were collected for food. Today African bush pigs introduced into the area threaten their existence by preying on tortoise eggs and young tortoises. Angonokas are legally protected under Malagasy law, although they are kept as pets by some rural residents throughout their range.

Early attempts to breed the angonoka began in 1971 at the Honolulu Zoo but were unsuccessful, perhaps because of a lack of understanding about the natural history of the species. Since then, attempts to breed eight captive angonokas at the Ampijoroa Forestry Station on Madagascar near the species' range have met with success. Since 1986, 10 hatchlings have been produced. Eventually the offspring from this project will be used, together with tortoises obtained from private individuals, to supplement the depleted populations.

Endangered birds have been the subjects of many captive breeding and reintroduction programs. Probably one of the best known and most successful examples is the reestablishment of the peregrine falcon in the eastern U.S. Populations of the peregrine, a diurnal bird of prey, were decimated over most of Europe and North America owing to the use of pesticides in the 1950s and 1960s, which made its eggshells very fragile. Some populations of the peregrine recovered dramatically after restrictions were imposed on some pesticides. Research on the peregrine in Great Britain reveals that there are now more than 1,000 occupied breeding territories (area claimed and defended by single breeding pairs)

203

A breeding pair of peregrine falcons (right) that were introduced to the "wild" of urban high rises tend their chicks on a building ledge in Baltimore, Maryland. The male was released within Baltimore and the female outside the city; the two subsequently encountered each other and mated. At a remote release site, a helicopter (below) delivers a hacking box into which will be placed young, captive-reared peregrines nearly ready to take their first free flights. They will be cared for in the box for several days before being given the opportunity to fly and to gradually begin fending for themselves.

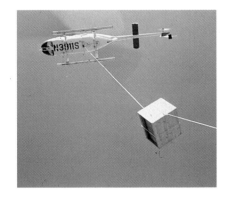

throughout the British Isles, making the species more numerous in that area of the world than ever before.

In some portions of its range including the eastern U.S., however, recovery of the peregrine falcon required more drastic measures. In 1942 estimates of the original nesting population of the eastern U.S. were about 350 pairs per year. By the 1960s the same habitat was completely vacant.

The recovery of the peregrine in the eastern U.S. was started by the Peregrine Fund at Cornell University, Ithaca, New York, which began its captive breeding program in 1969–70. Because the original population of indigenous "Appalachian" peregrines was extinct, breeding stock for the program was obtained from other parts of the world, including Alaska, Canada, Scotland, Spain, and the western U.S. Captive breeding was successful, and the first birds were released in 1974 by means of a technique known as hacking, whereby the young are placed outdoors and cared for until they can fend for themselves. Reintroduction efforts went so well that soon scientists were able to release about 100 birds per year. More than 1,000 captively bred peregrines have been released into 13 eastern states and the District of Columbia since the mid-1970s, although normal losses have reduced the numbers of survivors considerably. Monitoring indicates that the reintroduced breeding populations, which have taken up residence in both rural and urban locations, including the rooftops of city skyscrapers, are able to double in size about every two years. It is estimated that the recovery goal of 175 pairs established by the U.S. Fish and Wildlife Service will be achieved in the early 1990s.

Attempts at breeding peregrine falcons in captivity for reintroduction have also been successful in other countries. Christian Saar in Berlin has produced some 700 birds in captivity, 191 of which were reintroduced into vacant ranges in Germany during the 1980s. Peter Lindberg of the University of Göteborg, Sweden, began releasing birds into vacant ranges in that country in 1982. The Canadian Wildlife Service started a program in the early 1970s and has since established breeding populations in Montreal, Calgary, Edmonton, and Alberta.

Unfortunately, not every attempt at reestablishing birds in vacant ranges has been as successful. The endangered Guam rail, a small flightless bird, is gradually being eradicated from its native island. Although attempts to breed the rail in captivity have succeeded, scientists have been unable to release the bird on Guam because of the presence of the introduced brown tree snake. The snake, which arrived on Guam in the late 1940s, has been responsible for wiping out five native bird species on the island. While scientists decide how to remove the snake, the bird has been released on the nearby island of Rota. The program, being conducted by the Smithsonian Institution's National Zoological Park, Washington, D.C., aims to place 500 rails on Rota during the early 1990s.

Conservation programs geared toward mammals, particularly the large, more dramatic species, have gained increasing attention. The captive breeding of Siberian tigers, golden lion tamarins, and giant pandas by zoos has caught the eye of the general public.

The recovery of the European bison, or wisent, has been widely supported by Europeans and Soviets. A close relative of the American bison, the European bison has been extinct in the wild since about 1920. About 60 animals, some too old to breed, survived in captivity. In 1923 Polish scientists sought to reverse the decline by securing habitat in Bialowieza Forest and then breeding the animals in the safety of zoos. In spite of the limited knowledge of bison genetics, the newly founded Society for the Protection of the European Bison was able to breed bison and in 1952 release them into the wild. The herd that roams in the forest of Poland and the U.S.S.R. currently numbers 3,000. They survive on their own except for supplemental feedings during the harsh winter months. Today the species, which helped pioneer reintroduction schemes, is no longer considered endangered.

The black-footed ferret has gained less attention than some other endangered mammals, but its rarity and its subsequent progress toward recovery are worthy of discussion. Listed as federally endangered and considered to be the rarest mammal in the world, the species is the only ferret found in North America. The only known population was located in Wyoming, where the species was rediscovered in 1981 after having been thought extinct. Its severe decline is believed to have been the direct result of the decline of prairie dogs, the species' preferred prey.

During the mid-1980s the remnant population of black-footed ferrets was found to have been almost eliminated by disease, primarily canine distemper. Consequently, in 1986 officials with the Wyoming Game and Fish Department decided to capture the remaining handful of individuals. Since then the animals have bred extremely well in captivity, and by late 1990 the population had reached 118. Success of the program is attributed to some innovative techniques, including the use of a surrogate mother. A Siberian polecat, a closely related species, was used to raise a kit when its natural mother failed to lactate.

Smithsonian Institution
National Zoological Park; photos, Jessie Cohen

Begun in the early 1920s, the program responsible for recovery of the European bison, or wisent (above), helped pioneer wildlife-reintroduction efforts. About 3,000 wild bison currently roam the forest of Poland and the U.S.S.R., the result of a well-supported captive breeding program among zoos in Poland, the Soviet Union, and Germany. The flightless, endangered Guam rail (below), in decline on its native island for the past two decades, has been bred successfully in captivity. The presence of the introduced brown tree snake, however, has kept scientists from releasing new populations of the bird on Guam.

Like the California condor, the black-footed ferret (above) of Wyoming was spared extinction in the wild when the last surviving wild individuals were brought into a captive breeding program. Since then, excellent results in increasing the population have encouraged Wyoming game officials to consider reintroducing the animals. (Right) A wildlife service technician works with a ferret-release cage inside an enclosed prairie dog colony, which has been set up to allow the ferrets to learn to hunt their natural prey before being returned to the wild.

The good results from the captive breeding program have spurred game officials in Wyoming to consider releasing the animals back into the wild. To prepare the animals for the return, enclosed prairie dog colonies have been built that allow the ferrets to learn to hunt their natural prey—a key requirement for their survival in the wild. State officials hope to establish three separate populations in the wild by 1996.

The successfully reintroduced golden lion tamarin is another mammal that serves as a model for other efforts. This small monkey historically was found in the coastal forests in southeastern Brazil. However, because of deforestation of its rain-forest habitat and capture of many animals for exhibition in zoos, the species declined significantly.

International zoo involvement with the preservation of the tamarin began in the late 1960s. The National Zoological Park initiated a long-term

206

(Top and bottom) Smithsonian Institution National Zoological Park; photos, Jessie Cohen; (right) Walt Anderson

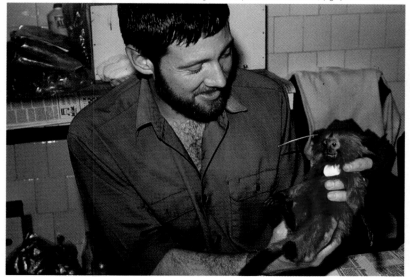

captive research and management program that has been instrumental in the recovery program. At the same time, a group of Brazilian scientists began efforts to preserve habitat in their own country and develop captive breeding programs. Efforts to breed the monkeys in captivity have been extremely rewarding. Scientists associated with the Smithsonian's Golden Lion Tamarin Conservation Program instituted both prerelease and postrelease training programs that teach the animals locomotion, foraging, and orientation skills. Since 1984, 67 golden lion tamarins have been reintroduced. Although not all of the animals have survived, the tamarin's stronghold in its native habitat is growing increasingly secure. These efforts not only have offered the last hope for the endangered tamarin but also have helped focus international attention on the plight of the vanishing rain forests.

A reintroduced golden lion tamarin (above) begins a new life in the wild at Poço das Antas Biological Reserve, Brazil. The technique of equipping the tamarins with radio collars before release (top left) and then monitoring them afterward with telemetry equipment (bottom left) is important for evaluating the success of the reintroductions. Long-term monitoring can reveal behavior patterns—e.g., group movements around and away from the release site—that indicate how well the released monkeys are adjusting.

207

Criticisms of captive breeding and reintroduction

While captive breeding and reintroduction programs have been hailed by many conservationists as a solution to the problem of diminishing species in the wild, they are not without their critics. These efforts have been faulted by scientists, politicians, wildlife managers, and the general public.

The high cost associated with breeding animals in captivity, releasing them into the wild, and monitoring their success is one target for attack. The cost is undoubtedly high; the price tag for reintroducing golden lion tamarins has been estimated at $22,000 per surviving animal. This includes costs associated with captive rearing, veterinary care, reintroduction, and research. To many taxpayers—and their legislators—who are unsympathetic toward endangered species, the spending of such funds is unjustified.

Some conservationists have been critical of the expenditure of such sums for another reason; namely, that the money could be better spent in other conservation efforts. Many scientists advocate supporting the preservation of habitat and intact ecosystems rather than concentrating on individual species. They argue that saving habitats is likely to assist far more species and individual animals than programs aimed at a single struggling species. Indeed, many scientists believe that the ultimate factor that will assure species survival is a safe habitat where endangered species can hold their own under natural conditions.

Another criticism raised by scientists is the concern that captive breeding and reintroduction programs do not properly address the problem. Nat Frazer of Mercer University, Macon, Georgia, who has studied sea turtles, has pointed out that too often such programs deal only with the short-term issue: too few animals. They do not pay enough attention to the factors that placed the species in jeopardy. Problems such as pollution, habitat destruction, or hunting pressure are not solved by the release of more animals; the released animals must deal with the same threats their ancestors could not handle. Reintroduction of the peregrine falcon worked only because the cause of the animal's decline—pesticides—had been removed as a threat before captive-bred peregrines were returned to the wild. On the other hand, the nene, or Hawaiian goose, has failed to establish a permanent population anywhere in the Hawaiian Islands despite the reintroduction of more than 1,600 captive-bred individuals since the 1970s. Scientists now believe that many of the nonaquatic birds, which spend much of their lives on the ground, have fallen victim to the same factors—hunters and introduced predators including dogs, cats, pigs, and mongooses—that reduced the original populations of the nene.

Scientists point out yet another problem with captive breeding programs—that they may foster the idea that the decline of animals in the wild is easily fixed. The public perception that these populations will somehow "bounce back" is dangerous because it allows for the continued degradation of the habitats on which animals depend, with little concern for the effects.

Captive breeding and introduction programs can work only when the factors that placed the species in jeopardy have been dealt with adequately. In the case of the nene, or Hawaiian goose (below), the reintroduction of more than 1,600 birds since the 1970s has failed to establish them permanently anywhere on the Hawaiian Islands. Many of the geese are thought to have been killed by hunters and introduced predators, the same factors responsible for the original population decline.

Bill Field

208

The future

As the world loses more and more natural habitats, increased management of the remaining natural areas seems inevitable. In fact, some scientists predict that managed nature preserves, zoos, and aquariums soon will completely replace the world's wild ecosystems. These may become the final refuges for some species in outdoor environments. With increased management will grow an increased need for such techniques as captive breeding.

Captive breeding and reintroduction efforts will not save all the species so close to extinction. Nevertheless, despite their weaknesses, they offer agencies an active option for preserving endangered species. With time and a greater understanding of the animals in danger, scientists may be able to improve the techniques so vital to the preservation of some species. For an increasing number of animals, there may be no other hope.

Overlooking a closely bordering urban sprawl, Ring Mountain Preserve in Marin County, California, offers a reminder of the seemingly inevitable encroachment of civilization upon the world's remaining natural areas. As more—and perhaps eventually all—wilderness becomes managed preserve, the need will grow for captive breeding and other techniques for preserving endangered wildlife.

FOR ADDITIONAL READING

R.L. DiSilvestro (ed.), *Audubon Wildlife Report 1987* (National Audubon Society, 1987).

Les Kaufman and Kenneth Mallory (eds.), *The Last Extinction* (MIT Press, 1986).

P.J.S. Olney (ed.), *1984/1985 International Zoo Yearbook* (Zoological Society of London, 1986).

C.M. Schonewald-Cox *et al.* (eds.), *Genetics and Conservation* (Benjamin/Cummings Publishing Co., 1983).

S.A. Temple (ed.), *Bird Conservation* (University of Wisconsin Press, 1983).

S.A. Temple (ed.), *Endangered Birds: Management Techniques for Preserving Threatened Species* (University of Wisconsin Press, 1978).

NATURE'S DETECTIVES:
BIOLOGICAL POLLUTION MONITORS

by Michael Root

From dogs with radon detectors to insect
larvae in wetlands, animals and plants
are providing scientists with a direct
look at the biological effects of a
wide range of environmental pollutants.

A vast array of pollutants is released into the environment each year, from heavy metals and carcinogenic (cancer-producing) organic chemicals to radioactive compounds and pesticides. According to a recent report by the National Wildlife Federation, in the United States during 1987 some 1.2 billion kilograms (one kilogram equals about 2.2 pounds) of toxic chemicals were released into the air, 680 million kilograms were dumped on the ground, and more than 225 million kilograms were poured into the water. More than 1.4 billion kilograms went to landfills and public sewers.

The situation is worse in Eastern Europe. Forty-five years of inefficient industrial practices combined with little or no controls on hazardous wastes have contributed to an environment that is choked by pollution. More than 50% of the drinking water in Czechoslovakia is reported to be contaminated with industrial and agricultural chemicals.

Wastes are not the only concern. Intentional chemical releases into the environment are also worrisome. Large quantities of pesticides, wood preservatives, paints, lubricants, heat exchangers, and other products containing hazardous chemicals as active ingredients are used each year. A U.S. Environmental Protection Agency (EPA) report estimated that 1.2 billion kilograms of these chemicals, including 500 million kilograms of pesticides, were used in the U.S. during 1988. Many of these chemicals are not broken down easily, and so they remain in the environment for many years.

The health effects of environmental pollution on humans and animals are frightening. The connection between disease and polluted air and water was recognized as early as the 17th century. Heavy metals, such as lead and cadmium, can cause liver and kidney damage. Polyaromatic hydrocarbons (PAHs) and such organochlorine compounds as polychlorinated biphenyls (PCBs) are implicated as carcinogens. Others can lead to

MICHAEL ROOT *is a research chemist and science writer.*

increased incidences of lung ailments, reproductive and developmental problems, and many other diseases.

A crucial challenge facing environmental scientists is early detection of these health hazards. If they are identified soon enough, remedial action may be taken before people are harmed further and environmental damage becomes widespread. Cleanup operations of polluted sites need to be watched closely to assure completeness. Habitat conservation is also necessary in order to safeguard wildlife. A clean environment is essential for preservation of a diversity of plant and animal species.

Chemical analysis and biomonitoring

Conventionally, environmental monitoring is accomplished by means of chemical analyses on samples collected from the air, soil, or water. This type of surveillance has become increasingly more sophisticated as new

212

analytic procedures and better instrumentation are developed. Concentrations on the order of parts per billion are now measured routinely through such methods as high-performance liquid chromatography, and atomic absorption spectroscopy.

There are certain limitations to chemical analysis, however, even with these high-powered tools. For example, the detection of infrequent pollution sources is subject to the time and place of sampling. This is particularly true for airborne pollutants or in aquatic systems where intermittent releases can be dispersed rapidly. In the soil, contaminants may be flushed away by rain. Consequently, finding such pollutants may be a hit-or-miss proposition. Nevertheless, some chemicals are so toxic that a single exposure to even low levels of them may cause harm. Failure to detect them could lead to severe consequences.

Constant chemical monitoring is logistically impractical and expensive, however, especially in remote wilderness areas. In addition, chemical

Researcher operates high-performance liquid chromatography equipment, which monitors the environment by analyzing the chemical contents of air, soil, and water samples. The time and place of the sampling vitally affect analyses of this type.

Courtesy, Waters Division of Millipore Corporation, Milford, Mass.

analysis alone does not evaluate the long-term biological consequences of toxicants in the environment, such as uptake by organisms, synergism (interactions among toxicants that lead to a stronger effect than each toxicant would have acting alone), and accumulation within the food chain. There is a subtle but important distinction between chemically measurable and biologically available pollutant concentrations. Waste sites are usually polluted with many different types of chemicals, some of which must be inferred from past operations at the location. The actual toxicity may be more than a simple sum of the effects of chemicals that are present, because there may be interactions between chemicals. Sometimes commercial formulations can be more poisonous than the active ingredient alone.

Traditional toxicological assays can also fall short. Laboratory toxicology studies generally involve exposing biologically controlled test animals

(Page 211) Illustration by John Zielinski

213

to varying doses of a particular chemical and observing the ensuing reactions, such as toxicity or tumor growth. Much of what is known about the biological effects of certain chemicals has been provided by laboratory testing of animals. However, while these assays have contributed significantly to the understanding of biological responses, they do not describe the intricate interactions between organism and environment. Neither do they accurately describe the responses of heterogenous populations, such as humans.

But scientists are discovering the advantages of biological monitoring by enlisting the very organisms affected by pollution to warn people of environmental hazards. Biomonitors (plants and animals used as environmental indicators) offer scientists a way of looking directly at biological effects instead of trying to predict those effects from chemical analysis.

Nothing new

Before the development of elaborate analytic procedures, people looked to animals to assess the status of the environment. The Bible records that Noah understood the value of biomonitors. He sent a raven and a dove out of the ark to determine if the floodwaters had receded. Coal miners used to carry caged birds, primarily canaries, with them into mines to serve as early-warning systems. There are a number of dangerous gases in mines, and canaries are sensitive to them. If they died or even became restless, it was a clear message to the miners: get out of the mine.

Biomonitors found their way into the trenches during World War I. In 1915 the German Army began deploying a terrible new weapon—

In one of the earliest depictions of biomonitors, a 12th-century mosaic (below) shows Noah using a dove and a raven to determine whether the floodwaters had receded. A rescue worker in the early 1920s carries a bird inside a cage to test for dangerous gases in a coal mine (below right). Should the bird die or become agitated, he would know to leave the mine quickly.

poison gas. A number of chemical warfare agents were tried, including chlorine, phosgene, and mustard gas. At first, soldiers were surprised, but eventually they learned to depend on biomonitors to warn them of approaching gas attacks. Guinea pigs, cats, owls, ducks, and a variety of other birds were used because they became agitated long before poison-gas clouds overtook the soldiers.

In a later incident, people would perhaps have been spared suffering and death if they had listened to what animals were telling them. During the 1950s residents of the small fishing villages around Minamata Bay on the southern Japanese island of Kyushu noticed unexplained fish and shellfish mortalities. Some birds began falling into the sea during flight. Then cats began to behave strangely. They would stagger as they walked, go into convulsions, and whirl uncontrollably. Death would often follow, sometimes because a cat had fallen into the sea. The local villagers called it "cat's dancing disease" or "strange disease." Nearly all of the cats in some areas died this way. After a time, people began showing signs of neurological problems and birth defects, eventually resulting in death for some. It was then discovered that a local chemical plant had for years been dumping methyl mercury, a potent central nervous system poison, into the bay, where it was then taken up by fish and shellfish. The people living near Minamata Bay—and their cats—consumed large amounts of fish and so absorbed the mercury themselves. Since then, methyl mercury poisoning has sometimes been referred to as "Minamata disease."

Scientists recently raised an alarm after discovering that frog, toad, salamander, and other amphibian populations are mysteriously declining at a rapid rate throughout the world. What this means and how people may be affected were not yet clear.

A mother carries her daughter, who is a victim of "Minamata disease." Caused by the dumping of methyl mercury into Minamata Bay on the Japanese island of Kyushu, the disease first made its presence known by killing fish, shellfish, birds, and cats; about 40% of the afflicted humans died.

215

Oak Ridge National Laboratory

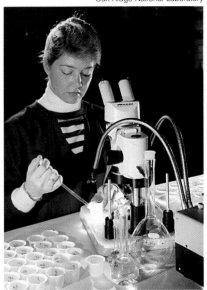

Freshwater organisms, including the microcrustacean Ceriodaphnia duba *and the larvae of the fathead minnow, are used to test the toxicity of various waste materials. Each test lasts seven days, during which the water is changed daily, the condition of the organisms is recorded with each change, and chemical analyses are performed.*

Biological responses to pollutants

Given the variety of plants and animals available, how do scientists select an appropriate biomonitor? Methods vary widely and to a large extent depend on the information that is required. One approach involves monitoring the biological responses of various organisms to pollutants, either in the field or in the laboratory, using samples collected from contaminated areas. The EPA is using this technique increasingly to identify the cause of toxicity in five organisms—fathead minnows, *Daphnia* and *Ceriodaphnia* (aquatic crustaceans), earthworms, and algae—by observing their responses to suspect water or soil samples.

Many other promising biomonitors are under investigation. Plants are the most prevalent organism in terrestrial ecosystems. Much of a plant is in contact with soil or water, depending on the type of vegetation. Pollution can affect plant germination, growth, and photosynthesis. Teresa Norberg-King of the EPA's Environmental Research Laboratory in Duluth, Minnesota, believes that duckweed plants are practical for examining the ecological impact of wastewater effluents. Norberg-King and co-workers relate chlorophyll loss and inhibition of frond growth to the presence of toxicants. Duckweed offers a number of benefits. This small aquatic plant is easy to grow and matures rapidly. Contrary to other plant-testing experiments, which check only one effluent sample, duckweed allows evaluation of chronic toxicity through the monitoring of many samples. In this way effluent variability over time may be appraised. Duckweed, like many other plants, also serves as food for a variety of animals, and so it transfers pollutants into the food chain.

John Thomas, a biochemist at Battelle Pacific Northwest Laboratories, found that lettuce-seed-germination assays were valuable for determining

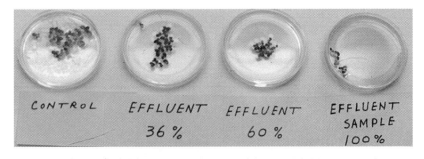

Duckweed (top right) reveals the effects of increased concentrations of industrial wastewater. (Bottom right) Wheat seeds (top) and lettuce seeds germinate to varying degrees depending on the soil in which they are planted. The soil in 6A, 7A, and 8A was taken from the bottom of a ditch containing hazardous wastes, while 9A was taken from the ditch's edge. Wheat seeds proved to be less sensitive than lettuce seeds to the toxic soils.

(Top) Wuncheng Wang, Illinois State Water Survey, Peoria, Ill.; (bottom) John M. Thomas, Battelle Pacific Northwest Laboratories

soil contamination at a site near Denver, Colorado. Chemical warfare agents and pesticides were manufactured there. Holding basins were utilized for chemical-waste disposal, and the movement of those wastes to surrounding soil and water was a concern. Thomas and co-workers planted lettuce seeds in soil samples taken from various locations, including areas known to be relatively free of pollution. In clean soils only about 20% of the lettuce plants died, whereas up to 100% died in the most heavily contaminated soils. Furthermore, soil samples from depths of 15 to 30 centimeters (6 to 12 inches) below ground were more toxic than those from the top 15 centimeters. With these results the researchers devised maps identifying areas where different levels of contamination exist, which should help in making cleanup decisions.

Veterinarian Lawrence Glickman of Purdue University, West Lafayette, Indiana, believes that household pets are underutilized as "sentinels" of environmental hazards that could affect people. The American Veterinary Medical Association estimates that there are more than 100 million cats and dogs living in homes in the U.S. Sharing the same household environment as people, they experience the same types of pollutants and routes of exposure to them. Since the latency period for manifestation of most diseases is shorter in pets than in humans, pet illnesses may forecast health problems for their owners. Pets also do not work or smoke cigarettes, two factors that can complicate human epidemiological studies.

Lung cancer in humans and dogs can be caused by asbestos fibers. Glickman correlated canine lung cancer with exposure of a household member to asbestos through his or her occupation or hobby. The latency period of this disease in humans is 20 to 30 years, but it is about 8 years in dogs. If diagnosed in the pet, appropriate action could be taken to identify and remove the source of asbestos before problems became evident in the owner. Household members could then be screened on a routine basis for asbestos-related diseases.

Radon has received much attention in the last few years. This naturally occurring gas is radioactive and has been associated with lung cancer. It can seep into homes from the ground. Chemical-testing procedures entail placing detectors in the home, especially in the basement. As an alternative Glickman and co-worker Robert Teclaw fitted dogs with radon detectors attached to collars. This will provide the researchers with information on the effect of radon on pets and household members as a function of actual exposure.

Scientists often construct mathematical computer simulations based on large arrays of data to help them predict the outcomes of certain events. Biomonitoring is no exception. Biologist Jerry Bromenshenk of the University of Montana developed a computer model to simulate the ways in which honeybee colonies respond to natural and chemical events. There are more than 50,000 bees in an average hive. A significant number of those are foragers that travel over a geographic area of more than 6.5 square kilometers (2.5 square miles) gathering nectar and pollen for food, water for evaporative cooling of the hive, and resin for

Lung cancer is revealed (below) in a dog that has been exposed to asbestos fibers. Because dogs develop asbestos-related cancer in about 8 years, compared with 20–30 years in humans, they can serve as an early warning to their owners to remove the source of the fibers. A dog wears a radon detector (bottom). Radon, a gas that can seep into homes from the ground, has also been associated with lung cancer.

Photos, Lawrence T. Glickman, Purdue University, West Lafayette, Ind.

217

Fish are collected from a section of a stream to help analyze fish communities. Using block nets, the crew makes three separate passes through the sampling site to collect most or all of the fish in each section. The fish are then anesthetized, identified, counted, weighed, and measured to provide information on species richness and biomass in the community.

holding the hive together. Hairs on their bodies electrostatically capture dust particles. Any pollutants in food, water, dust, or the air through which the bees fly will thus be carried back to the hive.

Bromenshenk's computer program describes honeybee population dynamics—how colony growth and decline evolve—as a function of several known parameters, such as the number of bees and weather conditions. Assuming a sufficient supply of food and no disease, weather is the primary driving force behind the two factors that contribute most to bee populations: egg laying by the queen and the longevity of forager bees. Every bee in a colony comes from a single individual, the queen. She increases or decreases egg laying in response to the ambient temperature, amount of light, and other natural factors. On the other hand, the lifetime of a forager is governed by the number of flights made. Foragers live about 10 flight days. Bees prefer to fly on warm, calm days. If it is windy, raining, or too cold, the foragers will not fly until the weather improves, and their life is extended.

Once the effect of weather on the colony population has been determined, Bromenshenk simulates the exposure of eggs or foragers to harmful agents such as pesticides. The program predicts mortality rates by drawing information from a large data base on the toxicity of various chemicals to bees. The model can also account for chronic effects, delayed death, and disease. Turning the model around, given the number of bee mortalities resulting from a known chemical, the program calculates the exposure level.

Comparisons of mortality rate results from experiments and calculations using the model are promising. Bromenshenk concluded that the computer simulation could be valuable both as a research tool to identify gaps in data and as an educational tool. For example, it could help train commercial pesticide applicators.

218

Photos, New Mexico Tech, Socorro;
(top) Carl Popp; (bottom) Tom Lynch

Residue analysis

Another important biomonitoring technique is the analysis of sublethal quantities of chemical residues in organisms. This method entails sampling wild populations of plants and animals and then analyzing their tissues for the presence of various contaminants. In this way researchers can determine the quantity of a particular chemical to which an organism has been exposed.

Invertebrates, especially insects, are abundant and thus provide an excellent resource for environmental biomonitoring. Chemist Carl Popp and aquatic toxicologist Tom Lynch at the New Mexico Institute of Mining and Technology and aquatic biologist Gerald Jacobi at New Mexico Highlands University found that the larvae of aquatic flies can point to localized pollution sources in streams and other wetlands. To demonstrate this they studied the impact of molybdenum-mining operations on the Red River in New Mexico, a tributary of the Rio Grande, by analyzing mayfly, stone fly, caddis fly, and true fly larvae. The larvae are benthic organisms; *i.e.*, they dwell on stream bottoms. Larvae found downstream from the mine contained higher concentrations of molybdenum, manganese, and copper (sometimes found with molybdenum mineral deposits) than those living upstream. A year after the last reported discharge, metal levels in the stream and sediments had diminished. Nevertheless, concentrations remained high in the fly larvae, indicating that the biological impact of exposure to these metals was more long-lived than chemical analysis would suggest.

Biologist Donald Steffeck of the U.S. Fish and Wildlife Service (FWS) in Washington, D.C., determined pollutant levels in animals within areas near three Gary, Indiana, hazardous-waste sites. Each was classified as an EPA Superfund site, containing a host of toxic organic and inorganic chemicals. Steffeck first looked for areas to which contaminants may migrate by studying how surface storm water flowed offsite. Both aquatic

Scientists collect insect larvae from the Red River in New Mexico (top) and separate the larvae from debris on a screen (above). Larvae found downstream from a molybdenum mine on the river contained higher concentrations of molybdenum, manganese, and copper than did those found upstream.

Donald W. Steffeck, Division of Environmental Contaminants, U.S. Fish and Wildlife Service

A wetland area near Gary, Indiana, contained many toxic organic and inorganic chemicals. A study of animals living in the wetland revealed that they contained high concentrations of the chemicals.

(fish and turtles) and terrestrial (earthworms and mice) species were selected for analysis. In most cases wherever the soil, groundwater, or surface water contained high levels of pollutants, high concentrations were also found in the test organisms. One of the sampling sites was in a residential neighborhood that had experienced intermittent stormwater runoff problems. Hazardous chemical levels in earthworms taken from residents' yards were intermediate between those removed from the nearby waste site and those from a reference site in a park with no known contamination. It was evident, therefore, that pollutants were being washed into the neighborhood during rainstorms.

This work is important for another reason. There is not much information concerning the ecological consequences of volatile organic compounds. Since they are easily evaporated, they are not generally believed to be accumulated in organisms. Steffeck found that these chemicals could indeed be taken up by animals; thus, biomonitoring provides a convenient way to trap volatile compounds for analysis and evaluation of potential effects.

Biochemical analysis

Techniques adapted from molecular biology are now being applied to environmental analysis. A wide range of biochemical tests are being designed to scrutinize any damage done by pollutants on a subcellular level. Although many are indirect measures of the presence of contaminants, these types of assay can be highly specific. Their promise is the potential of finding an environmental problem early, before adverse biological responses occur.

Analysis of DNA (deoxyribonucleic acid) from biomonitors is being used as a marker to identify exposure to toxic chemicals. The integrity of DNA is crucial for life. It controls what an organism is and how it functions. Despite the obvious differences between species, DNA consists essentially of the same components, whether it is from bacteria or from humans. Therefore, chemicals that harm DNA in one species are likely to produce similar effects in another. Mutagens are chemicals that modify DNA. They have been linked to such problems as reduced fertility, sterility, birth defects, and cancer. Looking at DNA reveals the early events after exposure to a mutagen. Effects become evident within minutes, hours, or days.

Clastogens are a class of mutagen capable of breaking DNA molecules. The damage they cause is detectable visually with a microscope. Karen McBee of Oklahoma State University performed analyses of DNA taken from wild mice living at a site that was contaminated with petroleum chemicals, heavy metals, and PCBs. Small mammals can be useful as biomonitors of contaminants in the soil if they are abundant, are easily caught, have a limited range, and have known feeding habits. McBee found DNA damage that indicated the presence of strong clastogens at the site.

Another way some chemicals modify DNA is by combining with it to create adducts. Following exposure to toxic chemicals, organisms me-

Arrow points to chromosomal damage in a bone marrow cell of a fulvous harvest mouse that inhabited an area contaminated by PCBs (polychlorinated biphenyls). Small mammals can serve as useful biomonitors of contaminants in soil if they have a limited range and known feeding habits.

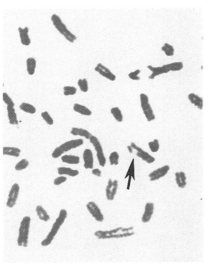

tabolize the chemicals in an attempt to detoxify them. It is a complex process and sometimes results in the formation of energetic compounds that react with DNA molecules to form adducts. The concentration of such adducts will correspond with the level of exposure. Lee Shugart, a biochemist at the Oak Ridge (Tennessee) National Laboratory, exploited this process to detect PAHs, including the highly carcinogenic benzo[*a*]pyrene (BaP).

Canadian scientists became concerned when beluga whales began dying in an estuary of the St. Lawrence River. Autopsies showed unusual bladder tumors. Coincidentally, there was a high incidence of bladder cancers in people from that area. BaP adducts with DNA were found in the whales' brains. The source was determined to be an aluminum smelting operation that released BaP. Workers at the plant and whales living downstream subsequently absorbed the compound.

Other researchers are investigating hemoglobin modification as an alternative to DNA testing. Hemoglobin is the oxygen-carrying molecule in red blood cells. Adducts formed with hemoglobin are not known to induce cancer, but they do correspond to exposure levels. The metabolites of more than 50 chemicals from many of the important classes of mutagenic chemicals have been shown to bind to hemoglobin. BaP adducts with hemoglobin can be detected in humans who smoke cigarettes. One cigarette contains 10 to 50 billionths of a gram of BaP.

Some contaminants induce organisms to synthesize certain biochemicals. Most animals, including humans, produce a metal-binding protein called metallothionein. It is an important factor in the detoxification of such harmful metal ions as cadmium, mercury, and lead. Organisms expedite production of this protein when confronted with toxic metals. Bromenshenk found that elevated metallothionein levels in bees are a convenient gauge of cadmium exposure.

Difficulties and drawbacks

Biomonitoring testing procedures must be implemented and interpreted with care. Even within a single species there is considerable biological heterogeneity. Pollution sources usually consist of a complex chemical mixture. Furthermore, the entangled ecological relationships between organisms and their surroundings defy simple explanation. Thus, the selection of an appropriate biomonitor species must take into account many factors.

One such factor is availability. If wild populations are to be sampled, it is important that they be present in sufficient numbers to provide meaningful data. Plants and animals raised in the laboratory can overcome this restriction. EPA scientist Clarence Callahan needed to bring his own biomonitors, earthworms, to a Superfund site near Boston. An old pesticide-repackaging firm had contaminated the area with DDT and other organochlorine compounds. Earthworms pass large amounts of soil through their digestive tracts as they feed. If pollutants are present, they may be absorbed. But Callahan was unable to find enough earthworms at the site, and so he placed worms he had purchased into containers

A normal earthworm (below) is contrasted with an earthworm (bottom) that was placed in a container along with soil contaminated by DDT and other organochlorine compounds. The latter worm suffered constrictions, swelling, and surface lesions and also was shortened, as can be seen by comparing each earthworm with the 2.5-centimeter (one-inch) line drawn in each photograph.

From "On-Site Methods for Assessing Chemical Impact on the Soil Environment Using Earthworms; A Case Study at the Baird & McGuire Superfund Site, Holbrook, MA," C.A. Callahan, C.A. Menzie, D.E. Burmaster, D.C. Wilborn, and T. Ernst, *Environmental Toxicology and Chemistry*, vol. 10, no. 6, 1991

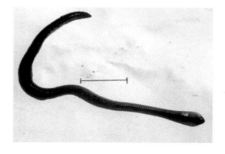

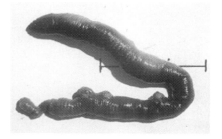

A wetland area in New Jersey is part of the Brigantine National Wildlife Refuge; Atlantic City is in the background. A decrease of about 50% in U.S. wetland acreage has increased the population densities of wetland animals. This crowding—in addition to the high levels of pollution—results in the spread of disease.

along with contaminated soil samples. Chemicals in the soil induced in these worms such behavioral-response changes as coiling, stiffening, shortening, and swelling. Skin lesions and deaths also occurred.

Another difficulty involves the capture of animals in the wild. Trapping and handling must be done with care to avoid harm to workers and animals. Wild animals can transmit diseases to workers. Some species are not amenable to handling; for example, shrews become hyperactive and die when enclosed. It is also important to know the home ranges of biomonitor animals in order to assess the extent of immigration and emigration within the study area.

Keeping test subjects in enclosures may be feasible in some cases. Fish pathologist John Grizzle and biochemist Ralph Strength, both of Auburn (Alabama) University, used cages containing bullheads and catfish in an oxidation pond at a Tuskegee, Alabama, water-pollution-control plant. Such oxidation ponds dissipate chlorine used as a disinfectant in the water-purification process, and officials were concerned that chlorine and organic compounds in the water might react to form carcinogenic chlorohydrocarbons. During the test the fish exhibited oral cancers, low growth rates, gill inflammation, enlarged livers, a predisposition toward bacterial infections, and death. Chemical analysis of the pond water and sediments had not detected carcinogenic organic compounds, and the fish were thus superior monitors of water quality.

Other factors must be considered in choosing a test method. Responses to environmental pollution generally differ among species. Residue analysis is sensitive and specific, but it is not appropriate for all situations. The chemicals must be stable and accumulate in tissues without being metabolized. Metals and certain organic compounds, such as PCBs, can be measured this way. Sporadic exposures to chemicals that leave no long-lived residues cannot be detected by residue analysis.

Careful study using statistical methods is necessary to establish a cause-and-effect relationship between pollutants and biological responses. Correlations observed under controlled conditions are not always observed in

222

the field. For example, waterfowl are susceptible to diseases such as avian cholera, botulism, and duck plague. Outbreaks of these diseases may be influenced by the presence of various chemicals in the environment. Experiments have demonstrated a link between reduced immunity to infectious diseases in ducks and the presence of selenium, DDT, PCBs, and crude oil, but there are other possible causes of the reduced immunity. Wetland acreage has decreased about 50% in the U.S. as a result of development. Fewer habitat areas result in more animals sharing the same space. The resultant high population densities are conducive to the spread of infections through contact with feces, carcasses, and sick individuals. Add industrial, agricultural, and urban pollutants, which are increasingly degrading wetlands, and it becomes difficult to establish a simple connection between disease and pollution in this case.

Future prospects

Scientists generally agree that groups of related tests with different end points are needed to overcome some of the disadvantages of individual assays. They also recognize the importance of predicting the consequences of pollution on the basis of their test results. For example, how does DNA damage affect biological responses such as tumor formation? How will an observed biological response alter population dynamics? These are some of the questions scientists will seek to answer.

Updated procedures will be required as new pollutants enter the environment. The FWS, along with several other federal agencies, began a national contaminant-biomonitoring program in the 1960s. Their mission was to track organochlorine pesticides, such as DDT and dieldrin, in the environment. As time passed, the types of pollutants changed. While organochlorine compounds are accumulated in organisms, newer organophosphate and carbamate agricultural pesticides are not. The FWS, therefore, was planning to revise and expand its biomonitoring program to counter these threats.

The advantages of environmental biomonitoring are legion. They provide a cost-effective way to determine the volume and mobility of pollutants while estimating the biological impact of those chemicals. Although more research is needed to evaluate its advantages and limitations more fully, biomonitoring seems certain to become more prevalent. Assurance of a clean environment demands it.

FOR ADDITIONAL READING

J.F. McCarthy and L.R. Shugart, eds., *Biomarkers of Environmental Contamination* (Lewis Publishers, 1990).

Michael Root, "Biological Monitors of Pollution," *BioScience* (February 1990, pp. 83–86).

S.S. Sandhu *et al.,* eds., *In Situ Evaluations of Biological Hazards of Environmental Pollutants* (Plenum Press, 1990).

R.G.M. Wang *et al.,* eds., *Biological Monitoring for Pesticide Exposure: Measurement, Estimation, and Risk Reduction* (American Chemical Society, 1989).

SOLVING THE TRASH CRISIS

by Barry Commoner

In an era of heightened concern for the health of the environment, governments and communities are awakening to the fact that the traditional strategy of dealing with solid waste after it has been produced is doomed to failure.

Archaeologists can learn a great deal about ancient societies by analyzing the contents of their kitchen midden—the residue of discarded material that has survived the long-departed people. In the contemporary United States, its own kitchen middens, the facilities that have been established to deal with that nation's accumulations of trash, are in a state of crisis. They have grown so large and hazardous that they threaten both the health and pocketbooks of the people who have created them.

Trash—more technically, municipal solid waste—is a particularly troublesome environmental problem. One reason is that until recently trash was a kind of orphan pollutant, relatively neglected by the public, government officials, and environmental researchers. Compared with air and water pollutants, information about trash has been rather sparse and incomplete. Only in recent years, largely because of public concern with the unsolved problem, has enough work been done to clarify it.

Composition of trash

The general composition of the typical stream of urban trash is now fairly well known. More than one-third of it is paper, including newspaper, corrugated cardboard, books and magazines, and a mixed category that appears to be chiefly junk mail. About one-fourth is made up of two types of residues from living things: yard waste (grass clippings and brush) and food garbage. The remainder includes about 8% discarded metal, chiefly aluminum and tin cans; about 7% glass, chiefly bottles and jars; about 8% plastics; and some 11% of miscellaneous discards such as wood, textiles, and rubber. Like the ancient kitchen middens, contemporary discards reflect the nature of modern society. For example, between 1960 and 1986 the amount of plastic in trash in the U.S. increased by a factor of 26, indicative of the development of a "throwaway" society during that time.

The overall composition of the trash stream varies from place to place and from season to season. In New York City, for example, trash generated by schools, hospitals, and city offices contains a higher percentage of

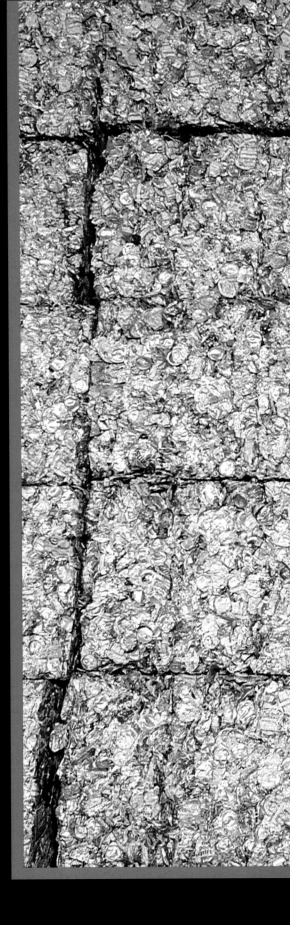

The changing composition of the typical trash stream in the U.S. reflects the nature and priorities of modern society. For example, between 1960 and 1986 the amount of plastic in trash increased by a factor of 26, pacing the development of a "throwaway" society serviced by systems of materials production that paid little heed to environmental compatibility.

BARRY COMMONER *is Director of the Center for the Biology of Natural Systems, Queens College, City University of New York.*

(Overleaf) Bales containing more than a million crushed aluminum beverage cans are readied for shipment to a reclamation plant; photograph, Hank Morgan—Science Source/Photo Researchers

paper and plastics than does residential trash, but it has proportionately less food garbage. The city's elementary and high schools discard much more plastic than do its colleges; hospitals, which use a great deal of disposable plastic equipment, discard more than either. The boroughs of Queens and Staten Island, where most homes have lawns, produce a higher proportion of grass clippings and yard waste than does the almost totally paved borough of Manhattan. In the summer the proportion of mixed paper waste falls to half of what it was in the spring, probably reflecting the seasonal flow of junk mail.

All this can be regarded as the approximate composition of what might be called "regular" trash—material routinely discarded from the city's households, offices, and institutions. At irregular intervals other discards are separately collected: bulky items such as furniture and appliances, old tires, and debris from construction or demolition. Hazardous household wastes—discards such as paint, solvents, pesticides, and batteries (which may contain toxic metals such as lead, cadmium, and mercury)—also require separate collection because they lead to serious environmental problems if mixed with regular trash. At present the United States generates some 450,000 tons per day of residential and commercial trash.

Landfills

In sum, urban trash is a complex and variable mélange of discards. New York City's trash has been classified into some 50 types of materials, and a survey made in Phoenix, Arizona, which classified trash at a level of detail that distinguished among discarded containers from different types of food, has listed more than 300 types. This built-in complexity has fostered the view that urban trash must be dealt with as a whole and the entire mixture simply discarded or otherwise disposed of without much consideration of its actual composition. For a long time, especially in rural areas, this approach meant simply carting the trash to a dump. Later, especially in larger urban areas, holes were dug, into which the trash was deposited and periodically covered with a layer of soil—the so-called sanitary landfill. In 1979 the U.S. Environmental Protection Agency (EPA), acting under the Resource Conservation and Recovery Act of 1976, prohibited open dumping of trash and, together with state environmental agencies, established criteria for the proper construction of landfills.

These actions reflected past experience with the environmental effects of landfills, which are still receiving about 80% of U.S. trash. In 1988 the EPA reported nearly 2,300 violations of environmental air- and water-quality standards at landfills. The violations included emissions into the air of about 20 different toxic synthetic organic (*i.e.*, carbon-containing) chemicals, some of them carcinogens (cancer-causing agents) such as vinyl chloride and carbon tetrachloride. More serious were the toxic materials that leached from landfills as rain drained through them into groundwater, often contaminating nearby drinking-water wells. Nearly half of the landfills are within a mile (1.6 kilometers), and upgrade, of such wells. According to an EPA survey, about 100 toxic metals and synthetic organic compounds have been found in leached material, or leachate, from landfills, nearly all of them in concentrations that consid-

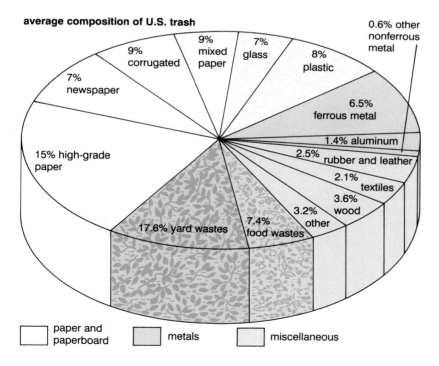

average composition of U.S. trash

9% corrugated
9% mixed paper
7% glass
8% plastic
0.6% other nonferrous metal
7% newspaper
15% high-grade paper
6.5% ferrous metal
1.4% aluminum
2.5% rubber and leather
2.1% textiles
3.6% wood
3.2% other
7.4% food wastes
17.6% yard wastes

paper and paperboard   metals   miscellaneous

Landfills are no longer simply holes in the ground. Rules now require that a landfill have a bottom lined with packed clay or plastic (above) and be provided with drainage systems for collecting rainwater that runs off the landfill cover or leaches through the trash inside. Once trash deposits have filled the landfill (opposite page, top), it must be covered with soil and vegetation and provided with a gas vent to allow decay gases to escape. The components of a carefully designed modern landfill are shown in the diagram (opposite page, bottom).

erably exceed the relevant exposure standards. For example, the median concentration of methylene chloride, a powerful carcinogen, in landfill leachates was more than 1,000 times the exposure standard.

Reacting to such observations, which together with less subtle afflictions like the odor of decaying garbage led to frequent public complaints, the EPA and state agencies have imposed new, more stringent rules on landfill construction. As a result, the modern landfill is no longer just a hole in the ground. First, landfills are now required to be sited in a location that minimizes the possibility of materials' leaching into the underlying groundwater. Then the landfill bottom must be lined with one or more layers—packed clay or plastic—that are more or less impervious to water. The landfill must be provided with a drainage system to collect the rainwater that falls on the landfill cover as well as any of it that leaches through the deposited trash and may penetrate the bottom liners. The leachate must be monitored for contaminants. Finally, when completely filled, the landfill must be suitably covered with soil and vegetation and supplied with a gas vent to allow methane (generated by the decay of organic debris) and other gases to escape.

These precautions against environmental contamination are not foolproof. Clay liners can crack and become leaky, and some toxic substances such as benzene can diffuse through an unbroken three-foot (nearly one-meter) clay liner in about five years. Plastic liners are better than clay

228

liners but are by no means perfect. They generally are made of high-density polyethylene, which is known to crack under stress (for example, due to uneven pressure from the weight of the overlying trash), especially after being exposed to chemicals such as acetic acid (vinegar), alcohol, and oil, all of which may be present in the trash deposited in the landfill. Finally, the drainage system may become clogged. Customarily, modern landfills are warranted by their builders against leakage for no more than 20 years. Nevertheless, their noxious contents will last much longer—some of them, like toxic metals, forever.

Even a perfectly leakproof landfill, however, has a fatal flaw—it fills up. It is, after all, still a hole, which is a nonrenewable resource. Eventually the landfill must be abandoned, and as the trash keeps coming, a more distant site must be found for a new one. Inevitably the new site is more expensive than the old one, leading to a progressive rise in the cost of landfilling. This problem has become particularly acute in heavily populated areas of the U.S. Between 1984 and 1988 the national average landfill "tipping fee"—the price charged for depositing trash in a landfill, which reflects its construction and operating costs as well as the cost of replacing it—doubled. In the Northeast the fee quadrupled in that period.

For all these reasons landfills are being phased out. The EPA estimated that there were 6,034 active trash landfills in the U.S. in 1986 and that the number would be reduced by about half by 1993 and by 80% 20 years later. Trash will, of course, continue to be produced—in ever larger amounts according to most estimates. This defines the "trash crisis" facing the United States; most of the landfills, which now receive 80% of the trash stream, must be closed, but a new, more satisfactory means of disposal is not yet in hand.

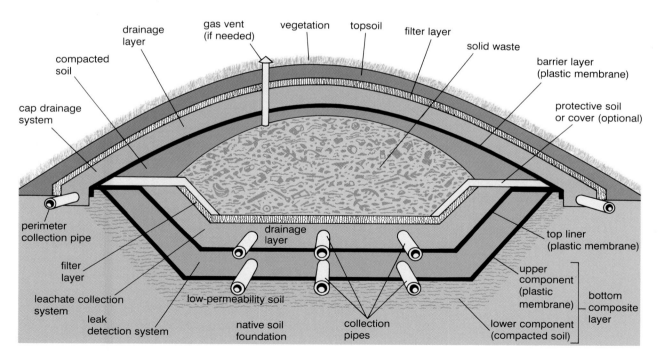

A crane in a trash-to-energy plant moves solid waste from a holding pit to the hoppers of high-temperature furnaces, which in turn heat steam to drive turbine generators. Trash-burning incinerators share an inherent design problem: although they reduce trash bulk, they generate pollutants that either enter the atmosphere directly or are concentrated in residual ash that still must be disposed of in the environment by landfilling.

Incineration

One possible alternative to landfilling is based on an old idea: burning the trash—a practice frequently employed in the past as a futile means of combating the odors generated by decaying town dumps. In the 1950s and 1960s trash-burning incinerators were built in a number of U.S. cities, and some were even installed in apartment houses. With the passage of the Clean Air Act in 1970, however, new emission standards were established that the incinerators could not meet, and most were closed down.

Late in the 1970s a new generation of trash-burning incinerators reached the market. They featured control devices designed to bring the stack emissions of standard air pollutants, such as dust, sulfur dioxide, and carbon monoxide, down to the permissible levels. Also, in response to the energy crisis precipitated by the oil embargoes in the 1970s, the new incinerators were frequently designed to recapture the heat generated by combustion, in the form of steam or electricity. According to the manufacturers, this feature justified a new terminology; they were no longer to be called incinerators but became "resource-recovery" or "trash-to-energy" plants.

By 1988 more than 160 such incinerators, capable of burning 70,000 tons per day of trash, were in operation in the United States. Like landfills, they received the total stream of regular trash and, again like

230

landfills, they created environmental problems. Although incinerators are generally able to destroy 99.99% of the combustible material in the trash, certain of the noncombustible materials are highly toxic and pass through the incinerator furnace unscathed; for example, lead, cadmium, and mercury. Most of the lead and cadmium is captured by the incinerator's emission-control devices, but mercury is not. Instead, nearly all the mercury in the trash, much of it originating in the batteries used in cameras and hearing aids, is emitted from the incinerator stack into the air.

Emissions of toxic organic compounds have been particularly troublesome. In the late 1970s, when dioxins, a group of extremely hazardous cancer-inducing chemicals, were first detected in the stack emissions of European incinerators, it was assumed that they resulted from incomplete combustion of dioxins that contaminated the trash. Later it was discovered that, instead, dioxins are literally synthesized in the incinerator. Synthesis reactions catalyzed by tiny fly ash particles occur in the cooler parts of the incinerator. These reactions form dioxins by combining certain residual chemicals in the gases leaving the furnace with chlorine, which may occur in the trash in the form of chlorinated plastics. Some of the dioxin is emitted from the stack, and the rest is deposited in the fly ash that is trapped, along with toxic metals, in the emission-control device.

Thus, trash-burning incinerators have a problem that is inherent in their design: while burning the trash, they generate pollutants that in one form or another enter the environment. The control devices do not eliminate the pollution problem but only shift it from one place to another. Instead of most of the toxic pollutants being emitted into the air, they occur chiefly in fly ash, which must be disposed of in the environment by landfilling.

There has been a good deal of debate about the seriousness of the health effects due to these environmental pollutants. The outcome has been a general recognition that fly ash nearly always contains enough lead and cadmium to qualify under EPA standards as a "hazardous substance" and that stack emissions of mercury are often high enough to violate regulatory standards. (In 1990 the largest U.S. trash-burning incinerator, in Detroit, Michigan, was closed down for a time because of its mercury emissions.) Finally, according to an EPA assessment of the health risks associated with the emissions from trash-burning incinerators, the resultant maximum individual lifetime risk of cancer—largely due to dioxins—ranges between one in a million to one in a thousand. Such risk estimates are used to judge the "acceptability" of pollution. In the past the EPA has called for remedial action when the cancer risk from dioxins exceeds one in a million. At best, then, the cancer risk from the incinerator emissions is borderline; at worst, it is clearly unacceptable by EPA standards.

Control or prevention?

Thus, the effort to solve the trash crisis by means of incineration, like the earlier effort based on landfills, has been plagued by environmental

About 85–90% of the typical residential and commercial stream of regular trash is recyclable. Old newspapers, for example, can be collected and shredded (right), then de-inked, pulped, and reformed into new newsprint, cardboard, or construction materials. Through the action of microorganisms, yard waste and food garbage can be converted into compost (opposite page, top; part of a municipal compost facility) for growing crops and other vegetation. Some plastics, chiefly beverage bottles, presently are recycled into such products as fiber for carpets. The park bench shown (opposite page, bottom), assembled from "lumber" of mixed plastic waste that has been melted together and molded to the desired shape, represents efforts to develop new processing methods and expand applications for recyclable plastic waste.

hazards. Landfills and incinerators share a generic fault with many other current efforts to cope with pollution; they attempt to deal with the pollutant after it has been produced, by containing it or otherwise using a control device to block its entry into the environment. It is now evident that this "control strategy," which has guided most environmental regulatory programs in the last 20 years, has failed. For example, perhaps the best-known control device, the catalytic converter mandated for automobile exhausts, was intended to reduce national annual emissions of carbon monoxide by 90% and of nitrogen oxides by 70% between 1975 and 1985. In fact, in that period carbon monoxide emissions were reduced by only 19%, while nitrogen oxide emissions increased by 4%.

(Below) Cornell Cooperative Extension of Westchester; (right) Syntech Products Division; AFCO Industries, Inc.

This generic fault recently was acknowledged by the EPA, which has called for a shift to a strategy of prevention—that is, avoiding generation of the pollutant to begin with. How can this strategy be applied to trash, which, after all, appears to be an inescapable accompaniment to domestic and commercial life? Can people literally prevent the production of trash and thereby avoid the environmental problems generated by futile efforts to control it?

Reuse and recycling

The answer becomes evident if one reflects on the history of some selected trash component—say, a discarded jam jar. When the last spoonful of jam has been eaten, the empty jar is not trash but a useful object. The jar can be reused and once more filled with jam, or it can be recycled—melted at a glass plant and made into a new container, perhaps once more fated to contain jam. The jar becomes trash if, instead of being reused or recycled, it is simply tossed into the waste can, joining food garbage and the rest of the discarded household debris that together constitute trash. If the jar is reused or recycled and thereby kept out of the trash stream, all of the environmental problems incident to the disposal of trash in an incinerator or a landfill are avoided. Thus, the newly mandated strategy of pollution prevention, applied to the trash problem, calls for reuse and recycling rather than incineration or landfilling.

Here a numerical question arises. When trash is deposited in a landfill, all of it is disposed of. When trash is incinerated, about 70% of it is burned up, although the remaining 30% is ash that is hazardous and still needs to be disposed of; for example, in a special landfill. By comparison, how much of the trash is capable of being recycled? Clearly, apart from refillable glass containers and bottles, which represent only a small part

233

Separate bins containing discarded newspaper, glass, and aluminum beverage cans that have been sorted by the householder await curbside pickup in San Diego, California. Recycling has become a workable alternative to incineration, and programs have been established in most cities and many smaller communities. In most large cities, however, recycling programs are still in an early state of development; recycling rates there are typically low.

of the trash stream, most of the present components of trash cannot readily be reused.

A theoretical answer is provided by examination of the list of trash components to determine which can be recycled by existing methods. Nearly all discarded paper can be recycled into the same or other paper products. Discarded newspaper, for example, can be de-inked, pulped, and made into new newsprint. Glass containers can be color sorted, crushed, remelted, and made into new containers, usually by being mixed with about three-fourths virgin material (although, in fact, glass containers could be made solely from recycled containers). Aluminum cans are readily remelted to make new ones; about 50% of them are now recycled in this way in the United States. After having their tin plating removed, tin cans become steel scrap, an important input to the steel industry. Some plastics, at present chiefly beverage bottles, are reprocessed and used to make new products such as polyethylene carpet. Finally, yard waste and food garbage—products of living things—can be returned to that state, if indirectly, by being converted into compost, which can then be used to grow crops and other vegetation. When all of these inherently recyclable components are added up, it appears that 85–90% of the typical residential and commercial stream of regular trash is recyclable.

Compost is produced when various bacteria and fungi that are normally found in soil act on the natural substances that occur in living things, for the most part breaking them down into simple molecules, with a humuslike residue remaining. Claims are sometimes made that certain commercially available plastics are "degradable" and therefore environmentally sound. At best, however, these materials only fragment under the influence of light or oxygen, becoming less obvious in the environment but still retaining their original chemical composition.

In practice, recycling is considerably more complicated than dumping the trash into a landfill or burning it. The recycled material must be homogeneous and uncontaminated by other trash components, such as food garbage. Some effort has been made to separate recyclable components from the trash mixture by mechanical means, but these have been largely unsuccessful. What does work, in keeping with the principle of preventing the formation of trash, is separation at the source.

The householder, for example, is asked to place the empty jam jar (or discarded newspaper, food garbage, or can) into an appropriate, separate container. If food garbage is separately bagged, it can be collected readily and processed into compost that is free of contaminating bits of glass or plastic or hazardous materials such as discarded batteries. One or more mixtures of the "dry" recyclables—paper, bottles and jars, tin and aluminum cans, and certain plastic containers—can be further separated in a "materials recovery facility" into marketable products such as various grades of paper, color-sorted crushed glass, tin cans, aluminum cans, and plastic beverage bottles. However, the numerical question remains: can such a system of household separation, collection, and further processing successfully recycle most of the trash stream and thereby qualify as the major means of dealing with it?

To answer this question, a practical test of such a recycling system was carried out by the Center for the Biology of Natural Systems at Queens College, City University of New York, in 1987. One hundred families in East Hampton, Long Island, volunteered to participate in a 10-week experiment. They were asked to separate their household discards into four containers: food garbage, paper, cans and bottles, and "all the rest" (nonrecyclables). These collections were weighed, further separated, and processed into compost and marketable materials. The measurements showed that 84.4% of the original household trash was actually recycled, representing 97% of the total recyclable material in the trash stream. Thus, it is in fact physically possible to recycle all but perhaps 15% of the residential trash stream. This is, of course, a maximum and presupposes that everyone participates in the program and that both the household sorting and subsequent mechanical separation are very efficient as well.

Making recycling work

In the past few years, communities have become disenchanted with trash-burning incinerators, not only because of their environmental hazards but also because of their rising cost, brought about by the addition of expensive control devices. By 1984 a survey for the State of California Waste Management Board had concluded that "the most formidable obstacle to waste-to-energy facilities [trash-burning incinerators] is public opposition." The result of this opposition was a sharp drop in incinerator orders after 1985. Between 1985 and 1989 some 40 proposed incinerators were blocked by public opposition, including projects in Los Angeles; Boston; Philadelphia; New York; Kansas City, Missouri; and Seattle, Washington.

Recycling has become an attractive alternative, and programs have been established in most cities and many smaller communities. A recent survey showed that the 17 most successful recycling programs are able to recover 32–57% of household and commercial trash. Most of these programs, however, are in suburban or rural communities ranging in pop-

ulation from about 300 to 27,000, almost entirely housed in single-family residences. The recycling rate, that is, the percentage of total residential trash that is actually recycled and converted into marketed materials, is the simplest measure of a recycling program's success. Recycling rates are typically low in large cities at present. As of 1990 some residential rates were: New York, 6%; Philadelphia, 14%; and Minneapolis, 11%; Seattle held the record, with 35%. Recycling programs are still in an early stage of development in most large cities.

As a nation the United States lags behind other countries in developing recycling. For example, while the U.S. recycles about 10% of its glass and 27% of its paper, in Europe and Japan an average of 31% of the glass and 40% of the paper is recycled. Composting is much more advanced in Europe than the U.S. In France, for example, nearly one million tons of compost is produced annually, much of it used in vineyards.

One reason why recycling rates are less than the theoretical maximum of about 85% is that recycling programs have not yet been targeted on all the recyclable components in the trash stream. For example, they generally exclude food garbage, which represents about 15% of the total regular trash stream. Another reason is that household participation rates average about 65%; much higher participation rates, ranging up to 95%, exist where recycling is mandatory and is accompanied by an intensive, ongoing public education program. In sum, it appears likely that through establishment of a mandatory, well-publicized intensive recycling program, which targets all of the recyclable components and achieves a high rate of participation, recycling rates of 70% or so could be reached.

Recycling rate does not alone determine the degree to which a recycling program achieves its basic purpose of reducing the production of

The success of a recycling program in reducing the production of trash depends not only on the recycling rate but also on the inherent recyclability of the trash components. Glass, for example, can be recycled again and again into jars and bottles (above). In theory, the glass container industry could be entirely self-contained, with essentially no glass containers entering the trash stream. By contrast, the propensity of plastics to change chemically in use and during recycling generally limits their recyclability at present to a single step. Thus, while the plastic from discarded beverage bottles (right) may find its way into carpet fiber, the carpets made from the fiber are likely to enter the trash stream when their useful life is over.

trash and hence the amount that must be disposed of in the environment. The recyclability of the trash components also influences the degree to which disposal is avoided. Certain of the components—for example, glass, aluminum, and steel—can be recycled again and again without limit. In theory, with these components a closed-loop system of recycling can be established in which, say, glass containers are made entirely from previously used glass containers. The glass container industry would then be entirely self-contained, with virtually all new containers made from old ones and none entering the trash stream.

On the other hand, when paper is recycled, about 10% of the fibers are broken down to a size that results in their being lost during processing. Consequently, paper cannot be infinitely recycled but is limited to the equivalent of perhaps 10 recycling steps before all of the starting material is lost to the environment. Plastics represent the extreme case of low recyclability. Unlike glass or metal, which remain unchanged in their chemical composition when they are used or reprocessed, plastics are appreciably altered in use and by recycling. The changes are so severe as to generally limit plastic recycling to a single step. For example, when plastic beverage bottles are recycled, they are converted to fiber, much of which is then used to produce carpets. In turn, the carpets are likely to be discarded as trash when their useful life (about 12 years) is over. Thus, if all plastic bottles were recycled (100% recycling rate) into carpets instead of both items being made from virgin material, the amount of plastic discarded into the environment would be reduced only by half. In contrast, 100% recycling of glass containers would reduce the discards into the environment to zero.

Thus, together with recycling rate, a trash component's recyclability— that is, the number of recycling steps it can undergo—determines the degree to which the component can be kept out of the trash stream and thereby avoid the environmental impact of landfilling or incinerating it. Indeed, recycling can do even more for the environment; for example, by reducing the pollution generated when glass is produced from virgin resources. About 25% less fuel is needed to produce molten glass from crushed glass than from sand. Hence, to the degree to which the glass factory uses recycled glass, it burns less fuel and creates that much less pollution. Indeed, more energy can be saved by recycling trash than can be gained by burning it.

Recycling has another advantage over incineration—it is cheaper. Several economic comparisons of incinerators and recycling systems of equal capacity, taking into account capital costs, financing, operating expenses, and returns from energy or recycled materials sold, have been made. They show that recycling is about one-third less expensive than incineration.

The most serious disadvantage of recycling compared with incineration is in the realm of administration. Incineration is attractive to the municipal executive because of its administrative simplicity; the present system of collecting unseparated bags of trash at curbside remains unchanged, and the administrator can seemingly dispose of the trash

Photos, Bill Swersey—Gamma/Liaison

Workers in New York City distribute recycling bins (right), while police take on the responsibility for ensuring compliance with recycling regulations (below). Recycling can be less appealing to municipal governments than incineration because of its greater administrative complexity. Recycling programs call for additional collection systems, ongoing public education about sorting trash components, enforcement of rules, contracts with recycling companies, and continuing efforts to find markets for recycled materials.

problem by signing a single contract with the incinerator operator. In contrast, a recycling program calls for ongoing public education about separating trash components, new collection systems and vehicles, probably separate contracts for composting and materials-recovery facilities, and a continuing effort to develop markets for the recycled materials.

Overcoming the "market problem"

The market aspect is particularly important. In the past, recycling programs generally were carried out by ecology-minded community groups, scout troops, and churches that organized depots to which people were encouraged to bring their discarded cans, bottles, and newspapers. Apart from aluminum cans, which were so valuable to aluminum companies that they took on the task of paying consumers to collect them, most of these early efforts sooner or later collapsed, frustrated by the vagaries of the secondary materials market.

Items collected at the recycling centers were usually sold to brokers for resale to the actual users. Whenever commodity prices fell, for example, in the recession years of the early 1980s, the value of secondary materials frequently dropped to zero. Since brokers, like all private entrepreneurs, must operate at a profit, they would then stop buying the collected cans and paper. The recycling depot would clog up and be forced to close. This experience has encumbered recycling with a "market problem" that is frequently cited to prove that the process is not a realistic means of coping with trash.

With the development of large-scale community-based recycling programs, the marketing situation has changed. Most important is the fact

238

A recycling sampler			
primary material	original product	recycling process	typical new products
newsprint	newspaper	paper mixed with water in pulping machine; may be de-inked; pulp screened and reformed into sheets	newsprint, cardboard, egg cartons, building materials
clay-coated paper	magazines, catalogs	repulped, like newsprint; clay removed with water during screening	building materials
mixed papers (with adhesive)	telephone books	repulped; may be bleached to remove paper dyes; machinery and additives may be used to remove adhesive	building materials
clear and colored glass	food jars, beverage bottles	separated by color; melted with raw materials and remolded	new glass containers
polyethylene terephthalate (PET)	plastic beverage bottles	separated by color, shredded, washed; particles separated from metal contaminants (caps and neck rings); remolded	chiefly carpets
aluminum	beverage cans	melted (and coatings burned off); recast	beverage cans, cookware, lawn furniture, siding
steel	tin cans for food and beverages	tin plating removed; melted and recast	food and beverage cans, building materials, tools, automotive materials

that any trash-handling system is a cost to the municipality and should not be expected to operate at a profit. The revenue from the sale of recycled materials represents a relatively small item in the overall cost of a recycling program. Even if the materials are given away, recycling is likely to be less costly than the alternative, incineration. In a fundamental sense the market for recycled materials is economically sound, for they are always less costly to the user industries than producing paper, glass, steel, or aluminum from virgin resources. What these industries require is an assured supply of the recycled materials on a long-term basis so that the necessary investment in dealing with them can be justified. The establishment of stable, ongoing community recycling programs can accomplish this goal.

Incompatible alternatives

Government agencies have begun to recognize the relative merits of the various means of dealing with trash, often proposing, as a policy guide, a hierarchy of preferences: reduction, reuse, recycling, incineration, and landfilling. Reduction—that is, elimination of the production and use of a product that unnecessarily adds to the trash stream—properly heads the list of preferences, for it totally eliminates the need to deal with the trash component. An example is the substitution of reusable net bags for carrying home one's groceries in place of the rapidly proliferating plastic bags now used for that purpose. Such possible reductions, however, are generally believed capable of eliminating no more than 10% of the present trash stream; thus, like reuse, this approach is unable to deal with the trash problem as a whole.

Most government agencies suggest that all of the elements in this hierarchy are needed to deal with trash—an approach usually called integrated waste management. This conclusion bears close examination, however. It is true that some landfilling will be needed to accommodate the disposal of nonrecyclable components (most plastics, for example) until their use is stopped. On the other hand, the same is not true of incineration. If a trash program is properly based on recycling, there is no need for incineration. As already noted, intensive recycling that is targeted on all the recyclable components can readily deal with more of the trash stream than incineration; recycling is therefore a viable alternative to incineration.

Indeed, incineration actually interferes with recycling. About 80% of the trash stream consists of components, such as paper and food garbage, that can be either burned or recycled but obviously not both. Modern incinerators must be fueled with trash to 85% of capacity so that sufficient steam or electricity can be sold to allow them to operate profitably. Most incinerator contracts require the town to supply the incinerator with enough trash to permit economic operation or, failing that, to pay for the lost revenue from energy sales. In Warren county, New Jersey, an incinerator was forced to operate, uneconomically, well below capacity because burnable trash components were diverted to conform to a state law requiring 25% recycling. In short, intensive recycling and incineration are inherently incompatible.

Need for environmental democracy

The trash crisis mirrors the experience of the 20-year effort to improve environmental quality in the U.S. That effort has failed to achieve the goals established by environmental legislation in the early 1970s because it was based on controls instead of prevention. The experience reflects the fact that pollution originates in the systems of production, which have not been designed with their environmental compatibility in mind. The same is true of the trash problem, for most trash originates in the ecologically unsound production processes that have been adopted, especially since 1950—in the substitution of refillable bottles with throwaways by the bottling industry; in the displacement of paper, glass, and metal, especially in packaging, by the plastics industry; in the increased sales of prepackaged products by the food industry. In contrast, recycling is a major example of the environmental superiority of the strategy of prevention.

The strategy of prevention represents a commitment, on the part of society, to participate in the hitherto wholly private decisions that determine what is produced and by what means. The recent history of the trash crisis—the growing movement under public pressure away from incineration toward recycling, and for the elimination of particularly intractable components of trash such as polystyrene foam, recently dramatized by the abandonment by the McDonald's fast-food chain of their plastic hamburger containers—is an encouraging sign that such environmental democracy will, before long, resolve the trash crisis.

240

Encyclopædia

Britannica

Science Update

Major Revisions from the 1991 *Macropædia*

The purpose of this section is to introduce to continuing *Yearbook of Science and the Future* subscribers selected *Macropædia* articles or portions of them that have been completely revised or written anew. It is intended to update the *Macropædia* in ways that cannot be accomplished fully by reviewing the year's events or by revising statistics annually, because the *Macropædia* texts themselves—written from a longer perspective than any yearly revision—supply authoritative interpretation and analysis as well as narrative and description.

Two articles have been chosen from the 1991 printing: GEOCHRONOLOGY (in part) and OCEANS (in part). Each is the work of distinguished scholars, and each represents the continuing dedication of the *Encyclopædia Britannica* to bringing such works to the general reader.

Geochronology: The Interpretation and Dating of the Geological Record

Precambrian time

GENERAL CONSIDERATIONS

The Precambrian is defined as the period of time that extends from a little more than 3.9 billion years ago, which is the approximate age of the oldest known rocks, to the beginning of the Cambrian Period, roughly 570 million years ago. The Precambrian era thus represents about 80 percent of the whole of geologic time. It has long been known that the Cambrian marks the earliest stage in the history of the Earth when many varied forms of life evolved and were preserved extensively as fossil remains in sedimentary rocks. It is not surprising that all life-forms were long assumed to have originated in the Cambrian, and therefore all earlier rocks with no obvious fossils were grouped together into one large era, the Precambrian. However, detailed mapping and examination of Precambrian rocks on most continents have since revealed that primitive life-forms already existed more than 3.5 billion years ago. The original terminology to distinguish Precambrian from all younger rocks, nevertheless, is still used for subdividing geologic time.

Major subdivisions. It is now internationally agreed that Precambrian time should be divided into the Archean and Proterozoic eons, with the time boundary between them at 2.5 billion years. The subdivision of these eons into early, middle, and late eras is not so widely agreed upon, but experts in the field have adopted a scheme according to which the relevant boundaries are at 3.4 billion and 3 billion and at 1.6 billion and 900 million years. These definitions are based on isotopic age determinations, and it is not possible to introduce smaller subdivisions. In the absence of fossils to permit the creation of small-scale subdivisions, relative chronologies of events have been produced for different regions based on such field relationships as unconformities and crosscutting dikes (tabular bodies of intrusive igneous rock that cut across original structures in the surrounding rock), combined with isotopic age determinations of specific rocks, as, for example, granites. This allows for some correlation between neighbouring regions.

Distinctive features. The Archean and Proterozoic are very different and must be considered separately. The Archean–Proterozoic boundary constitutes a major turning point in Earth history. Before that time the crust of the Earth was in the process of growing and so there were no large stable continents, whereas afterward, when such continents had emerged, orogenic belts were able to form marginally to and between continental blocks as they did during Phanerozoic times.

There are two types of Archean orogenic belts: (1) upper crustal greenstone–granite belts, rich in volcanic rocks which are probably primitive types of oceanic crust and island arcs that formed during the early rapid stage of crustal growth, and (2) granulite–gneiss belts that were recrystallized in the Archean mid-lower crust under metamorphic conditions associated with high-temperature granulite and amphibolite facies. Thus granulites, which typically contain the high-temperature mineral hypersthene, are a characteristic feature of many Precambrian orogenic belts that have been deeply eroded, as opposed to Phanerozoic orogenic belts, in which they are rare.

Archean orogenic belts

There are several other rock types that were developed primarily during the Precambrian and rarely later. This restriction is a result of the unique conditions that prevailed during Precambrian times. For example, the banded-iron formation mentioned above is a ferruginous sediment that was deposited on the margins of early iron-rich oceans. Anorthosite, which consists largely of plagioclase, forms large bodies in several Proterozoic belts. Komatiite is a magnesium-rich, high-temperature volcanic rock derived from a very hot mantle; it was extruded in abundance during the early Precambrian when the heat flow of the Earth was higher than it is today. Blueschist contains the blue mineral glaucophane; it forms in subduction zones under high pressures and low temperatures, and its rare occurrence in Precambrian rocks may indicate that temperatures in early subduction zones were too high for its formation.

The bulk of many of the world's valuable mineral deposits (for example, those of gold, nickel, chromite, copper, and iron) also formed during the Precambrian. These concentrations are a reflection of distinctive Precambrian sedimentary and magmatic rocks and their environments of formation.

PRECAMBRIAN ROCKS

General occurrence and distribution. Precambrian rocks as a whole occur in a wide variety of shapes and sizes. There are extensive Archean regions, up to a few thousands of kilometres across, that may contain either or both greenstone–granite belts and granulite–gneiss belts and that are variously designated in different parts of the world as cratons, shields, provinces, or blocks. Some examples are the North Atlantic craton that includes northwestern Scotland, central Greenland, and Labrador; the Kaapvaal and Zimbabwean cratons in southern Africa; the Dhārwār craton in India; the Aldan and Anabar shields in Siberia in the Soviet Union; the Baltic shield that includes much of Sweden, Finland, and the Kola Peninsula of the Soviet Union; the Superior and Slave provinces in Canada; and the Yilgarn and Pilbara blocks in Western Australia. There are linear belts, up to several thousand kilometres long, that are often though not exclusively of Proterozoic age, such as the Limpopo, Mozambique, and Damaran belts in Africa, the Labrador Trough in Canada, and the Eastern Ghāts belt in India. Also, small relic areas, only about a few hundred kilometres across, exist within or against Phanerozoic orogenic belts, as, for instance, the Lofoten islands of Norway, the Lewisian Complex in northwestern Scotland, and the Adirondack Mountains in the northeastern United States. Some extensive areas of Precambrian rocks are still overlain by a blanket of Phanerozoic sediments, as under the European and Russian platforms and under the central United States; these are mostly known from borehole samples (see Figure 15).

Adapted from Brian F. Windley, *The Evolving Continents*; John Wiley and Sons Ltd

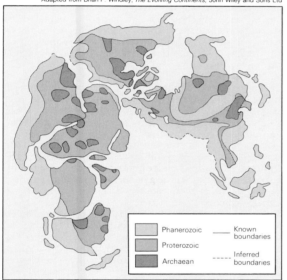

Phanerozoic	Known boundaries
Proterozoic	
Archaean	Inferred boundaries

Figure 15: Archean regions within Proterozoic cratons surrounded by Phanerozoic mobile belts. This distribution is shown here on a Permian predrift map of the continents.

Archean rock types. Archean rocks occur in greenstone–granite belts that represent the upper crust, in granulite–gneiss belts that formed in the mid-lower crust, and in sedimentary basins, basic dikes, and layered complexes that were either deposited on or intruded into the first two types of belts.

Greenstone–granite belts. These belts occur on most continents. The largest extend several hundred kilometres in length and measure several hundred metres in width. They range from aggregates of several belts (as in the southern Superior province of Canada) to irregular, even triangular-shaped belts (such as Barberton in South Africa) to synclinal basins (as in the Indian Dhārwār craton). Today, many greenstone–granite belts are regarded as tectonic slices that have been thrust between or against older rocks, such as gneisses. The irregular and synclinal shapes are commonly caused by the diapiric intrusion of younger granites. Important occurrences are the Barberton belt in South Africa; the Sebakwian, Belingwean, and Bulawayan–Shamvaian belts of Zimbabwe; the Yellowknife belts in the Slave province of Canada; the Abitibi, Wawa, Wabigoon, and Quetico belts of the Superior province of Canada; the Dhārwār belts in India; and the Warrawoona belt in the Pilbara block and the Yilgarn belts in Australia.

Greenstone–granite belts developed at many different times throughout the long Archean Eon. In the Zimbab-

wean craton they formed over three successive periods: the Selukwe belt at about 3.75–3.8 billion years ago, the Belingwean belts at about 2.9 billion, and the Bulawayan–Shamvaian belts at 2.7–2.6 billion. The Barberton belt in the Kaapvaal craton and the Warrawoona belt in the Pilbara block are 3.5 billion years old. Globally the most important period of formation was from 2.7 to 2.6 billion years ago, especially in the Slave and Superior provinces of North America, the Yilgarn block in Australia, and the Dhārwār craton in India. Some of the better documented belts seem to have formed within about 50 million years. It is important to note that while the Bulawayan–Shamvaian belts were forming in the Zimbabwean craton, flat-lying sediments and volcanics were laid down in the Pongola rift and the Witwatersrand Basin not far to the north.

The greenstone sequence in many belts is divisible into a lower volcanic group and an upper sedimentary group. The volcanics are made up of ultramafic and basaltic lavas noted for magnesian komatiites that probably formed in the oceanic crust, overlain by basalts, andesites, and rhyolites whose chemical composition is much like that of modern island arcs. Especially important is the presence in the Barberton and Yellowknife belts of sheeted basic dike complexes cutting across gabbros and overlain by pillow-bearing basalts. The uppermost sediments are typically terrigenous shales, sandstones, quartzites, graywackes, and conglomerates. The overall stratigraphy suggests an evolution from extensive submarine eruptions of komatiite and basalt (ocean floor) to more localized stratovolcanoes (island arcs), which become increasingly emergent with intervening and overlying clastic basins. There are, however, regional differences in the volcanic and sedimentary makeup of some belts. The older belts in southern Africa and Australia have more komatiites and basalts, more shallow-water banded-iron formations, cherts, and evaporites, and fewer terrigenous sediments. On the other hand, the younger belts in North America have a higher proportion of andesites, rhyolites, and terrigenous and turbidite debris, but fewer shallow-water sediments. These differences reflect a change from the older oceanic-type volcanism (effusion of lava from submarine fissures) to the younger, more arc-type phenomenon (explosive eruption of pyroclastic materials and lava from steep volcanic cones), an increasing amount of trench turbidites and graywackes with time, and an increasing availability of continental crust with time as a source for terrigenous debris.

Granitic rocks and gneisses occur within, adjacent to, and between many greenstone sequences. Some paragneisses, as in the Quetico belt in Canada, are derived from graywackes and were probably deposited in a trench or accretionary prism at the mouth of a subduction zone between the island arcs of the adjacent greenstone sequences. Many early granitic plutons were deformed and converted into orthogneiss. Late plutons commonly intruded the greenstones that were downfolded in synclines between them, or they intruded along the borders of the belts, deflecting them into irregular shapes.

The structure of many belts is complex. Their stratigraphic successions are upside down and deformed by thrusts and major horizontal folds (nappes) and have been subsequently refolded by upright anticlines and synclines. The result of this thrusting is that the stratigraphic successions have been repeated and thus may be up to 10–20 kilometres thick. Also, there may be thrusts along the base of the belts, as in the case of Barberton, showing that they have been transported from elsewhere. In other instances, the thrusts may occur along the borders of the belts, indicating that they have been forced against and over adjacent gneissic belts. The conclusion from structural studies is that many belts have undergone intense subhorizontal deformation during thrust transport and that subsequent compression, assisted by the diapiric rise of late granitic plutons, created synformal shapes and subvertical structures.

All the greenstone sequences have undergone recrystallization during metamorphism of greenschist facies at relatively low temperatures and pressures. In fact, the presence of the three green metamorphic minerals chlorite, horn-

Notable Archean regions

Regional differences in component rocks

blende, and epidote has given rise to the term greenstone for the recrystallized basaltic volcanics. Ultramafic rocks are commonly altered to talc schists and tremolite–actinolite schists, which may contain asbestos veins of economic value. There are some indications that several phases of metamorphism exist—namely, seafloor metamorphism associated with the action of hydrothermal brines perhaps at mid-oceanic ridges, syntectonic metamorphism related to thrust-nappe tectonics, and local thermal contact metamorphism caused by late intrusive granitic plutons.

Mineralization in greenstone–granite belts

One finds abundant mineralization in greenstone–granite belts. These belts constitute one of the world's principal depositories of gold, silver, chromium, nickel, copper, and zinc. In the past they were termed gold belts because the gold rushes of the 19th century took place, for example, at Kalgoorlie in the Yilgarn belt of Western Australia, in the Barberton belt of South Africa, and at Val d'Or in the Abitibi belt of southern Canada. The mineral deposits occur in all the major rock groups: chromite, nickel, asbestos, magnesite, and talc in ultramafic lavas; gold, silver, copper, and zinc in basaltic to rhyolitic volcanics; iron ore, manganese, and barite in sediments; and lithium, tantalum, beryllium, tin, molybdenum, and bismuth in granites and associated pegmatites. Important occurrences are chromite at Selukwe in Zimbabwe, nickel at Kambalda in southwestern Australia, tantalum in Manitoba in Canada, and copper–zinc at Timmins and Noranda in the Canadian Abitibi belt.

Clearly there are different types of greenstone–granite belts. In order to understand their origin and mode of evolution, it is necessary to correlate them with comparable modern analogues. Some, like the Barberton and Yellowknife belts, consist of oceanic-type crust and have sheeted dike swarms that occur in many Mesozoic–Cenozoic ophiolites, such as Troodos in Cyprus. They are a hallmark of modern oceanic crust that formed at a mid-oceanic ridge. Also, like modern ophiolites, a few seem to have been obducted by thrusting onto continental crust. Many belts, like those in the Superior province of Canada, are very similar to modern island arcs. The Wawa belt, for example, has been shown to consist of an immature island arc built on oceanic crust and overlain by a more mature arc. The Abitibi belt began as an island arc that was rifted to form an intra-arc basin in which developed a second arc. Between the Wawa and Wabigoon island arcs lies the Quetico belt, consisting of metamorphosed turbidites and slices of volcanics that probably developed in an imbricated accretionary prism in an arc–trench system, as seen today in the Japanese arcs. The Pilbara belts are similar to modern active continental margins, and they have been interthrust with older continental orthogneisses to form a very thick crustal pile that was intruded by diapiric crustal-melt granites. This scenario is quite comparable to that of a Himalayan type of orogenic belt formed by collisional tectonics. In conclusion, most greenstone–granite belts are today regarded by geologists as different parts of interthrust oceanic trench–island arc systems that collided with continental gneissic blocks.

High-grade metamorphism

Granulite–gneiss belts. The granulites, gneisses, and associated rocks in these belts were metamorphosed to a high grade in deep levels of the Archean crust; metamorphism occurred at a temperature of 750° to 980° C and at a depth of about 15–30 kilometres. These belts, therefore, represent sections of the continents that have been highly uplifted, with the result that the upper crust made up of volcanics, sediments, and granites has been eroded. Accordingly, the granulite–gneiss belts are very different from the greenstone–granite belts. They occur in a variety of environments. These may be extensive regions, such as the North Atlantic craton, which measures 1,000 by 2,000 kilometres across and includes, in its pre-Atlantic fit, the Scourian complex of northwestern Scotland, the central part of Greenland, and the coast of Labrador; the Aldan and Ukrainian shields in the Soviet Union; eastern Hopeh (Hebei) and Liaoning provinces of northeastern China; large parts of the Superior province of Canada and the Yilgarn block in Australia; and the Limpopo belt in southern Africa. Or they may be small areas, such as the Ancient Gneiss Complex of Swaziland; the Minnesota River valley and the Beartooth Mountains of the United States; the Peninsular gneisses and Sargur supracrustals of southern India; the English River gneisses of Ontario in Canada that form a narrow strip between greenstone–granite belts; the Sand River gneisses that occupy a small area between greenstone–granite belts in Zimbabwe; and the Napier complex in Enderby Land in Antarctica. Granulite–gneiss belts are commonly surrounded by younger, mostly Proterozoic belts that contain remobilized relicts of the Archean rocks, and the granulites and gneisses must underlie many Archean greenstone–granite belts and blankets of Phanerozoic sediment. In light of this, the granulite–gneiss belts may be regarded as minimally exposed and preserved sections of a widespread continental basement.

Types

Isotopic age determinations from the granulite–gneiss belts record an evolution from about 4.3 to 2.5 billion years—more than a third of geologic time. Most important are the few but well-determined detrital zircons at Mount Narryer and Jack Hills in Western Australia that are more than 4 billion years old (see above). Several regions have a history that began in the period dating from 3.9 to 3.6 billion years ago—*e.g.,* West Greenland, Labrador, the Limpopo belt, Enderby Land, and the Aldan Shield. Most regions of the world went through a major tectonic event that may have involved intrusion, metamorphism, and deformation in the period between 3.1 and 2.8 billion years ago; and some of these regions, like the Scourian in northwestern Scotland, show no evidence of any older crustal growth. The best-documented region is West Greenland, which has a long and complicated history from 3.8 to 2.5 billion years ago.

Orthogneisses of deformed and recrystallized tonalite and granite constitute the most common rock type. The geochemical signature of these rocks closely resembles that of modern equivalents that occur in granitic batholiths in the Andes. Where such rocks have been metamorphosed under conditions associated with amphibolite facies, they contain hornblende or biotite or a combination of the two. However, where they have been subjected to conditions of higher temperature associated with the granulite facies, the rocks contain pyroxene and hypersthene and so can be called granulites.

The granulites and gneisses enclose a wide variety of other minor rock types in layers and lenses. These types include schists and paragneisses, which were originally deposited on the Earth's surface as shales and which now contain high-temperature metamorphic minerals, such as biotite, garnet, cordierite, staurolite, sillimanite, or kyanite. There also are quartzites, which were once sandstones; marbles, which were either limestones or dolomites; and banded-iron formations, which were deposited as ferruginous sediments. Commonly intercalated with these metasediments are amphibolites, which locally contain relict pillows, demonstrating that they are derived from basaltic lavas deposited underwater. These amphibolites have a trace element chemistry quite similar to that of modern seafloor basalts. The amphibolites are often accompanied by chromite-layered anorthosite, gabbro, and ultramafic rocks, such as peridotite and dunite. All these rocks occur in layered igneous complexes, which in their well-preserved state may be up to 1 kilometre thick and 100 kilometres long. Such complexes occur at Fiskenaesset in West Greenland and in the Limpopo belt in southern Africa, as well as in southern India. These complexes may have formed at a mid-oceanic ridge in a magma chamber that also fed the basaltic lavas. In many cases, the complexes, the basaltic amphibolites, and the sediments were extensively intruded by the tonalites and granites that were later deformed and recrystallized, with the result that all these rocks may now occur as metre-sized lenses in the orthogneisses and granulites.

The structure of the granulite–gneiss belts is extremely complex, since the constituent rocks have been highly deformed several times. In all likelihood, it seems that the basalts and layered complexes from the oceanic crust were interthrust with shallow-water limestones, sandstones, and shales, with tonalites and granites from Andean-type batholiths, and with older basement rocks from a continental margin. All these rocks, which are now mutually conformable, were folded in horizontal nappes and then refolded. The picture that emerges is one of a very mobile Earth, where no rocks remained long after their formation before they were compressed and thrust against other rocks.

The mid-lower crust is relatively barren of ore deposits, as compared to the upper crust with its sizable concentrations of greenstones and granites, and so little mineralization is found in the granulite–gneiss belts. The few exceptions include a nickel–copper sulfide deposit at Selebi–Pikwe in the Limpopo belt in Botswana that is economic to mine and banded-iron formations in gneisses in the eastern Hopeh and Liaoning provinces of northwestern China that form the foundation of a major steel industry. There are uneconomic chromitite seams in anorthosites in West Greenland, southern India, and the Limpopo belt, a banded-iron formation in a 3.8-billion-year-old sedimentary–volcanic belt at Isua in West Greenland, and minor tungsten mineralization in amphibolites in West Greenland.

Correlation
It is impossible to correlate the rocks in different granulite–gneiss belts. One granitic gneiss is essentially the same as another, but it may be of vastly different age. There is a marked similarity in the anorthosites in various belts throughout the world, and their similar relationship with the gneisses suggests that the belts have undergone comparable stages of evolution, although each has its own distinctive features. Little correlation can be made with rocks of Mesozoic–Cenozoic age, because few modern orogenic belts have been eroded sufficiently to expose their mid-lower crust. The lack of modern analogues for comparison makes it particularly difficult to interpret the mode of origin and evolution of the Archean granulite–gneiss belts.

Sedimentary basins, basic dikes, and layered complexes. During the Late Archean (3 to 2.5 billion years ago), relatively stable, post-orogenic conditions developed locally in the upper crust, especially in southern Africa, where the development of greenstone–granite and granulite–gneiss belts was completed much earlier than in other parts of the world. The final chapters of Archean crustal evolution can be followed by considering specific key sedimentary basins, basic (basaltic) dikes, and layered complexes.

Pongola Rift
Along the border of Swaziland and South Africa is the Pongola Rift, which is the oldest such continental trough in the world; it is 2.95 billion years old, having formed only 50 million years after the thrusting of adjacent greenstone–granite belts. If there were earlier rifts, they have not survived, or more likely this was the first time in Earth history that the upper crust was sufficiently stable and rigid for a rift to form. It is 30 kilometres wide and 130 kilometres long, and within it is an 11-kilometre-thick sequence of lavas and sediments. It seems most likely that the rift developed as the result of the collapse of an overthickened crust following the long period of Archean crustal growth and thrusting in the Kaapvaal craton.

The 200-by-350-kilometre Witwatersrand Basin contains an 11-kilometre-thick sequence of lavas and sediments that are 2.8 billion years old. The basin is famous for its very large deposits of gold and uranium that occur as detrital minerals in conglomerates. These minerals were derived by erosion of the surrounding greenstone–granite belts and transported by rivers into the shoreline of the basin. In all probability, the gold originally came from the komatiitic and basaltic lavas in the early Archean oceanic crust.

Great Dyke of Zimbabwe
The Great Dyke, thought to be more than 2.5 billion years old, transects the entire Zimbabwe craton. It is 480 kilometres long and 8 kilometres wide and consists of layered ultrabasic rocks—gabbros and norites. The ultrabasic rocks have several layers of chromite and an extensive platinum-bearing layer that form economic deposits. The Great Dyke represents a rift that has been filled in with magma.

The Stillwater Complex is a famous, 2.7-billion-year-old, layered ultrabasic-basic intrusion in the Beartooth Mountains of Montana, U.S. It is 48 kilometres long and has a stratigraphic thickness of 6 kilometres. It was intruded

as a subhorizontal body of magma that underwent crystal settling to form the layered structure. It is notable for a three-metre-thick layer enriched in platinum minerals, which forms a major economic deposit.

The basins, dikes, and complexes described above cannot be mutually correlated. They most resemble equivalent structures that formed at the end of plate-tectonic cycles in the Phanerozoic. They represent the culmination of Archean crustal growth.

Proterozoic rock types. What happened geologically at the time of the Archean–Proterozoic boundary 2.5 billion years ago is uncertain. It seems to have been a period of little tectonic activity, and so it is possible that the earlier intensive Archean crustal growth had caused the amalgamation of continental fragments into a supercontinent, perhaps similar to Pangaea in the Permo–Triassic. The fragmentation of this supercontinent and the formation of new oceans gave rise to many continental margins on which a variety of distinctive sediments were deposited. Much evidence suggests that in the period from 2.5 billion to 570 million years ago Proterozoic oceans were formed and destroyed by plate-tectonic processes and that most Proterozoic orogenic belts arose by collisional tectonics. Sedimentary, igneous, and metamorphic rocks that formed in this period are widespread throughout the world. There are many swarms of basic dikes, important sedimentary rifts, basins, and layered igneous complexes, as well as many orogenic belts. The rocks commonly occur in orogenic belts that wrap around the borders of Archean cratons. The characteristic types of Proterozoic rocks are considered below, as are classic examples of their occurrence in orogenic belts. With a few exceptions the following types of rocks were formed during the Early, Middle, and Late Proterozoic, indicating that similar conditions and environments existed throughout this long period of time.

Basic dikes. The continents were sufficiently stable and rigid during the Proterozoic for an extremely large number of basic dikes to be intruded into parallel, extensional fractures in major swarms. Individual dikes measure up to several hundred metres in width and length, and there may be hundreds or even thousands of dikes in a swarm, some having transcontinental dimensions. For example, the 1.2-billion-year-old Mackenzie swarm is more than 500 kilometres wide and 3,000 kilometres long and extends in a northwesterly direction across the whole of Canada from the Arctic to the Great Lakes. The 1.95-billion-year-old Kangamiut swarm in West Greenland is only about 250 kilometres long but is one of the world's densest continental dike swarms. Many of the major dike swarms were intruded on the continental margins of Proterozoic oceans in a manner similar to the dikes that border the present-day Atlantic Ocean.

Layered igneous intrusions. There are several very important layered, mafic to ultramafic intrusions of Proterozoic age that were formed by the accumulation of crystals in large magma chambers. The well-known ones are several tens or even hundreds of kilometres across, have a dikelike or sheetlike (stratiform) shape, and contain major economic mineral deposits. The largest and most famous is the Bushveld Complex in South Africa, which is 9 kilometres thick and covers an area of 66,000 square kilometres. It was intruded nearly 2.1 billion years ago and is the largest repository of magmatic ore deposits in the world. The Bushveld Complex consists of stratiform layers of dunite, norite, anorthosite, and ferrodiorite and contains deposits of chromite, iron, titanium, vanadium, nickel, and, most important of all, platinum. The Sudbury Complex in southern Canada, which is about 1.9 billion years old, is a basin-shaped body that extends up to 60 kilometres across. It consists mostly of layered norite and has deposits of copper, nickel, cobalt, gold, and platinum. It is noted for its high-pressure structures and other manifestations of shock metamorphism, which suggest that the intrusion was produced by an enormous meteorite impact (see CONTINENTAL LANDFORMS: *Formation of impact craters*).

World's largest repository of magmatic ore deposits

Shelf-type sediments. Quartzites, dolomites, shales, and banded-iron formations make up sequences that reach up to 10 kilometres in thickness and that amount to more than 60 percent of Proterozoic sediments. Minor sediments include sandstones, conglomerates, red beds, evaporites, and cherts. The quartzites typically have cross-bedding and ripple marks, which are indicative of tidal action, and the dolomites often contain stromatolites similar to those that grow today in intertidal waters. Also present in the dolomites are phosphorites that are similar to those deposited on shallow continental margins against areas of oceanic upwelling during the Phanerozoic. Several early-middle Proterozoic examples of such dolomites have been found in Finland and northern Australia, as well as in the Marquette Range of Michigan in the United States, in the Aravalli Range of Rājasthān in northwestern India, and at Hamersley and Broken Hill in Australia. Still another constituent of these dolomites is evaporite, which contains casts and relicts of halite, gypsum, and anhydrite and which occurs, for example, at Mount Isa in Australia (1.6 billion years old) and in the Belcher Group in Canada (1.8 billion years old). These evaporites were deposited by brines in very shallow pools, like those encountered today in the Persian Gulf.

Ophiolites. Phanerozoic ophiolites are considered to be fragments of ocean floor that have been trapped between island arcs and continental plates that collided or that have been thrust onto the shelf sediments of continental margins. They consist of a downward sequence of oceanic sediments such as cherts, pillow-bearing basalts, sheeted (100-percent) basic dikes, gabbros, and certain ultramafic rocks (*e.g.,* serpentinized harzburgite and lherzolite). Comparable ophiolites occur in several Proterozoic orogenic belts and provide strong evidence of the existence of oceanic plates like those of today. The oldest is an ophiolite in the Cape Smith belt on the south side of Hudson Bay in Canada whose age has been firmly established at 1.999 billion years. There is a 1.8-billion-year-old ophiolite in the Svecofennian belt of southern Finland, but most Proterozoic ophiolites are 1 billion to 570 million years old and occur in the Pan-African belts of Saudi Arabia, Egypt, and The Sudan, where they occur in sutures between a variety of island arcs.

Greenstones and granites. Greenstone–granite belts, like those of the Archean, continued to form in the Proterozoic albeit in greatly reduced amounts. They are characterized by abundant volcanic rocks that include pillowed subaqueous basalt flows and subaerial and subaqueous volcaniclastic rocks. Magnesian komatiites are for the most part absent, however. Intrusive plutons are typically made of granodiorite. Examples occur at Flin Flon in central Canada and in the Birrimian Group in West Africa. Generally such rocks resemble those in modern island arcs and back-arc basins.

Granulites and gneisses. These highly deformed and metamorphosed rocks are similar to those of the Archean and occur in many Proterozoic orogenic belts, such as the Grenville in Canada, the Pan-African Mozambique belt in eastern Africa, and the Musgrave and Arunta ranges in Australia, and in Lapland in the northern Baltic Shield. They were brought up from the mid-lower crust on major thrusts as a result of continental collisions.

Orogenic belts. Some of the classic Proterozoic orogenic belts of the world are considered in this section.

One such belt is the Wopmay Orogen, situated in the Arctic in the northwestern part of the Canadian Shield. (It is beautifully exposed and has been well described by Paul F. Hoffman and his colleagues at the Geological Survey of Canada.) It formed within a relatively short time between 1.9 and 1.8 billion years ago and provides convincing evidence of tectonic activity in a modern form in the early Proterozoic. On the eastern continental margin occur red beds (sandstones), which pass oceanward and westward into stromatolite-rich dolomites deposited on the continental shelf to a thickness of four kilometres; these dolomites pass into submarine turbidite fans that were deposited on the continental rise. An island arc and a continental margin are found to the west. The history of the Wopmay Orogen can be best interpreted in terms of subduction of oceanic crust and collision tectonics.

The Svecofennian Orogen of the Baltic Shield extends in a southeasterly direction from northern Sweden through southern Finland to the adjoining part of the Soviet Union. It formed in the period from 1.9 to 1.7 billion years ago. A major lineament across southern Finland consists of the suture zone on which occur ophiolite complexes representing the remains of oceanic crust. At Outokumpu one encounters copper mineralization in these oceanic crust rocks similar to that in the Cretaceous ophiolite at Troodos in Cyprus. On the northern side of the suture is a shelf-type sequence of sediments and on the southern side a volcanic-plutonic arc. To the south of this arc lies a broad zone with thrusted gneisses intruded by tin-bearing crustal-melt granites, called rapakivi granites after their coarse, zoned feldspar megacrysts (*i.e.,* crystals that are significantly larger than the surrounding fine-grained matrix). The rocks in this zone are predictably equivalent to those that occur today under the Tibetan Plateau at a depth of about 20 kilometres.

The Grenville Orogen is a deeply eroded and highly uplifted orogenic belt that extends from Labrador in northeastern Canada to the Adirondack Mountains and southwestward under the coastal plain of the eastern United States. It developed from about 1.5 to 1 billion years ago. Apart from an island arc situated today in Ontario, most of the Grenville Orogen consists of highly metamorphosed and deformed gneisses and granulites, which have been brought to the present surface on major thrusts from the mid-lower crust. A result of the terminal continental collision that occurred at about 1.1 billion years ago was the formation of the Midcontinent (or Keweenawan) rift system that extends southward for more than 2,000 kilometres from Lake Superior.

A type of crustal growth—one very different from that described above—took place in what is now Saudi Arabia, Egypt, and The Sudan in the period from 1.1 billion to 500 million years ago. This entire shield, called the Arabian–Nubian Shield, is dominated by volcanic lavas, tuffs (consolidated rocks consisting of pyroclastic fragments and ash), and granitic plutons that formed in a variety of island arcs separated by several sutures along which occur many ophiolite complexes. Some of the ophiolites contain a complete stratigraphy that is widely accepted as a section through the oceanic upper mantle and crust. The final collision of the arcs was associated with widespread thrusting and followed by the intrusion of granitic plutons containing tungsten, tin, uranium, and niobium ore deposits. The island arcs grew from the subduction of oceanic crust in a manner quite comparable to that taking place today throughout Indonesia.

The Mozambique belt is one of the many Pan-African orogenic belts that formed in the period between 1 billion and 500 million years ago. It extends along the eastern border of Africa from Ethiopia to Kenya and Tanzania. It consists largely of highly metamorphosed, mid-crustal gneisses within which are a few peridotite bodies that may be relicts of ophiolites. The structure of the Mozambique belt is dominated by eastward-dipping thrusts very similar to the thrusts on the southern side of the Himalayas that resulted from the collision of India with Tibet during the Tertiary period hundreds of millions of years later.

During the Middle and Late Proterozoic, thick sequences of sediment were deposited in innumerable basins throughout Asia. The Riphean sequence spans the period from 1.7 billion to 900 million years ago and occurs in the Soviet Union. The Sinian in China extends from 850 to 570 million years ago (the end of the Precambrian) and roughly approximates the Vendian in the Soviet Union. The sediments are terrigenous debris, characterized by conglomerates, sandstone, siltstone, and shale, some of which are oxidized red beds, along with stromatolite-rich dolomite. Total thicknesses reach more than 10 kilometres. The terrigenous sediments were derived from the erosion of many Proterozoic orogenic belts.

Correlation. The fact that Phanerozoic sediments have been so successfully subdivided and correlated is attributable to the presence of abundant fossil remains of life-forms that evolved and underwent changes over time. The fact that Precambrian sediments lack such fossils pre-

Intrusive plutons of grano-diorite

Grenville Orogen

Riphean and Sinian basins

vents any comparable correlations. There are, however, stromatolites in Precambrian sediments ranging in age from 3.5 billion to 570 million years, and they reached their peak of development in the Proterozoic. Stromatolites underwent sufficient evolutionary changes that Russian biostratigraphers have been able to use them to subdivide the Riphean into four main zones throughout widely separated parts of the Soviet Union. Similar stromatolite-based stratigraphic divisions have been recognized in the Norwegian islands of Spitsbergen, China, and Australia. This stromatolite biostratigraphy still has relatively limited application, however. As a consequence, it is the chronometric time scale that is used to subdivide Precambrian time and to correlate rocks from region to region and from continent to continent.

The rocks within Proterozoic orogenic belts are invariably too deformed to allow correlation of units between different belts. Nonetheless, the techniques of geochronology have improved considerably in recent years, with the result that rocks of approximately similar age on different continents can be mutually compared and regarded as equivalent. Archean rocks have in general been far too highly deformed and metamorphosed to be correlated to any significant degree.

PRECAMBRIAN ENVIRONMENT

In this section the types of environment that may have existed during Precambrian time are considered. Several rock types, notably banded-iron formations, paleosols, and red beds, are very useful for deriving information about the conditions of the atmosphere, and tillites (indurated sedimentary rocks formed by the lithification of glacial till; see below) reveal what the climatic patterns were like during Precambrian glaciations.

Paleogeography. One of the most important factors controlling the nature of sediments deposited today is continental drift. This follows from the fact that the continents are distributed at different latitudes, and latitudinal position affects the temperature of oceanic waters along continental margins; in short, sedimentary deposition is climatically sensitive. At present, most carbonates and oxidized red soils are being deposited within 30 degrees of the equator, phosphorites within 45 degrees of it, and evaporites within 50 degrees. Most fossil carbonates, evaporites, phosphorites, and red beds of Phanerozoic age dating back to the Cambrian have a similar bimodal distribution with respect to their paleoequators. If the uniformitarian principle that the present is the key to the past is valid, then in the Precambrian such sediments would have likewise been controlled by the movement and geographic position of the continents. Thus it can be inferred that the stromatolite-bearing dolomites of the Riphean in the Soviet Union were deposited in warm tropical waters. Even the 3.5-billion-year-old, extensive evaporites in the Pilbara region of northwestern Australia could not have been formed close to their paleopole. Today, phosphate sediments are deposited primarily along the western side of continents, where they receive upwelling, nutrient-rich currents as they move toward the equator. The major phosphorite deposits in the Proterozoic Aravalli belt of Rājasthān in northwestern India are associated with stromatolite-rich dolomites and were most likely deposited within the tropics on the western side of a continental mass.

Significant geologic events. Outlined below are some of the main geologic events that occurred throughout the long history of the Precambrian and that reveal something about prevailing conditions and environments.

Oldest minerals and rocks. As was previously noted, the oldest minerals on Earth, the zircons from western Australia, crystallized 4.276 billion years ago. The most significant thing about them is that the environment in which they formed is totally unknown. The rocks from which they came may have been destroyed by some kind of tectonic process or by a meteorite impact. On the other hand, the rocks may still exist on the Earth's surface but simply have not been found. Perhaps their very absence is indicative of something important about early terrestrial processes. Comparisons with the Moon indicate that the Earth must have been subjected to an enormous number

of meteorite impacts about 4 billion years ago, but there is no geologic evidence of such events.

The oldest known rocks on Earth are found near Canada's Great Slave Lake; their age has been established radiometrically at 3.96 billion years. These rocks are of a granitic variety and are thought to have evolved from older basaltic crustal material that was melted and remelted by tectonic processes.

Archean events. During the first third of geologic history, until about 2.5 billion years ago, the Earth developed in a broadly similar manner. Greenstone–granite belts formed in the upper Archean crust and granulite–gneiss belts in the mid-lower crust. This was a time when the overall rate of heat production by the breakdown of radioactive isotopes was several times greater than it is today. This condition was manifested by very rapid tectonic processes, probably by some sort of primitive plate tectonics. Most of the heat that escapes from the Earth today does so at the mid-oceanic ridges, and it probably did likewise during the Archean but in much larger amounts. To permit this release of heat, the mid-oceanic ridges of the Archean were more abundant and longer and opened faster than those in the modern oceans. Although the amount of newly generated crust was probably enormous, a large part of this material was inevitably destroyed by equally rapid plate subduction processes. The main results of this early growth that can still be seen today are the many island arcs in greenstone–granite belts and the voluminous Andean-type tonalites that were deformed to orthogneiss in granulite–gneiss belts. Although most of the Archean oceanic crust was subducted, a few ophiolitic-type complexes have been preserved in greenstone–granite belts.

The Late Archean was an important interval of time because it marks the beginning of the major changeover from Archean to Proterozoic types of crustal growth. Significant events of this time were the formation of the first major rifts (such as the Pongola), the intrusion of the first major basic dikes (*e.g.,* the Great Dyke) and of the first large stratiform layered igneous complexes (*e.g.,* the Stillwater), and the formation of the first large sedimentary basins (as, for example, the Witwatersrand). All of these structures indicate that the continental crust had for the first time reached a mature stage with considerable stability and rigidity. The Late Archean represents the culmination that followed the rapid tectonic processes of the Early and Middle Archean. Because crustal growth was diachronous (*i.e.,* cut across time planes) throughout the world, similar structures can be found in the Early Proterozoic.

The Archean–Proterozoic boundary. There is no record of tectonic activity of any sort at the time corresponding to the Archean–Proterozoic boundary—about 2.5 billion years ago. This probably means that a supercontinent was created by the amalgamation of innumerable smaller continental blocks and island arcs. Accordingly, this was a period of tectonic stability that may have been comparable to the Permo–Triassic when the supercontinent of Pangaea existed. The main geologic events would have been the intrusion of basic dikes and the formation of sedimentary basins, like the Huronian on the U.S.–Canadian border, into which large volumes of clastic sediment were deposited. Such sediments would have been derived by erosion of high plateaus and mountains that are characteristic of a large continental mass.

Proterozoic developments. During the Early Proterozoic large amounts of quartzite, carbonate, and shale were deposited on the shelves and margins of many continental blocks. This would be consistent with the breakup of a supercontinent into several or many smaller continents with long continental margins. Examples of shelf sequences of this kind are found along the margins of orogenic belts, such as the Wopmay bordering the Slave province and the Labrador Trough bordering the Superior province in Canada, and the Svecofennian in Finland.

The fact that stable continental blocks existed by the Early Proterozoic meant that orogenic belts were able to develop against them by some form of collision tectonics. This was the first time that long, linear orogenic belts could form by "modern-style" plate-tectonic processes that involved seafloor spreading, ophiolite obduction, subduction that

Rapid tectonic processes

Development of long, linear mountain belts

created island arcs and Andean-type granitic batholiths in active continental margins, and the collision of arcs and continents that gave rise to sutures with ophiolites and to Himalayan-type thrust belts with abundant crustal-melt granites. These were key events in the evolution of the continents, and such processes have continued throughout Earth history.

During the Late Proterozoic some orogenic belts continued to develop, as in the case of the Pan-African belts of Saudi Arabia and East Africa. The intense crustal growth and the many orogenic belts that formed throughout the Proterozoic, however, began to create large continental blocks, which amalgamated to form a new supercontinent by the end of the Precambrian. Therefore, in the Late Proterozoic many sedimentary basins that were infilled with conglomerates and sandstones—the Riphean of the Soviet Union and the Sinian of China, for example—were able to form on extensive cratons of continental crust.

Climatic conditions. During the long course of Precambrian time the climatic conditions of the Earth must have changed considerably. Evidence of this can be seen in the sedimentary record, which suggests that the composition of the atmosphere and oceans changed appreciably over time. More importantly, however, the presence of tillites indicates that extensive glaciations occurred several times during the Precambrian. The tillites provide evidence of glacial conditions, although not necessarily at high latitudes. In general, they are complementary to the carbonates, evaporites, and red beds that are climatically sensitive and restricted to low latitudes.

The oldest extensive glaciation occurred 2.3 billion years ago during the Early Proterozoic. It can be recognized from the rocks and structures that the glaciers and ice sheets left behind on several continents. The most extensive occurrences are found in North America in a belt nearly 3,000 kilometres long extending from Chibougamau in Quebec through Ontario to Michigan and southwestward to the Medicine Bow Mountains of Wyoming. This probably represents the area of the original ice sheet. Most details are known from the Gowganda Formation in Ontario, which contains glacial deposits that are up to 200 metres thick and that occupy an area of about 20,000 square kilometres. Evidence that these rocks were of glacial origin has been obtained by comparing them with the rocks left behind by the Quaternary ice sheets and with the deposits associated with modern glaciers. The Early Proterozoic examples have the following features: The main glacial sediment is a tillite. This lithified till contains abundant pebbles and fragments of up to boulder size of various rocks distributed randomly in a fine-grained silty matrix. The surfaces of some pebbles have parallel scratches caused by having been rubbed against harder pebbles during ice transport. Locally, the basement rocks below the tillite also have been scratched, or striated, by the movement of the overlying boulder-strewn ice. Another type of glacial deposit is a laminated varved sediment composed of alternating millimetre-to-centimetre-thick layers of silt and clay, which closely resemble the layered varves that are laid down in modern glacial lakes at the front of retreating glaciers or ice sheets, each layer defining an annual accumulation of sediment. Within the Gowganda varved sediment are dropstones, which are fragments of rock that have dropped from an overlying floating ice sheet and that have sunk into and depressed the varved layers beneath them. When all these features are found together, they provide good evidence of an ancient glaciation. Similar, roughly contemporaneous glacial deposits can be found in the Transvaal and Cape Province in South Africa, where they reach only 30 metres in thickness but extend over an area of 20,000 square kilometres. Such deposits also are encountered in the Hamersley Basin of Western Australia, in central-east Finland and the adjoining part of the Soviet Union, near Lake Baikal in Siberia, and in central India. These occurrences suggest that there was one or more extensive glaciation during the Early Proterozoic.

The largest glaciation in the history of the Earth occurred during the Late Proterozoic in the period between 1 billion and 600 million years ago. It left its mark almost everywhere. The principal occurrences of the glacial

Evidence of Precambrian glaciation

deposits are in Europe (Scotland, Ireland, Sweden, Norway, France, and Czechoslovakia), the Western Cordillera (Yukon Territory, Can., to California, U.S.) and the Appalachians of the United States, East Greenland, Brazil, much of Africa (Congo, Angola, Namibia, Zambia, Zaire, and South Africa), and much of the Soviet Union, China, and Australia. One of the best described occurrences is in the Flinders Range of South Australia, where there is a four-kilometre-thick sequence of tillites and varved sediments occupying an area of 400-by-500 kilometres. Detailed stratigraphy and isotopic dating show that three glaciations took place at 850–800, 750, and 720–670 million years ago. The Port Askaig tillite on the island of Islay off northwestern Scotland is only 750 metres thick, but it records 17 ice advances and retreats and 27 periglacial periods, which are indicated by infilled polygons that formed under ice-free permafrost conditions. There are two major tillites in central Africa and Namibia (910–870 and 720–700 million years old, respectively) and two other such consolidated tills in East Greenland. What is the explanation for all these occurrences? It is interesting that some paleomagnetic studies have shown that the tillites in Scotland, Norway, Greenland, central Africa, North America, and South Australia were deposited in low or near-equatorial paleolatitudes. Such conclusions are, however, controversial, because it has also been suggested that the poles may have migrated across the globe, leaving a record of glaciations in high and low latitudes. There is the possibility that floating ice sheets could have traveled to low latitudes, depositing glacial sediments and dropstones below them. Whatever the answer, the existence of such vast quantities of tillites and of such extensive glaciations is intriguing and enigmatic. There is at present no broad agreement that resolves this Late Proterozoic phenomenon.

PRECAMBRIAN LIFE

Precambrian rocks were long ago defined to predate the Cambrian and therefore to predate all life, although the term Proterozoic was later coined from the Greek for "early life." It is now known that Precambrian rocks do in fact contain the evidence of the very beginnings of life on Earth (and thus the record of its evolution for more than 3 billion years), of the explosion of life-forms without skeletons before the Cambrian, and even of the development of sexual reproduction on Earth.

The first evidence of terrestrial life is found in the Early Archean sedimentary rocks of the greenstone–granite belts of Barberton in South Africa and of Warrawoona in the Pilbara block of Western Australia, which are both about 3.5 billion years old. There are two types of these early, simple, biological structures: microfossils and stromatolites.

The microfossils occur in cherts and shales and are of two varieties. One type consists of spherical carbonaceous aggregates, or spheroids, which may measure as much as 20 millimetres in diameter. These resemble algae and cysts of flagellates and are widely regarded as biogenic. The other variety of microfossils consists of carbonaceous filamentous threads, which are curving, hollow tubes up to 150 micrometres (0.006 inch) long. These tubes are most likely the fossil remains of filamentous organisms, and hundreds of them can be found in some rock layers. The 2.8-billion-year-old goldreefs (conglomerate beds with rich gold deposits) of the Witwatersrand Basin contain carbonaceous columnar microfossils up to seven millimetres long that resemble modern algae, fungi, and lichens. They probably extracted gold from the environment in much the way that modern fungi and lichens do.

Stromatolites are, as previously explained, stratiform, domal, or columnar structures made of sheetlike mats precipitated by communities of microorganisms, particularly filamentous blue-green algae. The Early Archean examples form domes as tall as about 10 centimetres (see Figure 16). Stromatolites occur in many of the world's greenstone–granite belts. In the 2.7-billion-year-old Steep Rock Lake belt in Ontario, Can., they reach three metres in height and diameter. Stromatolites continued to form all the way through the geologic record and today grow in warm intertidal waters, for example, at Shark Bay in Western

Microfossils and stromatolites

Figure 16: Stromatolites overlying the brecciated top of an ultramafic lava flow in Barberton Mountain Land, South Africa. The domal forms along the base are covered by larger, somewhat asymmetrical domes (see text).

By courtesy of Gary R. Byerly, Louisiana State University, Baton Rouge

Australia. They provide indisputable evidence that by 3.5 billion years ago life had begun on Earth by algal photosynthesis in complex, integrated biological communities.

These Archean organisms were prokaryotes that were incapable of cell division. They were relatively resistant to ultraviolet radiation and were able to survive during the early history of the Earth when the atmosphere lacked an ozone layer to block out such radiant energy. The prokaryotes were predominant until about 1.4 billion years ago, when they were overtaken by the eukaryotes. The latter make use of oxygen in metabolism and for growth and thus developed profusely in the increasingly oxygenic atmosphere of the Middle Proterozoic. The eukaryotes were capable of cell division, which allowed DNA (deoxyribonucleic acid), the genetic coding material, to be passed on to succeeding generations.

By Early Proterozoic time both microfossils and stromatolites had proliferated. The best-known occurrence of microorganisms is in the two-billion-year-old, stromatolite-bearing Gunflint iron formation in the Huronian Basin of southern Ontario. These microbial fossils include some 30 different types with spheroidal, filamentous, and sporelike forms up to about 20 micrometres across. Sixteen species in 14 genera have been classified so far. Microfossils of this kind are abundant, contain beautifully preserved organic matter, and are extremely similar to such present-day microorganisms as blue-green algae and microbacteria. There are comparable microfossils of the Early Proterozoic in Minnesota and Michigan in the United States, the Belcher Islands in Hudson Bay in Canada, southern Greenland, Western Australia, and northern China. These microbiota lived at the time of the transition from an anoxygenic to an oxygenic atmosphere.

During the Late Proterozoic stromatolites reached their peak of development and became distributed worldwide. The first metazoa (multicelled organisms whose cells are differentiated into tissues and organs) also appeared at this time. The stromatolites diversified into complex, branch-

ing forms. From about 700 million years ago, however, they began to decline significantly in number. Possibly the newly arrived metazoa ate the stromatolitic algae, and their profuse growth destroyed the habitats of the latter.

Metazoa developed rapidly from the beginning of the Cambrian, when they acquired protective shells and hard skeletons, which contributed to their preservation in fossil form. More primitive metazoa without skeletons, however, appeared before that time—at the outset of the Ediacaran period about 700 to 670 million years ago. The type locality for these remarkable organisms is the Ediacara Hills in the Flinders Range north of Adelaide in South Australia, where there is an enormous number of well-preserved impressions in shallow-water quartzite stratigraphically situated some 500 metres below the base of the Cambrian System (see below *Cambrian life*). These are impressions of soft-bodied organisms that resemble modern jellyfish, worms, sponges, and sea pens, among which more than 60 species have been named. Comparable impressions are known from many parts of the world in the youngest Precambrian sediments, such as those at Charnwood in central England, in the Ukraine and Siberia in the Soviet Union, Namibia, southeastern Newfoundland in Canada, and North Carolina in the eastern United States. Finally, there is the intriguing question as to when sexual division arose in life-forms. The American paleobiologist J. William Schopf has pointed out that in the abundant microflora of the 900-million-year-old Bitter Springs Formation of central Australia, some eukaryotic algae have cells in various stages of division into tetrahedral sporelike forms. These resemble the tetrad of spore cells of living plants known to develop by sexual division. In effect, by the end of the Precambrian the conditions were set for the explosion of life at the start of the Phanerozoic that ultimately led to the emergence of humankind.

(Brian Frederick Windley)

Paleozoic Era

The Paleozoic (from the Greek for ancient life) is bounded by major events in the history of life. It began about 570 million years ago with an extraordinary diversification of marine animals and ended about 245 million years ago with the greatest extinction event in Earth history. (New, more precise isotopic dates reported in 1990 suggest that the Paleozoic may have begun as late as 530 million years ago.) The major divisions of the Paleozoic Era, from oldest to youngest, are the Cambrian, Ordovician, Silurian, Devonian, Carboniferous, and Permian periods. Some geologists recognize the Mississippian and Pennsylvanian periods in place of the Carboniferous.

Paleozoic rocks are widely distributed on all continents. Most are of sedimentary origin, and many show evidence of deposition in or near shallow oceans. Among the more useful guide fossils for correlation are trilobites (Cambrian to Ordovician), graptolites (Ordovician to Silurian), conodonts (Ordovician to Permian), ammonoids (Devonian to Permian), and fusulinids (Carboniferous to Permian).

On a global scale, the Paleozoic was a time of continental assembly. Cambrian continents were scattered, but none covered either pole, and the average world climate was probably warmer than it is today. The continent of Laurentia, composed mostly of present-day North America and Greenland, lay across the equator and remained there even after joining with other continents. By Ordovician time the large continent of Gondwana, consisting primarily of present-day Africa, Antarctica, Australia, South America, southern Europe, much of the Middle East, and India, began to move over the South Pole. The distribution of extensive glacial deposits has been used to track the movement of parts of Gondwana over and around the South Pole during the remainder of the Paleozoic. Parts of Gondwana, because of its large size, also extended into tropical latitudes. Baltica, composed mostly of present-day northern Europe (including Scandinavia), moved across the equator from southern temperate into northern warm latitudes during the Paleozoic, and it collided with and joined Laurentia during Devonian time. Continued

Ediacaran fossils

Major divisions

tectonic plate movements resulted in the final assembly of the supercontinent of Pangaea by the end of the Paleozoic. Such mountainous regions as the Appalachians, Caledonides, and Urals were originally deformed by the Paleozoic collision of the lithospheric plates. Large areas of all continents were episodically inundated by shallow seas, with the greatest inundations during the Ordovician and early Carboniferous periods.

At the beginning of the Paleozoic, animals were restricted to the oceans, and land plants had not appeared. About half of all animal phyla, especially those with hard shells and mineralized skeletons, originated during the early and middle Cambrian. The biota rapidly diversified throughout the Cambrian and Ordovician as life-forms adapted to virtually all marine environments. In numbers of described marine species, trilobites are the dominant kind of fossil in Cambrian rocks, whereas brachiopods predominate in Ordovician to Permian rocks.

Conquest of the land by life-forms

Several different kinds of organisms independently adapted to living on land, primarily during the middle Paleozoic. Leafless vascular plants (psilophytes) and invertebrate animals (centipede-like arthropods) were both established on land at least by Silurian time. Vertebrate animals made the transition to land via evolution of amphibians from air-breathing crossopterygian fish during the Devonian. Further conquest of the land became possible during the Carboniferous as dependence on moist environments for depositing spores and shell-less eggs was overcome, as plants evolved seeds (seed-fern origin), and as animals evolved amniote eggs with protective shells (reptile origin). Flight was first achieved also during the Carboniferous, as insects evolved wings.

The great extinction event at the end of the Paleozoic Era eliminated such major invertebrate groups as the blastoids, fusulinids, and trilobites. Other major groups, as, for example, the ammonoids, brachiopods, bryozoans, corals, and crinoids, were severely decimated but managed to survive. It has been estimated that as many as 95 percent of the marine invertebrate species perished during the late Permian. Extinction rates were much lower among vertebrates, both aquatic and terrestrial, and among plants. Causes of the extinction are not clear, but they may be related to changing climate and exceptionally low sea level. Although of lesser magnitude, other important mass extinctions occurred at the end of the Ordovician and during the late Devonian.

CAMBRIAN PERIOD

General considerations. For years the Cambrian Period, the earliest time division of the Paleozoic Era, was thought to have extended from about 570 to 505 million years ago, but recent findings indicate that the period may have begun no more than 530 million years ago. Rocks formed or deposited during this time are assigned to the Cambrian System, which was named in 1835 by Adam Sedgwick for successions of slaty rocks in southern Wales and southwestern England. The corresponding period and system names are derived from Cambria, the Latinized name for Wales.

As originally described, the Cambrian System was overlain by the Silurian System, which was named, also in 1835, by Roderick I. Murchison. Subsequent disagreement between Sedgwick and Murchison over the definition and placement of the Cambrian–Silurian boundary led to a bitter controversy that involved many British geologists. The problem persisted until after the deaths of both Sedgwick and Murchison in the 1870s and the eventual adoption of an intervening system, the Ordovician, which was proposed in 1879 by Charles Lapworth.

Rocks in the Cambrian-type area were divided by Sedgwick into what he called Lower, Middle, and Upper Cambrian. These rocks, however, are so poorly exposed, structurally complicated, and sparsely fossiliferous that they have had little influence on development of modern concepts of the Cambrian and its subdivisions. In fact, much of the type Cambrian has been reassigned to either the Precambrian or the Ordovician. Rocks in Wales that are now assigned to the Cambrian System roughly correspond to Sedgwick's Lower Cambrian.

Boundaries and subdivisions. Boundaries of the Cambrian System are undefined in the sense that there are no internationally accepted limits to the unit. Nevertheless, working groups of the International Commission on Stratigraphy have reached a general consensus, based on global investigations beginning in 1972, about what the Cambrian System should and should not contain. Specific points, called boundary stratotypes, will eventually be selected in designated stratigraphic sections that will become standards for formal definitions of the system boundaries. Guidelines dictate that rocks in the boundary-stratotype sections must be of marine origin and that they should be as continuous and uniform in lithology as possible. The sections also should contain fossils and other indicators of time that will enable widespread identification of the system boundaries once they are formally defined.

The working group on the Precambrian–Cambrian boundary is seeking a boundary stratotype between strata containing soft-bodied Ediacaran fossils, considered to be late Precambrian in age, and strata with the earliest trilobites, regarded as Cambrian in age. This stratigraphic interval holds the earliest diverse shelly fossils and represents a pivotal time in biological evolution and Earth history. Therefore, the working group has agreed that the Precambrian–Cambrian boundary stratotype should be placed as close as practicable to the lowest appearance of these diverse shelly fossils. Several potential boundary stratotypes from around the world have been evaluated, and further study is concentrated on three leading candidates. One section is along the Aldan River of eastern Siberia in the Soviet Union, a second is near K'un-ming (Yunnan province) in southern China, and the third is on the Burin Peninsula of southeastern Newfoundland in Canada. Irrespective of which candidate is finally selected, the stratigraphic sections at all these boundary localities are important references for reconstructing the physical and biological histories of the boundary interval.

Precambrian–Cambrian boundary

The working group on the Cambrian–Ordovician boundary has agreed to select a boundary stratotype close in age to the base of the Tremadoc Series, which has its type area in northern Wales. British geologists have traditionally assigned rocks and fossils of Tremadoc age to the Cambrian, whereas many other geologists have assigned them to the Ordovician. From several potential boundary stratotypes, further study is concentrated on a section in the Kirin (Jilin in Pinyin) province of northeastern China and another on the coast of western Newfoundland. The stratotype for the Cambrian–Ordovician boundary is expected to be placed at the base of one of three closely spaced conodont zones and near the first appearance of planktonic (floating) graptolites. In rocks of this age, conodonts (toothlike microfossils produced by an extinct group of small, free-swimming marine animals) are among the best guide fossils for global time correlation, and planktonic graptolites have been used in defining the base of the Tremadoc Series and for zonation of the Ordovician System.

In most regions of the world, Cambrian rocks have been divided into lower, middle, and upper series (Table 5). The series boundaries, however, are not necessarily synchronous because of differences in definition as well as problems in correlation. Some series have been further divided into stages, but these are mostly identifiable only within individual regions.

Cambrian series and stages

Cambrian rocks have a special biological significance because they are the earliest to contain abundant and diverse fossils of animals. These rocks also include the first appearances of most animal phyla that have fossil records. Proliferation of organic lineages is called adaptive radiation, but Cambrian evolution produced such an extraordinary array of new body plans that the event has been referred to as the "Cambrian explosion." The beginning of this remarkable adaptive radiation has been used to divide the history of life on Earth into two unequal eons. The older, approximately 3-billion-year Cryptozoic Eon began with the appearance of life on Earth, and it is represented by rocks with mainly algae and similar primitive organisms. The younger, approximately half-billion-year Phanerozoic Eon, which began with the Cambrian explosion and con-

Table 5: Subdivisions of the Cambrian System

system	series	Great Britain	Scandinavia	U.S.S.R.	China	Australia	North America
		Tremadoc series				Datsonian	
Cambrian	Upper	Merioneth Series / no stages	Olenus Series / no stages	Aksayan / Saksian / Ayusokkanian	Fengshanian / Changshanian / Kushanian	Payntonian / unnamed stage / Idamean / Mindyallan	Trempealeauan / Franconian / Dresbachian
	Middle	Saint David's Series / no stages	Paradoxides Series / *Forchhammeri* / *Paradoxissimus* / *Oelandicus* / no stages	Mayan / Amagan	Changhian / Hsuchuangian / Maochuangian	Boomerangian / Undillan / Floran / Templetonian	no stages
	Lower	Comley Series / no stages	Holmia Series / no stages	Toyonian / Botomian / Atdabanian / Tommotian	Lungwangmiaoan / Tsanglangpuian / Chiungchussuian / Meishucunian	Ordian	no stages
				Vendian	Sinian	Ediacaran	

tinues to the present day, is characterized by rocks with conspicuous animal fossils.

Economic significance. Cambrian rocks are of moderate economic importance as they provide a variety of resources. For example, ore bodies rich in such metals as lead, zinc, silver, gold, and tungsten have secondarily replaced Cambrian carbonate rocks, especially in parts of North America and Australia. Other carbonate rocks have been widely used as building stone and for making lime and cement. Large Cambrian phosphorite deposits are major sources of agricultural fertilizer in northern Australia, southwestern China, and the central Soviet Union. Other Cambrian resources in China are mercury, uranium, and salt. The Soviet Union also has salt deposits of Cambrian age, as well as those of bauxite, the chief commercial source of aluminum.

Cambrian rocks. *Types and distribution.* Rocks of Cambrian age are present on all the continents, and individual sections range up to thousands of metres in thickness. The most fossiliferous and best-studied deposits are primarily from marine continental-shelf environments. Among the thicker and better-documented sections are those in the Rocky Mountains of western North America, the Siberian Platform of the eastern Soviet Union, and areas of central and southern China. Other well-documented, fossiliferous, but thinner sections are in Australia (especially western Queensland), the Appalachian Mountains of eastern North America, the southern Soviet Union (especially Kazakhstan), and the Baltic region (especially Sweden).

Lateral changes in the composition of Cambrian rocks resulted from regional differences in environments of deposition. Near-shore deposits are commonly composed of siliceous sandstone. This usually grades seaward into siltstone and shale, which formed by accumulation of finer-grained sediment in deeper water where the seafloor was less affected by wave action. Extensive carbonate platforms, analogous to the modern Bahama Banks, developed along some continental shelves that were in low latitudes during Cambrian time. Rapid production of

carbonate sediment in this warm, shallow-water environment resulted in massive deposits of Cambrian limestone and dolomite. Good examples are exposed in the Rocky Mountains of North America, in north-central Australia, along the Yangtze River in central China, and along the Lena River emanating in Siberia.

Few Cambrian rocks from land environments have been documented, and most of those are of limited areal extent. They mainly represent deposits of floodplains and wind-blown sand. Without plants or animals, the desolation of Cambrian landscapes must have rivaled that of any present-day desert. In the absence of plants with roots to hold soil in place, Cambrian lands in general probably eroded more rapidly than they do at present.

Relative sea level rose significantly during the Cambrian, but with fluctuations. This is indicated by both the geographic distribution and the stratigraphic succession of sedimentary deposits. In North America, for example, early Cambrian marine deposits covered only marginal areas, but late Cambrian marine deposits covered much of the continent. A similar distribution of marine rocks is present on other continents. In stratigraphic sections from continental shelves that were in low latitudes it is common for a basal, near-shore sandstone to be overlain by a transgressive succession of more seaward shale and carbonate rocks. Shelf sections from high latitudes may be mostly or entirely sandstone, or a basal sandstone may grade upward into shale, but most of these sections contain evidence of marine transgression. Exceptions to the general Cambrian sea-level pattern are commonly attributable either to local tectonism or to different rates of sediment accumulation. The most likely explanation for the general rise in Cambrian sea level seems to be increased thermal activity and related swelling of spreading ridges between lithospheric plates, which would displace vast quantities of seawater. It has been suggested that the general Cambrian transgression exerted an influence on adaptive radiation by greatly increasing the area of shallow seas where life was most abundant.

Development of carbonate platforms

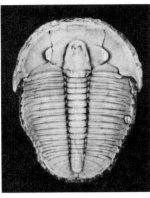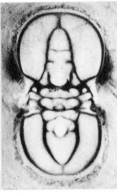

Figure 17: *Representative Cambrian trilobites.*
(Left) *Elrathia kingii* (order Polymerida) and (right)
Ptychagnostus gibbus (order Agnostida).
By courtesy of R.A. Robison

Correlation. Time correlation of Cambrian rocks has been based almost entirely on fossils. The most common fossils in Cambrian rocks are of trilobites (Figure 17), which evolved rapidly and are the principal guide fossils for biostratigraphic zonation in all but rocks of the basal Tommotian stage or those of equivalent age (Table 5). Until the mid-1900s almost all trilobite zones were based on members of the order Polymerida. Such trilobites usually have more than five segments in the thorax, and the order includes about 95 percent of all trilobite species. Most polymeroids, however, lived on the seafloor, and genera and species were mostly endemic to the shelves of individual Cambrian continents. Therefore, polymeroid trilobites are useful for regional correlation but have limited value for intercontinental correlation, which has been difficult and subject to significant differences in interpretation.

From the 1960s, investigators began to recognize that many species of the trilobite order Agnostida have intercontinental distributions in open-marine strata. These trilobites are small, rarely exceeding a few millimetres in length, and they have only two thoracic segments. Specialized appendages, which were probably useful for swimming but unsuitable for walking on the seafloor, suggest that they were pelagic. Agnostoids make up less than 5 percent of all trilobite species, but individuals of some agnostoid species are abundant. This fact, together with their wide geographic distribution and rapid evolution, makes them valuable for refined intercontinental correlation. Agnostoids first appear in upper Lower Cambrian rocks but did not become common or diversify significantly until the middle of the Cambrian. Therefore, agnostoids have their greatest biostratigraphic value in the upper half of the Cambrian System. A comprehensive trilobite zonation in Sweden has often been cited as a standard for correlation.

Other kinds of fossils have had more limited use in Cambrian biostratigraphy and correlation. Among them are spongelike archaeocyathids in the Lower Cambrian and brachiopods throughout the Cambrian, but use of both groups has been hampered by problems of endemism. Small mollusks and other small shelly fossils, mostly of problematic affinities, have been employed for biostratigraphy in the Tommotian Stage, but their utility is also limited by endemism. Conodonts appear in the uppermost Precambrian but are rare in most Cambrian rocks except those of latest Cambrian age, when adaptive radiation of conodont animals accelerated. Wide species distributions, rapid evolution, and abundance make conodonts excellent indexes for global biostratigraphy in uppermost Cambrian to uppermost Triassic rocks.

Cambrian environment. *Paleogeography.* The geography of the Cambrian world differed greatly from that of the present. The geographic reconstruction in Figure 18 is based on combined geologic and biological evidence. Fossils in continental-shelf deposits indicate the presence of at least three major faunal provinces during much of the Cambrian Period.

The most distinct faunal province surrounded the continent of Laurentia. Paleomagnetic evidence indicates that

Laurentia was located over the equator during most or all of Cambrian time. This geographic interpretation is supported by the presence of thick, warm-water, carbonate-platform deposits that accumulated in a broad belt encircling the continent. These carbonates are commonly flanked on the inner shelf by lagoonal shale and nearshore sandstone. On the outer shelf, the carbonates commonly grade into laminated mudstone and shale that accumulated in deeper water. At times, two almost mutually exclusive subfaunas were separated by temperature and salinity barriers in the shallow water on the carbonate platforms. Inner, restricted-shelf deposits are characterized by sparse, low-diversity faunas that tend to be highly endemic. Outer, open-shelf deposits are characterized by common to abundant, high-diversity faunas that are widely distributed around the continent. Fossils are usually most abundant and most diverse near the outer margin of the carbonate platform. Because Laurentia has remained nearly intact structurally, it is ideal for studying the relationships between Cambrian environments and faunas around a low-latitude Cambrian continent.

Another Cambrian faunal province surrounded the small continent of Baltica, which was located in middle to high southern latitudes. Cambrian shelf deposits of Baltica are relatively thin, rarely exceeding 250 metres in thickness, and are composed of primarily sandstone and shale. Seemingly as a consequence of cool-water environments, carbonate deposits are relatively minor and very thin. The wide distribution of many species from the nearshore to deep-shelf environments of Baltica suggests no significant restriction in shelf dispersal like that caused by the shallow carbonate platforms of Laurentia.

The largest Cambrian faunal province is that around the continent of Gondwana, which extended from the low northern latitudes to the high southern latitudes, just short of the South Pole. Rocks and faunas of Gondwana show major changes that correspond to its great size and wide range of climates and environments. The Antarctic and Australian sectors of Gondwana were in low latitudes and have extensive carbonate deposits, although those of Antarctica are poorly exposed through the present-day polar ice cap and have received little study. China, with massive carbonate-platform deposits and close faunal affinities with Australia, was also in the low latitudes. It is unclear, however, whether China was attached to Gondwana near the Australian sector, or whether it was a microcontinent separated from Gondwana by a narrow seaway.

Several terranes seem to have been near or attached along the margin of Gondwana in high southern latitudes (the northern Africa sector), but many details of their Cambrian geographic relations are unknown. (Terranes are fault-bounded fragments of the Earth's crust characterized by a geologic history markedly different from that of neighbouring crustal segments.) These terranes now make up much of southern Europe and parts of northeastern North America. Cambrian deposits in all the terranes are chiefly sandstone and shale and include few or no carbonates. Their faunas closely resemble those of Baltica at generic and higher taxonomic levels, but differences at the species level suggest some geographic separation.

Siberia and Kazakhstania were in the low latitudes, probably on separate tectonic plates. Faunal affinities suggest closer proximity to China and equatorial Gondwana than to Laurentia. Some Cambrian rocks in present-day Kazakhstan show evidence of deposition in seamount environments.

Few Cambrian faunas from continental-slope and deep-ocean environments are known. Limited information from these is important, however, for demonstrating affinities between deep, cool-water faunas from all latitudes and shallow, cool-water faunas from high latitudes. Close similarity between the observed distribution patterns of Cambrian and modern marine arthropods has been used as persuasive evidence for thermally stratified Cambrian oceans in lower latitudes and for a thermocline separating warm-water and cool-water layers (Figure 19). The inferred thermocline as well as wide oceanic separation were likely causes for the high endemism of the Laurentian faunal province. This interpretation is supported by

Use of
agnostoid
fossils for
inter-
continental
correlation

Largest
Cambrian
faunal
province

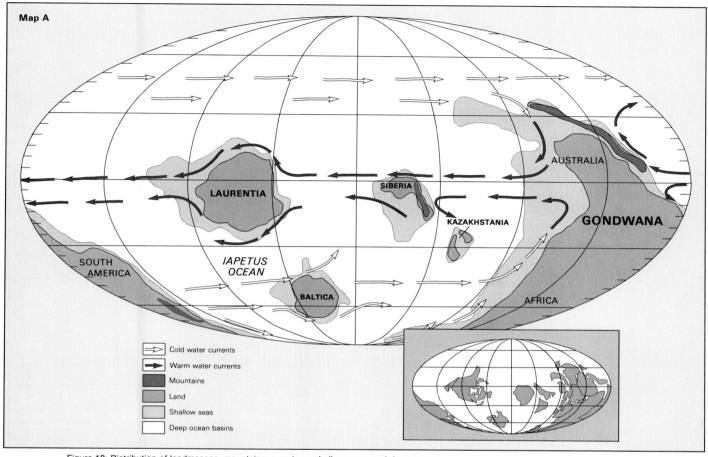

Figure 18: Distribution of landmasses, mountainous regions, shallow seas, and deep ocean basins during the Late Cambrian. Included in the paleogeographic reconstruction are cold and warm ocean currents. The present-day coastlines and tectonic boundaries of the configured continents are shown in the inset at the lower right.

Adapted from: C.R. Scotese, The University of Texas at Arlington

Middle Cambrian deposits in North Greenland where, in a few tens of kilometres, normal Laurentian shelf-margin trilobite faunas grade into deepwater faunas like those in the shallow-shelf deposits of Baltica. In a similar pattern, trilobite species in deepwater faunas of Late Cambrian age in the western United States and southeastern China are the same, but shallow-water faunas of the same age in the two regions have neither genera nor species in common.

As large lithospheric plates continued to move during the Phanerozoic Eon, terranes of various sizes were displaced. Endemic Cambrian fossils, in conjunction with such other geologic evidence as physical stratigraphy, have been useful in helping to identify the geographic origins of some terranes, particularly those that have undergone substantial displacement. Examples are northern Scotland with Laurentian faunas, eastern Newfoundland with Baltic faunas, southern Mexico (Oaxaca) with Gondwanan (South American) faunas, and west-central Argentina (Precordillera) with Laurentian faunas.

Another important consequence of the continued movement of lithospheric plates has been the formation of large mountain ranges by crumpling where plates have collided. Pressure and heat generated during collisions since the Cambrian have folded, faulted, and metamorphosed significant volumes of Cambrian rock, especially that from the outer margins and slopes of many continental shelves.

No oceanic crustal rocks have been found to be older than Mesozoic in age, and apparently most pre-Mesozoic deposits that accumulated in the deep ocean basins have been either metamorphosed beyond recognition or destroyed by subduction into the Earth's interior.

Relatively abrupt changes in sea level may have significantly influenced Cambrian environments and life. A global drop in sea level is suggested by extensive unconformities (i.e., interruptions in the continuity of depositional sequence) and changes in sedimentary rocks near the Early–Middle Cambrian boundary. The time represented by such unconformities in sectors of Laurentia and Baltica bounding the Iapetus Ocean has been called the Hawke Bay event. An apparent absence of a coeval unconformity in western North America seems to be an anomaly. Thick, uninterrupted shelf deposits in this sector of Laurentia, however, may have resulted from abnormal shelf subsidence that was caused by cooling of crustal rocks following a late Precambrian plate-rifting event. Temporal correlations with unconformities on other continents lack precision. Nevertheless, it is perhaps significant that a number of characteristic Early Cambrian animal groups were either exterminated or severely restricted in their geographic distribution at about the same time in the shallow-shelf environments of the world. Among biostratigraphically important trilobites, the olenellids were exterminated around Laurentia, the holmiids were killed off around Baltica, and the redlichiids vanished around Gondwana. In addition, diverse and abundant reef-forming archaeocyathids disappeared from most low-latitude, warm-water continental shelves.

A significant rise in sea level is suggested by rather abrupt and extensive displacements in sedimentary environments and biotas in the middle Middle Cambrian (the *Ptychagnostus gibbus* zone). Lowland areas were flooded, as in

Abrupt global changes in sea level

low latitudes   Iapetus Ocean   high latitudes

Laurentia   warm water   thermocline   cool water   Baltica

Figure 19: Hypothetical cross-section of the Iapetus Ocean during Middle Cambrian time (vertical scale greatly exaggerated).

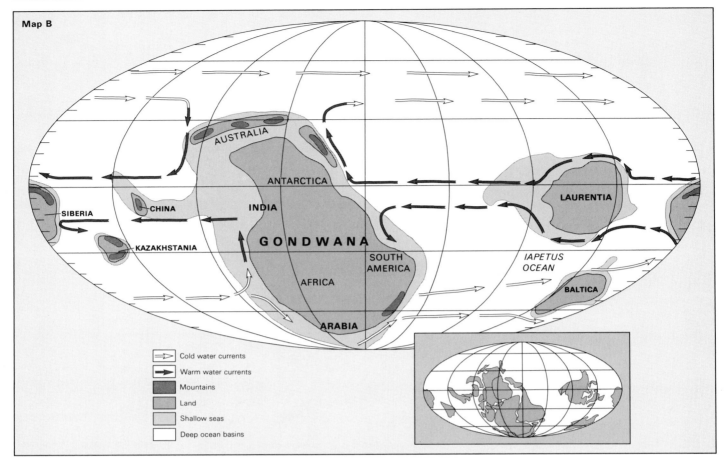

Map B

Legend:
- Cold water currents
- Warm water currents
- Mountains
- Land
- Shallow seas
- Deep ocean basins

parts of Baltica. In warm-water shelf sections of the world, it is common for coarse-grained, shallow-water, carbonate rocks to be abruptly overlain by fine-grained, deeper-water, laminated limestone or shale. Adaptive radiation of the pelagic agnostoid trilobites was greatly accelerated in open-oceanic environments following this event, perhaps in response to expanded habitats.

Missing faunas and an unconformity, which define the boundary between the Dresbachian and Franconian stages in peripheral areas of North America, suggest another significant drop in sea level during the early Late Cambrian. Evidence for two other lesser changes in Cambrian sea level has been identified near the Cambrian–Ordovician boundary. Associated minor unconformities have provided a problem for selection of a boundary stratotype, which ideally should be located in an uninterrupted stratigraphic section.

Several regions of Cambrian volcanism have been identified. Australia was especially active, with large areas in the northern and central regions covered by flood basalts during the Early Cambrian and with residual activity into the Middle Cambrian. Basalts and mafic intrusives in southeastern Australia formed in a volcanic island-arc setting during the Early and Middle Cambrian. Volcanic suites of similar age also are present in New Zealand and in parts of Antarctica (Ellsworth and Victoria lands). Other significant Lower and Middle Cambrian volcanic deposits are present in northeastern China, western Mongolia, northwestern China (Tien Shan mountains), and adjacent regions of the Soviet Union (Altai–Sayan mountains). Cambrian volcanics are scattered along the eastern-most margin of the United States, but most are probably island-arc deposits that were accreted to Laurentia after the Cambrian. In the southern United States (Oklahoma), granitic intrusives and basaltic and rhyolitic extrusives are associated with a large tectonic trough that was formed by Early and Middle Cambrian crustal extension.

Minor volcanic deposits, mainly ash beds and thin flows, are widely known. In general, these have received little

study, but some are suitable for determination of isotopic ages. Volcanic tuffs near inferred Tommotian–Atdabanian boundaries in both Morocco and southwestern China have yielded similar dates of 521 million years.

The tectonic history of the Paleozoic is much better known than that of the Precambrian. In general, however, late Precambrian history seems to have been characterized by continental fragmentation, whereas Paleozoic history was characterized by continental accretion. The Cambrian was a period of transition between those tectonic modes and seems to have been a time of reduced orogenic activity. Continents were scattered, apparently by fragmentation of a late Precambrian supercontinent. Collision of tectonic plates seems to have affected parts of Gondwana, especially in areas represented by present-day Australia, Antarctica, and Argentina, but details and timing are still largely unclear. At least some of the volcanic activity noted above, particularly that of volcanic island arcs, is evidence that seafloor spreading and crustal subduction were active geologic processes, although perhaps at somewhat reduced levels.

Paleoclimate. The overall climate during Cambrian time was probably warmer and more equable than it is today. An absence of Cambrian glacial deposits and an abundance of widespread, warm-water, carbonate deposits both suggest higher average temperatures than at present. The absence of glacial deposits of Cambrian age is more notable because such deposits are common and widespread in the upper Precambrian, and they accumulated again during the Ordovician in northern Africa as Gondwana began to move over the South Pole. An apparent absence of either land or landlocked seas at the Cambrian poles may have prevented the accumulation of polar ice caps.

Cambrian life. The long history of life on Earth has been punctuated by relatively abrupt changes. Some have argued that the greatest change of all occurred in marine environments near the Precambrian–Cambrian boundary. Fossils from Cambrian rocks include the oldest representatives of most animal phyla having mineralized shells or skeletons. A lack of observed connecting links suggests that processes of biomineralization evolved independently in several phyla. Whether or not soft-bodied representatives of some of these phyla originated during the Precambrian but have no preserved record is a debated question. Nevertheless, the hard parts of Cambrian animals had a much greater potential for preservation than soft parts, and they mark the beginning of a diverse fossil record.

Fossil record of the Precambrian–Cambrian transition

Preservation of the record of the Precambrian–Cambrian transition was significantly affected by global changes in sea level. During latest Precambrian time, the sea level was relatively low, resulting in areally restricted oceans and expanded continents. Throughout much of the Cambrian, rising seas gradually flooded vast land areas. Sediment was eroded from the continents and deposited in adjacent seas. Because of low sea level, the sedimentary and fossil records of the Precambrian–Cambrian transition are generally most complete toward the outer margins of continental shelves. As a corollary, the time gap represented by the boundary surface generally increases in landward directions. Absence or serious incompleteness of a transitional record in most areas, particularly in those of classical Cambrian studies, contributed significantly to the long-held notion of an abrupt or sudden appearance of Cambrian fossils. This was compounded by a general deficiency in knowledge of Precambrian biotas before the mid-1900s.

Considering the biological importance of the Precambrian–Cambrian transition, it is somewhat surprising that the primary impetus for its detailed study has come from a project undertaken to establish international agreement on a suitable boundary stratotype. Before the project was initiated in 1972, reasonably complete stratigraphic sections across the transition were either largely unrecognized or ignored. Since 1972, information about the transition has accumulated at an accelerating rate. Although many details remain to be learned, the general history of this momentous interval is becoming clear.

The Precambrian–Cambrian biotic transition, once thought to be sudden or abrupt, has been found to include a succession of events spread over many millions of years. It commences with the appearance of the animal kingdom (*i.e.,* multicelled organisms that ingest food), but the date and details of that event remain obscure. At least three informal phases in the transition can be identified by progressively more diverse and complex biotas.

The earliest phase, generally considered to be of late Precambrian age, is characterized by fossils of soft-bodied animals known from many localities around the world. These organisms may have appeared as early as 650 million years ago and are commonly called the Ediacaran fauna (see above *Precambrian Era: Precambrian life*). The fossils are predominantly the imprints of soft-bodied animals. Their extraordinary preservation, usually in sandstone, was probably the result of rapid burial and protection by smothering sediment. Most of the fossils are relatively simple, and many resemble worms, sea pens, and jellyfish. Dwelling traces like those of modern sea anemones are also common. Higher taxonomic assignments are controversial, however, because critical diagnostic features are not evident. Some paleontologists have assigned Ediacaran body fossils to the extant phyla Annelida, Coelenterata, and Arthropoda, whereas others have regarded them as members of extinct taxonomic groups of high rank. Some adherents of the latter viewpoint have suggested that the Ediacaran fauna was terminated by a major extinction event, but direct evidence of an abrupt faunal replacement has not been detected in any stratigraphic section.

Other kinds of fossils also provide valuable information about life during Ediacaran time. Photosynthetic organisms include unicellular blue-green algae (cyanobacteria) and acritarchs (probable algae), both of low diversity. Individuals of some species were probably abundant, however, and may have been an important source of food for Ediacaran animals. Hard parts of animals, primarily known from Africa and China, are mainly dwelling tubes composed of calcium carbonate and other compounds. Most were probably secreted by sessile, filter-feeding, wormlike animals. Although rare and of low diversity, these forms

are significant because they signal the advent of biomineralization. The oldest unequivocal trace fossils, mainly crawling trails, are also of Ediacaran age. The trails suggest that locomotion of the trace makers was accomplished by waves of muscular contraction, like that in annelids and sea slugs, and not by legs. All but the latest Ediacaran trace fossils are relatively simple, suggesting limited and primitive behaviour patterns. Their low diversity further suggests that few kinds of mobile animals lived on the Ediacaran seafloor. **Oldest trace fossils**

The second phase of the Precambrian–Cambrian biotic transition is characterized by a marked increase in the diversity of its shelly fauna and a lack of trilobites. It is near the lowest stratigraphic occurrence of this fauna that the Precambrian–Cambrian boundary stratotype is likely to be placed. The fauna includes that of the Tommotian Stage, as applied in the Soviet Union, and it has often been referred to as the Tommotian fauna. It is known from many localities around the world, but time correlations lack precision. A general acceleration in biotic diversity during this second phase is the beginning of the so-called Cambrian explosion.

Fossils of the second phase, which may be locally abundant, represent several new animal groups of Paleozoic aspect. Cup-shaped archaeocyathans, considered to be sponges by some paleontologists and assigned to a separate phylum by others, became common in carbonate environments and were the first animals to form reefs. Mollusks, preserved in both shale and limestone, include at least four classes (Monoplacophora, Gastropoda, Hyolitha, and Rostroconchia). Brachiopods made their appearance but are low in diversity. Several problematic groups are represented by an astonishing array of small mineralized tubes, scales, and spicules. The presence of arthropods, the first animals to develop legs, is indicated by characteristic trace fossils. The skeletal remains of arthropods are not preserved in the fauna, however, presumably because they were not mineralized. Other trace fossils show a marked increase in abundance and diversity as well as an expansion of behaviour patterns that reflect improvements in locomotion, greater ability to penetrate sediment, and new foraging strategies.

The third phase of the Precambrian–Cambrian biotic transition commenced with the appearance of mineralized trilobite skeletons, which approximately correlates with the base of the Atdabanian Stage of the Lower Cambrian, as conceived in the Soviet Union. Subsequent adaptive radiation of the trilobites was exceptional, and their remains dominate most Cambrian deposits. For this reason, the Cambrian Period has sometimes been called the "Age of Trilobites," and one of the more widely used informal definitions for the base of the Cambrian System has been the first appearance of trilobites. Appearance of the diverse shelly fauna of phase two, however, is considered to be a more significant biological event by most members of the international working group that will eventually select a boundary stratotype. **Predominance of trilobites**

The known Cambrian biota was restricted to marine environments. At least 11 extant animal phyla (Annelida, Arthropoda, Brachiopoda, Chordata, Ctenophora, Echinodermata, Hemichordata, Mollusca, Onychophora, Porifera, and Priapulida), including most of those with a fossil record, first appear in Cambrian rocks. Most of these rapidly diversified as they seemingly adapted to numerous unfilled ecological niches. The only extant animal phylum with a good fossil record that is not known from Cambrian rocks is the Bryozoa, which appears in rocks of Early Ordovician age. A summary of the principal biotic groups of the Cambrian is given below.

Cambrian photosynthetic organisms, the primary food of animals, are entirely unicellular. These organisms include a variety of bacteria and algae of the kingdoms Monera and Protista. Their evolution, like that in associated animals, shows a marked acceleration in adaptive radiation and biomineralization near the base of the Cambrian. A new calcareous benthic (bottom-dwelling) flora dominated by blue-green algae appeared. Some of these organisms formed mounds on the seafloor. Others formed small, concentrically laminated, marble- or biscuit-shaped structures **Photosynthetic organisms** called oncoids, which were locally abundant. Although it was rarely preserved, there existed a noncalcareous benthic flora that also was dominated by blue-green algae. By at least Middle Cambrian time, some noncalcareous green algae (Chlorophyta) had became common. In North America and Siberia, the axes of one species, *Margaretia dorus,* exceeded two centimetres in diameter and were probably more than one metre in height. Such large size is attained by modern green algae only in warm, equatorial oceans. The phytoplankton, consisting of acritarchs and blue-green algae, also diversified near the base of the Cambrian. Acritarchs are widespread in many kinds of marine rocks and seem to have potential for an improved zonation of Lower Cambrian rocks. They are difficult to study, however, because of their microscopic size.

Cambrian faunas, like those of the present day, are commonly dominated in numbers and kind by members of the phylum Arthropoda. Calcification of skeletons by the beginning of Atdabanian time contributed to an abundant fossil record of the class Trilobita, of which some details have been discussed above. Many hundreds of genera and thousands of species of Cambrian trilobites have been described worldwide. Rates of evolution in Cambrian trilobites were relatively rapid, resulting in short stratigraphic ranges and giving them much value for biostratigraphic correlation. Representatives of the class Ostracoda, characteristically enclosed by a bivalved carapace, also appeared near the base of the Atdabanian. Compared to trilobites, however, ostracods are generally rare and of low diversity throughout the Cambrian, except in some rocks of Australia and China. Extraordinary preservation at rare localities indicates that many other kinds of arthropods were at least locally more abundant and more diverse than the trilobites. These other arthropods had unmineralized skeletons, and some may represent extinct classes.

Sponges (phylum Porifera) are commonly represented in Cambrian faunas. Their remains are mostly simple siliceous spicules, which readily disaggregated after death, making their identification at lower taxonomic levels difficult, if not impossible. At rare localities where preservation is exceptional, including articulated skeletons and associated soft-bodied taxa, sponges are second only to arthropods in species diversity. This suggests that Cambrian sponges were much more common and more diverse than is indicated by the known fossil record. Limited information indicates that species of Cambrian sponges evolved slowly, resulting in relatively long stratigraphic ranges.

Archaeocyathans are probable sponges that typically have cup-shaped skeletons with double calcareous walls and numerous pores. Some formed small reefs. The group is common and diverse in some Early Cambrian deposits and has been used for provincial biostratigraphic zonation, especially in Australia and Siberia. Archaeocyathans are common only in regions that were in low Cambrian latitudes, including Antarctica, Australia, China, Kazakhstan, Siberia, and North America. Their latitudinal distribution is similar to that of modern colonial corals, suggesting adaptation to similar ecological controls in warm shallow seas. Archaeocyathans nearly disappeared at the end of the Early Cambrian, but rare species survived until at least middle Late Cambrian time, after which the group became extinct.

Brachiopod shells are present in many Cambrian continental-shelf deposits. In total number of species that have been described from Cambrian rocks, brachiopods are second only to trilobites. Species diversity, however, is generally low to moderate at most localities. Phosphatic shells of the class Inarticulata are normally much more common and more diverse than are calcareous shells of the class Articulata. These abundance and diversity relationships are usually reversed in post-Cambrian rocks.

The phylum Echinodermata (some present-day representatives of which are sea urchins and starfish) had a major adaptive radiation during the Cambrian Period. The number of classes increased from three in the Early Cambrian to eight in the Middle Cambrian. Only one of these, the Eocrinoidea, is known from many species, but the described record seems to be grossly incomplete. Skeletal plates in early echinoderms were not rigidly connected, and they readily disaggregated after death of an animal. Consequently, it is rare to find articulated skeletons that can be identified at lower taxonomic levels. In some Cambrian limestones, however, skeletal plates of echinoderms are a dominant sedimentary constituent, indicating the existence of innumerable animals and suggesting far greater diversity, especially at low taxonomic levels, than has been recorded. As in some modern echinoderm species, it is common for those in the Cambrian to show evidence of a gregarious habit and patchy distribution. Most of the Cambrian echinoderms were suspension and detritus feeders, and it was only after the Cambrian that herbivores and carnivores became common. All classes of echinoderms that were present during the Cambrian, except the Crinoidea, subsequently became extinct.

The phylum Mollusca also underwent significant adaptive radiation during the Cambrian, with the appearance of the classes Monoplacophora, Gastropoda, Pelecypoda (synonymous with Bivalvia), Cephalopoda, Polyplacophora, Rostroconchia, Hyolitha, and Stenothecoida. (The latter three are now extinct.) The only molluscan class that appeared after the Cambrian is the Scaphopoda (tusk or tooth shells), which originated during the Ordovician. A small variety of mollusks is present in the shelly fauna of Tommotian and time-equivalent rocks of the earliest Cambrian. Mollusk shells are absent or rare in most Cambrian rocks, but at a few localities they are common to abundant. The small conical shells of hyoliths are the kind most commonly preserved in Cambrian rocks.

Other new Cambrian phyla largely lack biomineralization and have a poor fossil record. The Hemichordata is represented by rare sessile graptolites (order Dendroidea) of the class Graptolithina, which appeared during the Middle Cambrian. Appearance of the more common planktonic graptolites (order Graptoloidea) has been informally used to define the Cambrian–Ordovician boundary, and the formal boundary stratotype is expected to be established close to this biohorizon. Cambrian worm phyla include the Annelida, Priapulida, and probable Pogonophora, but these are mainly known from localities where preservation was extraordinary. Other rarely represented phyla are the Onychophora, with leglike lobopodia, and Ctenophora (comb jellies).

The origin of the phylum Chordata is unclear. If primitive conodonts are included, as argued by some paleontologists, the phylum appeared during the late Precambrian. Rare, soft-bodied, possible chordates have been described from Middle Cambrian rocks. The oldest unequivocal chordate remains are isolated bony plates of jawless fish in Upper Cambrian rocks of the western United States.

Trace fossils, as discussed above, provide independent evidence of accelerated animal diversification and an increase in the complexity of animal behaviour near the beginning of the Cambrian. Other evidence from trace fossils indicates changes in Cambrian bioturbation, the churning and stirring of seafloor sediment by animals. Late Precambrian (Ediacaran) trace fossils from around the world are mainly surface trails and show little evidence of sediment burrowing. Quantitative study in the western United States has shown that a significant increase in bioturbation, occurs between pretrilobite (Tommotian) and trilobite-bearing (Atdabanian) Lower Cambrian rocks. Throughout the Cambrian, bioturbation was more intensive in nearshore and inner-shelf environments than in more offshore settings. Depth of bioturbation in carbonate environments of the inner shelf was consistently less than six centimetres throughout Cambrian time.

Modern biotas are largely dominated by soft-bodied organisms, whereas the fossil record is overwhelmingly dominated by the hard parts of organisms. Rare deposits of fossils with soft parts are therefore of great importance in helping to establish the original diversity and ecology of ancient biotas. Among the most famous soft-bodied biotas is that in the Burgess Shale of western Canada (British Columbia), which is early Middle Cambrian in age. Tens of thousands of complete specimens, many with soft parts preserved in remarkable detail, were apparently buried by submarine slumping of sediment on the continental shelf of Laurentia. Fossils from the Burgess Shale have been

Abundance of sponges and related forms

Proliferation of mollusks

Cambrian deposits with soft-bodied organisms

used to demonstrate the presence of a complex community as diverse in habit, structure, and adaptation as many modern communities. If isolated, fossils with hard parts would constitute a typical Cambrian fauna, but they represent only about 40 percent of the genera in the Burgess Shale, a proportion similar to that in modern faunas on continental shelves.

Other less diverse Cambrian deposits with soft-bodied organisms have been discovered in such places as South Australia, China (Yunnan), North Greenland, Sweden, and the United States (Utah and Pennsylvania). Some of these are important in demonstrating that the biota of the Burgess Shale is unusual only in preservation and not in composition. They also demonstrate that some of the soft-bodied taxa have substantial geologic ranges and wide geographic distributions. Extraordinary preservation of Late Cambrian arthropods in Sweden is especially notable, as the bodies and appendages remain largely uncrushed and the integument retains many fine structures, including setae and pores.

Minor extinction events occurred sporadically throughout the Cambrian Period. One near the end of the Early Cambrian was apparently related to global marine regression. At least three Late Cambrian events primarily affected low-latitude shelf faunas and have been used in North America to define biostratigraphic units called biomeres. (Such units are bounded by sudden nonevolutionary changes in the dominant elements of a phylum.) Each of the Cambrian biomere events eliminated several trilobite families, which collectively contained most of the genera and species that were living on the continental shelves. Less attention has been paid to extinction patterns among other invertebrates, but some evidence of corresponding extinctions among brachiopods and conodonts is available. Geochemical evidence suggests that the biomere extinctions were probably caused by abrupt drops in water temperature. Oxygen isotopes from the skeletons of bottom-dwelling trilobites associated with one biomere boundary in Texas indicate a drop in water temperature of about 5° C (9° F) at the boundary. A comparable decrease in temperature would kill the larvae of many modern marine invertebrates that live in warm oceans. Following each Cambrian extinction, shelf environments were repopulated by low-diversity trilobite faunas of relatively simple form, which apparently emigrated from deeper and cooler off-shelf environments. In effect, every one of the biomere events was followed by an adaptive radiation of new taxa, especially among the trilobites.   (Richard A. Robison)

Oceans

Ocean basins

The first major undersea survey was undertaken during the 1870s, but it was not until the last half of the 20th century that scientists began to learn what lies beneath the ocean surface in any detail. It has been determined that the ocean basins, which hold the vast quantity of water that covers nearly three-quarters of the Earth's surface, have an average depth of almost four kilometres. A number of major features of the basins depart from this average, as, for example, the mountainous ocean ridges, deep-sea trenches, and jagged, linear fracture zones. Other significant features of the ocean floor include aseismic ridges, abyssal hills, and seamounts and guyots. The basins also contain a variable amount of sedimentary fill that is thinnest on the ocean ridges and usually thickest near the continental margins.

While the ocean basins lie much lower than sea level, the continents stand high—about one kilometre above sea level. The physical explanation for this condition is that the continental crust is light and thick, whereas the oceanic crust is dense and thin. Both the continental and oceanic crust lie over a more uniform layer called the mantle. As an analogy, one can think of a thick piece of styrofoam and a thin piece of wood floating in a tub of water. The styrofoam rises higher out of the water than the wood.

The ocean basins are transient features over geologic time, changing shape and depth while the process of plate tectonics proceeds. The surface layer of the Earth, the lithosphere, consists of a number of rigid plates that are in continual motion. The boundaries between the lithospheric plates form the principal relief features of the ocean basins: the crests of oceanic ridges are spreading centres where two plates move apart from each other at a rate of several centimetres per year. Molten rock material wells up from the underlying mantle into the gap between the diverging plates and solidifies into oceanic crust, thereby creating new ocean floor. At the deep-sea trenches, two plates converge, with one plate sliding down under the other into the mantle where it is melted. Thus, for each segment of new ocean floor created at the ridges, an equal amount of old oceanic crust is destroyed at the trenches, or so-called subduction zones (see below *Deep-sea trenches* and also the article PLATE TECTONICS). It is for this reason that the oldest segment of ocean floor, found in the far western Pacific, is apparently only about 200 million years old, even though the age of the Earth is estimated to be at least 4.6 billion years.

The dominant factors that govern seafloor relief and topography are the thermal properties of the oceanic plates, tensional forces in the plates, volcanic activity, and sedimentation. In brief, the oceanic ridges rise about two kilometres above the seafloor because the plates near these spreading centres are warm and thermally expanded. In contrast, plates in the subduction zones are generally cooler. Tensional forces resulting in plate divergence at the spreading centres also create block-faulted mountains and abyssal hills, which trend parallel to the oceanic ridges. Seamounts and guyots, as well as abyssal hills and most aseismic ridges, are produced by volcanism. Continuing sedimentation throughout the ocean basin serves to blanket and bury many of the faulted mountains and abyssal hills with time. Erosion plays a relatively minor role in shaping the face of the deep seafloor, in contrast to the continents. This is because deep ocean currents are generally slow (they flow at less than 50 centimetres per second) and lack sufficient power.

EXPLORATION OF THE OCEAN BASINS

Mapping the characteristics of the ocean basin has been difficult for several reasons. First, the oceans are not easy to travel over; second, until recent times navigation has been extremely crude, so that individual observations have been only loosely correlated with one another; and, finally, the oceans are opaque to light—*i.e.*, the deep seafloor cannot be seen from the ocean surface. Modern technology has given rise to customized research vessels, satellite and electronic navigation, and sophisticated acoustic instruments that have mitigated some of these problems.

Notable topographic features of the ocean basins

Factors governing seafloor relief and topography

The Challenger Expedition, mounted by the British in 1872–76, provided the first systematic view of a few of the major features of the seafloor. Scientists aboard the HMS *Challenger* determined ocean depths by means of wireline soundings and discovered the Mid-Atlantic Ridge. Dredges brought up samples of rocks and sediments off the seafloor. The main advance in mapping, however, did not occur until sonar was developed in the early 20th century. This system for detecting the presence of objects underwater by acoustic echo provided marine researchers with a highly useful tool, since sound can be detected over several thousands of kilometres in the ocean (visible light, by comparison, can only penetrate 100 metres or so of water).

Modern sonar systems include the Seabeam multibeam echo sounder and the GLORIA scanning sonar (see EXPLORATION: *Undersea exploration: Methodology and instrumentation: Exploration of the seafloor and the Earth's crust*). They operate on the principle that the depth (or distance) of the seafloor can be determined by multiplying one-half the elapsed time between a downgoing acoustic pulse and its echo by the speed of sound in seawater (about 1,500 metres per second). Such multifrequency sonar systems permit the use of different pulse frequencies to meet different scientific objectives. Acoustic pulses of 12 kilohertz (kHz), for example, are normally employed to measure ocean depth, while lower frequencies—3.5 kHz to less than 100 hertz (Hz)—are used to map the thickness of sediments in the ocean basins. Very high frequencies of 100 kHz or more are employed in side-scanning sonar to measure the texture of the seafloor. The acoustic pulses are normally generated by piezoelectric transducers. For determining subbottom structure, low-frequency acoustic pulses are produced by explosives, compressed air, or water-jet implosion. Near-bottom sonar systems, such as the Deep Tow of the Scripps Institution of Oceanography (in La Jolla, Calif., U.S.), produce even more detailed images of the seafloor and subbottom structure. The Deep Tow package contains both echo sounders and side-scanning sonars, along with associated geophysical instruments, and is towed behind a ship at slow speed 10 to 100 metres above the seafloor. It yields very precise measurements of even finer-scale features than are resolvable with Seabeam and other comparable systems.

Another notable instrument system is ANGUS, a deep-towed camera sled that can take thousands of high-resolution photographs of the seafloor during a single day. It has been successfully used in the detection of hydrothermal vents at spreading centres (see below *Oceanic ridges*). Overlapping photographic images make it possible to construct photomosaic strips about 10–20 metres wide that reveal details on the order of centimetres.

Three major navigation systems are in use in modern marine geology. These include electromagnetic systems such as loran and Earth-orbiting satellites (see EXPLORATION: *Undersea exploration: Basic elements of undersea exploration: Navigation*). Acoustic transponder arrays of two or more stations placed on the seafloor a few kilometres apart are used to navigate deeply towed instruments, submersibles, and occasionally surface research vessels when detailed mapping is conducted in small areas. These systems measure the distance between the instrument package and the transponder sites and, using simple geometry, compute fixes accurate to a few metres. Although the individual transponders can be used to determine positions relative to the array with great accuracy, the preciseness of the position of the array itself depends on which system is employed to locate it.

Satellite measurements

Such Earth-orbiting satellites as SEASAT and GEOSAT have uncovered some significant topographic features of the ocean basins. SEASAT, launched in 1978, carried a radar altimeter into orbit. This device was used to measure the distance between the satellite path and the surfaces of the ocean and continents to 0.1 metre. The measurements revealed that the shape of the ocean surface is warped by seafloor features: massive seamounts cause the surface to bulge over them owing to gravitational attraction. Similarly, the ocean surface downwarps occur over trenches. Using these satellite measurements of the ocean surface,

William F. Haxby computed the gravity field there. The resulting gravity map provides comprehensive coverage of the ocean surface on a 5′ by 5′ grid (five nautical miles on each side at the equator). Coverage as complete as this is not available from echo soundings made from ships. Because the gravity field at the ocean surface is a highly sensitive indicator of marine topography, this map reveals various previously uncharted features, including seamounts, ridges, and fracture zones, while improving the detail on other known features. In addition, the gravity map shows a linear pattern of gravity anomalies that cut obliquely across the grain of the topography. These anomalies are most pronounced in the Pacific basin; they are apparently about 100 kilometres across and some 1,000 kilometres long. They have an amplitude of approximately 10 milligals (0.001 percent of the Earth's gravity attraction) and are aligned west-northwest—very close to the direction in which the Pacific Plate moves over the mantle below.

OCEANIC CRUST

Structure and composition. The oceanic crust differs from the continental crust in several ways: it is thinner, denser, younger, of different chemical composition, and created in a different plate-tectonic setting. The oceanic crust is formed at spreading centres on the oceanic ridges, whereas continental crust is formed above the subduction zones. The oceanic crust is about six kilometres thick. It is composed of several layers, not including the overlying sediment. The topmost layer, about 500 metres thick, includes lavas of basaltic composition (*i.e.*, rock material consisting largely of plagioclase [feldspar] and pyroxene). The lavas are generally of two types: pillow lavas and sheet flows. Pillow lavas appear to be shaped exactly as the name implies—like large overstuffed pillows about one metre in cross section and one to several metres long. They commonly form small hills tens of metres high at the spreading centres. Sheet flows have the appearance of wrinkled bed sheets. They commonly are thin (only about 10 centimetres thick) and cover a broader area than pillow lavas. There is evidence that sheet flows are erupted at higher temperatures than those of the pillow variety. On the East Pacific Rise at 8° S latitude, a series of sheet flow eruptions (possibly since the mid-1960s) have covered more than 220 square kilometres of seafloor to an average depth of 70 metres.

Below the lava is a layer composed of feeder, or sheeted, dikes that measures more than one kilometre thick. Dikes are fractures that serve as the plumbing system for transporting magmas (molten rock material) to the seafloor to produce lavas. They are about one metre wide, subvertical, and elongate along the trend of the spreading centre where they formed, and they abut one another's sides—hence the term sheeted. These dikes are also of basaltic composition. There are two layers below the dikes totaling about 4.5 kilometres in thickness. Both of these include gabbros, which are essentially basalts with coarser mineral grains. These gabbro layers are thought to represent the magma chambers, or pockets of lava, that ultimately erupt on the seafloor. The upper gabbro layer is isotropic (uniform) in structure. In some places, this layer includes pods of plagiogranite, a differentiated rock richer in silica than gabbro. The lower gabbro layer has a stratified structure and evidently represents the floor or sides of the magma chamber. This layered structure is called cumulate, meaning that the layers (which measure up to several metres thick) result from the sedimentation of minerals out of the liquid magma. The layers in the cumulate gabbro have less silica but are richer in iron and magnesium than the upper portions of the crust. Olivine, an iron-magnesium silicate, is a common mineral in the lower gabbro layer.

The oceanic crust lies atop the Earth's mantle, as does the continental crust. Mantle rock is composed mostly of peridotite, which consists primarily of the mineral olivine with small amounts of pyroxene and amphibole.

Investigations of the oceanic crust. Knowledge of the structure and composition of the oceanic crust comes from several sources. Bottom sampling during early exploration brought up all varieties of the above-mentioned rocks, but the structure of the crust and the abundance of the constituent rocks were unclear. Simultaneously, seismic refraction experiments enabled researchers to determine the layered nature of the oceanic crust. These experiments involve measuring the travel times of seismic waves generated by explosions (*e.g.*, dynamite blasts) set off over distances of several tens of kilometres. The results of early refraction experiments revealed the existence of two layers beneath the sediment cover. More sophisticated experiments and analyses led to dividing these layers into two parts, each with a different seismic wave velocity, which increases with depth. The seismic velocity is a kind of fingerprint that can be attributed to a limited number of rock types. Sampled rock data and seismic results were combined to yield a model for the structure and composition of the crust.

Study of ophiolites

Great strides in understanding the oceanic crust were made by the study of ophiolites. These are slices of the ocean floor that have been thrust above sea level by the action of plate tectonics. In various places in the world, the entire sequence of oceanic crust and upper mantle is exposed. These areas include, among others, Newfoundland and the Pacific Coast Ranges of California, the island of Cyprus in the Mediterranean Sea, and the mountains in Oman on the southeastern tip of the Arabian Peninsula. Ophiolites reveal the structure and composition of the oceanic crust in astonishing detail. Also, the process of crustal formation and hydrothermal circulation, as well as the origin of marine magnetic anomalies (see below), can be studied with comparative clarity. Although it is clear that ophiolites are of marine origin, there is some controversy as to whether they represent typical oceanic crust or crust formed in settings other than an oceanic spreading centre—behind island arcs, for example.

The age of the oceanic crust does not go back farther than about 200 million years. Such crust is being formed today at oceanic spreading centres. Many ophiolites are much older than the oldest oceanic crust, demonstrating continuity of the formation processes over hundreds of millions of years. Methods that may be used to determine the age of the crustal material include direct dating of rock samples by radiometric dating (measuring the relative abundances of a particular radioactive isotope and its daughter isotopes in the samples) or by the analyses of fossil evidence, marine magnetic anomalies, or ocean depth. Of these, magnetic anomalies deserve special attention.

A marine magnetic anomaly is a variation in strength of the Earth's magnetic field caused by magnetism in rocks of the ocean floor. Marine magnetic anomalies typically represent 1 percent of the total geomagnetic field strength. They can be stronger ("positive") or weaker ("negative") than the average total field. Also, the magnetic anomalies occur in long bands that run parallel to spreading centres for hundreds of kilometres (Figure 30) and may reach up to a few tens of kilometres in width.

Marine magnetic anomalies were first discovered off the coast of the western United States in the late 1950s and completely baffled scientists. The anomalies were charted from southern California to northern Washington and out several hundred kilometres. Victor Vacquier, a geophysicist, noticed that these linear anomalies ended at the fracture zones mapped in this area. In addition, he noticed that they had unique shapes, occurred in a predictable sequence across their trends, and could be correlated across the fracture zones. Soon thereafter, linear magnetic anomalies were mapped over the Reykjanes Ridge south of Iceland. They were found to occur on both sides of the ridge crest and parallel to it. Simultaneously, Alan Cox and several other American geophysicists documented evidence that the Earth's magnetic field had reversed in the past: the north magnetic pole had been the south magnetic pole about 700,000 years ago, and there were reasons to believe older reversals existed. Also at this time, Robert S. Dietz and Harry H. Hess were formulating the theory of seafloor spreading—the hypothesis that oceanic crust is created at the crests of the oceanic ridges and consumed in the deep-sea trenches.

It remained for Frederick J. Vine and Drummond H. Matthews of Great Britain and Lawrence W. Morley of Canada to put these observations together in a theory that explained marine magnetic anomalies. The theory rests on three assumptions: (1) that the Earth's magnetic field periodically reverses polarity; (2) that seafloor spreading occurs; and (3) that the oceanic crust is permanently magnetized as it forms and cools at spreading centres. The theory expresses the assumptions—namely, that the oceanic crust records reversals of the Earth's field as it is formed during seafloor spreading. Positive anomalies result when the crust is magnetized in a "normal" polarity parallel to the ambient field of the Earth, and negative anomalies result when the crust is "reversely" magnetized in an opposite sense. As the magnetized crust moves down the flanks of a ridge away from the spreading centre, it remains permanently magnetized and "carries" the magnetic anomalies along with it. (For further details about paleomagnetism and seafloor spreading, see PLATE TECTONICS: *Historical overview: Renewed interest in continental drift.*)

A brilliant leap in understanding was now possible. If the age of the field reversals were known, the age of the ocean crust could be predicted by mapping the corresponding anomaly. By the mid-1960s, Cox and his colleagues had put together a schedule of reversals for the last four or five million years by studying the ages and magnetic polarities of lava flows found on land. Vine and the Canadian geologist J. Tuzo Wilson applied the time scale to marine magnetic anomalies mapped over the Juan de Fuca Ridge, a spreading centre off the northwest United States (Figure 30). They thus dated the crust there and also computed the first seafloor spreading rate of about 30 millimetres per year. The rate is computed by dividing the distance of

Calculation of seafloor spreading rate

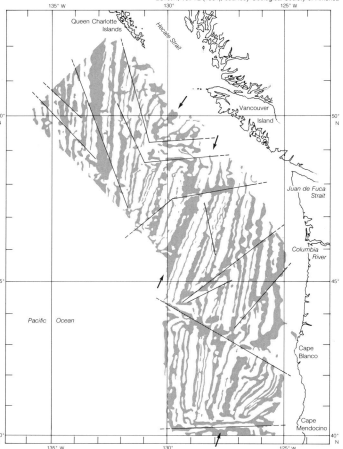

From J.P. Kennett, *Marine Geology* (1982); Prentice-Hall, Inc., Englewood Cliffs, N.J.; after R.G. Mason and A.D. Raff, *Geological Society American Bulletin*, vol. 72 (1961); courtesy Geological Society of America

Figure 30: *Magnetic anomalies off the west coast of the United States.*
The gray areas represent positive anomalies formed during periods of normal polarity of the Earth's magnetic field. The white (open) areas mark negative anomalies formed when the field was reversed. The arrows show the central magnetic anomaly over three spreading centres (from north to south): Explorer, Juan de Fuca, and Gorda (see text).

an anomaly from the ridge crest by the age of the anomaly twice. Thus the oceanic crust at the Juan de Fuca Ridge is moving at about 15 millimetres per year away from the ridge crest and at about 60 millimetres per year away from the crustal segment on the opposite side of the crest.

During the 1960s and '70s marine magnetic anomalies were mapped over wide areas of the ocean basins. By using estimates of the ages of oceanic crust obtained from core samples by deep-sea drilling, a magnetic anomaly time scale was constructed, and at the same time the spreading history for the ocean basins covering the last 200 million years or so was proposed.

It is thought that the most important contributor to marine magnetic anomalies is the layer of lavas in the upper oceanic crust. A secondary contribution originates in the upper layer of gabbros. The dike layer is essentially demagnetized by the action of hydrothermal waters at the spreading centres. The dominant mechanism of permanent magnetization is the thermoremanent magnetization (or TRM) of iron-titanium oxide minerals. These minerals lock in a TRM as they cool below 200° to 300° C in the presence of the Earth's magnetic field. Although several processes are capable of altering the TRM, including reheating and oxidation at the seafloor, it is remarkably robust, as is evidenced by magnetic anomalies as old as 165 million years in the far western equatorial Pacific.

OCEANIC RIDGES

The largest features of the ocean basin are the oceanic ridges. In the past these features were referred to as mid-ocean ridges, but, as will be seen, the largest oceanic ridge, the East Pacific Rise, is far from a mid-ocean location, and the nomenclature is thus inaccurate. Oceanic ridges are not to be confused with aseismic ridges, which have an entirely different origin (see below).

Principal characteristics. Oceanic ridges are linear mountain chains comprising the largest features on Earth. They are found in every ocean basin and appear to girdle the Earth. The ridges rise from depths near 5 kilometres to an essentially uniform depth of about 2.6 kilometres and are roughly symmetrical in cross section. They can be thousands of kilometres wide. In places, the crests of the ridges are offset across transform faults, or fracture zones, which can be followed down the flanks of the ridges. (Transform faults are those along which lateral movement occurs.) The flanks are marked by sets of mountains and hills that are elongate and parallel to the ridge trend.

New oceanic crust (and part of the upper mantle, which, together with the crust, makes up the lithosphere) is formed at seafloor spreading centres at the crests of the oceanic ridges. Because of this, certain unique geologic features are found there. Fresh basaltic lavas are exposed on the seafloor at the ridge crests. These lavas are progressively buried by sediments as the seafloor spreads away from the site. The flow of heat out of the crust is many times greater at the crests than elsewhere in the world. Earthquakes are common along the crests and in the transform faults that join the offset ridge segments. Analysis of earthquakes occurring at the ridge crests indicates that the oceanic crust is under tension there. A high-amplitude magnetic anomaly is centred over the crests because fresh lavas at the crests are being magnetized in the direction of the present geomagnetic field.

The depths over the oceanic ridges are rather precisely correlated with the age of the ocean crust; specifically, it has been demonstrated that the ocean depth is proportional to the square root of crustal age (Figure 31). The theory explaining this relationship holds that the increase in depth with age is due to the thermal contraction of the oceanic crust and upper mantle as they are carried away from the seafloor spreading centre in an oceanic plate. Because such a plate is ultimately about 100 kilometres thick, contraction of only a few percent predicts the entire relief of an oceanic ridge. It then follows that the width of a ridge can be defined as twice the distance from the crest to the point where the plate has cooled to a steady thermal state. Most of the cooling takes place within 70 or 80 million years, by which time the ocean depth is about 5 to 5.5 kilometres. Because this cooling is a function of age,

slow-spreading ridges, such as the Mid-Atlantic Ridge, are narrower than faster-spreading ridges, like the East Pacific Rise (see below). Further, a correlation has been found between global spreading rates and the transgression and regression of ocean waters onto the continents. During the Early Cretaceous period about 100 million years ago, when global spreading rates were uniformly high, oceanic ridges occupied comparatively more of the ocean basins, causing the ocean waters to transgress (spill over) onto the continents, leaving marine sediments in areas now well away from coastlines.

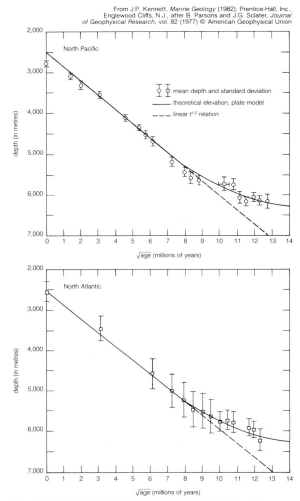

From J.P. Kennett, *Marine Geology* (1982); Prentice-Hall, Inc., Englewood Cliffs, N.J., after B. Parsons and J.G. Sclater, *Journal of Geophysical Research*, vol. 82 (1977) © American Geophysical Union

Figure 31: Relationship between depth of oceanic crust and its age. Error bars are one standard deviation (see text).

Besides ridge width, other features appear to be a function of spreading rate. Global spreading rates range from 10 millimetres per year (mm/yr total rate) or less up to 160 mm/yr. Oceanic ridges can be classified as slow (up to 50 mm/yr), intermediate (up to 90 mm/yr), and fast (up to 160 mm/yr). Slow-spreading ridges are characterized by a rift valley at the crest. Such a valley is fault-controlled. It is typically 1.4 kilometres deep and 20 to 40 kilometres wide. Faster-spreading ridges lack rift valleys. At intermediate rates, the crest regions are broad highs with occasional fault-bounded valleys no deeper than 200 metres. At fast rates, an axial high is present at the crest. The slow-spreading rifted ridges have rough faulted topography on their flanks, while the faster-spreading ridges have much smoother flanks (Figure 32).

Distribution of major ridges and spreading centres. Oceanic spreading centres are found in all the ocean basins. In the Arctic Ocean a slow-rate spreading centre is located near the eastern side in the Eurasian basin. It can be followed south, offset by transform faults, to Iceland. Iceland has been created by a hot spot (see below) located directly below an oceanic spreading centre. The

Global seafloor spreading rates (margin note)

ridge leading south from Iceland is named the Reykjanes Ridge, and, although it spreads at 20 mm/yr or less, it lacks a rift valley. This is thought to be the result of the influence of the hot spot.

The Mid-Atlantic Ridge extends from south of Iceland to the extreme South Atlantic Ocean near 60° S latitude. It bisects the Atlantic Ocean basin, which led to the earlier designation of mid-ocean ridge for features of this type. The Mid-Atlantic Ridge became known in a rudimentary fashion during the 19th century. In 1855 Matthew Fontaine Maury of the U.S. Navy prepared a chart of the Atlantic in which he identified it as a shallow "middle ground." During the 1950s the American oceanographers Bruce Heezen and Maurice Ewing proposed that it was a continuous mountain range.

In the North Atlantic the ridge spreads slowly and displays a rift valley and mountainous flanks. In the South Atlantic spreading rates are between slow and intermediate, and rift valleys are generally absent, as they occur only near transform faults.

After K.C. Macdonald, *The Geology of North America*, vol. N (1989); Geological Society of America

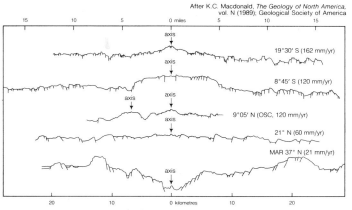

Figure 32: *High-resolution bathymetric profiles across the East Pacific Rise and Mid-Atlantic Ridge.*
The spreading rate varies from fast (159 millimetres per year) to slow (21 millimetres per year) on the Mid-Atlantic Ridge.
OSC stands for overlapping spreading centre: MAR signifies Mid-Atlantic Ridge.

A very slow oceanic ridge, the Southwest Indian Ridge, bisects the ocean between Africa and Antarctica. It joins the Mid-Indian and Southeast Indian ridges east of Madagascar. The Carlsberg Ridge is found at the north end of the Mid-Indian Ridge. It continues north to join spreading centres in the Gulf of Aden and Red Sea. Spreading is very slow at this point but approaches intermediate rates on the Carlsberg and Mid-Indian ridges. The Southeast Indian Ridge spreads at intermediate rates. This ridge continues from the western Indian Ocean in a southeasterly direction, bisecting the ocean between Australia and Antarctica. Rifted crests and rugged mountainous flanks are characteristic of the Southwest Indian Ridge. The Mid-Indian Ridge has fewer features of this kind, and the Southeast Indian Ridge has generally smoother topography. The latter also displays distinct asymmetric seafloor spreading south of Australia. Analysis of magnetic anomalies shows that rates on opposite sides of the spreading centre have been unequal at many times over the past 50 or 60 million years.

The Pacific-Antarctic Ridge can be followed from a point midway between New Zealand and Antarctica northeast to where it joins the East Pacific Rise off the margin of South America. The former spreads at intermediate to fast rates.

East Pacific Rise The East Pacific Rise extends from this site northward to the Gulf of California, where it joins the transform zone of the Pacific-North American plate boundary. Offshore from Chile and Peru, the East Pacific Rise is currently spreading at fast rates of 159 mm/yr or more. Rates decrease to about 60 mm/yr at the mouth of the Gulf of California. The crest of the ridge displays a low topographic rise along its length rather than a rift valley. The East Pacific Rise was first detected during the Challenger Expedition of the 1870s. It was described in its gross form

during the 1950s and '60s by oceanographers, including Heezen, Ewing, and Henry W. Menard. During the 1980s, Kenneth C. Macdonald, Paul J. Fox, and Peter F. Lonsdale discovered that the main spreading centre appears to be interrupted and offset a few kilometres to one side at various places along the crest of the East Pacific Rise. However, the ends of the offset spreading centres overlap each other by several kilometres. These were identified as a new type of geologic feature of oceanic spreading centres and designated overlapping spreading centres. Such centres are thought to result from interruptions of the magma supply to the crest along its length and define a fundamental segmentation of the ridge on a scale of tens to hundreds of kilometres.

Many smaller spreading centres branch off the major ones or are found behind island arcs. In the western Pacific, spreading centres occur on the Fiji Plateau between the New Hebrides and Fiji Islands and in the Woodlark Basin between New Guinea and the Solomon Islands. A series of spreading centres and transform faults lie between the East Pacific Rise and South America near 40° to 50° S latitude. The Scotia Sea between South America and the Antarctic Peninsula contains a spreading centre. The Galápagos spreading centre trends east-west between the East Pacific Rise and South America near the equator. Three short spreading centres are found a few hundred kilometres off the shore of the Pacific Northwest. These are the Gorda Ridges off northern California, the Juan de Fuca Ridge off Oregon and Washington, and the Explorer Ridge off Vancouver Island. In a careful study of the seafloor spreading history of the Galápagos and the Juan de Fuca spreading centres, the American geophysicist Richard N. Hey developed the idea of the propagating rift. In this phenomenon, one branch of a spreading centre ending in a transform fault lengthens at the expense of the spreading centre across the fault. The rift and fault propagate at one to five times the spreading rate and create chevron patterns in magnetic anomalies and the grain of the seafloor topography resembling the wake of a boat.

Spreading centre zones and associated phenomena. From the 1970s highly detailed studies of spreading centres using deeply towed instruments, photography, and manned submersibles have resulted in new revelations about the processes of seafloor spreading. The most profound discoveries have been of deep-sea hydrothermal vents (see below) and previously unknown biological communities.

Spreading centres are divided into several geologic zones. The neovolcanic zone is at the very axis. It is 1 to 2 kilometres wide and is the site of recent and active volcanism and of the hydrothermal vents. It is marked by chains of small volcanoes or volcanic ridges. Adjacent to the neovolcanic zone is one marked by fissures in the seafloor. This may be 1 to 2 kilometres wide. Beyond this point occurs a zone of active faulting. Here, fissures develop into normal faults with vertical offsets. This zone may be 10 or more kilometres wide. At slow spreading rates the faults have offsets of hundreds of metres, creating rift valleys and rift mountains. At faster rates the vertical offsets are 50 metres or less. A deep rift valley is not formed because the vertical uplifts are cancelled out by faults that downdrop uplifted blocks. This results in linear, fault-bounded abyssal hills and valleys trending parallel to the spreading centre.

Warm springs emanating from the seafloor in the neovolcanic zone were first found on the Galápagos spreading centre. These waters were measured to have temperatures about 20° C above the ambient temperature. In 1979 hydrothermal vents with temperatures near 350° C were discovered on the East Pacific Rise off Mexico (Figure 33). Since then, similar vents have been found on the spreading centres off the Pacific Northwest coast of the United States, on the south end of the northern Mid-Atlantic Ridge, and at many locations on the East Pacific Rise.

Hydrothermal vents are localized discharges of heated seawater. They result from cold seawater percolating down into the hot oceanic crust through the zone of fissures and returning to the seafloor in a pipelike flow at the axis of the neovolcanic zone. The heated waters often carry sulfide minerals of zinc, iron, and copper leached from the

Seafloor vents

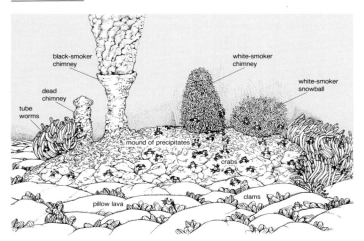

Figure 33: *Hydrothermal field at a spreading centre.*
The black-smoker chimney is one or two metres high and
is composed of sulfide minerals precipitated from hot water
of approximately 350° C. The white-smoker chimney is
precipitated from cooler water near 300° C and consists
chiefly of silica.

crust. Outflow of these heated waters probably accounts
for 20 percent of the Earth's heat loss. Exotic biological
communities exist around the hydrothermal vents. These
ecosystems are totally independent of energy from the
Sun. They are not dependent on photosynthesis but rather
on chemosynthesis by sulfur-fixing bacteria. The sulfide
minerals precipitated in the neovolcanic zone can accumulate in substantial amounts and are sometimes buried
by lava flows at a later time. Such deposits are mined as
commercial ores in ophiolites on Cyprus and in Oman.

Magma chambers have been detected beneath the crest
of the East Pacific Rise by seismic experiments. (The principle underlying the experiments is that partially molten
or molten rock slows the travel of seismic waves and
also strongly reflects them.) The depth to the top of the
chambers is about two kilometres below the seafloor. The
width is more difficult to ascertain, but is probably one to
four kilometres. Their thickness seems to be about two to
six kilometres based on studies of ophiolites (Figure 34).
The chambers have been mapped along the trend of the
crest between 9° and 13° N latitude. The top is relatively
continuous, but is apparently interrupted by offsets of
transform faults and overlapping spreading centres.

FRACTURE ZONES AND TRANSFORM FAULTS

Fracture zones. As was noted above, oceanic ridges
(and their associated spreading centres) are offset along
their trend by fracture zones. These are ridges and valleys
on the order of tens of kilometres wide that cut across the
crests of the ridges at approximately right angles and offset
their trend (Figure 35). Typically, a regional depth offset is
present across a fracture zone, owing to the juxtaposition
of crust of different ages (and, therefore, depth) across
it. In the Atlantic, on the slow spreading Mid-Atlantic
Ridge, fracture zones are numerous and occur every 55
kilometres on average along the trend of the ridge. They
offset the crest between 5 and 40 kilometres. Some of the
larger fracture zones in the North Atlantic are the Gibbs
at 52° N, the Atlantis at 30° N, and the Vema at 11° N.
These and others can be followed across both flanks of
the ridge for some 3,000 kilometres. The Vema Fracture
Zone offsets the Mid-Atlantic Ridge 320 kilometres to the
left. It is marked by a sediment-filled valley more than
5 kilometres deep and 10 to 20 kilometres wide and is
flanked by mountains 3,500 metres high. Basalts, gabbros,
and serpentinized peridotites (*i.e.*, those peridotites that
have been altered in varying degrees to serpentine) of the
oceanic crust and mantle have been recovered from the
mountain flanks.

Fracture zones occur less frequently on the East Pacific
Rise, but they offset the ridge by a greater amount. More
than a dozen can be found between 20° N and 30° S.

Typical offsets are roughly 100 kilometres. Several fracture zones more than 3,000 kilometres long are found off
the shore of western North America. These include the
Mendocino, Murray, Molokai, and Clarion fracture zones.
They are not associated with a ridge crest. Rather, they
occur on the west flank of the defunct Pacific-Farallon
oceanic ridge. The Farallon Plate has all but disappeared
down a subduction zone that extended along the entire
coast of California and Baja California until about 25 to
30 million years ago. Subduction now occurs north of the
Mendocino Fracture Zone. These fracture zones off western North America were among the first mapped. Menard
has traced them almost 10,000 kilometres westward across
the Pacific. The continental margin of northern California
is displaced to the right where the Mendocino Fracture
Zone and its transform portion, the Gorda Escarpment,
intersect it.

Transform faults. The portion of a fracture zone between different offset spreading centres constitutes a
transform fault. Transform faults also connect spreading
centres to subduction zones (deep-sea trenches). Faults
of this kind are the only segments of fracture zones that
are seismically active. J. Tuzo Wilson recognized this and
other features and explained the phenomenon as a transfer of motion from one spreading centre to another. The
American geologist W. Jason Morgan, one of the several
outstanding pioneers in plate tectonics, recognized that
transform faults are zones where opposing lithospheric
plates slip past one another. Morgan proposed that opposing plates along an oceanic ridge crest offset by fracture
zones are divided by the spreading centres and transform
faults. The inactive portions of the fracture zone on the
ridge flanks are scars on the ocean floor created in the
transform faults.

This theory made a very dramatic prediction: namely,
that the direction of motion on the transform faults was
opposite to the offsets of the ridge crests. For example, if
a ridge crest was offset to the left by a transform fault,
implying leftward movement on a fault joining the offset crests, the movement across the transform fault was
instead to the right (Figure 35). This is clear when it
is realized that the plate boundaries are confined to the
spreading centres and transform faults, not to the inactive
part of the fracture zone. Seismic studies of earthquakes

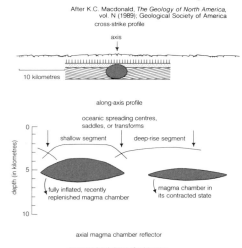

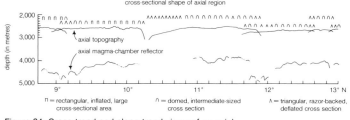

Figure 34: Cross-trend and along-trend views of an axial
magma chamber on the East Pacific Rise. The two upper
diagrams are idealized; the one at the bottom is made from
seismic reflection surveys (see text).

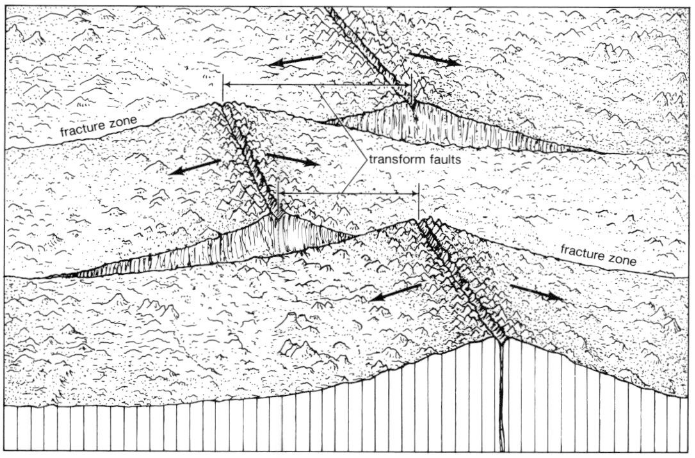

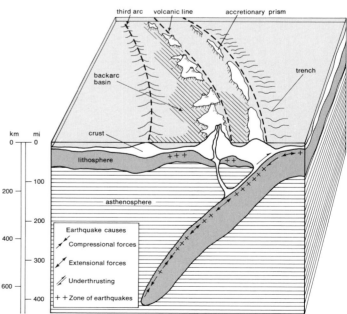

Figure 35: Oceanic ridges offset by transform faults and fracture zones. The arrows show the direction of movement across the transform faults.

from transform faults soon revealed that the motion was opposite, as predicted.

Not everywhere in the ocean basins are plate motions exactly parallel to transform faults. In places where a component of opening motion occurs across the transform, volcanic activity results, and the fracture zone is termed a leaky transform fault. South of New Zealand, between it and the Pacific-Antarctic Ridge, a component of shortening is occurring across a transform called the Macquarie Ridge. Here, subduction may be taking place at a slow rate.

DEEP-SEA TRENCHES

Types. Although the term trench has been applied to many deep, long linear troughs in the ocean floor, the most common and accurate usage relates it to subduction zones. According to plate tectonic theory, subduction zones are locations where a lithospheric plate bearing oceanic crust slides down into the upper mantle under the force of gravity. The result is a topographic depression where the oceanic plate comes in contact with the overriding plate, which may be either oceanic or continental. If the overriding plate is oceanic, an island arc develops (Figure 36). The trench forms an arc in plan view, and islands with explosive volcanoes develop on the overriding plate. If the overriding plate is continental, a marginal trench forms where the topographic depression appears to follow the outline of the continental margin. Explosive volcanoes are found here too. Both types of subduction zones are associated with large earthquakes that originate at a depth of as much as 700 kilometres. The deep earthquakes below subduction zones occur in a plane that dips 30° or more under the overriding plate. Typical trench depths are 8 to 10 kilometres. The longest trench is the Peru-Chile Trench, which extends some 5,900 kilometres along the west side of South America. Trenches are relatively narrow, usually less than 100 kilometres wide.

The Pacific basin is rimmed by trenches of both marginal and island arc varieties. Marginal trenches bound the west side of Central and South America from the Gulf of California to southern Chile. Although they are deeply buried in sediment, trenches are found along the western North American continental margin from Cape Mendocino (in northern California) to the Canadian border. The Aleutian Trench extends from the northernmost point in the Gulf of Alaska west to the Kamchatka Peninsula in the Soviet Union. It can be classified as a marginal trench in the east but is more properly termed an island arc west of Alaska.

In the western Pacific, the trenches are associated with island arcs. These include the Kuril, Japan, Bonin, Mariana, Ryukyu, and Philippine trenches that extend from Kamchatka to near the equator. A complex pattern of island arcs is found in Indonesia. The major island arc here is the Java Trench extending from northern Australia

Formation of island arcs

to the northwestern end of Sumatra in the northeast Indian Ocean. The region of New Guinea and the Solomon Islands includes the New Britain and Solomon trenches, the latter of which joins the New Hebrides Trench directly to the south. East of this area the Tonga and Kermadec trenches extend south from the Fiji Islands to New Zealand.

Two island arcs occur in the Atlantic Ocean. The South Sandwich Trench is located west of the Mid-Atlantic Ridge between South America and Antarctica. The Puerto Rico Trench joins the Lesser Antilles Island arc in the eastern Caribbean.

Some seafloor features bear the name trench and are deep linear troughs but are not subduction zones. The Vema Trench on the Mid-Indian Ridge is a fracture zone. The Vityaz Trench northwest of Fiji is an aseismic (inactive) feature of unknown origin. The Diamantina trench (Diamantina Fracture Zone) extends westward from the southwest coast of Australia. It is a rift valley that was formed when Australia separated from Antarctica between 60 and 50 million years ago.

The deepest water on Earth (11,034 metres) is located in the southern end of the Mariana Trench near Guam. A few trenches are partially filled with sediments derived from the bordering continents. The Aleutian Trench is effectively buried east of Kodiak Island in the Gulf of Alaska. Here, the ocean floor is smooth and flat. To the west farther from the sediment supply on Alaska, the trench reaches depths of more than seven kilometres. The Lesser Antilles trench in the eastern Caribbean also is buried by sediments originating from South America.

Structure. Oceanward of trenches the seafloor is usually bulged upward in an outer ridge or rise of up to 1,000 metres relief. This condition is thought to be the elastic response of the oceanic plate bending down into a subduction zone. The landward or island-arc slope of the trench is often interrupted by a submarine ridge, which sometimes breaks the ocean surface, as in the case of the Java Trench. Such a ridge is constructed from deformed sediments scraped off the top of the descending oceanic plate and is termed an accretionary prism. A line of explosive volcanoes, extruding (erupting) a lava that forms the volcanic rock andesite, is found on the overriding plate usually 100 kilometres or so from the trench. In marginal trenches these volcanoes form mountain chains, such as the Cascades in the Pacific Northwest or the great volcanoes of the Andes. In island arcs they form active volcanic island chains, such as the Mariana Islands.

Figure 36: *Features of a typical island arc.*
The deep-sea trench, volcanic line, accretionary prism, backarc basin, and third arc generally associated with island arcs are shown here.

Behind the volcanic line of island arcs are sometimes found young, narrow ocean basins. These basins are bounded on the opposite side by submarine ridges. Such interarc, or backarc, basins are sites of seafloor spreading directly caused by the dynamics of subduction. They originate at the volcanic line, so that the outer bounding submarine ridge, or third arc, represents an older portion of the volcanic line that has spread away. These backarc basins bear many of the features characteristic of oceanic spreading centres. Well-studied examples of these features are found in the Lau Basin of the Tonga arc and also west of the Mariana Islands. The Sea of Japan originated from backarc spreading behind the Japanese arc that began some 30 million years ago. At least two backarc basins have opened behind the Mariana arc, creating seafloor in two phases from about 30 to 17 million years ago in the western Parece Vela Basin and from 5 million years ago in the Mariana Trough next to the islands.

ASEISMIC RIDGES

In some oceans the basin floors are crossed by long, linear and mountainous aseismic ridges. The term aseismic distinguishes these ridges from oceanic spreading centres because the former lack earthquakes. Most aseismic ridges are constructed by volcanism from a hot spot and are composed of coalescing volcanoes of various sizes. A hot spot is a magma-generating centre fixed in the Earth's deep mantle and leaves a trail of volcanic outpourings on the seafloor as an oceanic plate travels over it. This form of volcanism is not associated with the volcanism at spreading centres and is distinct from it chemically in that the magma extruded onto the surface has a higher alkali composition. (For additional information on hot spots, see VOLCANISM: *Volcanism and tectonic activity: Intraplate volcanism.*)

Formation by hot spot volcanism

The Hawaiian-Emperor chain is the best displayed aseismic ridge. Earthquakes do occur here, but only at the end of the ridge where volcanism is current—in this case, on the island of Hawaii (commonly known as the Big Island) to the southeast end of the island chain. Taking into account the relief of the island of Hawaii above the seafloor, it is the largest volcanic edifice on Earth. The Hawaiian-Emperor chain stretches from the Big Island to the intersection of the Kuril and Aleutian trenches in the northwest Pacific. There are roughly 18 volcanoes or seamounts (see below) per 1,000 kilometres along the Hawaiian segment and 13 per 1,000 kilometres on the Emperor portion beyond the bend. The Hawaiian Islands are a part of the chain—the young part—that rises above sea level. The Hawaiian-Emperor chain has two main trends: (1) from the Hawaiian Islands west to the Kammu and Yūryaku seamounts (near 32° N, 168° W), the trend of the Hawaiian portion is just west of northwest; and (2) from this point to the Aleutian Trench, the trend of the Emperor segment is north-northwest. The hot spot interpretation infers that this change in trend is due to a change in the direction of Pacific Plate motion, from north-northwest prior to 38 million years ago (the age of the ridge at the change in trend) to west of northwest until the present day. Radiometric dating of rocks from the ridge indicates that it is 70 million years old at its extreme north end.

Other prominent aseismic ridges include the Ninetyeast Ridge and the Chagos-Laccadive Plateau in the Indian Ocean and the Walvis Ridge and Rio Grande Rise in the South Atlantic. The Ninetyeast Ridge is thought to have originated from hot spot volcanic activity now located at the Kerguelen Islands near Antarctica. These islands lie atop the Kerguelen Plateau, which also originated from volcanism at this hot spot. The Ninetyeast Ridge stretches parallel to 90° E longitude in a long, linear chain of seamounts and volcanic ridges from the Andaman Islands in the Bay of Bengal more than 4,500 kilometres to the south where it intersects Broken Ridge at 30° S latitude. Broken Ridge is an aseismic ridge and was once part of the Kerguelen Plateau. It was split away from the plateau as Australia separated from Antarctica.

Core samples of the seafloor along the Ninetyeast Ridge have been retrieved through deep-sea drilling. Analyses of the samples show that the ridge is slightly less than 30 mil-

lion years old in the south and about 80 million years old in the north. Additionally, sediments on the ridge indicate that parts of it were above sea level while it was being built near a spreading centre. The ridge then subsided as it rode north on the Indian Plate.

The Walvis Ridge and Rio Grande Rise originated from hot spot volcanism now occurring at the islands of Tristan da Cunha 300 kilometres east of the crest of the Mid-Atlantic Ridge. The Walvis Ridge trends northeast from this location to the African margin. The Rio Grande Rise trends roughly southeast from the South American margin toward the Mid-Atlantic Ridge. Both the Walvis Ridge and Rio Grande Rise began forming from the same hot spot near the spreading centre as the South Atlantic was in its initial opening stages 100 to 80 million years ago. The spreading centre shifted west of the hot spot about 80 million years ago, ending construction of the Rio Grande Rise but continuing to build the Walvis Ridge. Volcanic activity has since diminished, resulting in the younger part of the latter ridge being smaller. The findings of ocean drilling on the Rio Grande Rise show that it was once a volcanic island some two kilometres high.

SEAMOUNTS, GUYOTS, AND ABYSSAL HILLS

Submarine volcanoes

Seamounts are submarine volcanoes with more than 1,000 metres of relief. Aseismic ridges are built by chains of overlapping seamounts. A seamount is akin to a subaerial shield volcano in that it also has gently sloping sides (5° to 15°) and is constructed by nonexplosive eruptions of alkaline basalt lavas that are thought to originate from depths of roughly 150 kilometres. About 2,000 seamounts are known; they are most common in the Pacific and on fast-spreading ridges. Like the Hawaiian-Emperor chain, the lines of seamounts and islands trending northwest-southeast in the central and south Pacific (Marshall Islands, Line Islands, Tuamotu Archipelago, and Cook and Austral Islands) may be due to hot spot volcanism. Isolated seamounts also occur, and many of these are located in the far western Pacific. Another group of smaller seamounts is found in the northeastern Pacific.

Flat-topped seamounts are called guyots. They are particularly abundant in the western Pacific and along the Emperor seamount chain. Bottom samples and drill cores of shallow-water sediments and fossils capping guyots have been retrieved. The presence of such geologic materials suggest that guyots are seamounts that have had their peaks planed off by wave action and have since subsided below sea level. The western Pacific guyots are capped by drowned coral atolls and reefs. These reefs are generally of Late Cretaceous age (about 95 million years old). The cause of the subsidence is attributed to the sinking of the seafloor as it moves down the flanks of an oceanic ridge. However, the reason for the demise of the coral reefs on the Cretaceous guyots is less clear. Under normal conditions, coral growth can easily keep up with sinking due to seafloor spreading. The Cretaceous guyots may have resulted from the northward drift of seamounts and reefs on the Pacific Plate away from the tropical zone of favourable growth. Another hypothesis is that the reefs were killed by unusually anoxic (oxygen-depleted) conditions that developed suddenly, a situation possibly related to intense seafloor volcanism in the Pacific at this time.

Abyssal hills are low-relief (less than 1 kilometre) features usually 1 to 10 kilometres wide and elongate parallel to spreading centres or to marine magnetic anomalies located in the vicinity of the latter. The tops of the hills are often flat, in which case they have steep sides. Gently sloping sides, however, are equally common. Abyssal hills are extremely numerous, so much so that Menard declared them "the most widespread physiographic forms of the face of the earth." Abyssal hills are most common in the Pacific basin, where they cover 80 to 85 percent of the seafloor. Because they cover the entire flanks and crests of the oceanic ridges, such hills are thought to form during crustal accretion at spreading centres. They are commonly associated with intermediate- and fast-spreading ridges. On slow-spreading ridges, such as the Mid-Atlantic, the topographic features are much larger and have steeper sides. Bottom-sampling and seismic reflection studies reveal that abyssal hills are relief features on the top of the oceanic crust; they are not constructed from ocean-bottom sediments. In areas such as the abyssal plains (see below), abyssal hills are buried by sediments.

Apparently the hills are constructed by two processes: volcanism and block faulting. The relative contribution of each may depend on the spreading rate. At slower rates, faulting of the oceanic crust is a dominant factor in forming the relief, and the relief of the hills is greater as the rate is slower. At the crest of a spreading centre, volcanism in the neovolcanic zone initiates the construction of volcanic hills. The zone of active faulting is where they form or are modified by block faulting. The existence of discrete and separate volcanic hills indicates that volcanism at a spreading centre is episodic.

DEEP-SEA SEDIMENTS

The ocean basin floor is everywhere covered by sediments of different types and origins. The only exception are the crests of the spreading centres where new ocean floor has not existed long enough to accumulate a sediment cover. Sediment thickness in the oceans averages about 450 metres. The sediment cover in the Pacific basin ranges from 300 to 600 metres thick, and that in the Atlantic is about 1,000 metres. Generally, the thickness of sediment on the oceanic crust increases with the age of the crust. Oceanic crust adjacent to the continents can be deeply buried by several kilometres of sediment. Deep-sea sediments can reveal much about the last 200 million years of Earth history, including seafloor spreading, the history of ocean life, the behaviour of the Earth's magnetic field, and the changes in the ocean currents and climate.

The study of ocean sediments has been accomplished by several means. Bottom samplers, such as dredges and cores up to 30 metres long, have been lowered from ships by wire to retrieve samples of the upper sediment layers. Deep-sea drilling has retrieved core samples from the entire sediment layer in several hundred locations in the ocean basins. The seismic reflection method has been used to map the thickness of sediments in many parts of the oceans. Besides thickness, seismic reflection data can often reveal sediment type and the processes of sedimentation. (For more information on the equipment and techniques used by investigators to study deep-sea sediments, see EX-PLORATION: *Undersea exploration.*)

Sediment types. Deep-sea sediments can be classified as terrigenous, originating from land; biogenic, consisting largely of the skeletal debris of microorganisms; and authigenic, formed in place on the seafloor (Figure 37). Pelagic sediments, either terrigenous or biogenic, are those that are deposited very slowly in the open ocean either by settling through the volume of oceanic water or by precipitation. The sinking rates of pelagic sediment grains are extremely slow because they ordinarily are no larger than several micrometres. However, fine particles are normally bundled into fecal pellets by zooplankton, which allows sinking at a rate of 40 to 400 metres per day.

Terrigenous sediments are transported to the oceans by rivers and wind. The sediments that reach the continental shelf are often stored in submarine canyons on the continental slope. Turbidity currents carry these sediments down into the deep sea (see above *Density currents in the oceans: Turbidity currents*). These currents create sedimentary deposits called turbidites, which are layers up to several metres thick composed of sediment particles that grade upward from coarser to finer sizes. The turbidites build sedimentary deep-sea fans adjacent to the base of the continental slope. Turbidites also are found below the major river deltas of the world where they build features called abyssal cones. The largest of these is the Ganges Fan (also called the Ganges Cone or Bengal Cone) in the Bay of Bengal east of the Indian subcontinent. It measures 3,000 kilometres long (north-south) by 1,000 kilometres wide (east-west) and is up to 12 kilometres thick. The Bengal Cone is forming from rock material eroded from the Himalayas and transported by the Ganges and Brahmaputra rivers.

Abyssal plains are formed by the accumulation of turbidites beyond the limits of deep-sea fans and abyssal cones in locations where there is a very large sediment supply. In contrast to fans and cones, abyssal plains are flat and featureless. They are prominent near both margins of the Atlantic and in the northeast Pacific. Tectonic and climate controls have influenced the formation of abyssal plains. The last major glaciation near the end of the Pleistocene epoch about 10,000 years ago greatly increased erosion and sediment supply to the deep sea, but deep-sea trenches interrupted the flow of turbidity currents to the ocean floor. Off the Pacific Northwest coast of the United States, however, the trenches were filled by turbidites, and subsequent turbidity currents passed beyond them to form the Alaska and Tufts abyssal plains.

Brown clays are a variety of pelagic sediment, mostly of terrigenous origin, which are composed largely of four different clay minerals: chlorite, illite, kaolinite, and montmorillonite. By definition, clays have less than 30 percent biogenic components. Quartz, volcanic ash, and micrometeorites are common as minor constituents. Brown clays are widespread in the deeper areas of the oceans below four kilometres. They dominate the floor of the

Abyssal plains

From J.P. Kennett, *Marine Geology* (1982); Prentice-Hall, Englewood Cliffs, N.J., after W.H. Berger in *The Geology of Continental Margins*, C.A. Burk and C.L. Drake (eds.), (1974); Springer-Verlag, New York

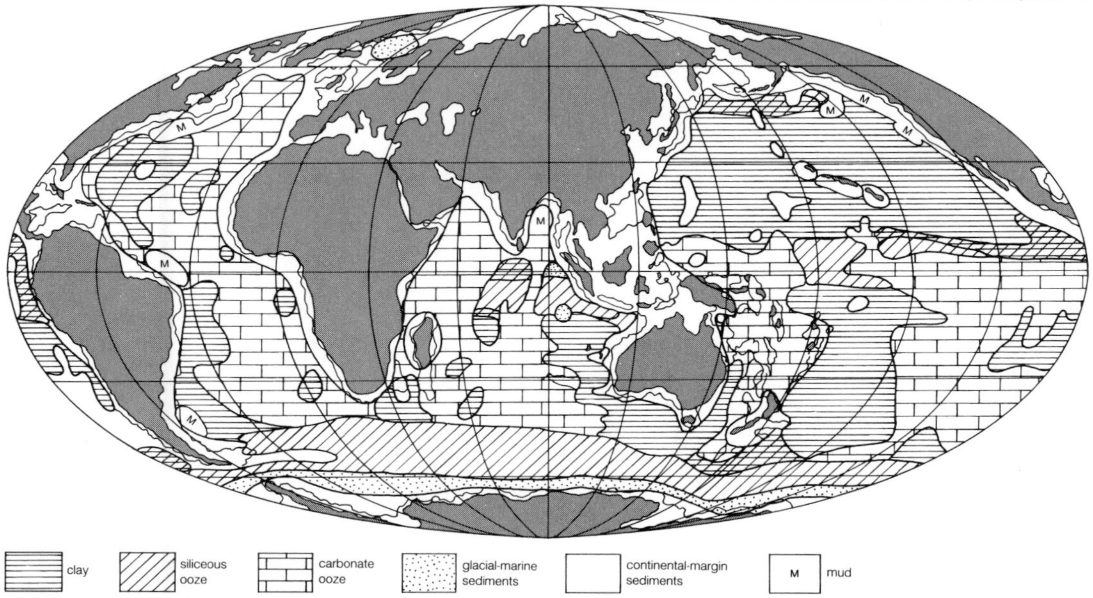

| clay | siliceous ooze | carbonate ooze | glacial-marine sediments | continental-margin sediments | M mud |

Figure 37: Global map of the distribution of sediment types on the ocean floor.

central North Pacific. Clays accumulate very slowly, averaging about one millimetre per 1,000 years. The type of clay found in a given area is a function of the source region on land and the climate. For example, chlorite is dominant in polar regions and kaolinite in the tropics. Clays are introduced into the oceans by river transport, although kaolinite is also carried by the wind from the arid regions of Africa and Australia. Montmorillonite is an alteration product of volcanic material and can form from either wind-blown volcanic ash or basaltic glass on the seafloor.

Sediments composed mostly or entirely of volcanic ash are commonly found adjacent to the island arcs and marginal trenches. These are normally deposited as turbidites. Volcanic ash that has been ejected higher than five kilometres during an eruption can be carried by wind and settle out through the atmosphere and oceans as pelagic sediment. The ocean floor encircling Antarctica is covered by glacial marine sediments. These sediments are carried by icebergs from the continent as far north as the Antarctic Convergence at 45° to 55° latitude.

Biogenic oozes are pelagic sediments that have more than 30 percent skeletal material. They can be either carbonate (or calcareous) ooze or siliceous ooze. The skeletal material in carbonate oozes is calcium carbonate usually in the form of the mineral calcite but sometimes aragonite. The most common contributors to the skeletal debris are such microorganisms as foraminiferans and coccoliths, microscopic carbonate plates that coat certain species of marine algae and protozoa. Siliceous oozes are composed of opal (amorphous, hydrated silica) that forms the skeleton of various microorganisms, including diatoms, radiolarians, siliceous sponges, and silicoflagellates. The distribution of biogenic oozes depends mainly on the supply of skeletal material, dissolution of the skeletons, and dilution by other sediment types, such as turbidites or clays.

Primary productivity in the ocean surface waters controls supply to a large extent. Productivity is high at the equator and in zones of coastal upwelling and also where oceanic divergences occur near Antarctica. Productivity is lowest in the central areas of the oceans (the gyres) in both hemispheres. Siliceous oozes are more reliable indicators of high productivity than carbonate oozes. This is because silica dissolves quickly in surface waters and carbonate dissolves in deep water; hence, high surface productivity is required to supply siliceous skeletons to the ocean floor. Carbonate oozes dominate the deep Atlantic seafloor, while siliceous oozes are most common in the Pacific; the floor of the Indian Ocean is covered by a combination of the two (see Figure 37).

Carbonate oozes cover about half of the world's seafloor. They are present chiefly above a depth of 4,500 metres; below that they dissolve quickly. This depth is named the Calcite Compensation Depth (or CCD). It represents the level at which the rate of carbonate accumulation equals the rate of carbonate dissolution. In the Atlantic basin the CCD is 500 metres deeper than in the Pacific basin, reflecting both a high rate of supply and low rate of dissolution in comparison to the Pacific. The input of carbonate to the ocean is through rivers and deep-sea hydrothermal vents. Variation in input, productivity, and dissolution rates in the geologic past have caused the CCD to vary over 2,000 metres. The CCD intersects the flanks of the world's oceanic ridges, and as a result these are mostly blanketed by carbonate oozes.

Calcite
Compensa-
tion Depth

Siliceous oozes predominate in two places in the oceans: around Antarctica and a few degrees of latitude north and south of the Equator. At high latitudes the oozes include mostly the shells of diatoms. South of the Antarctic Convergence diatom oozes dominate the seafloor sediment cover and mix with glacial marine sediments closer to the continent. Seventy-five percent of all the oceans' silica supply is being deposited in the area surrounding Antarctica. Radiolarian oozes are more common near the Equator in the Pacific. Here, both siliceous oozes and calcareous oozes occur, but carbonate deposition dominates the region immediately near the Equator. Siliceous oozes bracket the carbonate belt and blend with pelagic clays farther north and south. Because siliceous skeletons dissolve so quickly in seawater, only the more robust skeletal remains are found in the siliceous oozes. Thus, fossils of this kind are not completely representative of the organisms living in the waters above.

The most significant authigenic sediments in the ocean basins today are metal-rich sediments and manganese nodules. Metal-rich sediments include those enriched by iron, manganese, copper, chromium, and lead. These sediments are common at spreading centres, indicating that processes at the centres are responsible for their formation—specifically, hydrothermal circulation is the controlling factor. Deep-sea drill cores have revealed the presence of metal-rich sediments on top of ancient oceanic crust away from ridge crests. It can be inferred from this that the processes controlling their formation existed in the past, but with variations. Which type of enriched sediment is deposited depends on the degree of mixing between the hydrothermal water deep in the crust at a spreading centre and the cold seawater percolating down into the crust. Little mixing produces sulfides, liberal mixing yields manganese-rich crustal material, and intermediate conditions give rise to sediments enriched in iron and manganese.

Manganese nodules are pebbles or stones about the size of walnuts that are built of onionlike layers of manganese and iron oxides. Minor constituents include copper, nickel, and cobalt, making the nodules a potential ore of these valuable elements. Mining of manganese nodules has been the subject of study and experimentation since the 1950s (see below *Economic aspects of the oceans: Sources of minerals and other raw materials*). The nodules grow very slowly, about one to four millimetres per million years. They are found in areas of slow sedimentation, usually five millimetres per thousand years or less. The North and South Pacific hold the greatest concentration of manganese nodules; in some places, the nodules cover 90 percent of the surface of the ocean floor. Coverages this high also are found in the southernmost South Atlantic. The Indian Ocean floor is largely devoid of manganese nodules. Because seawater is supersaturated in manganese, the direct precipitation of the element onto an available surface is the most likely mode of nodule formation.

Manganese
nodules

Two significant mysteries surround manganese nodules. Drilling and coring in the sediment column has shown that nodules are vastly more abundant at the seafloor than below it and that the rate of growth of nodules is 10 times slower than the lowest known sedimentation rates. If such is the case, the nodules should be quickly buried and should be common in the sediment below the seafloor. Current theories for explaining these observations propose that bottom currents keep areas of nodule growth free of sediment deposition and that burrowing organisms nudge and roll the nodules in the process of feeding, thereby keeping them at the surface of the seafloor. Observations in the deep sea support both explanations.

Sedimentation patterns. The patterns of sedimentation in the ocean basins have not been static over geologic time. The existing basins, no more than 200 million years old, contain a highly variable sedimentary record. The major factor behind the variations is plate movements and related changes in climate and ocean water circulation. Since about 200 million years ago, a single vast ocean basin has given way to five or six smaller ones. The Pacific Ocean basin has shrunk, while the North and South Atlantic basins have been created. The climate has changed from warm and mild to cool, stormy, and glacial. Plate movements have altered the course of surface and deep ocean currents and changed the patterns of upwelling, productivity, and biogenic sedimentation. Seaways have opened and closed. The Strait of Gibraltar, for example, was closed off about 6 million years ago, allowing the entire Mediterranean Sea to evaporate and leave thick salt deposits on its floor. Changes in seafloor spreading rates and glaciations have caused sea level to rise and fall, greatly altering the deep-sea sedimentation pattern of both terrigenous and biogenic sediments. The CCD has fluctuated more than 2,000 metres in response to changes in carbonate supply and the corrosive nature of ocean bottom waters. Bottom currents have changed, becoming erosive or nondepositional in some regions to produce unconformities and redistributing enormous volumes of sediment to other locations. The Pacific Plate has been steadily moving northward, so that biogenic sediments of the equatorial regions are found in drill cores taken in the barren North Pacific.

EVOLUTION OF THE OCEAN BASINS
THROUGH PLATE MOVEMENTS

Through most of geologic time, probably extending back 2 billion years, the ocean basins have both grown and been consumed as plate tectonics continued on Earth. The latest phase of ocean basin growth began just less than 200 million years ago with the breakup of the supercontinent Pangaea, the enormous landmass composed of nearly all the present-day continents. Since that time, the major developments have included a shrinking of the Pacific basin at the expense of the growing Atlantic and Arctic basins, the opening of the Tethys seaway circling the globe in tropical latitudes and its subsequent closing, and the opening of the Southern Ocean (see above *General considerations*) as the southern continents moved north away from Antarctica.

As was noted earlier, the oldest known oceanic crust (estimated to be about 200 million years old) is located in the far western equatorial Pacific, east of the Mariana Island arc. The Pacific ocean floor at this site was generated during seafloor spreading from a pattern of ridges and plates that had existed for some unknown period of time. At least five different seafloor spreading centres were involved (Figure 38). In the Indian Ocean the oldest segment of seafloor was formed about 165 to 145 million years ago by the rifting away of Africa and South America from Gondwana, a supercontinent consisting largely of the present-day continents of the Southern Hemisphere. At this time, Africa was joined to South America, Eurasia, and North America. Today, this old seafloor is found along the east coast of Africa from the Somali Basin to the east coast of South Africa and adjacent to Queen Maud Land and Enderby Land in East Antarctica.

Close to 180 million years ago (but before 165 million years ago), North America and Eurasia, which together made up most of the large northern continent of Laurasia, began drifting away from Africa and South America, creating the first seafloor in the central region of the North Atlantic and opening the Gulf of Mexico. The Tethys seaway also opened during this rifting phase as Europe pulled away from Africa. Shortly after this time continental fragments, including possibly Tibet, Myanmar (Burma), and Malaya, rifted away from the northwest coast of Australia and moved northward, thereby creating the oldest seafloor in the Timor Sea. During this period spreading continued in the Pacific basin with the growth of the Pacific Plate and the consumption by subduction of its bordering plates, including the Izanagi, Farallon, and Phoenix. The Pacific Plate moved northward during this phase and continues to do so today.

India and Madagascar, as a unit, rifted away from Australia and Antarctica prior to 130 million years ago and began drifting northward, creating seafloor adjacent to Western Australia and East Antarctica (Figure 39). Possibly simultaneously or shortly after this rifting began, South America started to separate from Africa, initiating the formation of seafloor in the South Atlantic Ocean.

Between 90 and 80 million years ago, Madagascar and India separated, and the spreading ridges in the Indian Ocean were reorganized. India began drifting northward directly toward Asia. During this same period Europe, joined to Greenland, began drifting away from North America, which resulted in the emergence of the seafloor in the Labrador Sea and the northernmost Atlantic Ocean. This spreading phase affected the passages in the Tethys seaway between Europe (Iberia) and northwest Africa, intermittently opening and closing it. In the southwest Pacific, New Zealand, along with the Lord Howe Rise and the Norfolk Ridge, rifted away from Australia and Antarctica between 80 and 60 million years ago, opening the Tasman Sea.

About 60 million years ago a new rift and oceanic ridge formed between Greenland and Europe, separating them

Opening of the Caribbean and the Gulf of Mexico

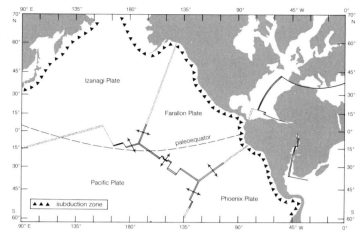

Figure 38: Possible configuration of spreading centres in the Pacific Ocean about 110 million years ago (see text).

From J.P. Kennett, *Marine Geology* (1982); Prentice-Hall, Inc., Englewood Cliffs, N.J., after R.L. Larson and W.C. Pitman III, *Geological Society America Bulletin*, vol. 83 (1972); Geological Society of America

and initiating the formation of oceanic crust in the Norwegian Sea and the Eurasian basin in the eastern Arctic Ocean (Figure 40). The Amerasian basin in the western Arctic Ocean had formed during an earlier spreading phase from about 130 to 110 million years ago. Between 60 and 50 million years ago, significant events occurred in the Indian Ocean and southwest Pacific. Australia began drifting northward, away from East Antarctica, creating seafloor there. The northward movement of Australia resulted in the emergence of several subduction zones and island arcs in the southwest and equatorial Pacific. The Indian sub-

From C.Mc.A. Powell, S.R. Roots, and J.J. Veevers, *Tectonophysics*, vol. 155 (1988); Elsevier Science Publishers P.V.

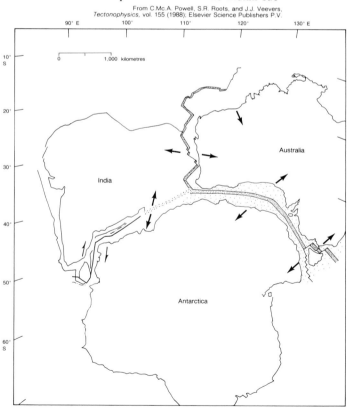

Figure 39: *Early phase of seafloor spreading in the eastern Indian Ocean.*

The rift between Australia and Antarctica developed into seafloor spreading between 60 and 50 million years ago. The arrows show the relative motion between these segments of Gondwana. The heavy stipple between Australia and Antarctica represents the amount of continental extension, and the light stipple indicates the continental extension over the whole area.

Figure 40: Reconstruction of the North Atlantic and Arctic basins for 56 million years ago. Seafloor spreading began at this time in the Norwegian Sea and Eurasian (eastern Arctic) basin areas.

From D.B. Rowley and A.L. Lottes, *Tectonophysics*, vol. 155 (1988); Elsevier Science Publishers P.V.

ocean floor of
the North American Plate

ocean floor of the Eurasian Plate

ocean floor of
the Greenland Plate

ocean floor of
the Iberian Plate

continent first touched against the Asian continent about 53 million years ago, developing structures that preceded the main Himalayan orogeny (mountain-building event), which began in earnest some 40 million years ago.

Less than 30 million years ago, seafloor spreading ceased in the Labrador Sea. Along the west coast of North America, the Pacific Plate and the North American Plate converged along what is now California shortly after 30 million years ago. This resulted in the cessation of a long history of subduction in the area and the gradual conversion of this continental margin to a transform fault zone. Continued closure between Africa and Europe, which began about 100 million years ago, caused the isolation of the Mediterranean Sea, so that by 6 million years ago it had completely evaporated.

The present-day Mediterranean seafloor was formed during a complex sequence of rifting between small plates in this region, beginning with the separation of North America and Europe from Africa about 200 million years ago. In the eastern Mediterranean, the seafloor is no older than about 100 million years. West of Italy it was created during subsequent spreading between 30 and 20 million years ago.

The Caribbean Sea and the Gulf of Mexico formed as a result of the relative movement between North America and South America. The seafloor of the Gulf of Mexico began forming some 160 to 150 million years ago. A proto- or ancient Caribbean seafloor also was formed during this period but was later subducted. The present Caribbean seafloor consists of a captured piece of the Farallon Plate (from the Pacific basin) and is estimated to be for the most part of Cretaceous age (*i.e.*, about 120 to 85 million years old).

The seafloor in the western portion of the Philippine Sea developed between 60 and 35 million years ago. In the east, it was formed by backarc spreading from 30 million years ago (see above). The origin of the older crust is not completely clear. It either was created by spreading in the Pacific basin and subsequent capture by the formation of the Bonin and Mariana arcs, or it resulted from backarc spreading behind trenches to the south.

PALEOCEANOGRAPHY

Through knowledge of the ocean sedimentary record, the history of plate motions, glacial changes, and established relations between present sedimentation patterns and environmental factors, it is possible to reconstruct an oceanographic history for approximately the past 200 million years. This is the emerging field of paleoceanography.

Prior to the breakup of Pangaea, one enormous ocean, Panthalassa, existed on Earth. Currents in this ocean would have been simple and slow, and the Earth's climate was, in all likelihood, warmer than today. The Tethys seaway formed as Pangaea broke into Gondwana and Laurasia (see above). In the narrow ocean basins of the central North Atlantic, restricted ocean circulation favoured deposition of evaporites (halite, gypsum, anhydrite, and other less abundant salts). Evaporites also were deposited some 100 million years ago in the equatorial regions of the South Atlantic during the early opening of this ocean.

Sequences of organic-rich, black shales were deposited during the early phases of spreading in the North and South Atlantic. These sediments indicate anoxic conditions in the deep ocean waters. The oceans must have been well stratified into dense layers to prevent the overturning and mixing required to replace depleted oxygen. Black shales also were deposited in the older areas of the eastern Indian Ocean.

During the time interval between 200 and 65 million years ago, but especially from 100 to 65 million years ago, microplankton abundance and diversity increased enormously in the oceans. This resulted in increased deposition of biogenic sediments in the ocean basin. During Cretaceous time (from 144 to 66.4 million years ago),

Pantha-
lassa

sea level was often high, and shallow seas lapped onto the continents. This may have provided an environment favourable to the explosion in the numbers of species of foraminiferans, diatoms, and calcareous nannoplankton. Increased abundance of calcareous nannoplankton shifted the locus of carbonate sedimentation from shallow seas to the deep ocean. The end of Cretaceous time is marked by a sudden extinction of many life-forms on Earth, and marine organisms were no exception (see GEOCHRONOLOGY: *Cretaceous Period*). Coccolithophores (calcareous nannoplankton) and planktonic foraminiferans were particularly affected, and only a few species survived. Ocean sediments were suddenly less biogenic, and clays became widespread.

After Cretaceous time the Earth underwent a gradual cooling, especially at high latitudes. Deep-sea sedimentation changed as thermohaline bottom water circulation became fully developed (see above *Circulation of the ocean waters: Thermohaline circulation*). The CCD rose in the Pacific and dropped in the Atlantic as a result of changes in thermohaline circulation. An event of major significance was the spreading away of Australia from Antarctica beginning about 53 million years ago. This separation initiated limited circum-Antarctic circulation, which isolated Antarctica from the warmer oceans to the north, and led to cooling, which set the stage for later major glaciation.

Formation of Antarctic Bottom Water and its effects

At the Eocene-Oligocene boundary (36.6 million years ago), Antarctic Bottom Water began to form, resulting in greatly decreased bottom-water temperatures in both the Pacific and Atlantic oceans. Bottom-living organisms were strongly affected, and the CCD suddenly dropped from about 3,500 metres to approximately 4,000 to 5,000 metres in the Pacific. Bottom-water temperatures were generally warm, 12° to 15° C, during the time preceding this event. In a study of deep-sea sediment core material from near Antarctica, J.P. Kennett and Lowell D. Stott of the United States discovered that there was a period between roughly 50 and 35 million years ago when deep waters were very warm (20° C) and salty. The origin of these ocean waters was most likely in the low latitudes and resulted from high evaporation rates there.

The modern oceans are distinguished by very cold bottom water. The gradual changes toward this condition began 10 million years after the origination of Antarctic Bottom Water. Particularly significant among these changes was the closing of the Tethys seaway as Australia and several microcontinents moved north into the Indonesian region. Also, Australia moved far enough north that circum-Antarctic surface circulation became fully established.

The modern ocean circulation patterns and basin shapes were mostly in place by the beginning of Miocene time (nearly 24 million years ago). An exception was an ocean connection between the Pacific and Caribbean Sea in Central America that persisted until about 3 million years ago. Major and probably permanent ice sheets on Antarctica formed during Miocene time, and glacial sediments began to dominate the seafloor surrounding the continent shortly thereafter. Siliceous oozes also became widespread around Antarctica. Siliceous sedimentation increased in this area at the expense of siliceous sedimentation in equatorial regions. Ocean circulation became more vigorous, global climate became cooler, and sedimentation rates in the ocean basins increased. Planktonic microorganisms were segregated into latitudinal belts. Bottom-water flow north through the Drake Passage between South America and Antarctica began in Miocene time, resulting in erosion and nondeposition of sediments in the southwest Atlantic and southeast Pacific oceans. Also during Miocene time rifting between Greenland and Europe had progressed to a point where a connection was established between the North Atlantic and the Norwegian Sea. This resulted in the formation of North Atlantic Deep Water (see above *Circulation of the ocean waters: Thermohaline circulation*), which began flowing south along the continental rise of North America at this time. Sediments redistributed and deposited by this deep current are called contourites and have been extensively studied by Bruce Heezen, Charles D. Hollister, and Brian E. Tucholke, among others.

Sudden global cooling set in near the end of the Miocene some 6 million years ago. The strength of ocean circulation must have increased, as evidence of increased upwelling and biological productivity is present in ocean sediments. Diatomaceous sediments were deposited in abundance around the rim of the Pacific. This cooling event is synchronous with a drop in sea level, thought to be about 40 or 50 metres by various authorities, and probably corresponds to the further growth of the Antarctic ice sheet. This lowered sea level, coupled with the closure of narrow seaways probably due to plate movements, isolated the Mediterranean Sea. Subsequently, the sea dried up, leaving evaporite deposits on its floor. The Swiss geologist Kenneth J. Hsü and the American oceanographer William B.F. Ryan have concluded that the Mediterranean probably dried up about 40 times as seaways opened and closed between 6 and 5 million years ago. This evaporation removed about 6 percent of the salt from the world ocean, which raised the freezing point of seawater and promoted further growth of the sea ice surrounding Antarctica.

Enormous ice sheets emerged in the Northern Hemisphere between 3 and 2 million years ago, and the succession of Quaternary glaciations began at 1.6 million years ago. The exact cause of the glacial period is unclear, but it is most likely related to the variability in solar isolation, increased mountain building, and an intensification of the Gulf Stream at 3 million years ago due to the closing off of the Pacific-Caribbean ocean connection in Central America. The Quaternary glaciations, of which there were probably 30 episodes, left the most dramatic record in ocean sediments of any event in the previous 200 million years. Terrigenous sedimentation rates greatly increased in response to fluctuations in sea level of up to 100 metres and a more extreme climate. Biogenic sedimentation also increased and fluctuated with the glacial episodes. Deep-sea erosion began in many places as a result of intensified bottom-water circulation. (Bruce Peter Luyendyk)

Science

Year in

Review

Contents

The Year in Science: An Overview

by Robert P. Crease

The year 1990 was the one in which *Big Science* became a term of disrepute. The culprit was the Hubble Space Telescope. Big Science was never an expression of unalloyed praise, of course. The phrase entered public discourse three decades ago in the context of the sharp increase in scale of science projects following World War II. Instruments such as nuclear reactors and particle accelerators were beginning to require unprecedented levels of money and teamwork to build and operate, beyond the capabilities and resources of even the largest universities. In partial response the U.S. government established a string of national laboratories to coordinate the activities of many institutions. These laboratories included Brookhaven National Laboratory, Upton, Long Island, N.Y.; Oak Ridge (Tenn.) National Laboratory; Argonne (Ill.) National Laboratory; Berkeley (Calif.) Radiation (later Lawrence Berkeley) Laboratory; and others.

In 1961 Alvin Weinberg, then the director of the physics division of Oak Ridge National Laboratory, commented on this development—and promoted the term *Big Science* for the first time—in an influential article in *Science* magazine entitled "Impact of Large-Scale Science on the United States." He was neither praising nor condemning the trend but merely drawing attention to certain "diseases" to which it made scientific activity prone. These included "moneyitis," or the spending of money instead of thought; "journalitis," or the debating of the value of projects in the popular rather than the scientific press; and "administratitis," or the hiring of administrators rather than scientists.

Weinberg believed, however, that these dangers could be circumvented—and that there was no alternative to trying to do so. "It is fruitless to wring one's hands over the bad effects of Big Science," he wrote. "Big Science is an inevitable stage in the development of science and, for better or worse, it is here to stay. What we must do is learn to live with Big Science. We must make Big Science flourish without, at the same time, allowing it to trample Little Science."

In the ensuing years Big Science undertakings grew still larger, more numerous, and more publicly

ROBERT P. CREASE *is an Assistant Professor of Philosophy at the State University of New York, Stony Brook, and Historian at the Brookhaven National Laboratory, Upton, New York.*

visible. Some, such as U.S. Pres. John F. Kennedy's Apollo project to land a human being on the Moon, were ultimately successful, while others, such as Pres. Richard Nixon's National Cancer Act (the "war on cancer"), were not. Nearly all were infected to some extent by the diseases Weinberg had diagnosed, but whether the projects succeeded or failed seemed almost beside the point. The attempt to marshal all available resources to meet social and environmental challenges seemed to be an intrinsic part of the cultural duty of an advanced civilization.

By the late 1970s and early 1980s, however, such projects had become so numerous, and their scale so large, that the peaceful coexistence between Big Science and Little Science that Weinberg had envisioned grew uneasy. Still, Big Science projects continued to be embarked on with more than a trace of pride by participants and proponents: How could Big Science be insignificant science?

Hubble's troubles. Then came Hubble. The Hubble Space Telescope, a 12-ton device 13 m (43 ft) long and 4 m (14 ft) in diameter at its widest point, had taken about $1.5 billion and 12 years to build; it was launched on April 24, 1990. Though seven years behind schedule and some four to five times over budget, it was initially heralded as a triumph of modern astronomy. The triumph did not last, however. Hubble was soon discovered to have a serious flaw called a spherical aberration, which inhibited the fine focusing powers of the telescope, bathing points of light in a blur. As a result, many of the most important capabilities of the five onboard instruments were seriously impaired; hardest hit was the wide-field and planetary camera, which was able to execute only about 15 to 20% of the programs it was originally designed to do. A few functions escaped unscathed, however, and the U.S. National Aeronautics and Space Administration (NASA) was able to release a number of relatively clear photographs—including one of a supernova and another of a storm on Saturn—throughout the remainder of the year. A month of tests eventually tracked the cause of the distortion to a 1.3-mm spacing error in the assembly of an instrument used to guide the machines that ground the telescope's primary mirror. A tiny error had practically done in a $1.5 billion project.

A few in the scientific community emphasized Hubble's remaining capabilities and the fact that the distortion ultimately could be compensated for and found the episode an illustration that to dare greatly is to risk greatly. Critics, however, used it to illustrate another lesson: the risk of Big Science projects. Hubble's problems provided new and more powerful ammunition for critics who were already sniping at Big Science and helped provoke others to attack it for the first time. Within a few weeks the term *Big Science* was widely used as one of disrepute.

A month after Hubble's launch, the *New York Times* began a series of feature articles entitled "Big Science: Is It Worth the Price?" The answer implied by the *Times* was no. In September *Reader's Digest* published an article entitled "Let's Get Serious About Cutting the Budget," which offered a supposedly painless way to slash the deficit by $50 billion through the elimination of "needless, wasteful expenditures." The sixth category of these expenditures was entitled "End funding for research extravaganzas," and included in that category were the Superconducting Super Collider, the Human Genome Initiative, and the space station *Freedom*. Newspapers throughout the U.S. published editorials condemning large scientific undertakings.

Allergic reactions to the term *Big Science* broke out everywhere. Proponents of large scientific endeavors began developing ingenious arguments to the effect that their projects should not be thought of as Big Science, lest they be seen as running the danger of becoming "another Hubble." Even small projects suffered consequences. A proposal from one national laboratory to jointly sponsor, with the Smithsonian Institution's Air and Space Museum, an exhibit on the convergence of particle physics and cosmology was rejected by the government, partly owing to fears of possible damage to the laboratory if it were associated in any way, however loosely, with the (cosmologically oriented) Hubble telescope.

Beneath this sensitivity was a usually implicit but occasionally explicit comparison between Big Science and Big Business. The elements of the comparison ran something like this: There is only a limited amount of science (akin to a market share) that can be done at any given time, based on what society can afford to set aside for pure research. Inevitably, a competition develops between large and small projects, similar to the way that large and small businesses compete for shares in a limited market. Those who made this comparison freely admitted that big projects, like big businesses, often can accomplish things that little ones cannot, but small projects, they said, are like small businesses in that they have their own virtues and exert a beneficial impact. These include a greater flexibility to respond to changing conditions, a larger role for the initiative, imagination, and ingenuity of the individual researcher, and an increased ability to tolerate risk.

The increasing size and numbers of large scientific projects, it was argued, have soaked up a larger and larger share of the total, driven out more and more individual investigators, and led to increasing conservatism. Therefore, Big Science projects should be curtailed.

Big Science and Big Business are not analogous, however, for scientific knowledge cannot be compared with market shares. Much scientific knowledge, especially in such areas as high-energy physics and astronomy, can be gained only through large projects and not by any amount of small ones. Thus, the scale of a scientific project is mandated by the kind of thing one wishes to know. Moreover, that knowledge is publicly disseminated and belongs to the entire community; the fruit of businesses is profit and belongs to the particular enterprise that generated it. Science projects of all sizes can benefit from Big Science initiatives; the knowledge obtained from them becomes an integral part of the scientific background on the basis of which new initiatives are planned. Many small science projects, such as high-temperature superconductor experiments, succeed only because knowledge gained by Big Science instruments has been incorporated into the planning.

A scientific project creates a kind of "window" on nature that is otherwise unavailable. The windows in the various areas of science differ in many respects, including the scale of the undertaking needed to create them, the percentage of the scientific community that benefits from seeing through them, the risks involved in constructing them, the political value of having them, the clarity and significance of the view, and the cost and possible practical benefits. Some idea of these differences—and, thus, how the meaning of *Big Science* changes from field to field—can be seen from a brief examination of some major "windows" under discussion during the past year.

Human Genome Initiative. A gene is an "atom" of heredity, the basic unit through which inheritable characteristics are transmitted from one generation to the next. Genes are arranged along chromosomes and are composed of DNA (deoxyribonucleic acid), which is, in turn, made of pairs of four nitrogenous bases (adenine, cytosine, guanine, and thymine). A genome is the sum total of all the genes in an organism. The Human Genome Initiative (HGI) is the attempt to map and sequence all the genes in the human organism; that is, determine the linear order of the genes on each chromosome as well as the order of the base pairs in the DNA they comprise.

The path to the HGI began in 1953 with the discovery of the basic structure of DNA. With the revolution in recombinant DNA techniques that began in 1973, scientists discovered ways to trace the location of genes through the use of "markers" that indicate where on the various chromosomes a particular gene is found. About 1980 the realization set in that it was within the capability of the scientific community to map and sequence in a systematic way every single one of the 50,000 to 100,000 human genes—the human genetic code. Proposals to do so were made in the mid-1980s, and the Human Genome Initiative was launched by the U.S. Department of Energy in 1987. It has been estimated that it will cost $3 billion over approximately 15 years.

During the past year a battle raged over the project's value. Proponents argued that the HGI would revolutionize biology, accelerate the search for cures for the 4,000 or so hereditary diseases, stimulate the development of faster and cheaper sequencing equipment, and keep the U.S. ahead in biotechnology. Critics called it largely a waste of time, pointing out that more than 95% of the human genome may well be "junk," unrelated to recognizable functions; they believed that it would be far better to sequence only the interesting parts of the genome, at least for the time being. Moreover, they said, the work is tedious and repetitive; one scientist suggested, tongue in cheek, that a penal colony be built to supply labor for the sequencing projects, while another wrote that the project was "about as difficult as mapping every tree in Borneo." The controversy reached a peak of sorts in the fall, with editorials and letters to the editor of science journals (one was titled "Mediocre Science, Terrible Science Policy") and even shouting matches at public conferences and congressional hearings over the value of the project.

Whatever the scientific merits of the HGI, what was striking about the debate was the way in which it degenerated whenever the Hubble Space Telescope and/or Big Science was invoked. The HGI was often attacked under the rubric of Big Science, but it bears little resemblance to Hubble and other projects purported to be in that category. For example, it cannot fail the way that Hubble did; the work involved has no single piece of hardware whose malfunction could doom the entire project, will not take place in a single laboratory, and will not be performed by a single team of scientists. The project has been likened to the building of an interconnected highway system across a continent; the work by nature is done in segments, and problems at one location do not affect work at others. The mapping and sequencing technology consists of standardized techniques available in laboratories throughout the U.S. and, far from squeezing out small investigators, it is composed of them; the largest part of the HGI consists of research sponsored by single investigators in small research laboratories.

To be sure, one can still debate the value of the research being coordinated by the project and point to other possibly more significant research that the small investigators could be funded to execute. For instance, knowledge of the genetic map and the sequence of base pairs in the DNA of its components would not answer many critical questions about complex functions such as the behavior of proteins. No doubt the debate over the value of the HGI will continue for some time. Nevertheless, it has little to do with the debate over Big Science. It is thus small wonder that Nobel laureate James Watson, head of the National Center for Human Genome Research of the U.S. National Institutes of Health, was able to protest quite legitimately that the HGI was "nothing like the 'big science' research and development initiatives with which it is continually compared."

Materials sciences. Materials scientists study the structure of solid matter. Practical applications of their work have included stronger metals, ceramics, and plastics; more efficient heat-conversion techniques; new magnetic materials; high-temperature superconductors; more transparent glass; tinier integrated circuits; and sharper and more durable tools. Materials scientists use two kinds of facilities—research reactors and synchrotron light sources—that have grown to such a scale as to be routinely cited as instances of Big Science. These facilities produce two different kinds of beams—neutron beams and photon beams, respectively—that are useful for probing the structure of solids. Neutrons and photons make good probes because they are nondestructive; they do not interact to any great extent with the material being studied, and so the structure of that material can be analyzed without being taken apart or otherwise ruined. Neutron and photon probes have complementary capabilities. Neutrons can penetrate more deeply into objects and are more sensitive to light elements than are photons, while photons are better for studying surface structures. It is also easier to create intense beams of photons, allowing them to provide sharper images. Neutrons have a magnetic moment; i.e., they can deliver information about the magnetic structure of a material. Photons, on the other hand, provide information about a material's charge properties. Moreover, photons of different wavelengths or energies are suited to different tasks; X-rays are used for structural studies, while ultraviolet light is employed for studying the surface features of a material.

During the past 25 years, materials scientists have come to rely increasingly on large facilities to produce beams of neutrons and photons. In 1965 the High Flux Beam Reactor went into operation at Brookhaven; it was the first major research reactor designed principally for the creation of beams of neutrons rather than for irradiation or the production of energy. Within a few years similar reactors had been

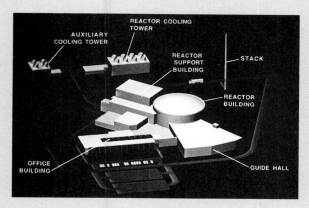

At the Advanced Neutron Source facility, planned for Oak Ridge (Tennessee) National Laboratory, scientists would generate beams of neutrons for research on materials.
Oak Ridge National Laboratory

built at Oak Ridge and by the U.S. Bureau of Standards (run by the U.S. Department of Commerce, which was interested in such a reactor for its long-term beneficial effect on industrial competitiveness); in 1971 one was built at the Institut Laue-Langevin in Grenoble, France. By the mid-1970s neutron beams were proving so important that materials scientists began urging the building of a reactor of a more advanced design. Pressure for such a facility grew with the sudden development of high-temperature superconductors—for which neutron-scattering work is critical, since neutrons are the only method of determining the magnetic properties of materials on the atomic level. The outcome was the Advanced Neutron Source (ANS) at Oak Ridge. It was estimated that the ANS, still in the conceptual design stage, would cost about $500 million over 10 years.

Meanwhile, materials scientists who were photon partisans were also feeling pinched. At first they had to piggyback experiments off of electron accelerators built by high-energy physicists. About 1980, however, several large "synchrotron radiation" sources—named after the method by which the light is generated—were constructed. The first was Brookhaven's National Synchrotron Light Source (NSLS), which provided beams of both X-ray and ultraviolet light. These facilities were remarkable in that they brought together materials scientists from industry, academia, and national laboratories. Like neutron beams, photon beams proved so important that pressure mounted for a new generation of sources, giving rise to plans for the Advanced Photon Source (APS) at Argonne National Laboratory, to cost $453 million over about six years, and the Advanced Light Source (ALS) at Lawrence Berkeley Laboratory, to cost $100 million over about seven years.

The ANS, APS, and ALS make regular appearances on lists of Big Science projects, but they bear little resemblance to either the Hubble or the HGI. Unlike the HGI, they are large and expensive devices and the work done with them will be centralized. Unlike Hubble, their reason for being is to serve as utilities—to produce intense neutron and photon beams for many small experiments. The ANS will have about 50 instrument stations; the Advanced Photon Source, 68 beam lines (with more than one experiment possible on each); and the Advanced Light Source, potentially 60 beam lines. If some genie were to bring materials scientists tiny but intense sources of neutron and photon beams, these groups could all work at home. That genie has not appeared, and the next best solution is for materials scientists to create large facilities where those interested can work simultaneously. Proponents are quite right to deny that the science done at such centers is Big Science; indeed, what these centers do is allow the field to remain Small Science.

Superconducting Super Collider. The Superconducting Super Collider (SSC) will be a particle accelerator, a device that boosts particles to high speeds, slams them into other particles, and then tracks the fragments—the basic high-energy physics experiment. The SSC—to be built in an area surrounding Waxahachie, Texas, south of Dallas, over the next decade at a cost of about $8 billion—will accelerate counterrevolving beams of protons and collide them into each other inside detectors. Scientists believe that they will thereby learn certain things about the nature of matter—in particular, how it obtains mass—that they can discover in no other way.

In an article about Big Science during the past year, the *New York Times* published a photograph of Ernest Lawrence, a pioneer in the development of particle accelerators, holding his earliest version, a circular object about the size of a bagel that he had built for less than $10. Juxtaposed with this was a photograph of a 16-m (52-ft)-long magnet core for the SSC, which will require some 10,000 magnets along its 84-km (52-mi) circumference. The pair of photographs dramatized quite nicely the apotheosis of Big Science—the huge increase in scale of particle-physics experiments over 60 years.

Nevertheless, in Hubble's wake during the past year, one SSC official made the case (though, to be sure, largely tongue in cheek) that the SSC was not Big Science. For, he said, just as one could say that materials sciences centers were not Big Science but utilities for the service of experimenters in the community, so one could say that the SSC was likewise a service facility for experimenters. When it was pointed out that the SSC experiments themselves were huge undertakings (at least one would cost

$500 million and involve hundreds of collaborators), he replied that the advanced detection techniques and equipment for the SSC experiments were being developed and put together in pieces at dozens of small laboratories and institutes. Thus, Small Science prevails—at least until everything comes together just before the SSC begins operation.

Ending the Big Science debate. Three different models of large and expensive projects in three different fields have been described. Others range from huge optical telescopes under construction (where the large amount of private funding is an important complicating factor) to cancer and AIDS research, which, though consisting largely of studies sponsored by single investigators, are the fruit of large, billion-dollar, multi-institutional projects centrally directed by agencies in Washington. Which of these may properly be called Big Science?

If the term is to be construed narrowly, to apply only to the construction of large pieces of hardware principally to meet social, political, or military agendas, then the only Big Science projects currently under development are the space station *Freedom* and the Strategic Defense Initiative. A society quite legitimately may decide that it wants and can afford a manned space station to satisfy a craving to explore the universe or a space-based laser missile system to protect itself against aggression; critics may argue whether the particular projects envisioned will fulfill expectations. Nevertheless, the question of their social value should not be confused with that of their scientific worth. It would be difficult, for instance, to present a convincing scientific case for either the space station or the Strategic Defense Initiative, both of which are extraordinarily expensive (the cost of the space station alone, for instance, is about three times the combined cost of all of the large projects mentioned above, and SDI is many times more expensive than even that).

If, on the other hand, Big Science is broadly defined as any comprehensive and centrally directed national effort to coordinate and direct research, then virtually all of the science in the U.S. is Big Science, for nearly all of the civilian basic research in the U.S. is controlled by programs and panels of the National Institutes of Health and the Department of Energy. In the terms of such a broad definition, existing cancer and AIDS research would be Big Science.

The term *Big Science* is, consequently, a poor conceptual tool with which to understand and make judgments about science and would be a poor framework with which to think about the developments presented in the articles that follow. The overwhelming majority of the work described in them was either sponsored by a Washington-based group such as NIH or DOE, actually done on a large instrument such as a particle accelerator, or affected in some way by the knowledge of other investigators who had used such instruments. Science consists of a highly interwoven fabric of knowledge from which different groups of researchers borrow different strands in different ways. That is not to say that researchers do not have cultural differences about how that knowledge is conceived, applied, and pursued. Nevertheless, it would be useless and indeed impossible to try to pick apart from this densely woven tapestry the respective contributions of Big and Little Science however they are defined, let alone to evaluate which is more important.

That large scientific projects are changing the ways in which science is carried out so that they involve new dangers and temptations is indisputable. These projects continue to be susceptible to the dangers Weinberg mentioned and also to run the risk of stifling individual creativity and encouraging conservatism. Moreover, their existence will force trade-offs between the various fields—materials sciences versus molecular biology, perhaps, or high-energy physics versus astronomy. Nonetheless, these problems must be faced head-on as issues themselves and not disguised and misrepresented within the framework of Big versus Little Science. What must be judged is the legitimacy and value of the science itself in each case.

In the final days of 1990, two scientists wrote in the *New York Times* that "the time has come to end the small science vs. big science debate." If this hope is fulfilled, the result will certainly be an elevation in the quality of public discussion of the nature and value of science.

Engineer at the Superconducting Super Collider Laboratory in Dallas, Texas, checks the results of a low-frequency vibration test on the superconducting dipole magnet in the background.
The Super Collider Laboratory

Anthropology

In most parts of the world, anthropology continued to develop during the past year, both in theory and in practice, although serious setbacks occurred in China. In the U.S.S.R. and Eastern Europe, the discipline was in a state of confusion, yet there appeared to be a strong potential for growth.

Among the outstanding works of research was Ernest Gellner's *Plough, Sword and Book: The Structure of Human History*. The book reflected anthropology's traditional interest in the major transformations of human society, beginning with food-collecting peoples, advancing to the discovery of agriculture, and ending with the transition to the Industrial Revolution and modern times. Changes in society follow the changes in modes of production, but Gellner made it clear that production need not cause only one kind of response. Modes of production cause common problems; humans are able to provide a variety of solutions with different responses. Gellner did not opt for any particular solutions, but he offered hope that social science can aid peoples in finding those that are most satisfying.

Anthropology's potential for helping achieve solutions was best demonstrated in 1990 by the $100,-000 Right Livelihood Award, the so-called alternative Nobel Prize. It was given to Survival International by the Right Livelihood Awards Foundation. The award cited Survival International for its "longest serving and most effective campaigning and education organization working with tribal peoples to secure their rights, livelihood and self-determination." One ex-ample of its work was the campaign to stop Scott Paper Co. from a $600 million project in western New Guinea that threatened the destruction of tropical forests that support 15,000 tribal peoples. Survival International also published a special issue of its journal that was devoted to the harmful effects of tourism on tribal peoples, but it noted alternative possibilities for tourism that do not harm the environment or endanger tribal peoples.

In New Zealand anthropologist Michèle Dominy found herself in a position in her relationship with tribal peoples that was new for anthropology but likely to become more frequent in the future. She had been working among white sheep farmers in the high country who had leased Crown lands for more than three generations to support their operations. These farmers had developed close ties to the land that were far more than economic; the ties paralleled Maori attitudes toward the land. The Maori, meanwhile, were suing the New Zealand government for redress of treaty violations and seeking Crown lands in the South Island as compensation for past injustices. If their claims are met, the sheep farmers will lose their leases. They turned to Dominy for support of their claim to the land, asking her to explain their emotional and cultural ties to the countryside.

A similar issue troubled Australian anthropologists, as reflected in the circulation of a paper presented by a geologist to the July 1990 annual general meeting of the Australian Anthropological Society, which met in Brisbane. The geologist argued that proponents of Aborigine rights, including Aborigines, have often hurt themselves and the nation economically

Yanomami woman (above) belongs to a tribe of Brazilian Indians facing extinction because their rain forest habitat is being destroyed. An airstrip used by gold prospectors particularly threatened the Yanomami and was blown up by Brazilian authorities (left).

(Left) Carlos Humberto—Contact; (right) Survival International; photo, V. Englebert

Sheep farmer in New Zealand faces the possible loss of his land if a lawsuit by the Maori is settled in their favor. As compensation for past injustices, the Maori are seeking the Crown lands leased by sheep farmers.

in demanding rights as citizens and special rights as Aborigines. He argued that insistence on equal wages had led to loss of jobs and self-esteem and that the conflict profited only lawyers and irresponsible media that inflamed the situation in order to make news. The papers presented by anthropologists at the annual meeting showed that they continued to pursue applied and theoretical paths; for example, one paper dealt with the ways in which anthropologists perceive a situation in fieldwork, and others examined attitudes toward AIDS. An emphasis on Aborigines also continued, with reports of investigations on their education, health, and employment. Members also mourned the loss of one of their most famous anthropologists, Ronald Murray Berndt, who died in May.

In the U.K. the continuing interest in theory and practice was exemplified at the Edinburgh meeting of the Association of Social Anthropologists. The conference theme, "Anthropology of the Future," allowed for considerable variation in the papers presented, but two major categories were covered, one examining how various peoples perceive the past and future and another speculating on possible future developments in the field that require new anthropological perspectives. Several of the ethnographic papers explored how people saw their future in regard to changes in the environment, a theme also investigated by many U.S. anthropologists during the year. Among the Edinburgh papers reflecting on the future of the discipline, one called for predictions about how new technologies would affect peoples' lives, while another asked if it was possible for the discipline to make predictions.

In Germany the emphasis was on more practical matters. A small number of professionals in museums and universities were working to place a growing number of students in applied positions. The interest of the young, nonacademic anthropologists in political and ecological problems motivated them to use their talents in a variety of positions. A number of these anthropologists, who in Germany identified themselves as ethnologists, were particularly interested in economic and social development in Third World countries; they formed a working group within the Deutsche Gesellschaft für Volkerkund (German Society for Ethnology). A theoretical development that received much attention from German scholars was shaped by a question of ethics and the shadow of National Socialism (Nazism) over German ethnology. The depth of this introspection on the Nazi era was illustrated by the publication in 1990 of *Ethnologie im Nationalsozialismus* by Dietrich Reimer Vergla and the convening of a congress at the University of Cologne on the same topic.

U.S. anthropologists revived their past tradition in research by reasserting the integration of the subfields of the discipline, such as cultural anthropology and physical anthropology. This new emphasis was most evident at the annual meetings of the American Anthropological Association. There, Floyd Lounsbury used linguistics, cultural anthropology, physical anthropology, and archaeology to show how knowledge in all four fields helped to decipher Mayan writing systems. Although not all symbols had yet been deciphered, Lounsbury proved that Mayan combines both phonetic and ideogram script, as did Egyptian hieroglyphics.

278

During other sessions of the annual meetings, integration was further highlighted in panel discussions such as "Reproduction Risks and Outcomes," where biological and cultural anthropologists joined interests. A session on "Human Evolution" integrated biological, cultural, and prehistoric anthropology. The session "Conditions for Urbanism in the Humid Tropics" discussed the ways in which archaeological studies of prehistoric Mayan sites contributed to the work of cultural anthropologists who were studying coastal Mexican towns and cities.

Applied research covered the usual broad range of topics, but two areas of concern received notable attention. At least 12 sessions centered on gender issues. Since the study of such issues has become well advanced, research interests have diversified. Session titles reflected this diversity: "Impact of AIDS on Women and Children in Africa," "Pseudo-Procreation Symbolism and Culture Theory," "Gender and the Interplay of Hierarchies in Complex Societies," "Women, Economic Development and Social Change in Latin America," "Political Economy Aspects of Violence Against Women," "Gender in Sacred Spaces," and "Women as Ritual Specialists." The importance of gender issues was further reflected in articles appearing in the *American Anthropologist*. These reported on women's roles in Israel, Spain, and among the Creek Indians; other research investigated ovarian function and reproductive ecology and examined dowry as a form of female competition.

The second issue drawing increased concern was the environment. Study of the environment ranged from the particular to the general. Two sessions were held on the oil spill off the coast of Alaska, the first dealing with its cultural and psychological effects and the second with the spill's social and economic effects. Another example of focus on a particular issue was a session on cocoa farmers in Bolivia.

Concentration on selected aspects of environmental problems resulted in further specialization of environmental anthropology. Four different sessions were held on "Tropical Forest Ecology, the Changing Human Niche, and Deforestation," along with a session on "Development and Amazonian Forest Peoples." The session "Natural Resources Management: Who Can Protect the Commons, and for Whom?" described anthropologists' findings of how people, in adapting to an environment, discover numerous ways to share its resources. These discoveries have lessons for contemporary peoples, ranging from Maine lobster fishers to people in Borneo making multiple uses of their swampland.

A central issue for anthropologists in their study of environmental problems is tropical deforestation, with particular emphasis on the Amazon rain forest. Large numbers of tribal people in the Amazon Basin are threatened with the extinction of their way of life, if not life itself, not only by timber interests but also by gold miners, ranchers, and the resettlement necessitated by the construction of large dams to generate hydroelectric power. The problem attracted to the area many North American anthropologists, who then began working with Brazilian and other South American anthropologists. In seeking solutions for the problems that had arisen, anthropologists found it necessary to integrate knowledge from the subfields of their discipline along with that of other disciplines. The process was illustrated by a 1990 report of the Wenner-Gren Foundation for Anthropological Research, which described a symposium that the foundation had sponsored on "Amazonian Synthesis: An Integration of Disciplines and Methodologies." Ethnohistorians, social anthropologists, archaeologists, and physical anthropologists sought a new theoretical synthesis to understand the nature and history of Amazonian cultures, with a focus on changing relationships among social structure, ideology, and economy in the new ecological setting.

Because of a concern for the discipline itself, the American Anthropological Association established a Committee on Anthropology in Predominantly Minority Institutions, which sought to encourage careers in anthropology among minority students. Retired anthropologists or those on sabbatical were placed in universities with large minority enrollments to make the field available to students for whom anthropology is especially relevant. During the past year Bea Medicine, herself a Dakota Indian, was the first to serve in the program, volunteering to teach at Standing Rock College, Fort Yates, N.D. The committee planned to place 15 volunteers during future months.

—Ernest L. Schusky

Archaeology

Since its formalization as a discipline in the late 19th century, archaeology has been aligned with both art and technology. Modern archaeologists have refined those alignments with many kinds of scientific advances, especially in restoration and analysis, but the wonder and appreciation for the beauty of ancient art and technology remain intact. The following summary of events in 1990 reflects some of the ways archaeologists find evidences of ancient art and technology, study them, and present them to the world. The record includes a spectacular Moche tomb in Peru, a race to record colorful but disappearing Maya art in Central America, and mass extinctions in ancient New Zealand because of human colonization and technology.

An 1,800-year-old Moche lord. A remarkable find reported in 1990 was the tomb of the "Old Lord of Sipán," in the lowest platform level of the ceremonial complex at Sipán, Peru. Surrounded by ceramic, copper, shell, silver, and gold artifacts, the Old Lord was probably an ancestor of the "Lord of Sipán," a spectacular burial in the uppermost platform reported in 1988. Each find by itself was truly astonishing, but finding two rich, intact, and relatively unvandalized tombs in the same site was unique in modern New World archaeology. Project directors Walter Alva and Susana Meneses, from the Bruning Archaeological Museum in Lambayeque, Peru, anticipated five more years of work uncovering at least three more little-disturbed tombs of Moche warrior-priests.

The Old Lord probably was alive in the 1st century AD. He was a member of the Moche culture, known from the fertile valleys along the Peruvian coast. The Moche were superb artists and technicians who, among other things, created a method for electroplating precious metals on copper some 1,500 years before the advent of electricity. Their art, well known from ceramics, fabrics, and metals, depicts a variety of human, animal, fish, bird, spider, and other effigies, as well as a panoply of human-animal deities. They were skilled in portraying individual personalities in facial features, and they often pictured everyday or special events in clay sculpture on vessels. Most of their head and figure sculptures were produced in molds, allowing reproduction of individual pieces. Mold-making technology is itself a form of advanced ceramic production, and the Moche were very adept at these techniques by at least 1,500 years ago.

Moche metalsmithing reached high levels of refinement, and what might be some of the best work was revealed during excavation of the Old Lord's tomb. An assortment of metal figures, jewelry, and ornaments was found with the body in the tomb, along with six large, intricate necklaces. The first necklace encountered was decorated with gold spiders atop golden webs. Another contained 10 gold human heads and an abundance of shell and stone beads. The Old Lord's death mask had one shell eye and, like the other masks in the grave, contained an empty left eye socket. This might signify a wound suffered by the warrior-priest during battle. Other items included a small, beautiful gold, silver, and turquoise figurine, a gold-plated deity figure, copper and gold rattles, solid gold nose and ear ornaments, a shell chest protector, bundles of broken spears, a spear-thrower, textiles, and a solid gold backflap.

Among all these riches, a 0.6-m (2-ft)-tall crab deity figure was perhaps most impressive. Made of gilded copper, this figurine has a human face and legs and the carapace, legs, and claws of a crab. It is inlaid with gold disks and rods and has a necklace of gilded bird skulls and an owl face on its headdress. Its eyes are made of shell and coral. It had been mounted on a fabric banner covered with gilded plates. The excavators called it Ulluchu Man, after the papaya-like fruit depicted on the banner. Ulluchu fruit was associated with warfare and the ritual drinking of prisoners' blood, perhaps because the fruit contains anticoagulant properties that kept the blood fresh before it was drunk. Why such bloody business was accompanied by masterful craftsman-

Metal figures, ornaments, and jewelry, including a necklace of gold spiders atop golden webs, were discovered during 1990 in the tomb of the "Old Lord of Sipán" at Sipán, Peru. The Old Lord probably lived during the first century AD and was a member of the Moche culture, which flourished in the fertile valleys along the coast of Peru.

The Maya Temple of the Sun at Palenque stands starkly white against the southern Mexican rain forest (left). Basing her work on the drawings of Adela Catherine Breton in the early 1900s, Merle Robertson re-created the brightly colored friezes that adorned the temple before they were destroyed by air pollution, volcanic ash, acid rain, and vandals (far left).

ship in metal, fabric, and clay remains one of the great mysteries of Moche archaeology.

Disappearing Maya art. At almost the same time that the Moche lords were living and dying in what is now Peru, another New World culture was producing great art in Central America. The Maya created murals and plaster bas-reliefs showing events and stories related to their world in what are now the jungles of Mexico and Guatemala. These murals and reliefs depict moments of great importance, as well as events in everyday life, and are invaluable for interpreting who and what the Maya were. According to Arthur Miller of the University of Maryland, they were "packed with information carried by color," and the color schemes are important in interpreting the art. Unfortunately, many of the pigments have been lost to increasingly acidic rain, vandals, and the loving but destructive touch of conservators and tourists. In some cases, all that is left are colored renditions of some of the scenes painted and sketched by Victorian visitors during the early 1900s.

One such visitor, Adela Catherine Breton, spent eight years traveling between Britain and Chichén Itzá and other Maya sites in the Yucatán region of Mexico. Today her sketches and paintings comprise the only records of some of the once brightly colored murals on the limestone walls of these ruins. June Kinoshita, in a recent issue of *Scientific American*, describes Breton's diligence in recording the beautifully painted walls, which are now almost obliterated. The importance of Breton's and similar work is growing as more Maya murals and reliefs are discovered and exposed to view. Once-vibrant colors fade rapidly; simply exposing them to light,

air, and visitation causes almost immediate deterioration, especially of areas painted with the indigo-based "Maya blue."

Archaeologists now know that color expressed a major part of the meaning of many Maya objects, including murals, reliefs, and buildings, and the way it was used reflected much of the Maya cosmology. For example, colors stood for the cardinal directions: red symbolized the east, black the west, white the north, yellow the south, and blue-green the center. A whole system of abstract associations permeating every aspect of Maya life grew out of these basic color-coded directional elements. The colors of deities' costumes were associated with directions, and the combination of color and direction gives clues to relationships between gods and goddesses in the Maya pantheon. In depictions of humans, colors signified status and place of origin. The use of color on murals reflects its use on sculptural pieces that are now bare limestone. Buildings in cities were also once brightly colored, and murals give us glimpses of how impressive these must have been.

Modern efforts to preserve and restore Maya art have been less than successful. For example, the famous murals at Bonampak, dated to AD 800, depicting a battle, its glorious aftermath, and the victory celebrations, have been deteriorating since they were discovered in the 1940s. These are some of the most important of all Maya murals, and several attempts have been made to preserve them. First, the site was stripped of trees, and portions of it were sheltered under tin roofs. This process changed the conditions surrounding the murals from the dark and damp of the rain forest that had prevailed for nearly 1,000

281

years to an environment with more abundant light that was alternately hot and moist or cool and dry. The murals quickly began to fade. They were also disappearing under a coating of calcium carbonate deposited as moisture seeped through the surrounding limestone walls.

Injections of silicon in the 1960s temporarily stabilized the walls, but eventually this process contributed to even more rapid deterioration as the silicon material began to slide downward. Concrete patches on several large cracks also obliterated portions of the murals. More recently, the calcium carbonate layers were stripped away with acids, revealing the painted murals in their full glory. However, cleaning may have hastened their destruction, because the coating protected them from temperature changes, light, moisture fluctuations, and air pollution. Furthermore, the newly revealed spectacular colors and details increased visitations to the site, and while this builds interest and revenues, it also introduces a host of problems, including more abundant plant spores that grow on the walls and destroy the paints.

Major projects have been undertaken during the past few years to record as much as possible of Maya art. The work is difficult and trying and requires, as Adela Breton put it, "not modern artistic skill, but the very different capacity of seeing them as ancient Americans did." Even the most important of the Bonampak murals have never been completely recorded. Several attempts have been made, but with mixed results. All started with great detail and accuracy but, as Breton noted, the toll on "brain and nerves as well as to eyes and hand" tends to lower the quality of the work at later stages. Even the most accurate and ambitious Bonampak replication, by Felipe Dávalos at the Florida Museum of Natural History, shows this loss of steam. Dávalos' replication of murals in the second and third rooms does not compare with his reconstruction of the first room. More recently, a Mexico City artist did well replicating murals in the third room but flagged by the time she worked on the others.

Several archaeologists and artists are attempting to convince the Mexican government that the murals could be preserved only by being removed from their natural environment. The goal is to have accurate replicas on display at the site but to remove the originals to museums. With a growing number of colorful murals being found and exposed throughout the Maya area, the need for replication and protection has never been greater. The eccentric Victorian Adela Breton not only set the stage for such work, she also set the standards by which modern replications must be measured.

Archaeology and mass extinctions in New Zealand. Recent evidence has shown that the unique fauna of

New Zealand was drastically altered in a very short time by human colonization of the islands. This was one result of the development of sophisticated ocean sailing and navigational skills by the ancient Polynesians. Their high level of sailing skill was associated with more elementary tool technologies, but even these were apparently enough to destroy a large number of the island's faunal species.

As described by Jared Diamond of the University of California at Los Angeles, the problem for archaeologists has been to associate the mass extinctions with the early human inhabitants. Few of the original animals on New Zealand remained by the time of European colonization, but hints of their relatively recent demise could be seen in fossils, in specialized plants, and in a few small remnant populations on nearby islands. Now direct evidence has come from the ancient campsites of the first human colonists.

New Zealand had evolved a suite of animals to fill the usual niches: large and medium-sized herbivores that were preyed upon by carnivores of corresponding sizes. In this case, however, most of the animals in both categories were birds. The large, flightless bird species, collectively called moas, were the major herbivores. They ranged in size from about 1 m (3 ft) tall and approximately 18 kg (40 lb) in weight up to 3 m (10 ft) tall weighing 225 kg (500 lb). Other large flightless species were also herbivores, including a large goose, a giant kagu, a big duck, and a giant coot. These were joined by flighted birds, among them pelicans, swans, and a giant raven. All these species filled the niches usually filled by large mammals. Major predators were also birds, including two large hawks. One, a giant goshawk, weighed up to 3 kg (7 lb), double the size of the largest currently living European and American goshawks. The other, however, was truly awesome: a giant eagle weighing around 15 kg (30 lb), then the largest and most powerful bird of prey in the world.

The goshawks preyed on small and medium-sized birds, and the eagle sought the large moas. It is probable that these large hunters preyed on adult moas, taking advantage of their bipedal posture by crippling their legs, then killing them with attacks to their heads and long necks. Eagles probably remained in the vicinity of such a kill for several days, eating slowly, much as lions consume a giraffe. None of these strange creatures was alive at the time of European contact in the 17th and 18th centuries. Were all of them alive around AD 800 when humans, the ancestral Maori, first settled the islands? Until recently, it was thought that by then many if not most of these animals were already on their way out. Now, archaeological evidence points to human hunters as the primary cause of their demise.

A growing number of radiocarbon dates on bird bones in Maori sites suggest that all known species of moas were still abundant at the time of colonization. They were all extinct a few hundred years later. The number of butchered moas in Maori sites is estimated to be around 100,000. Their large eggs were used as canteens, their skin as clothes, and their bones for needles, harpoons, and fishhooks. The Maori not only killed and used the birds but contributed to their extinction by clearing some of the forests where the birds lived.

Maori technology would not have been very advanced, but it was sufficient to allow humans to reach the islands and to exploit their flora and fauna. Most likely, the moas and other animals were so naive regarding humans that they became easy prey. Unlike large mammals in similar niches, such as deer and antelope, moas and other large birds probably had relatively low reproduction rates. Even the small numbers of hunters in the first colonizing parties could kill them faster than they could breed. It is easy to understand the relatively rapid human-caused extinction of all New Zealand's large flightless birds: they were surely killed for food, and they had no way to escape. The demise of the large birds of prey followed the reduction in their prey, but the ancestral Maori may also have fought the giant eagle in self-defense. Here was a bird used to attacking and killing large bipedal animals. Individual Maori, being smaller than large moas, must have seemed like fairly easy prey to such a bird. Even today, much smaller Manchurian hunting eagles sometimes kill their human handlers, and New Zealand's giant eagle was preadapted to hunting human bipeds.

Whole suites of other, smaller animals also became extinct in New Zealand, but some small populations maintain footholds on nearby islands. Archaeological evidence shows that the first human colonizers brought with them another efficient predator, the rat. These animals were probably responsible for the rapid extinction on New Zealand of several hundred species of smaller birds, bats, and reptiles. Some of these species remain alive on small islands that have no rats.

Although this evidence is becoming overwhelming, the idea that ancestral Maori caused the extinction of the majority of the country's indigenous fauna is controversial in New Zealand. European colonizers have recently begun to try to reverse discrimination against and dispossession of the Maori, and some see the evidence for Maori-caused extinction as "negative" information. The Maori themselves see the issue as one more excuse to deny them their rights. Here, as in many other places around the world, archaeological evidence is subject to political interpretation and can cause dissension between those in and out of power, and between those whose ancestors are studied and those who do the studying.

—James D. Wilde

Architecture and civil engineering

Rarely does a new approach to architectural design receive international acceptance and take on worldwide significance. Few architects develop innovative styles and problem-solving approaches. Most architecture, therefore, tends to reflect established regional preferences, and trends respond to socially accepted aesthetics.

Modern technology provides the ability to mimic regional styles that evolved out of the inherent virtues of the materials with which they were built and the social functions they served. Today architects curve steel beams into the shape of masonry arches, etch concrete to look like stone, and cast ancient Greek and Roman column forms in plastic. Designers borrow and intermingle incongruous styles.

Europe's tallest building, the Messeturm office tower, rises 256 meters (845 feet) in Frankfurt, Germany. The granite-covered concrete structure was designed by Murphy/Jahn.

Courtesy, Murphy/Jahn

Architects looking to the future foresee a variety of opportunities and possibilities. Richard Rogers, Norman Foster, and Peter Cook envision vastly different buildings that will respond to changing needs and adopt new technologies. As energy efficiency becomes an ever-pressing issue, an increasing number will contain systems to store and reclaim heat. Revolving buildings will be built to follow the Sun's path, and walls will change color in reaction to its intensity. The Marseille Civic Center, in France, was designed with self-adjusting louvers in front of the windows, and concrete floor slabs cooled by night air act as heat sinks during the day.

Economic and political events will always affect construction. One of the many casualties of Iraq's invasion of Kuwait was a $30 billion project to build two new suburbs near Kuwait City, Ras Az Zour and Sabiyah, which together were planned to house some 350,000 people. In Nairobi, the capital of Kenya, a project by the country's ruling political party to build the African continent's tallest structure, a 60-story office building, came to a halt. Its planned location, within a city park, raised such an environmental and political furor that it might never be built.

During the past year many competent, and some excellent, structures were conceived and built. Although many of these buildings were of significance to those they were designed to serve, no one underlying, single-minded design philosophy prevailed. In addition to the regional, national, or even international significance a building may obtain on the basis of its use and function, size or quantity alone can make a structure noteworthy. The most difficult criterion to pinpoint or select, because it is by far the most subjective, is excellence in terms of aesthetic quality. Often new trends evolve in the less pressured atmosphere of small, low-budgeted projects whose clients are more likely to encourage innovation.

Architecture. The Messeturm office tower in Frankfurt, Germany, became Europe's tallest building. Designed by Murphy/Jahn, the 256-m (1 m = 3.3 ft) granite-covered concrete structure dominates the city's skyline. In plan, its lower floors are 41-m squares with cut-out corners. At the 53rd floor, the building shape starts to transform into a cylinder, and the top 10 floors form a pyramid. The structure is supported by an octagonal core and perimeter columns. Above the lobby level, a 7.5-m-deep posttensioned concrete girder (in which tension is applied to steel cables embedded in the concrete) receives the loads from the columns above and carries them over to four giant corner supports. The tower rests on a 6-m-thick concrete mat, one of the largest in the world.

Soaring 282 m, One Liberty Place in Philadelphia looks down on William Penn's statue atop City Hall, the world's tallest building in 1880. City Hall, by

unwritten agreement, had remained Philadelphia's highest structure for more than 100 years. Murphy/Jahn's new office tower, while not duplicating prior forms, carries the distinct flavor of the early heyday of skyscraper construction, evoking images of New York City's Chrysler Building. The structural framing system, weighing only 112 kg per sq m (23 lb per sq ft), bears little resemblance, however, to the 200 + kg per sq m (40 + lb per sq ft) used by the Empire State Building and others of that era or to the column grids of the 1930s with spans of less than 6.1 m. One Liberty Place has 12.8 m of column-free space between its core and column-supported perimeter, which includes two supercolumns located in the facade opposite the corners of the core. These supercolumns are tied back into the core with diag-

One Liberty Place in Philadelphia, designed by Murphy/Jahn, recalls the skyscrapers of the 1920s and 1930s, especially the Chrysler Building in New York City. The office tower rises to a height of 282 meters (930 feet).

Exchange House in London, built over railroad tracks, features an exposed structural system. Supporting its 10 floors are a pair of seven-story-high parabolic steel arches, whose stability is maintained by two radial braces.

onal members that pass through tenant floor spaces at eight locations on 12 different floors. The amount of glass in the building's curtain wall gradually increases to all glass at the top. Stacked chevron-shaped masses on each building face step back as they approach the tower's apex, merging into a spire. Visible for kilometers, One Liberty Place has redefined Philadelphia's skyline.

One of the most handsome buildings recently completed in London's Broadgate complex is Exchange House. Designed by Skidmore, Owings & Merrill, it features an exposed structural system and spans 78 m over a complex of railroad tracks. Its 10 floors are supported by a pair of exterior seven-story-high parabolic steel arches, whose stability is maintained under unequal loading conditions (wind) by a pair of radial braces.

Bahrain acquired a museum of unusual merit. The design molded traditional cultural forms and spaces without condescension or superficiality. Designed by Knud Holscher, the museum is distinctively modern yet manages to incorporate traditional Islamic delicacy. It acquires strength through spatial proportions and texture, achieving it without resorting to eclecticism or literal references.

Toronto boasted a new police headquarters. Its design, by Shore Tilbe Henschel Irwin Peters Architects and Engineers and Mathers & Haldenby, aimed to break the somber stereotypical image of police buildings and create an open and friendly image. It features an atrium that unites a 10-story stepped, L-shaped mass with a 4-story front that opens into a well-defined courtyard.

The trend of restoring and renovating rather than demolishing and rebuilding continued to make social and economic sense. The government buildings on Ellis Island, arrival point for millions of immigrants to the United States, underwent a careful and sensitive refurbishing. Under the guidance of architects Beyer Blinder Belle and Notter Finegold + Alexander, the Main Building—the most important and majestic of the complex of 33 structures built between the 1890s and the 1930s—was restored as a museum. Interior spaces were carefully analyzed to determine which were appropriate for new use and which should be preserved and restored to demonstrate their historic function. The Registry Room was returned to its prior glory, and the sequence of spaces that the immigrants followed on their path to a new life was re-created.

A prosaic metal-drum factory in São Paulo, Brazil, was transformed by Lina Bo Bardi into a magnificent social center for recreation and sports. She demolished the interior partitions under the old iron trusses and created free-flowing spaces for play and exercise, a theater, and a library. Two new vertical structures were added to the complex. One contains a swimming pool and series of stacked gymnasiums, and the other encloses dressing rooms linked to the former by seven enclosed bridges arranged in an asymmetrical but balanced pattern.

Frank Gehry (winner of the 1989 International Pritzker Prize) designed the new American Center in Paris and the Vitra Museum in Weil-am-Rhein, Germany. Both are outstanding examples of his individualistic expressionistic architecture. His exuberant use of forms is a fascinating personal interpretation of space and juxtapositioned volumes.

The American Institute of Architects' Gold Medal was awarded to Charles Moore, designer of the Tegel Harbor development and four other AIA honor award buildings and perhaps best known for a mod-

The American Center in Paris exemplifies architect Frank Gehry's exuberant use of forms. Gehry was awarded the 1989 International Pritzker Prize for his entire body of work.

est early project known as Sea Ranch. The International Pritzker Prize went to Italy's Aldo Rossi, whose work reflects the mood of classical architecture while remaining distinctly modern. The recently completed Hotel Il Palazzo in Fukuoka, Japan, is a staid example of his style. The Praemium Imperiale, like the Pritzker an international award based on a lifetime portfolio of work, was bestowed on James Stirling of the U.K. His pioneering designs include the Leicester Engineering Building and the University of Cambridge History Faculty. Louis Kahn of the U.S. received the Aga Khan Award for his National Assembly Building in Dhaka, Bangladesh.

Civil engineering. More than a century after the French started tunneling toward England in 1878, and only three years after commencing current construction, crews digging from both the French and British shores met some 90 m under the English Channel. Owing to British fears that it might serve as an invasion route, the original effort was abandoned in 1882 with 1,828 m dug. The completed tunnel was designed to consist of two rail tubes (each carrying traffic in one direction) with a smaller interconnecting service tube between them. The tunnels extend almost 39 km (24 mi) through the chalk marl under the channel plus an additional 9.7 km (6 mi) to the Castle Hill portal in England and another 3.2 km (2 mi) to the Beussingue portal in France. Complex terminal structures were under construction in both countries. The world's largest civil engineering project, the tunnel was entirely privately financed.

Twenty years after the first celebration of Earth Day, the world has become more populated, and concerns about environmental contamination have increased. The need for industrial chimney scrubbers; safe disposal of chemical, nuclear, and human waste; and the recycling of nonbiodegradable items has generated a number of structures. For example, in Connecticut one of the world's largest enclosed composting facilities was completed along with another to burn 10 million tires a year in order to produce electricity. The U.K. agreed to stop dumping sewage sludge into the North Sea by 1998, a practice ended by its neighbors in 1987.

The Superconducting Super Collider, designed to be the world's most powerful proton accelerator, was under construction south of Dallas, Texas. Costing almost $8 billion, it would be one of the world's premier scientific research facilities. The Super Collider's main ring would measure three meters in diameter and form an oval 87 km (54 mi) in circumference.

Tokyo's new City Hall complex includes Japan's tallest tower. Rising to a height of 243 m, it has 19×109-m columnfree floors that are supported by eight supercolumns. Each column consists of four steel tubes arranged to form a 6.4-m square. Construction was begun on an even taller 296-m tower in Yokohama.

The Mount Baker Ridge Tunnel and Lid Complex in Seattle, Wash., won the American Civil Engineering Society's Outstanding Achievement Award for 1990. The project provides a traffic link between Seattle and Bellevue. Measuring 19.3 m in diameter, it was the world's largest-diameter tunnel constructed in soft soil and was equipped with the country's largest foam sprinkler system.

—David Guise

286

Astronomy

During the past year the Hubble Space Telescope began operating, and the Magellan spacecraft started mapping the surface of Venus. New evidence was found that disks of matter from which planetary systems can form are quite common around newly formed solar-type stars (those similar to the Sun). Clues to the early evolution of our Galaxy were uncovered. The 30-year-old determination that spiral galaxies are essentially transparent to visible light was strongly challenged.

Instrumentation. The long-awaited and much-delayed launch of the Hubble Space Telescope (HST) occurred on April 24, 1990. The space shuttle *Discovery* reached a record altitude of 614 km (382 mi) before deploying the telescope. At that height atmospheric drag is low enough to ensure the HST an orbit with a lifetime of at least five years. Space shuttle astronauts were tentatively scheduled to service the telescope in mid-1993. The orbit of the HST also was to be corrected for any changes caused by atmospheric drag.

During the engineering tests and checkout of the telescope, two major difficulties were found. One involved telescope pointing. Whenever the HST enters or leaves sunlight, each of which occurs 15 times every 24 hours, the telescope oscillates. Though the guidance system eventually corrects this, observations are restricted or degraded until the oscillations are removed. In addition, the design guiding error of 0.07 second of arc is attained only by using guide stars 2.5 times brighter than the faintest that had been planned. A lack of guide stars bright enough to attain good guiding will limit the ability of the telescope to observe some objects. Improvements to the software controlling the HST's guidance system and possible corrections to its solar power panels when the telescope is next serviced should bring the guidance problems within acceptable bounds.

The other problem was more devastating, at least at first. The telescope could not be focused to design specifications. The best image attainable with a point source of light had a sharp central core of 0.1 second of arc in diameter surrounded by a fuzzy halo of light. According to the design specifications, 70% of the light should have been found in the central core instead of the 15% that was. The reason for this was that the shape of the primary mirror was slightly in error and caused a type of image distortion known as spherical aberration. Fortunately, the distortion could be corrected by insertion of additional optics in the light path, much the same as eyeglasses correct the vision of an eye. Corrective optics are being prepared for insertion when the HST is visited in 1993 (*see* Year in Review: OPTICAL ENGINEERING).

Until then, computer-enhancement techniques developed for radioastronomy data could be used to improve the images of brighter objects. Unfortunately, the images of the very faint objects for which the HST was to have been particularly effective could not be improved. Faint sources were essentially lost in the background light. The loss of light in the central core also effectively reduced the distances

The best ground-based image of Pluto and its moon Charon (left) contrasts with the photograph of the same two bodies taken by the faint-object camera of the Hubble Space Telescope (right).

Photos, NASA/ESA

Image of Saturn obtained by the Hubble Space Telescope was enhanced by computer to yield greater spatial detail in the planet's ring system and cloud belts than could be achieved with ground-based telescopes.

at which galaxies and quasars could be measured. Even so, the application of computer-enhancement techniques to HST images had already produced some startling results that gave promise for effective observation by the telescope before its aberration was corrected.

As an example of such techniques, the enhanced image of the center of 30 Doradus, a star cluster in the Large Magellanic Cloud, showed some 60 stars in a region that is seven arc seconds wide. This was an improvement of nearly six times over the best ground-based images of the region. Hubble completely resolved the images of Pluto and its satellite Charon at a separation of 0.9 arc second even without image processing. The enhanced image of Saturn that it obtained approached the quality of images of the planet and its rings by the Voyager spacecraft. An image of Supernova 1987A revealed an elongated ring of glowing gas about 1.6 arc seconds long around the supernova's location. The ring is the compressed inner edge of a cloud of gas expelled by the supernova precursor during its red-giant stage and then excited into emission by ultraviolet light from the supernova event.

HST also imaged ionized gas clouds in the central 150 light-years of the Seyfert galaxy NGC 1068. This represented about one second of arc on the sky. In ground-based optical images this central region appeared only as a starlike image. When HST viewed the elliptical galaxy NGC 7457, the very center of the galaxy was revealed as a bright, distinct nucleus where the star density had to be at least 30,000 times that in the neighborhood of the Sun.

Solar system. An eclipse of Pluto by its satellite Charon was observed by David Tholen of the University of Hawaii on Sept. 3, 1990. Charon barely grazed the disk of Pluto, causing a 3% drop in the combined light of the two bodies. The last event of the current series of eclipses, when Charon's disk would have appeared just tangent to Pluto, occurred on October 15 when Pluto was too close to the Sun to be observed. The work of observing these eclipses, which took place every 6.39 days (the orbital period of the system), now had to be placed aside for 124 years. At that time Pluto would again be at a position in its orbit that would provide observers on Earth with another edge-on view of Charon's orbit. The six-year duration of observations allowed the sizes of Pluto and Charon to be determined with an uncertainty of less than 2%. Pluto's diameter is 2,302 km, and Charon's is 1,186 km (1 km = 0.62 mi). Observations of the system by the Hubble Space Telescope could improve the accuracy by permitting a better determination of the size of the mutual orbit of the two bodies.

The Magellan spacecraft of the U.S. National Aeronautics and Space Administration (NASA) arrived at Venus and entered orbit around the planet on Aug. 10, 1990. It circled Venus once every 3.26 hours in an elliptical orbit with an altitude that varied from 294 to 8,450 km. The orbit was inclined 85.5° to the equator of Venus. After some initial difficulties the spacecraft began performing magnificently.

Magellan was equipped with two radar systems. One was a side-viewing radar, and the other was a radar altimeter that measured the spacecraft's height above the surface of Venus to within about 10 m (33 ft). The side-viewing radar operated at a wavelength of 12.6 cm (5 in), which easily penetrated the dense atmosphere of the planet. During the 37 minutes of each orbit when Magellan was closest to Venus, the radar mapped a strip of the planet's surface that was roughly 15,000 km long and 20 to 25 km wide. During 243 days, the rotation period of Venus, Magellan was expected to have made 1,790 orbits, and its radar would have mapped 70 to 80% of the surface. Eventually Magellan should map all of Venus from its north pole to about latitude 67° S. The resolution of the radar was 10 times better than that achieved by the Soviet Venera orbiters and by the Arecibo antenna in Puerto Rico. Details as small as 120 m (394 ft) across were recorded.

Although only a tiny fraction of the surface of Venus had been mapped, the detail in the radar images was so exceptional that ideas about Venus were already being reshaped. The surface of the planet appeared to be extremely young, only 100 million to one billion years old, compared with the 4.5 billion years of the solar system. (The age of a planetary surface is taken to be the time since it was last reshaped or modified significantly.) Extremely intricate networks of faults, terraced volcanic calderas, folded mountain ranges, and what appeared to be large lava flows all indicated that Venus must have considerable internal activity. Many impact craters appeared to have smooth lava-filled bottoms. This implied that there is a thin surface crust lying above a hot interior. There was not yet enough evidence to indicate whether the Venusian surface undergoes tectonic plate activity similar to that which occurs on the Earth.

Many strange features were seen on Venus. Among them were eroded objects resembling riverbeds. Since no fluid water can exist at the high surface temperature of Venus, about 450° C (840° F), possibly very fluid lava or hot gas and dust ejected from an impact shaped these objects. A number of asymmetrical impact craters were also found. One kidney-shaped crater could have been formed when an incoming body was broken up by the dense Venusian atmosphere. The several broken parts could have struck the surface together to form the irregular crater.

Magellan arrived with an ample supply of fuel to power its attitude-control system. Barring unforeseen difficulties, the spacecraft could continue to map Venus for decades. This would allow the comparison of sequential maps that might reveal changes on the Venusian surface as they occurred.

What might be the largest visible object in the solar system was found by Michael Mendillo, Jeffrey Baumgardner, Brian Flynn, and W. Jeffrey Hughes of Boston University. They used a specially designed camera to record an image of the environs of Jupiter in the light of the strong yellow emission lines of the sodium atom. They also obtained images of the nearby sky in the light of sodium and images of the sky and Jupiter through a filter that transmitted light of a color slightly different from the yellow sodium light. By combining these images with the first, they could correct for extraneous sodium light scattered into the image. The corrected image revealed a huge, approximately elliptical-shaped cloud with its long axis in the plane of Jupiter's equator. The cloud spanned nearly 29 million km in its largest direction. The density of the sodium atoms in the clouds was extremely low.

Three craters 37 to 50 kilometers (23 to 31 miles) in diameter are revealed on the surface of Venus in an image provided by the orbiting space probe Magellan. Features of the craters indicate that they were caused by meteorite impact.

The cloud was visible only because the sodium is so efficient in scattering sunlight. The sodium atoms escape from the ring, or torus, of ionized gases lost by Jupiter's satellite Io and trapped by Jupiter's magnetic field. There are more abundant elements and molecules present in the gas given off by Io, but they scatter sunlight much more weakly than sodium at visible wavelengths. The investigators suggested that the cloud if observed from space should be detectable at ultraviolet wavelengths in sunlight scattered by the other components.

Stars. The faint nearby star known as Gliese 22 has been recognized as a double star for many years. The brighter component of the system also shows a small movement induced by another, but unseen, companion. Recent observations with a speckle camera by astronomers of the University of Arizona and Kitt Peak (Ariz.) National Observatory were used to provide the first image of this third component. In all, 7,000 frames of the unresolved pair of stars and of a control star that was known to be single were analyzed. By using suitable computational methods, the team was able to reconstruct the image of the brighter component and its newly resolved companion. The separation of the two stars was only 0.45 second of arc. The research team determined that the mass of the major component of the system is 0.36 solar mass. (One solar mass is the mass of the Sun, 2×10^{33} grams.) The other two components are 0.12 and 0.18 solar mass. The two smaller stars orbit about the primary star in the same plane at distances of 5 and 40 times the Earth's distance from the Sun. The system is similar in scale and orbital mechanics to our solar system.

The T Tauri stars are a class of stars that display an irregular variation in brightness. They invariably are found in regions where recent star formation has occurred. One of their distinguishing features is that they radiate more energy in the ultraviolet and infrared than would be expected, based on their visible radiation. They are believed to be very young solar-type stars surrounded by dust-rich accretion disks. (An accretion disk is a rapidly rotating disk of gas, and sometimes dust, surrounding a star, formed from material spiraling toward the star from an external source.) The excess ultraviolet radiation is generated when disk material falls onto the stellar surface. The excess infrared radiation is generated when the dust component of the disk is heated by direct starlight and by gravitational energy released as disk material spirals in toward the star.

Calculations indicated that the disks are of the same order of size as Pluto's orbit, about 5.9 billion km from the Sun. However, none of these stars is close enough to have had an accretion disk resolved. Because the disks are opaque in visible and infrared light, observers could receive energy only from the outer regions of the disks that lie in the Earth's direction. Consequently, there was no way to estimate the mass of the disks from the amount of visible energy received from the disks because only the outermost matter contributes. The disks do become transparent at microwave and millimeter wavelengths, however. For these wavelengths the amount of energy emitted is proportional to the total amount of emitting matter. Two different teams used this fact to estimate the masses of T Tauri accretion disks. One team, Fred Adams of the Harvard-Smithsonian Center for Astrophysics, Cambridge, Mass., James Emerson of Queen Mary and Westfield College, London, and Gary Fuller of the University of California at Berkeley, observed seven different T Tauri stars from Mauna Kea, Hawaii, at submillimeter wavelengths. The other team, Steven Beckwith of Cornell University, Ithaca, N.Y., Anniela Sargent of the California Institute of Technology, and Rolf Chini and Rolf Güsten of the Max Planck Institute für Radioastronomie, Bonn, Germany, observed 86 young stars in the Taurus-Auriga region from Pico Veleta, Spain, at the 1.3-mm wavelength. The team observing at submillimeter wavelengths detected radiation which implied that their sample of stars had disks that ranged in mass from 0.05 to 1.0 solar mass. The team observing at 1.3 mm found that 42% of the stars they observed had detectable emission from dust particles. They found evidence for disks ranging from 0.01 to 1.0 solar mass. These results indicate that approximately one-third of newly formed stars of the solar type have disks and that these disks contain enough mass to form planetary systems.

The strongest X-ray sources in our Galaxy are close binary stars in which one member of the system accretes matter from the other member. The X-ray source designated A0620-00 that erupted in 1975 to become momentarily the brightest X-ray source in the sky is that type of binary. A0620-00 is a system in which the spectrum of only one star is seen undergoing periodic Doppler shifts due to orbital motion of the star. Carole Haswell of the University of Texas at Austin and Allen Shafter of San Diego (Calif.) State University obtained time-resolved spectroscopic observations of emission from hydrogen in the accretion disk around the unseen companion. (Time-resolved spectra are those in which exposure times are short compared with the characteristic time of any changes in the spectrum. In this case the observations consisted of 30-minute exposures. This is short enough compared with the eight-hour period of the binary to freeze Doppler displacements in the spectra.) They detected a wobble in the hydrogen-line emission corresponding to a velocity variation slightly less than one-tenth that of the visible star. This velocity variation in the accretion disk reflects the movement of the unseen component. For this to be the case, the component must have a mass of more than 10 times the visible component. It has a mass of 3.82 solar masses or greater depending on the inclination of the orbital motion to the line of sight to the system. Thus, the unseen component is not a neutron star because the mass of a neutron star cannot exceed three solar masses. Therefore, A0620-00 is the first binary system in which the mass of an unseen component has been measured to be large enough to conclude that it is a black hole.

Galactic astronomy. A study of the age differences among globular clusters in our Galaxy by Don VandenBerg of the University of Victoria, B.C., and Michael Bolte and Peter B. Stetson of Dominion Astrophysical Observatory, Victoria, provided new insight into the evolution of the Galaxy. The age of globular clusters can be estimated by comparing observations of the brightness and colors of cluster stars with values found from computations of stellar evolution. The age of a particular cluster also depends on the assumed chemical composition of the cluster members, however. VandenBerg and his colleagues reduced the uncertainties introduced by these varying compositions by dividing the globular clusters into groups based on composition. They found that metal-poor clusters have nearly the same ages to within 500 million years. By contrast, the metal-rich clusters have an age spread in excess of two billion years. The metal-poor clusters formed from the original matter in the Galaxy. The metal-rich clusters, on the other hand, could form only after heavy elements had been generated during the evolution of massive stars and released by supernova explosions. The investigators, therefore, suggested that the age ranges they measured require that the collapse of the Galaxy from its original shape to the present one was prolonged rather than brief (less than one billion years), as had been commonly believed prior to their work.

Extragalactic astronomy. The cluster of galaxies known as Abell 2029 is centered on a large cD galaxy (cD galaxies are giant elliptical galaxies surrounded by a fainter envelope of stars). The immensity of this galaxy was revealed in measurements made by Juan Uson of the National Radio Astronomy Observatory, Green Bank, W.Va., Stephen Boughn of Haverford (Pa.) College, and Jeffrey Kuhn of Michigan State University. They used a charge-coupled device (CCD) camera to obtain 16 overlapping images that formed a cross centered on the cluster of galaxies. Their objective was to search for a possible, diffuse background of light from matter that might have been stripped from cluster members by collisions and tidal interactions. They used the CCD camera because its linearity and great dynamic range allowed them to measure diffuse light levels only 0.0002 times that of the night sky. After subtracting

light scattered from bright foreground stars and the central region of the cD galaxy by the telescope optics and the Earth's atmosphere, all the remaining diffuse light was associated with the cD galaxy itself. The elliptically shaped haze extended roughly eight million light-years in the longest direction. The combined light of the diffuse haze and that of the bright inner parts of the galaxy was the equivalent of two trillion Suns. Also, because the haze displayed no clumping, the matter in the haze must have been there from the early existence of the galaxy and not introduced later by collisions with other galaxies in the cluster. The galaxy is, therefore, an old supergiant, the largest yet measured.

In the late 1950s Erik Holmberg of the Lund (Sweden) Observatory concluded that spiral galaxies are mostly transparent in visible light. He reached his conclusion by comparing the average surface brightness of galaxies with their inclinations to the lines of sight to the galaxies. The inclination angle is found by comparing the minor with the major axis of an ellipse fitted to the observed outline of a galaxy. (If the disk of a spiral galaxy is assumed to be circular, the galaxy will appear elliptical in shape whenever it is viewed from a direction not perpendicular to the plane of the disk.) If a galaxy is perfectly transparent, it will appear equally bright no matter from which angle it is viewed. If it is totally opaque, it will appear brightest when the disk is viewed face-on. Since it is not possible to vary the angle of view to a given galaxy, Holmberg proceeded by collecting data on 119 spiral galaxies and then analyzing this information statistically to determine how brightness changed with viewing angle. On the basis of this analysis, he concluded that spiral galaxies are transparent.

Edwin Valentijn at the European Southern Observatory in Chile repeated this type of analysis but with a much more extensive and more accurate data base. From roughly 16,000 galaxies photometrically measured on the European Southern Observatory Survey plates, he selected a sample of 9,381 galaxies for which full surface-brightness profiles had been determined. Not only were the brightness measures much more accurate than those available to Holmberg 30 years earlier but Valentijn also had enough galaxies to select groups according to type of galaxy. He also could compare the analyses of different subsamples to test for statistical consistency in his results. He concluded that spiral galaxies are not transparent. The obscuring matter in the galaxies could supply enough mass to explain the flat rotation curves of spiral galaxies, thus removing the need to invoke so-called dark-matter haloes around them.

—W.M. Protheroe

See also Feature Articles: Colors for a Cosmic Canvas; Space Art: Visualizing the Unknown.

Chemistry

Had there been an annual award for "most popular chemical discovery," chemists in 1990 probably would have chosen buckminsterfullerene, a soccer-ball-shaped form of carbon finally made in a quantity sufficient to confirm its existence. In other highlights chemists explored compounds whose properties appeared intermediate between those of small molecules and bulk solids and synthesized a variety of organic compounds including many of biological importance. Continuing developments in the "cold fusion" controversy further ensured a special place for the affair in the history and sociology of science.

Inorganic chemistry

A common textbook definition of an atom is "the smallest unit having the properties of the element." In general, however, individual atoms do not have properties of bulk matter. This observation holds especially for metallic and semimetallic elements, whose atomic behavior conforms to a straightforward quantum mechanical model but whose ordinary bulk phases exhibit unique mechanical, electronic, magnetic, and optical properties that can be described only as properties of ensembles of atoms.

It has been known for some time that many simple binary compounds, i.e., compounds formed from only two elements, exist in the solid state as giant molecules. In cadmium sulfide, for example, each cadmium ion is surrounded by four sulfur atoms arranged at the apexes of a tetrahedron. Each sulfur atom is similarly surrounded by a tetrahedral array of four cadmium ions. This diamondlike, or adamantine, structure is sufficiently large that it imparts very low water solubility to the bulk solid.

There exist a growing number of large, discrete molecules, often possessing strikingly simple structures, whose behavior appears to be intermediate between that of small molecules and that of bulk solids. These so-called cluster compounds, of predictable size and composition, are of enormous theoretical interest because they may provide a conceptual link between theories that describe atoms and small molecules and those that describe the bulk solid state. This understanding, in turn, could help guide the development of solid-state devices ranging from microscopic circuits to high-temperature superconductors to catalysts that mimic natural processes.

This article focuses on recent developments in the chemistry of inorganic cluster compounds and of polyacids, the latter being complex ionic structures built up out of simple acids. Both topics fall within the field of frontier research that strives to bridge the chemistry of discrete molecules and that of the bulk solid state.

Cluster compounds. The earliest proven structure of a cluster compound is that of trimethylplatinum(IV) chloride. The compound consists of a platinum(IV) ion (Pt^{4+}) apparently bonded to three methyl groups (derivatives of methane having the chemical formula $-CH_3$ and bonded through the carbon atom to platinum) and one chloride ion (Cl^-). This formulation, however, is contrary to all prior experience with platinum(IV), which forms compounds with six substituents arrayed at the apexes of an octahedron (a geometric solid that can be represented by two square-based pyramids joined base to base). In 1947 it was shown by X-ray diffraction that trimethylplatinum(IV) chloride is a tetramer; i.e., four units of trimethylplatinum(IV) chloride form the discrete molecular structure. The gross structure is a cube—hence the generic name cubane for this and similar structures—with platinum(IV) and chloride ions at alternate apexes, thus forming a Pt_4Cl_4 cluster (see 1). Three methyl groups are bonded to each platinum(IV) ion, extending the edges of the cube. The platinum(IV) ions thus have the expected six substituents—three methyl groups and three shared chloride ions—arrayed at the apexes of an octahedron. Each chloride ion is bonded to three platinum(IV) ions.

In the course of 20 years of research led by Richard H. Holm and co-workers, the iron atoms in such iron-containing proteins as the ferridoxins have been found in a planar, rhombic cluster structure with two iron(III) ions (Fe^{3+}) and two sulfide ions (S^{2-}) arranged at alternate apexes and with two additional groups bonded to the iron(III) ion. Cubic Fe_4S_4 iron-sulfur clusters, with alternate apexes of the cube occupied by iron ions and sulfide ions, have also been found in abundance in iron-containing proteins. Each of the irons in these Fe_4S_4 cores (see 2) is bonded to only one additional group, usually a thiolate ($R-S-$, in which R is some organic group) from a sulfur-containing amino acid or a convenient synthetic analogue, an alcoxylate ($R-O-$, in which O is oxygen), or a halide ion (e.g., iodide, or I^-).

In contrast with the octahedral geometry around the platinum(IV) ion in trimethylplatinum(IV) chloride, the geometry around the iron in Fe_4S_4 cores is approximately tetrahedral, consisting of three shared sulfur ions and one "external" thiolate bonded to the iron. Although the iron ions are structurally equivalent, they need not have the same formal oxidation state. Thus, the formal charge carried by a cluster varies as the ratio of iron(II) to iron(III) ions.

Holm and other researchers showed that these iron-sulfur cores may be removed from and reinserted in proteins, that they can be synthesized easily from simple starting materials, and that they can be used as building blocks for the preparation of a variety of more complex structures. By 1990, according

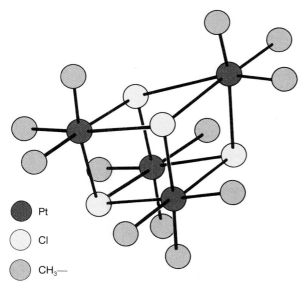

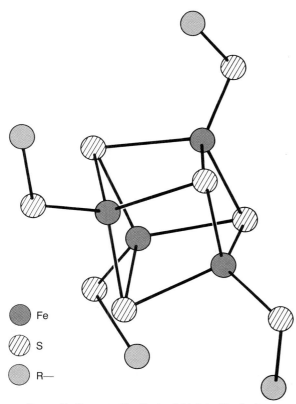

1   structure of trimethylplatinum(IV) chloride

Pt

Cl

CH₃—

Fe

S

R—

2   Fe₄S₄ core with attached thiolate (R—S—) groups

the iron-molybdenum-sulfur cofactor in the nitrogenases, enzymes that participate in the process of biological nitrogen fixation. Both Holm and his students at Harvard University and Dimitri Coucouvanis and his students at the University of Michigan have succeeded in substituting other metals for iron in some of these clusters. Holm described the synthesis and characterization of $[MoFe_3S_4]^{n+}$ core structures (the overall charge on the cluster is a variable) from precursors containing $[Fe_3S_4]^+$ and molybdenum (Mo). In 1990 he reported making a nickel (Ni)-containing cluster, $[NiFe_3S_4]^+$, from the reaction of $[Fe_3S_4]^+$ with tris(triphenylphosphine)nickel (see 3, on p. 294). In these reactions a molybdenum or nickel atom is inserted into an iron site in the cubane structure. By contrast with Holm's strategy of "folding a box" around the second kind of metal atom, Coucouvanis has used conditions that result in the addition of the second metal to a complete iron-sulfur cluster. As an example, he reported the synthesis and characterization of a $[Mo_2Fe_6S_6]^{n+}$ cluster, in which a molybdenum atom is added to opposing hexagonal faces of the $[Fe_6S_6]^{3+}$ prismane structure (see 4, on p. 294). The core of the new cluster is structurally similar to that of $[Fe_8S_6]^{5+}$.

In 1990 Holm described synthesizing a cyclic iron-sulfur cluster with a $[Fe_{18}S_{30}]^{10-}$ core that also contains two sodium atoms (Na). Though made under spontaneous self-assembly conditions, which often produce iron-sulfur clusters, the structure may be viewed as a torus (a donut-shaped structure) formed by closing the ends of an 18-iron strip of the linear polymeric $[FeS_2]_x^{n-}$ anion found in bulk iron sulfide. The structural building block is an iron(II) or iron(III) ion in a tetrahedral array of shared sulfide ions. Although the magnetic features of the cluster conform closely to those of some other, smaller iron-sulfur clusters, the absorption spectrum is similar to that of colloidal $Na_2[FeS_2]$. Holm described the bonding in $[Fe_{18}S_{30}]^{10-}$ as more similar to that of bulk semiconducting phases than to that of any of the familiar smaller iron-sulfur clusters.

The past year also saw advances in the chemistry of clusters containing elements other than iron and sulfur. As a part of studies of the large iron- and oxygen-containing cores that occur in such proteins as hemerythrin and methane monooxygenase, Stephen Lippard and co-workers of the Massachusetts Institute of Technology prepared what they described as a molecular "ferric wheel": $[Fe(OCH_3)_2(O_2CCH_2Cl)]_{10}$, which contains 10 iron ions, all as iron(III). As the trivial name suggests, this cluster is also toroidal in shape (see 5, on p.295). The spectroscopy and magnetism of the cluster conform to those expected of iron(III), with no special features attributable to the novel cluster structure. In contrast to the iron-sulfur cores, it is interesting to note that the oxygen-

to Holm, clusters were known with iron-to-sulfide ratios of 2:2, 3:4, 4:4, 4:6, 6:6, 6:8, 6:9, 7:6, 8:6, and 18:30.

In recent years Holm has applied the chemistry of iron-sulfur clusters toward an understanding of

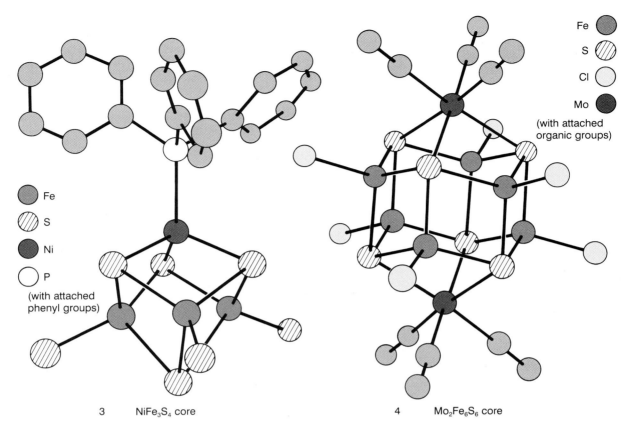

3   NiFe₃S₄ core

4   Mo₂Fe₆S₆ core

Fe
S
Ni
P
(with attached phenyl groups)

Fe
S
Cl
Mo
(with attached organic groups)

bridged species discovered in 1990 appear to have all of the metal ions in a single oxidation state.

G. Atillio Ardizzoia and co-workers at the University of Milan discovered a ring-shaped copper (Cu) compound, $[Cu_8(C_5N_2H_7)_8(OH)_8]$, in which the oxygen atoms in the hydroxide (OH) are shared between copper(I) ions; each copper ion is also bonded to a nitrogen atom residing in each of two adjacent 3,4-dimethylpyralolate $(C_5N_2H_7)$ groups. The largest previously known copper cluster contains five copper ions. The new eight-copper cluster compound is particularly interesting for its apparent ability to substitute a variety of alcohols for the hydroxide ions and to catalytically oxidize carbon monoxide to carbon dioxide in the presence of oxygen and pyridine.

Together, research reported in the past year showed the versatility of cluster compounds as models for biological processes and electronic and magnetic phenomena in bulk solids and as chemical catalysts.

Polyacids. The chemistry of polyacids, studied for more than a century, remains a subject of contemporary research. The solution chemistry of polyacids have been a major source for scientific understanding of complex equilibriums. Crystalline polyacids have found application as chemical catalysts. More recently various polyacids called poly "blues" have

been found to have antiviral and antitumor activity. Furthermore, there is particular interest in polyacids as models for the electronic and catalytic characteristics of bulk solid metal oxides.

Nonmetallic elements—for example, phosphorus or sulfur—combine with oxygen to form oxides. When phosphorus is burned in air, the oxide formed is diphosphorus pentoxide, whose formula is actually P_4O_{10}. Many of these oxides react on dissolution in water to form acids; e.g., $P_4O_{10} + 6H_2O \rightarrow 4H_3PO_4$ (phosphoric acid).

These oxides are known generically as acid anhydrides. In addition to the nonmetallic elements, many transition metals react with oxygen to produce anhydrides. Molybdenum and tungsten (W), for example, give MoO_3 and WO_3 respectively, which react with water to form molybdic and tungstic acids. The expected product, however, H_2MoO_4 in the case of molybdenum, reacts with itself to produce an equilibrium mixture of complex polymeric anions; e.g., $6MoO_4^{2-} + 7H_3O^+ \leftrightarrows [HMo_6O_{21}]^{5-} + 10H_2O$. It is such complex ions as $[HMo_6O_{21}]^{5-}$, built up out of simple acids, that are referred to as polyacids.

With the advent of semiautomatic X-ray diffraction apparatus, the structures of many crystalline polyacids have been determined. These structures are based on MO_6^{n-} octahedra (M representing an unspecified metal atom) sharing one "apex" or two "edge" oxide ions. All of the known polyacid structures contain cavities, which can accommodate additional octahedral XO_6^{n-} or tetrahedral XO_4^{m-} moieties (groups). If the element X is the same as element M, the product is called an isopolyacid; if X is different from M, the product is known as a heteropolyacid. An example of a heteropolyacid is $H_7[PMo_{12}O_{42}]$, with two $[Mo_6O_{21}]^{6-}$ units per phosphorus(V) ion. With 6 or 12 molybdenum(VI) ions per structural unit, these and other transition metal polyacids are easily reduced to produce compounds known as poly "blues" because of their characteristic intense blue color.

In 1990 several groups reported research results that began to forge links between polyacids and bulk solid metal oxide surfaces. Richard Finke and co-workers of the University of Oregon reported the synthesis and characterization of (1,5-cyclooctadienyl)iridium$[P_2W_{12}Nb_3O_{62}]^{8-}$ (*see* 6, on p. 296). This compound incorporates 3 NbO_6 octahedra, 2 PO_4 tetrahedra, and 12 WO_6 octahedra that share edges and apexes. One end of the polyacid ion is capped by the three NbO_6 groups, to which the iridium(I) complex is bonded. When the compound was dissolved in acetone and exposed to hydrogen gas under moderate pressure, the cyclooctadienyl moiety reacted to form cyclooctane, which departed, leaving H_2 (or perhaps two H atoms) and acetone in

its place. In this intermediate state, the compound catalytically reduced cyclohexene to cyclohexane in an atmosphere of hydrogen under pressure. All evidence indicated that this acetone-soluble, heteropolyacid-supported catalyst is chemically equivalent to the traditional catalyst; *i.e.*, a bulk solid supported on aluminum oxide.

Jon Zubieta and Qin Chen of the State University of New York at Albany prepared the polyoxovanadate $[V_6O_{13}\{O_2NC(CH_2O)_3\}_2]^{2-}$, in which tris(hydroxymethyl)nitromethane, $O_2NC(CH_2OH)_3$, caps an octahedral array of vanadium(V) ions in the $[V_6O_{19}]^{8-}$ cluster. This class of compound enables a chemist to bond organic fragments to a structure resembling a metal oxide. The organic fragments, in turn, may be used as "anchors" for catalytically active metal sites as in the case described by Finke. In particular, Zubieta and Chen's research indicates how similar features may be incorporated on bulk solid metal oxide phases.

Rafael Acerete and co-workers at the universities of Valencia and Madrid, Spain, isolated the sodium salt of $[P_6W_{18}O_{79}]^{20-}$, the first phosphotungstate proved to have a phosphorus-to-tungsten ratio of 1:3. The crystal structure revealed some unusual features, which included external PO_4 tetrahedra and an overall chiral structure. *Chirality* is the term applied to compounds having mirror-image isomers, molecular structures related to one another as the right hand

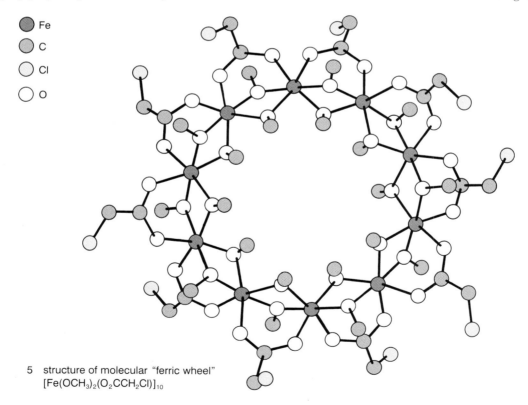

Fe
C
Cl
O

5   structure of molecular "ferric wheel"
     $[Fe(OCH_3)_2(O_2CCH_2Cl)]_{10}$

is to the left. Chirality is a characteristic of the molecular building blocks of living systems—amino acids and proteins, for example—but its occurrence is exceedingly rare in compounds that contain no carbon atoms.

In other developments Rosemarie Szostak and co-workers at the Georgia Institute of Technology discovered that heteropoly aluminophosphate analogues of zeolite molecular sieves can be prepared without organic "templates" and have used their discovery to produce aluminophosphate molecular sieves with exceedingly large cavities. (For a discussion of zeolites, see *1991 Yearbook of Science and the Future* Year in Review: CHEMISTRY: *Inorganic chemistry*.) The chemists modified an all-inorganic reaction mixture that had long been known to produce aluminophosphates having relatively small cavity dimensions. By adding hydrochloric acid, which is an occasional impurity in commercial aluminum oxide, and increasing the aluminum-to-phosphorus ratio, they produced a structure having pores the size of 18-member rings.

Robert Haushalter and co-workers at Exxon Research and Engineering Co., Annandale, N.J., prepared and characterized a heteropoly molybdophosphate that contains 35% empty space. The new compound, $Mo_8O_{12}(PO_4)_4(HPO_4)_2 \cdot 13H_2O$, reversibly absorbs 12% water by weight without changes in the crystal structure. Edge- and apex-shared MoO_6 octahedra are held together by apex-shared PO_4 tetrahedra incorporating molybdenum as an integral, covalently bonded member of a rigid, very porous zeolite-like structure. If these new compounds prove

6   representational structure of $[P_2W_{12}Nb_3O_{62}]^{8-}$ (only oxygens shown) with bonded (1,5-cyclooctadienyl)iridium

to exhibit electron-transfer behavior resembling that of bulk solids, the presence of molybdenum in the structure may lead to materials that perform both separation (zeolite-like cavities) and catalysis (molybdenum electron transfer).

—George R. Brubaker

Organic chemistry

Several themes marked the progress of organic chemistry during the past year. Extraordinary advances were made in the synthesis and characterization of nonnatural products—designed molecules that have no counterparts in nature. The laboratory synthesis of biologically important natural products reached new levels of efficiency and complexity, and insights were gained in understanding the details of biochemical molecular recognition. Finally, progress was reported on the development of substances that may be of use in molecular electronics.

Nonnatural products. Few scientific events caused as much excitement among chemists in 1990 as the isolation and preliminary characterization of C_{60}, a new form of elemental carbon whose structure had been proposed five years earlier. Nicknamed buckminsterfullerene because of its structural resemblance to the geodesic domes designed by architect R. Buckminster Fuller, C_{60} is a spherical molecule made up of hexagonal and pentagonal rings curved into a geometry resembling that of a soccer ball. The diameter of the sphere is 7.1 Å (one angstrom, Å, is a hundred-millionth of a centimeter), and the individual molecules appear to cluster into hexagonal arrays with an intermolecular spacing of 3.9 Å, approximately the same as in graphite. Although full and unambiguous characterization had not yet been completed, preliminary spectroscopic and chemical evidence made it almost certain that C_{60} has the predicted spherical structure.

Despite the structural complexity of C_{60}, research groups led by Donald R. Huffman of the University of Arizona and Wolfgang Krätschmer of the Max Planck Institute for Nuclear Physics, Heidelberg, Germany, discovered that it can be made in gram amounts by the vaporization of graphite electrodes by means of an electric current in a helium atmosphere at low pressure. The material had yet to find uses, and the reasons for the excitement over its preparation were still largely aesthetic. Nevertheless, work to discover the properties of this new form of carbon was continuing. (For additional information on C_{60} see *Physical chemistry*, below, and Feature Article: CLUSTERS: STRANGE BITS OF MATTER.)

It is almost an article of faith among organic chemists that a substituent group bonded to a six-membered ring of carbon atoms (cyclohexane) will orient itself so that it occupies an equatorial posi-

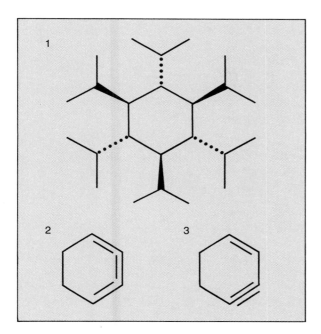

tion roughly in the plane of the ring rather than an axial position perpendicular to the ring plane. However, Z. Goren and S. Biali of the Hebrew University of Jerusalem reported that all-*trans*-1,2,3,4,5,6-hexaisopropylcyclohexane (*see* 1) adopts a geometry in which not just one but all six of the substituents are axial. Yet another surprising piece of nonnatural-products chemistry was the report of two new isomers of benzene. Most chemists would have guessed that little new work was possible in a research area dating back to the mid-1800s, but W.C. Shakespeare and Richard P. Johnson of the University of New Hampshire found that 1,2,3-cyclohexatriene (*see* 2) and cyclohexen-3-yne (*see* 3) can be prepared. Both substances are extremely strained and highly reactive.

Two other remarkable substances described during 1990 are 1,4-dehydrocubane (*see* 4), the first 1,4-diradical that has a ground-state singlet electronic structure, and the *in*-bicyclo[4.4.4]-1-tetradecyl cation (*see* 5), the first stable material with a three-center, two-electron C − H − C bond. In collaborative work reported by Philip Eaton and J. Tsananktsidis of the University of Chicago, Josef Michl and K. Hasenrück of the University of Texas, and Weston T. Borden and D.A. Hrovat of the University of Washington, 1,4-dehydrocubane was implicated as an intermediate formed in the reaction of 1,4-dihalocubanes with organolithium reagents. The diradical product (the molecule has two unshared electrons, represented in structure 4 by dots on the two trivalent, diagonally positioned carbon atoms) is unstable above 40 K (−233° C, or −388° F), and theoretical calculations suggested that there is a

slight antibonding interaction between the two trivalent carbons.

Hydrogen normally bonds to a single carbon atom by sharing two electrons in a covalent bond—the standard two-center, two-electron bond that makes up a part of every known organic substance. It now appears, however, than hydrogen can also bond to two carbons simultaneously by forming a three-center, two-electron C − H − C bond. Thomas Lectka, Carl N. Hodge, and John McMurry of Cornell University, Ithaca, N.Y., as well as Theodore Sorensen of the University of Calgary, Alta., prepared a series of rigid, cagelike ions such as structure 5, whose geometry makes possible the formation of stable C − H − C bonds. A full characterization and spectroscopic examination were carried out to elucidate the nature of the electronic interactions.

Natural products. The laboratory synthesis of complex naturally occurring molecules has been a major research area since the late 1940s and continues to attract scientists today. The importance of the field was recognized during the past year by the award of the 1990 Nobel Prize for Chemistry to Harvard University's Elias J. Corey (*see* SCIENTISTS OF THE YEAR), a man who played a major role in the development of laboratory organic synthesis and who has been one of its most successful and creative practitioners.

Several notable achievements in synthesis were recorded, including full descriptions of two extraordinarily complex examples of the art, chlorophyll a (*see* 6) and amphoteronolide B (*see* 7, both structures on p. 298). The synthesis of chlorophyll a, the green photosynthetic pigment of green plants and certain microorganisms, was completed in 1960 by an 18-person team led by Robert B. Woodward at Harvard, but complete details of that historic accomplishment did not become available until 1990 in a paper authored by Raymond Bonnett of Queen Mary and Westfield College, London. The synthesis of amphoteronolide, an equally complex molecule prepared by K.C. Nicolaou and his colleagues of the University of Pennsylvania was also detailed in the past year.

Among notable examples of new synthetic work were reports on the daphniphylline alkaloids, derived

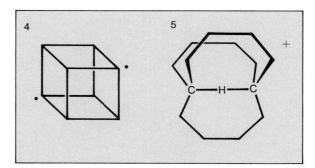

from the oriental Yuzuriha tree, by Clayton H. Heathcock and his students at the University of California at Berkeley; on the tumor promoter phorbol, from an Asian shrub, by P.A. Wender and F.E. McDonald at Stanford University; and on the immunosuppressant agent FK-506 by S.L. Schreiber's group at Harvard. FK-506, a bacterial metabolite, stirred much recent excitement in the medical community because of its apparently safe and extraordinarily effective use for the prevention of organ rejection following liver, kidney, and pancreas transplants in humans.

A large number of newly characterized natural products were reported in 1990, including the fungal compound dynemicin A (see 8) and 3-methyl-2-hexenoic acid (see 9). Isolated by a team led by M. Konishi at the Bristol-Myers Research Institute, Tokyo, and structurally elucidated by Jon Clardy and Gregory Van Duyne at Cornell University, dynemicin A is one of the most potent anticancer agents yet dis-

covered. It appears to act by intercalating into DNA chains and initiating chain breakage. The compound 3-methyl-2-hexenoic acid, isolated by George Preti of the Monell Chemical Senses Center, Philadelphia, is far less complex than dynemicin A and has no known medical benefits, but it is nevertheless of interest because, after a long search, it was identified as the molecule primarily responsible for the unpleasant odor of human sweat.

Bioorganic chemistry. Investigations into the chemical details of biological processes remain among the most important and fruitful areas of organic chemistry. Certain RNA molecules are known to have the ability to remove parts of themselves catalytically without the aid of enzymes, and during the past year a group led by Julius Rebek, Jr., at the Massachusetts Institute of Technology reported another self-catalytic process using simple organic molecules in the laboratory. Rebek constructed a synthetic template molecule that is able to bring together two molecular building blocks of itself into close proximity and then accelerate their coupling to form a new template molecule. A close mimic of a fundamental biological process was reported by Karl W. Hahn, Wieslaw A. Klis, and John M. Stewart of the University of Colorado Medical School, who successfully designed and synthesized a small protein comprising 73 amino acids and having an enzymelike ability to hydrolyze amide bonds. The synthetic enzyme consists of four polypeptide chains linked together to form a binding pocket similar to that of chymotrypsin. Hydrolysis rate-acceleration factors as high as 100,000 were observed.

Jean-Marie Lehn, Margaret M. Harding, and Ulrich Koert of Louis Pasteur University, Strasbourg, France, devised a new class of compounds dubbed nucleohelicates that spontaneously self-assemble into double-helical metal complexes. These complexes have selective interactions between strands similar to those of double-stranded DNA, although they more closely resemble DNA turned inside out, with their nucleosides (sugar-nucleotide base units) on the outside of the double helix rather than within.

The nucleic acids DNA and RNA, which encode the genetic heritage of all living organisms, are each constructed from just four different nucleotide monomer units. These nucleotides form the alphabet of the genetic code that specifies how a given protein is to be assembled with the cells of an organism. Steven A. Benner, J.A. Piccirilli, T. Krauch, and S.E. Moroney of the Swiss Federal Institute of Technology, Zürich, showed that this genetic alphabet can be expanded by the addition of a new pair of monomer units. The new units are smoothly incorporated into growing DNA strands and make possible, in principle, the preparation of RNA strands having greater structural diversity and greater catalytic potential.

The ability to bind and cut double-stranded DNA at a specific sequence of nucleotides is one of the most important challenges of molecular biology. Enzymic methods are normally used to meet this challenge, but Peter B. Dervan and Scott A. Strobel of the California Institute of Technology developed nonenzymic methods that are capable of recognizing and cutting a specific 20-nucleotide sequence in a 340,000-unit chromosome of the yeast *Saccharomyces cerevisiae*. The workers used pyrimidine oligonucleotides (short chains of pyrimidine nucleotides) bonded to ethylenediaminetetraacetic acid-iron units that form a triple helix with particular tracts of double-stranded DNA. In related work Dervan and David A. Horne designed oligonucleotides capable of simultaneously binding two alternate DNA strands by incorporation of a linker that allows the oligonucleotide to cross from one side of the DNA major groove to the other.

Organic chemicals for electronics. Organic materials continued to receive close scrutiny for possible use in new electronic devices. In work carried out by a team led by Jack M. Williams of Argonne (Ill.) National Laboratory, the highest known superconducting transition temperature for an organic material, *i.e.*, the temperature at or below which the material shows no resistance to electrical flow, was raised to 12.8 K for the tetrathiofulvalene derivative shown in structure 10. Progress also was made in the development of single molecules that might function as self-contained electronic switches. Following the suggestion of Ari Aviram of IBM's Thomas J. Watson Research Center, Yorktown Heights, N.Y., James M. Tour, Ruilian Wu, and Jeffry S. Schumm of the University of South Carolina prepared a compound (*see* 11) that contains two polymeric chains fixed at a 90° angle and connected by a single-atom-centered bridge. In theory, the bridge would control the flow of electrons from one chain to the other. When suitably doped, polymers based on such a structure could function as semiconductors.

—John E. McMurry

Physical chemistry

During the past year the feverish interest in cold fusion largely vanished, while a promising avenue of inquiry opened up following the discovery of a large-scale method of making a new form of elemental carbon, the elusive buckminsterfullerene. Researchers appeared to have solved the old problem of fabricating light sources that are smaller than the desired wavelength of light by taking advantage of "molecular excitons" in crystals of organic chemicals, thus making possible very high-resolution optical microscopy and possibly high-density optical computer memory. Chemists' understanding of the way chemical bonds are made and broken was extended in experiments that selectively break the O−H bond in the substituted water molecule HOD.

Cold fusion cools off. The excitement that erupted during 1989 over the prospects of a revolutionary new source of energy from nuclear fusion at room temperature—so-called cold fusion (see *1991 Yearbook of Science and the Future* Year in Review: CHEMISTRY: *Physical chemistry*)—faded during 1990. The original experiments that were claimed to have produced excess heat and the emission of nuclear particles during the electrolysis of heavy (deuterated) water were repeated in many laboratories worldwide with a general lack of success. Some laboratories did continue to find unrepeatable strange effects, which most workers attributed to contamination or experimental error. Nevertheless, it was not discounted that some form of nuclear process could be occurring, but only at extremely low levels insufficient to produce the effects claimed for cold fusion. (See *Applied chemistry*, below.)

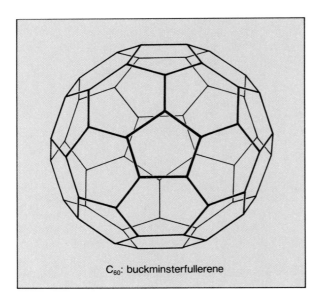

C₆₀: buckminsterfullerene

C_{60}: buckminsterfullerene

"Buckeyballs": a new area of research. The past year witnessed a veritable explosion of interest in the 60-carbon, soccer-ball-shaped molecule C_{60} (*see* Figure), named buckminsterfullerene or, more colloquially, a buckeyball, because of the resemblance of its structure to architect R. Buckminster Fuller's geodesic domes. The all-carbon molecule was originally postulated by Richard E. Smalley of Rice University, Houston, Texas, and Harold W. Kroto of the University of Sussex, Brighton, England, to be an important component of soot and to possibly be present in interstellar space. Unfortunately, as the material could be made only in microscopic quantities, it was difficult to characterize properly and remained an interesting curiosity, its very existence being challenged by some chemists.

The situation changed dramatically in 1990 when a team led by Donald R. Huffman of the University of Arizona and Wolfgang Krätschmer of the Max Planck Institute for Nuclear Physics, Heidelberg, Germany, announced that they had found a simple way to make large quantities of C_{60} mixed with a small fraction of C_{70}, another member of a postulated family of ball-shaped "fullerene" molecules. Their achievement opened up a new direction in research opportunities that was eagerly followed by many groups worldwide.

One of the first results emerging from the newfound availability of buckeyballs was a confirmation of their unusual spherical shape. A scanning tunneling microscope image of a layer of the material on gold foil, taken by Donald Bethune and co-workers of the IBM Almaden Research Center, San Jose, Calif., clearly showed their ball-like appearance but not their internal structure. Larger objects that appeared in the image were believed to be egg-shaped

C_{70} fullerenes. Chemists speculated over the possibility of growing other fullerene structures, some of them containing hundreds of carbon atoms. Smalley and Kroto theorized that fullerenes grow by addition of carbon atoms to a molecular structure, made up of pentagonal and hexagonal rings, resembling chicken wire. The framework extends in a spiral fashion, somewhat like that of the shell of the mollusk known as the chambered nautilus. Under the right conditions, which are apparently particularly favorable in the case of 60 carbon atoms, the mesh closes in on itself and joins at the edges to form a spherical fullerene.

The burst of initial experiments on this material, which many scientists hailed as a third form of carbon in addition to graphite and diamond, suggested some practical applications. The C_{60} molecule contains strong carbon-carbon bonds and, because of its symmetrical shape, has no obvious weak points for reaction. Consequently, it may prove to be both an excellent lubricant and a source of hard coatings. If a fluorine atom could be bonded to each carbon atom, it might form a slippery Teflon-like material highly resistant to mechanical and chemical damage. Chemists at Rice University and other laboratories expected to be able to cage electrically charged metal atoms inside a buckeyball. In quantity such a material might find use in lightweight replacements for electrical storage batteries. (See *Organic chemistry,* above, and Feature Article: CLUSTERS: STRANGE BITS OF MATTER.)

Ultrasmall light sources. It has been known since the time of Isaac Newton that when a beam of light is passed through a small hole, the light waves bend as they travel past the edge of the hole, causing the beam to spread out and its component waves to interfere with one another. This phenomenon of diffraction has been a bugbear for optical microscopists because it has limited the resolution of optical microscopes to that of the wavelength of light being used. Because visible light comprises a range of wavelengths that are hundreds or thousands of times larger than the sizes of even large molecules like proteins, optical microscopy has not been able to probe the molecular or atomic world. Hence, other techniques like scanning electron microscopy and scanning tunneling microscopy, based on the use of electrons rather than light, were developed to study materials at very small molecular dimensions.

During 1990 a new discovery based on the physical chemistry of organic crystals made it possible to surmount this apparently insuperable barrier and generate beams of visible light that are as small as a nanometer (nm; a billionth of a meter) across yet have a wavelength of hundreds of nanometers. According to the discoverers—Klonimus Lieberman, Schlomo Harush, and Aaron Lewis of the Hebrew

University of Jerusalem and Raoul Kopelman of the University of Michigan at Ann Arbor—the ultrasmall light sources are bright over a wide range of wavelengths and fairly simple to make; moreover, because they can image surfaces at very high resolution, they may find important uses in biology and materials research.

The method for making the light sources starts with a very fine glass tube, about 100 nm in diameter, that is drawn out to as little as one nanometer across. The most difficult part of the process is to persuade a crystal of an organic compound to grow right in the mouth of this micropipette. Once that task has been accomplished, a laser beam is directed at the crystal. The light does not pass through the crystal but instead is converted into molecular excitons—excitations of the electrons in the crystal—that are passed along from atom to atom within the crystal. When these excitons reach the crystal surface at the tip of the pipette, they are converted back into light having a wavelength that is much larger than the size of the crystal from which the light is emerging. Different types of crystal give light of different wavelengths, and the light is bright because the crystal actually amplifies the laser light signal.

The most obvious application for tiny light sources is in the nondestructive imaging of biological ma-

An array of molecules interpreted to be spherical C_{60} and egg-shaped C_{70} fullerenes (the latter appear taller and brighter) is shown in a scanning tunneling microscope image. Spacing between C_{60} molecules is 11 angstroms (44 billionths of an inch), center to center.

IBM Almaden Research Center, San Jose, Calif.

terials under ambient conditions, accomplished by scanning the light source across the surface of the material to be studied. Another possible use is in high-density optical computer memories and integrated optical switches.

Selective bond breaking. One long-awaited goal in the branch of chemistry known as chemical dynamics is an understanding of how to break just one chemical bond among all those present in a molecule. By doing so, it may be possible to make one reaction pathway dominant and therefore obtain compounds that are presently difficult or impossible to synthesize.

The first example of such a bond-selective reaction was reported by F. Fleming Crim, Mark C. Hsiao, and Amitabha Sinha of the University of Wisconsin at Madison. They chose an extremely simple molecule on which to test their procedure, a water molecule in which one hydrogen atom is replaced by deuterium (D), a heavy isotope of hydrogen having a neutron in its nucleus in addition to the single proton of the hydrogen nucleus. The HOD molecule provides a particularly good test case, as it is small enough to enable theoreticians to perform accurate calculations that can be tested experimentally.

The Wisconsin team's experiment begins with the use of a laser to deposit energy into the HOD molecule. The wavelength of laser light chosen is such that the energy goes into making only the oxygen and hydrogen atoms in HOD vibrate wildly, stretching the $O-H$ bond. Because a deuterium atom is twice as heavy as a hydrogen atom, the $O-D$ pair of atoms is out of tune with the laser light, and its bond is not affected. The excited molecules (HOD*) then are mixed with hydrogen atoms, whereupon either of the following reactions occurs:

(1) $H + H-OD^* \rightarrow OD + H_2$, or
(2) $H + HO-D^* \rightarrow OH + HD$.

When the laser beam is off, no reaction occurs, but when the laser beam is turned on, the ratio of OD to OH produced is more than 100:1, indicating that $O-H$ bond breaking of the type in reaction (1) is occurring almost exclusively. The laser beam is putting the HOD molecule in a state in which the oxygen and hydrogen atoms are vibrating in just the manner required for easing the breaking of the $O-H$ bond, thus leading to a highly selective reaction.

Crim and co-workers acknowledged that although the isotopically substituted water molecule is probably nearly the ideal case for this sort of investigation, the work nevertheless pointed the way toward exploring bond selectivity in a more general fashion. The key step will be containing the energy put into the molecule within the bond that is to be broken and not have it leak away into other parts of the molecule.

—Philip R. Watson

Applied chemistry

During the past year progress in applied chemistry led to developments in so-called cold fusion, superconductors, synthetic diamonds, and a class of solids of extremely low density called aerogels.

Cold fusion. In March 1989, at a press conference at the University of Utah, chemists B. Stanley Pons of the University of Utah and Martin Fleischmann of the University of Southampton, England, announced that they had achieved room-temperature, or cold, nuclear fusion by passing an electric current through a platinum wire electrode coiled around an electrode of palladium (one of the metal elements of the platinum group) in an electrolyte solution of alkaline heavy water. (Heavy water, or D_2O, contains atoms of deuterium, a heavy isotope of hydrogen, in place of the common hydrogen atoms present in ordinary water, H_2O.) Their "discovery" was hailed as a source of unlimited energy and the greatest scientific breakthrough of the last 40 years, and it immediately became the most publicized—and most controversial—scientific event of 1989. (See *1991 Yearbook of Science and the Future* Year in Review: THE YEAR IN SCIENCE: AN OVERVIEW; CHEMISTRY: *Physical chemistry* and *Applied chemistry;* U.S. SCIENCE POLICY.)

The media had a field day with the story, for scientists in laboratories throughout the world obtained conflicting results (which one journal characterized as "Elvis sightings") in their attempts to detect the heat, neutrons, and tritium (another heavy isotope of hydrogen) that Pons and Fleischmann cited as evidence that fusion was actually occurring. No consensus was reached by the end of 1989, and the situation continued unresolved throughout 1990 with additional events in the form of scientific reports (both experimental and theoretical), conferences devoted to the alleged phenomenon, rumors of fraud, a threatened lawsuit, and the resignation of a university president.

In a *New York Times Magazine* article, Nicholas P. Samios and Robert P. Crease, the director and historian, respectively, of Brookhaven National Laboratory, Upton, N.Y., called the cold fusion confusion "pathological science," a term first used by 1932 Nobel chemistry laureate Irving Langmuir to characterize the kind of "discovery" made by outsiders (chemists rather than nuclear physicists in the case of cold fusion) who claim miraculous results and who respond with ad hoc excuses to the inability of others to replicate their results. In February 1990 at a meeting of the American Association for the Advancement of Science (AAAS) in New Orleans, La., a symposium featuring a physicist, two sociologists, and two philosophers was held to interpret the cold fusion "happening" and put it into historical context.

In the March 29, 1990, issue of the international journal *Nature,* physicist Michael H. Salomon of Pons's institution, together with eight Utah colleagues and S.M. Seltzer of the National Institute of Standards and Technology, Gaithersburg, Md., reported no evidence of fusion activity during their nearly continuous monitoring, at the university's request, of Pons and Fleischmann's cold fusion cells in Pons's laboratory during a five-week period. In an accompanying editorial, "Farewell (not fond) to cold fusion," *Nature* declared the demise of cold fusion, while in an accompanying article *Nature*'s associate editor David Lindley agreed and stated that "one of the reasons that Pons and Fleischmann prospered early on was that few people were willing to stand up and say why they thought cold fusion was nonsense."

Paradoxically, on the same day that these articles appeared, the First Annual Conference on Cold Fusion began three days of deliberations in Salt Lake City, Utah, at which Pons and about 40 researchers continued to report formation of unexplained heat, tritium, and neutrons. Electrochemist John O'M. Bockris of Texas A&M University declared that his own and at least eight other laboratories had detected tritium in their experiments. Fleischmann stated that "one year's time is too short" to reach a decision on cold fusion. In a rebuttal to Salomon's negative findings, Pons argued that his fusion cells were not working while the neutron detectors were operating and that Salomon had excluded positive data; the latter claim Salomon denied.

In an action most unusual for a scientific controversy, C. Gary Triggs, Pons's attorney, wrote in April to Salomon demanding that he retract his *Nature* article or face "such legal action as is deemed appropriate." Two months later, in response to widespread criticism, from both cold fusion supporters and skeptics, of this legal attempt to limit academic and scientific freedom, Triggs apologized to Salomon in writing.

In June, Texas A&M nuclear chemist Kevin Wolf, whose reports of low-level tritium detection had been among the strongest evidence bolstering Pons and Fleischmann's claims, announced that his low-level tritium was due to contamination of the palladium supplied by a commercial source to his group and to some others reporting positive results. He also stated that in Bockris' laboratory, which had produced the most compelling evidence to date for cold fusion, "things were so uncontrolled and so sloppy [that] those studies don't mean anything." Bockris pointed out that 26 laboratories, including 3 U.S. national laboratories, that had reported tritium detection had obtained their palladium from sources other than Bockris' and that the high levels of tritium reported by him and independent laboratories could not be due to contamination.

In June Chase N. Peterson, president of the University of Utah, pressured by his faculty because of administrative problems and two cold fusion revelations, announced his resignation effective at the end of the 1990–91 academic year. First, he had represented a $500,000 grant to the newly established university-based National Cold Fusion Institute (NCFI) as coming from an anonymous donor when it had actually come from the university's own research foundation. Second, Pons's attorney, Triggs, was found to be on the university payroll.

In August the Cornell University (Ithaca, N.Y.) Cold Fusion Archive—funded by the U.S. National Science Foundation (NSF) and containing mass media print, audio, and video reports, taped interviews, preprints, and other pertinent materials—was opened to historians, sociologists, and other scholars interested in the controversy, which had become a cause célèbre in the history and sociology of science. During the same month, chemist Robert Huggins of Stanford University reported obtaining energy levels 10–1,000 times higher than would be expected from an ordinary chemical reaction, thus suggesting that cold fusion may indeed be possible. At a subsequent meeting, which he organized, Steven E. Jones, who had been studying independently the same type of electrochemical cells that Pons and Fleischmann had used but whose less flamboyant claims reported smaller amounts of neutrons, declared, "This is a legitimate field with a lot of evidence, and we'd appreciate it if people wouldn't associate us with Pons and Fleischmann."

In December a four-member extramural panel—two chemists, a physicist, and a metallurgist—that had been charged with discovering whether the NCFI had been making valid efforts to investigate cold fusion, not whether the phenomenon is real, concluded that the research was scientifically sound. Their report increased the likelihood that funding would be continued in 1991 for the state-funded institute, which had been granted $4.5 million by the Utah legislature in 1989. Thus, *Science* magazine's Nov. 9, 1990, proclamation that "like the Cheshire cat, cold fusion has slowly faded away" proved premature, and the controversy—about which one scientist commented that if a Hollywood writer had produced the script, it would be rejected for being too unrealistic—seemed ready to continue in the coming year.

Superconductors. Superconductors are materials that lose all electrical resistance when cooled below a particular critical temperature. Since the discovery in 1986 of the mixed metal oxide high-temperature superconductors (HTSs), physicists, ceramicists, and chemists have attempted to increase critical temperatures, to develop new classes of superconductors, and to devise theories to explain their operation. (See

1989 Yearbook of Science and the Future Feature Article: THE NEW SUPERCONDUCTORS: A SCIENTIFIC BREAKTHROUGH; Year in Review: CHEMISTRY: *Inorganic chemistry* and MATERIALS SCIENCES: *Ceramics*.) About $450 million annually was being spent worldwide on such research, and according to Sumitomo Electric of Japan, the market for HTS applications could reach $36 billion annually by the year 2000.

Physicist William J. Nellis of California's Lawrence Livermore Laboratory, together with colleagues at Livermore and the University of California at San Diego, reported that subjecting a powdered HTS crystal to a shock wave from a gas gun produces a material that can carry seven times more electrical current than the original material. The shock wave creates tiny defects (flux-pinning sites) that bind the lines of magnetic flux, allowing the superconductor to carry higher currents. The process can be scaled up by use of conventional explosives.

A breakthrough in HTS fabrication was reported in May by Paul Chu, Ru Ling Meng, Pei-Herng Hor, and co-workers of the University of Houston, Texas, who developed a continuous process involving a zone furnace for the bulk production of an yttrium-barium-copper oxide compound ($YBa_2Cu_3O_7$) in the form of small superconducting bars about the size of a pencil stub. The achievement, which advanced the bulk production of HTSs beyond thin wires or grains, was expected to be adaptable to the manufacture of rods, wire, ribbons, and other shapes, as well as thick coatings. In November David S. Ginley, supervisor of Sandia (N.M.) National Laboratories' Semiconductor Materials Division, and co-workers at Sandia and the University of Wisconsin announced fabrication of the first transistor made exclusively of high-temperature superconductor—in this case, thin films of thallium-calcium-barium-copper oxide compounds. According to Ginley, the new product, a superconducting flux-flow transistor (SFFT), was coupled with "passive microwave components to make real circuits that have exciting high-performance properties."

All known organic superconductors had been charge-transfer salts containing either selenium- or sulfur-bearing electron donors until May 1990, when Mark A. Beno of Argonne (Ill.) National Laboratory and researchers at Argonne and North Carolina State University reported the first ambient-pressure organic superconductor based on an oxygen-containing electron-donor molecule—a salt based on bis(ethylenedioxy)tetrathiafulvalene (BEDO-TTF) and a copper-containing anion—which becomes superconducting at 1.04 K ($-457.8°$ F). According to the report, the discovery "could be important for systematically expanding the range of possible organic superconductors and for potentially establishing a link between organic superconductors and

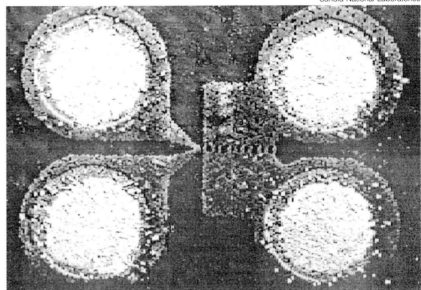

Sandia National Laboratories

A superconducting flux-flow transistor, the world's first transistor made from a high-temperature superconductor, is visible in the center of the photomicrograph at right. Patterned from a single piece of superconducting film, the device consists of a set of short, vertically aligned superconducting links that bridge two rectangular pieces of superconductor, plus a V-shaped control line. The prominent bright pads are silver electrical contacts.

the recently discovered high temperature oxide superconductors." Although inorganic copper oxide HTSs have critical temperatures as high as 125 K ($-235°$ F), organic superconductors possess advantages, such as lighter weight, that could enhance commercial applications.

Diamonds. In 1989 *Science* magazine initiated a new feature titled "Molecule of the Year" to honor "the scientific development of the year most likely to have a major impact on scientific advances and societal benefits." The 1990 winner of this honor was diamond because of its unique properties (*e.g.*, great hardness, electrical resistance, corrosion resistance, and thermal conductivity) and the developments in diamond research during the year. Diamonds, both natural and synthetic, are not only prized as gemstones but also valued for their numerous scientific and industrial applications.

Diamonds have been made in various laboratories since they were first synthesized at the General Electric (GE) Research and Development Center, Schenectady, N.Y., in 1955. A recent case is unique in that the inventor of a new synthesis process was a high school student, Andrew Good of Adelaide, Australia, who won Australia's Beyond 2000 Award in Science and Technology for his work. Good injected a stream of hot methane (CH_4) gas surrounded by a stream of cool hydrogen (H_2) gas into an electrostatically focused oxyacetylene plasma (a high-temperature flame similar to that of a welding torch) and grew a hard diamond coating on stainless steel at a rate of 0.5 micrometers (about 0.00002 in) per minute.

At the Institute of Physical Chemistry of the U.S.S.R. Academy of Sciences in Moscow, Boris V.

Deryagin, who began working on the synthesis of diamonds in 1955, and Dmitry V. Fedoseyev produced diamond powders by passing a 50-w infrared laser beam over graphite and soot. The laser pumped so much energy so quickly into the carbon that the carbon was compressed as if exposed to extremely high pressure, a condition (along with very high temperature) that had been previously required for making diamonds from graphite. The process was too inefficient (about 1% conversion) to be industrially useful, but its efficiency would probably be increased in the future.

Naturally occurring carbon, the element of which diamond is composed, consists of two stable isotopes, carbon-12 (^{12}C; 98.89%) and carbon-13 (^{13}C; 1.11%). Nearly 50 years ago a Russian physicist predicted that isotopically pure diamonds (composed of a single isotope of carbon) should possess properties superior to those composed of the natural mixture. His prediction was confirmed in July when chemical engineer William F. Banholzer and co-workers at the GE Research and Development Center reported success in synthesizing diamonds composed of almost pure ^{12}C. The new diamonds conduct heat 50% better and can withstand 10 times more laser energy than natural diamonds, which had held the records for these properties. The researchers first used a low-pressure technique known as chemical vapor deposition to rearrange the carbon atoms of methane gas molecules into diamond films. A mixture of hydrogen gas and methane, isotopically enriched to contain 99.97% ^{12}C, is atomized and ionized by microwave energy to a plasma, from which a layer of polycrystalline diamond is deposited onto a substrate. The deposit is powdered and added to a catalyst (a molten transition-metal element) in the presence of a diamond seed crystal, which at 1,500° C (2,700° F) and a pressure of 55,000 atmospheres (808,000 psi) grows to a weight as great as 1.3 carats.

According to GE researcher Tom Anthony, isotopically pure carbon is presently much more expensive than natural carbon, but if companies order it in large quantities, its price should decrease quickly, leading to prices only a few dollars more per carat for isotopically pure diamonds than for normal diamonds. Isotopically pure ^{13}C diamonds should also possess superior properties but remain to be prepared. By 1993 production of ^{12}C diamonds should begin at GE Superabrasives, Worthington, Ohio.

Aerogels. One of the 10 runners-up to diamond for *Science*'s 1990 Molecule of the Year was a class of materials called aerogels—strong, light, airy gels from which all the liquid has been removed, leaving a porous framework having interstices filled with air. Although aerogels have been known since the 1930s, recently the number of articles about them and their possible applications has increased tremendously. Thomas Tillotson, Lawrence Hrubesh, and Ian Thomas of Lawrence Livermore Laboratory prepared a new aerogel that set a record for lightness. Consisting of 99.8% air and a tenuous web (0.2%) of silicon dioxide (the main constituent of sand), the wispy, bluish material, which has been likened to frozen or solid smoke, has a density of five milligrams per cubic centimeter, one-fifth that of the lightest aerogel previously known and only four times denser than air at sea level.

In the standard aerogel-making process, a gel (a mixture of interlinked polymer molecules—silicon, aluminum, or zirconium oxides—swollen with a liquid) is dried at a very high temperature and pressure at which the liquid is in a supercritical state. Under these conditions the liquid and its gaseous phase are physically the same; consequently, no liquid surfaces form to create surface tension, and the gel does not collapse as the liquid molecules are slowly removed. The new process from the Livermore group contains an additional step; instead of a silica gel, a "condensed silica form," having the consistency of oil and containing short polymers with two, three, or four units of silicon dioxide with methoxy (CH_3O-) groups attached to each silicon atom, is treated with water, a solvent, and a basic catalyst to form a gel, which is then dehydrated by the usual process. The beads in the resulting aerogel are less than a nanometer (about 0.00000004 in) in diameter rather than the five to six nanometers characteristic of the beads in previous, much denser aerogels.

Because the atoms in an aerogel are linked only weakly, energy does not pass through the material easily. Aerogels thus conduct heat and sound very slowly and should make excellent insulators; *e.g.*, in refrigerators, where they can replace flammable, rigid polyurethane foams containing environmentally damaging chlorofluorocarbons. A given thickness of aerogel insulates as well as fiberglass having seven times the thickness. Because they transmit heat only $\frac{1}{100}$ as quickly as ordinary glass, nearly transparent aerogel layers may be inserted within double-pane windows. The Livermore researchers were developing even lighter aerogels for the U.S. National Aeronautics and Space Agency for use as heat-storage elements in solar collectors or as traps for fast-moving particles in space, such as micrometeorites.

Three golden anniversaries. The year 1990 marked the 50th anniversary of three important discoveries. Before 1940 the heaviest known element, uranium (element 92), had been believed to be the upper limit of the periodic table of elements. In that year the first two transuranic elements (those heavier than uranium) were discovered: neptunium (element 93), by American physicists Edwin M. McMillan and Philip H. Abelson, and plutonium (element 94), by American chemists Glenn T. Seaborg, Arthur C. Wahl, and Joseph W. Kennedy. The discoveries added a new dimension to the periodic table, revealing the existence of an unknown family of actinide elements. In 1940 American chemists Martin D. Kamen and Samuel Ruben discovered carbon-14, the long-lived radioisotope used for dating archaeological and historical artifacts. Also in 1940, Dale R. Corson, K.R. MacKenzie, and Emilio Segrè bombarded bismuth with alpha particles and obtained the radioactive element 85, the heaviest of the halogens, which they named astatine (Greek, "unstable") because it is the only halogen without stable isotopes.

—George B. Kauffman

See also Feature Articles: BIOTECHNOLOGY FOR THE '90s; CLUSTERS: STRANGE BITS OF MATTER.

A new kind of synthetic diamond, made by General Electric researchers from nearly pure carbon-12 isotope, is 10 times more resistant to damage from high-power laser light and conducts heat 50% better than natural diamond.

GE Research and Development Center

305

Defense research

The turbulent world conditions that characterized 1990, marked by the eradication of the Berlin Wall early in the year and Iraq's invasion of Kuwait in August, began reshaping the very nature of military research and development. The defense industry—and particularly the electronics industry, which has long been at the forefront of military technology—by year's end had begun tailoring weapons to the changing realities. This meant more rugged and more mobile equipment able to operate in places like the Arabian desert and the Persian Gulf. It also meant equipment that is more lethal, since it would have to be operated by a shrinking force of military manpower. And it meant equipment that is more affordable through maximum use of commercial off-the-shelf components, both hardware and software, rather than equipment designed from the beginning to demanding—and costly—military specifications.

Even before the Berlin Wall was torn down, the pendulum had begun to swing away from strategic systems intended primarily to counter the Soviet Union and toward tactical weapons to maintain stability in an increasingly volatile Third World. This resulted in stretchouts and cancellations for major weapons-development programs in the U.S. such as the Strategic Defense Initiative to counter Soviet nuclear missiles, next-generation aircraft such as the Navy's Advanced Tactical Aircraft, and the Navy's long-sought 600-ship fleet. In their place the U.S. Department of Defense (DOD) put increased emphasis on upgrading existing weapons systems with the new very high-speed integrated circuit (VHSIC) and microwave and millimeter wave monolithic integrated circuit (MIMIC) electronic components and on the introduction of "smart" weapons and robotic fighting vehicles, all with a high electronics content. Tying together this new, more mobile, and more lethal force would be advanced command, control, communications, and intelligence (C_3I) systems. Two of these new-generation weapons that performed well in the Persian Gulf war were the Tomahawk cruise missile and the Patriot air defense missile.

One thing that became clear was that overall defense spending was dropping sharply. Spending on research and development was also expected to drop, although not quite as rapidly. "The defense budget will decline one-third in constant 1991 dollars by the year 2000, and national defense as a percentage of the gross national product will drop to pre- World War II levels of 3 percent," Geoffrey K. Bentley told an Electronic Industries Association (EIA) conference at the year's end. Bentley was business research manager at Textron Defense Systems, Wilmington, Mass.

Of those categories of the defense budget of primary concern to the defense research community—research, development, test and evaluation, and procurement—the EIA estimated that electronics would account for approximately $365 billion of the $868 billion to be spent during the 1990s. (This was expressed in constant 1991 dollars; if estimates of 4.5% annual inflation hold, actual defense spending for the decade would be about $1 trillion.) The resulting decline from previous projections of defense spending for the decade has been called a $500 billion "peace dividend."

More important than these numbers, however, is where the dollars will be spent—and what technologies will be needed to support the planned programs. In its annual forecast, the EIA listed seven areas of defense research that would require increased efforts:
(1) surveillance and verification activities for military and economic threats; (2) small, mobile systems for light forces; (3) air and sea lift; (4) simulators, training and support services; (5) product improvements (as an alternative to new weapons programs); (6) commercial off-the-shelf components; and (7)

Two of the new-generation, highly technical weapons that performed well for U.S. and allied troops in the Persian Gulf war were the Tomahawk cruise missile (right) and the Patriot air defense missile (far right). The Patriot became particularly noted for intercepting and destroying Iraqi Scud missiles.

(Left) U.S. Navy; (right) Raytheon Company

A B-52 Stratofortress bomber is refueled in the air. Although the last B-52 rolled off the assembly line in 1962, the U.S. strategic bomber has been upgraded to improve its strength, accuracy, and navigation, and it played an important role for the U.S. and its allies in the Persian Gulf war.

continued emphasis on research and development as a hedge and potentially an enabling factor for conversion to commercial production.

In these areas advanced technologies were expected to play a major role. For example, surveillance and verification of the new treaties limiting strategic and conventional forces will result in increased emphasis on surveillance satellites. The reductions in total U.S. military manpower (from 3.2 million to 2.2 million by 2000) and a parallel trend toward greater reliance on reserve and National Guard units (36% of the total force in 1990 and projected to increase to 41% by 2000) were expected to increase requirements for simulation systems, particularly affordable part-task trainers not built to costly military specifications, and training services provided under contract. This situation should also increase demand for advanced displays and microprocessors.

An important example of the trend to upgrade present-day equipment rather than develop new systems was the U.S. Air Force's Microelectronics Technology Support Program, which was established at McClellan Air Force Base, California, as a program that eventually may embrace the U.S. National Aeronautics and Space Administration (NASA), Federal Aviation Administration (FAA), and other federal agencies. The purpose was to insert VHSIC and MIMIC components into existing weapons. Military officials anticipated two benefits from the program: increased overall mission capability and elimination of the logistics problem of trying to maintain inventories of obsolete parts.

Four companies—Control Data, Honeywell, Hughes Aircraft, and TRW—were "prequalified" in December 1989 to perform the avionics upgrades on aircraft such as the Air Force's F-111 fighter-bomber and B-52 long-range bomber, which were developed during the late 1950s and early 1960s and which still used discrete transistors. These early-vintage electronic components were no longer being produced,

so the military services have had to build their own— much as antique automobile owners have to build replacement parts by hand.

Accompanying this emphasis on introducing state-of-the-art parts was increased concern about adapting the hardware for the environment in which it will have to be used. The crisis in the Persian Gulf set a high priority for research on the effects of a desert climate on personnel and matériel. The Army was also concerned with weather predictions at the local level, where battles are actually fought, and this posed another challenge for the defense research industry. "Conditions within two kilometers can affect a helicopter," explained Richard Vitali, director of corporate laboratories at the Army's Laboratory Command in Adelphi, Md. "In dust storms the effects of particles on cooling systems, optics and electro-optics are non-trivial effects."

Other areas where more research is needed, according to Vitali, include sensors to monitor the temperatures of individual soldiers. These would work like the sensors on a car, warning the soldier (or his commander) when he was overheating and needed to slow down. Another issue that has attained increased importance is visibility, which determines the need for such sensors as radars and night-vision devices. "A hundred meters is a long distance in the jungle," Vitali said, "where we used to be concerned about six kilometers in the north German plain."

One of the lessons learned by the U.S. early in the Gulf crisis was that both the Navy and the Air Force lacked adequate rapid-deployment capabilities. DOD had to lease 15 cargo ships, and this could strain the economy in future crises. Experts predicted that new airlift and sea-lift systems would have to be developed.

On March 15 DOD released a list of 20 critical technologies intended to improve the performance, quality, and versatility of weapons. The list was a refinement of a similar tabulation of 22 technologies released the previous year and served as a guideline for maintaining the military technology base into the next century. The 20 technologies are: semiconductor materials and microelectronic circuits; software producibility; parallel computer architectures; machine intelligence and robotics; simulation and modeling; photonics; sensitive radars; passive sensors; signal processing; signature control; weapons system environment; data fusion; computational fluid dynamics; air-breathing propulsion; pulsed power; hypervelocity projectiles; high-energy density materials; composite materials; superconductivity; and biotechnology materials and processes.

In the spring of 1990 the Department of Commerce released its own list of 12 emerging technologies in four categories estimated to have a combined U.S. market potential of $350 billion in annual product sales by the year 2000 and a world market approaching $1 trillion. The list, which closely parallels DOD's estimates and which was coordinated between the two, is as follows:

Materials

(1) Advanced materials: structural and functional ceramics, ceramic and metal matrix composites, intermetallic and lightweight alloys, advanced polymers, surface-modified materials, diamond thin films, membranes, biomaterials

(2) Superconductors: high-temperature ceramic conductors, advanced low-temperature conductors

Electronics and Information Systems

(3) Advanced semiconductor devices: new compounds as semiconductors (such as gallium arsenide), ultra-large-scale integration (ULSI) memory chips, X-ray lithography

(4) Digital imaging technology: high-definition television, large displays, data compression, image processing

(5) High-density data storage: high-density magnetic storage, magneto-optical storage

(6) High-performance computing: modular and transportable software, numerical simulation, neural networks

(7) Optoelectronics: integrated optical circuitry, optical fibers, optical computing, solid-state lasers, optical sensors

Manufacturing Systems

(8) Artificial intelligence: intelligent machines, intelligent processing of materials and chemicals, expert systems

(9) Flexible computer-integrated manufacturing: computer-aided design, engineering, logistics and manufacturing, integrated control architectures, adaptive-process control

(10) Sensor technology: active and passive sensors, feedback and process control, nondestructive evaluation, industrial and atmospheric environmental monitoring and control

Life Sciences Applications

(11) Biotechnology: bioprocessing, drug design, genetic engineering, bioelectronics

(12) Medical devices and diagnostics: cellular-level sensors, medical imaging, in vitro and in vivo analysis, targeted pharmaceuticals, fiber-optic probes

Experts varied on the details, but they all agreed that the new international climate placed a premium on high-quality weapons capable of deterring or fighting small wars anywhere in the world. Sal Monaco, defense and aerospace analyst at DRI/McGraw-Hill, said that the principal need would be for retrofit, modification, and maintenance of existing military equipment. He also cited such needs as antisubmarine warfare, unmanned autonomous vehicles, space vehicles, air traffic management, software engineering, advanced power generation, simulators and trainers, surveillance and verification, secure communications, and smart munitions.

A significant trend in future defense procurement seemed certain to be increasing emphasis on what have come to be known as "force multipliers." Originally intended to achieve parity with the numerically superior Soviet forces, they were expected to become even more important during a time of declining defense budgets. Force multipliers required by the military included high-tech weapons systems, real-time intelligence, smart munitions, secure command and control, and simulators.

Another opportunity for defense research was in what were coming to be known as dual-use technologies. A report prepared in 1989 by the American Electronics Association and the accounting firm Peat Marwick pointed out that most of the $21 billion per year spent on research and development in federal laboratories was for defense or basic research, missions not directly relevant to commercial manufacturing. "By capitalizing commercially on this research, defense contractors would have a buyer besides the government for research and product developments, and the nation's manufacturing and technological base would benefit as well," the report noted. "The Office of Technology Assessment identified fiber optics, software and polymer matrix composites as three dual-use industries, industries critical for both defense and non-defense applications."

The AEA/Peat Marwick report warned that the U.S. faced severe international competition almost across the board. The competition was expected to come from allies and adversaries alike. "Europe leads in high-power microwaves and kinetic and kill energy, and Japan is running away in microelectronic circuits, gallium arsenide, parallel computer architecture, robotics, integrated optics, fiber optics, data fusion and superconductivity—all vital to defense and commercial products," the report noted. "And as [U.S. Secretary of Defense] Dick Cheney continually warned, the Soviet Union and Warsaw Pact members lead the United States in parallel computer architecture, robotics, integrated optics and air-breathing propulsion," the AEA/Peat Marwick study team concluded. "Moscow's expenditures in these areas, despite the easing of tensions, is still growing."

These findings echoed an earlier report by Congress's Office of Technology Assessment: "Technological superiority has been a cornerstone of United States security and industry since World War II. That cornerstone is not crumbling, but over the past decade it has weathered significantly. Foreign companies have made deep inroads into high-technology markets that had been more or less the exclusive domain of U.S. industry."

—John Rhea

Earth sciences

Climate change, mass extinctions, explosive volcanoes, and hydrothermal vents were among the many subjects of investigation by Earth scientists during the past year. A significant trend throughout the disciplines was the increasing use of computers to aid scientists in developing models for research.

Atmospheric sciences

In 1990 the atmospheric sciences continued to receive considerable international public attention. In particular, possible climate change due to the human-caused input of such greenhouse gases as carbon dioxide and methane and ozone depletion in the polar stratosphere were subjects of scientific and political attention. Other important scientific issues included continued implementation of state-of-the-art meteorological monitoring systems, revolutionary advancements in numerical weather prediction technology, and evaluations of air-quality modeling. International cooperation in atmospheric science research and prediction also continued during the year.

Climate change. During the past four years, carbon dioxide levels—as monitored by the National Oceanic and Atmospheric Administration's (NOAA's) Climate Monitoring and Diagnostic Laboratory in Boulder, Colo.—increased at an average rate of 0.5% per year (1.71 parts per million per year), with a peak annual rate of increase of almost 1% per year in late 1987, associated with an El Niño event in the Pacific Ocean. Methane, one of the other greenhouse gases, increased at an average annual rate of about 0.8% (12 parts per billion). Nitrous oxide concentrations increased at an average yearly rate of 0.25% (0.7 parts per billion). Chlorofluorocarbons, which are associated with the depletion of ozone in the stratosphere, increased by about 4% per year.

The Intergovernmental Panel of Climate Change (IPCC) in the summer of 1990 reported on the current understanding of global climate change. Created by the World Meteorological Organization and the United Nations Environment Program, the panel concluded that on the basis of current models and without controls on greenhouse-gas emission, the global mean temperature would increase at a rate of 0.3° C (0.5° F) per decade during the next century, with an uncertainty range of 0.2°–0.5° C (0.36°–0.9° F) per decade. By 2025 the predicted temperature would be 1° C (1.8° F) above the current value. If this should occur, global mean sea level rise would be 6 cm (2.4 in) per decade, with an uncertainty range of 3–20 cm (1.2–7.9 in) per decade. By 2030 the predicted rise would be 20 cm.

James K. Angell of NOAA's Air Resources Laboratory in Maryland reported unusually warm surface-air temperatures in the Arctic in the spring of 1990; they were 4° C (7.2° F) above average and 2.5° C (4.5° F) higher than previously observed during 30 years of records. The Arctic stratosphere, in contrast, was abnormally cold, with values 6° C (10.8° F) below normal in the 9,000–21,000-m (30,000–70,000-ft) range. Using 63 measurement sites around the Earth, Angell found that the March–May 1990 values were 0.3° C (0.54° F) warmer than reported previously during this 30-year period of record. The World Meteorological Organization reported in July 1990 that the global average annual surface temperature in 1989 was 0.23° C (0.41° F) greater than the 1951–1980 average.

There are natural and human-caused effects on global climate that could significantly modify greenhouse-gas warming, however. As reported by the U.S. National Aeronautics and Space Administration (NASA)-Langley Research Center's Earth Radiation Budget Experiment team in February 1990, the solar irradiance of the Sun decreased at a rate of 0.03% per year from September 1984 to the solar sunspot minimum about two years later and then increased at a rate of about 0.02% per year. About 90 scientists from the U.S.S.R., France, Canada, Hungary, Australia, and elsewhere in April 1990 attended a conference at Goddard Space Flight Center in Maryland entitled "The Climate Impact of Solar Variability." The conference concluded that during the last decade the solar irradiance varied on the order of 0.1% and that variations of 0.5% over a century could explain recent natural climatic changes such as the "little ice age" of the 17th century. In terms of greenhouse-gas warming, current estimates of the change in global temperature due to a doubling of CO_2 would correspond to a roughly equivalent 2% increase in the solar constant.

B.A. Kimball, Sherwood B. Idso, and associates at the U.S. Water Conservation Laboratory and Western Cotton Research Laboratory in Phoenix, Ariz., used laboratory and field experiments to investigate the impact of an enriched carbon dioxide atmosphere on plant growth and productivity. Among their findings was that the growth of orange trees was greatly stimulated. During the first year the mean cross-sectional areas of the trunks of the CO_2-enriched trees at 60 cm (23.6 in) above the soil surface were 102% greater than those of the trees in the control group (using the current atmosphere). After two years of growth the total trunk-plus-branch volume of the trees enriched with carbon dioxide was 2.79 times that of the control orange trees. Kimball concluded that yields, in general, would increase on the order of 33% with a doubling of atmospheric CO_2 concentrations. Ed Glenn of the Environmental Research Laboratory of the University of Arizona proposed planting salt-tolerant vegetation (referred to as halophytes) in coastal areas and inland salty areas as a mechanism for removing carbon dioxide from the atmosphere.

During the past year Michael King of NASA's Laboratory for Atmospheres of the Goddard Space Flight Center in Maryland and several colleagues from universities reported, using the NOAA-10 satellite and the University of Washington C-131A research aircraft, that pollution from ocean vessels increases the reflectivity of shallow-layer clouds. Such an effect, which results from a greater concentration of long-lived cloud droplets due to the presence of pollution particles on which the droplets can grow, would act to cool the Earth's climate.

On Oct. 11, 1990, NASA announced that the

Spectrometer on board the Nimbus 7 space satellite reveals an area of severe ozone depletion over Antarctica in October 1990, as indicated by the dark patch and surrounding ring at the center; the white spot is missing data.

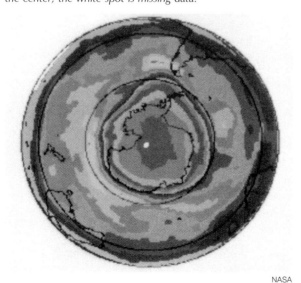

NASA

stratospheric ozone depletion over Antarctica at that time matched that of 1987 and 1989, which had the previous existing lowest levels of ozone concentration. In addition, the ozone hole persisted into December 1990 as the polar vortex remained strong over the continent, thereby preventing the relatively rich stratospheric ozone air from lower latitudes from mixing with the ozone-depleted atmosphere over the southern polar region. A reduction of ozone in the stratosphere could cause an increase in skin cancer in areas beneath the ozone hole, as well as change weather patterns over larger areas.

Meteorological monitoring systems and field programs. The new radar capability of the U.S. National Weather Service, referred to as the Weather Surveillance Radar-1988 Doppler (WSR-88D), continued to be installed. Originally referred to as NEXRAD, it would comprise 137 radars installed in the contiguous U.S. by July 1995. Such weather radars would assist in the identification of such atmospheric features as low-level wind shear associated with cumulus cloud downdrafts and tornadoes. The availability of Doppler radar could, for example, have facilitated the early identification of the tornado that cut through the Illinois communities of Plainfield and Crest Hill on Aug. 28, 1990, killing 29 people. A special-use Doppler radar, referred to as the Terminal Doppler Weather Radar (TDWR), was being developed under Federal Aviation Administration (FAA) support to provide more detailed wind monitoring at approximately 50 U.S. airports. Such a system was designed to prevent aircraft accidents, such as the August 1985 crash in Dallas, Texas, that are caused by rapid changes in wind speed and direction during takeoffs and landings.

The University of Oklahoma and Oklahoma State University were using over $2 million from oil rebate funds to establish a 107-station surface meteorological network across the state. Expected to become operational in two years, the stations would be about 40 km (1 km = 0.62 mi) apart and would provide weather updates every 15 minutes.

Planning for the Stormscale Operational and Research Meteorology (STORM) program continued in 1990. Both a field study in January–April 1992 in the U.S. Middle West to investigate winter extratropical cyclones and a study in the central plains in April–July 1993 to study mesoscale convective systems were planned. Mesoscale convective systems are organized areas of rainfall that often produce severe weather, including tornadoes, over the central U.S. These weather systems also frequently occur in China east of the Tibetan Plateau. They are poorly predicted by current numerical weather-prediction models.

In 1991 the second Winter and Icing Study Program (WISP) began on January 15 and extended

New Doppler radar system being introduced by the U.S. National Weather Service (above) will provide early identification of tornadoes, such as the one that struck an apartment complex in Crest Hill, Illinois, in August 1990 (left).

through March 31. Sponsored by the FAA, the National Science Foundation, and NOAA, WISP investigated winter storms along the Colorado Front Range with aircraft and surface-based monitoring systems. Icing associated with those storms has been implicated in aircraft crashes.

Continuously updated weather-forecast information was becoming routinely available in the U.S. and Canada. The Weather Channel, for example, based in Atlanta, Ga., and available through cable television in 46 million households, was providing local, regional, national, and selected international weather conditions 24 hours a day.

Air quality. The 1990 United States Clean Air Act amendments were passed into law in the fall. The first changes since 1977, the legislation mandated the phasing out of chlorofluorocarbons and carbon tetrachloride by Jan. 1, 2000. Methyl chloroform was to be banned by Jan. 1, 2002, and hydrochlorofluorocarbon production was to cease in 2030. These controls were designed to reduce the destruction of stratospheric ozone and also to provide health benefits by eliminating methyl chloroform and carbon tetrachloride. Acid deposition, commonly referred to as acid rain, was also to be reduced as part of the legislation. Annual sulfur dioxide emissions in the U.S. were to be reduced by almost 10 million tons by 2000, with half of those reductions completed by January 1995. By 1995 two million tons per year of nitrogen oxides were to be eliminated. Acid deposition has been associated in the eastern U.S., western Europe, and elsewhere with such environmental effects as forest-growth deterioration and damage to surface coverings (*e.g.*, paint) of building structures and automobiles.

As reported by Jaakko Kukkonen and associates of the Finnish Meteorological Institute, 2,100 tons of ammonium (NH_4) were released in Ionava, Lithua-

nia, on March 20, 1990, in a severe chemical accident. The accident resulted from the catastrophic failure of a storage container and the resulting fire. Using a model, scientists estimated that the material would reach southern Finland in concentrations of 5 to 20 mg per cu m. New modeling tools for assessing the transport and dispersion of pollution were being developed in response to such accidents. For example, a comparison of model simulations of the transport, dispersion, and deposition of emissions from the Chernobyl (U.S.S.R.) nuclear reactor accident of April 1986 was being reported in March 1991 in Varese, Italy.

International cooperation. The World Meteorological Organization (WMO) and International Council of Scientific Unions (ICSU) initiated the WMO/ICSU World Climate Research Program (WCRP) to coordinate studies of the Earth's climate system. The WMO, with 156 nations and four territories as members, continued to help facilitate international cooperation in weather and climate analysis, forecasting, and investigation. WCRP instituted three major projects to investigate the climate system. These were the study of Tropical Ocean and Global Atmosphere (TOGA) interactions; the Global Energy and Water Cycle Experiment (GEWEX) to model and predict the Earth's radiation, heat, and water budget, including the impact of climate change on rainfall patterns; and the World Ocean Circulation Experiment (WOCE), which sought to obtain simultaneous measurements of the oceans in a similar fashion as routinely accomplished for the atmosphere. As an example of international collaboration, the TOGA board had members from Australia, Brazil, Chile, China, Ecuador, France, India, Indonesia, Japan, Mauritius, New Zealand, Pakistan, Peru, the U.K., the U.S., and the U.S.S.R. For additional information, see *Oceanography*, below.

The successful use of the United Kingdom Meteorological Office general circulation model to simulate rainfall in the Sahel region of Africa for four distinctly different years (1950, 1958, 1983, and 1984) was reported in the July 1990 issue of the *Bulletin* of the WMO. Observed sea-surface temperatures were used in the model integrations. For model forecasts that used June data, the predictions of rainfall for the following season had considerable accuracy. The model, however, was less skillful in predicting summer monsoon rainfall in India, suggesting that the atmospheric circulation patterns over India depend more on local influences than does the circulation associated with rainfall over the Sahel region in Africa.

—Roger A. Pielke

Geologic sciences

Geology and geochemistry. A decade ago it appeared that the very creative or, as some would have it, revolutionary period engendered by the introduction of the theory of plate tectonics in the 1960s might be entering a more normal phase, in which the gains of the previous 20 years would be consolidated. With the introduction of the Alvarez hypothesis of asteroid impact and mass extinction in 1980, however, many geologists believed that yet another revolution had occurred, the results of which would supplement, rather than supersede, those of the previous one. Whatever the outcome of the debates currently raging, the fact that the Alvarez hypothesis was so profoundly influencing the direction of research in the Earth sciences was, in itself, sufficient to establish it as one of the most significant geologic ideas of the 20th century.

Impact theory. The increasing interest in impact phenomena raised once again the question of the role of catastrophes in the history of the Earth, a question debated among geologists for more than 200 years. Although it is sometimes said that anything can happen, science, as well as meaningful discourses in everyday life, is grounded on the assumption that some things are impossible. Scientists suppose that there is an unchanging natural order, which, to one degree or another, serves to limit expectations. One would be ill-advised, for example, to invest in a corporation formed to manufacture perpetual-motion machines because physical theory forbids one to suppose that such a venture would succeed. Geologists, owing to historical circumstances, have seen themselves as having a special stake in this principle of uniformity. During the 18th century, catastrophic and even miraculous events, some of which had been suggested by the Old Testament, were invoked to explain the physical features of the Earth's surface. James Hutton of Edinburgh saw this practice as a threat to a rational understanding of

the history of the Earth. In order to impose a limit on the kinds of events that might be introduced into historical accounts, he formulated a principle assuring that chaos in geologic discourse could be avoided. He said, in 1795,

Not only are no powers to be employed that are not natural to the globe, no actions to be admitted of except those of which we know the principle, and no extraordinary events to be alleged in order to explain a common experience, the powers of nature are not to be employed in order to destroy the very object of those powers; we are not to make nature act in violation of that order, which we actually observe, and in subversion of that end which is perceived to be in the system of created things.

This principle, which has become a methodological cornerstone of geology, leaves some issues unresolved. Hutton spoke confidently of the order of nature that is actually perceived, but disputes in science arise from just the fact that not everyone perceives the same order in nature. Geologists whose perception allowed for the transmutation of species—their change in form and/or appearance—imposed a different order of nature on the past than those whose perception did not. There is yet another source of conflict that Hutton identified when he said, "We have been representing the system of this Earth with a certain regularity, which is not perhaps in nature, but which is necessary for our clear conception of the system of nature." Because knowledge of the past presupposes some initial assumption about the uniformity of nature, this uniformity cannot be tested independently of that initial assumption. Even though geologists may agree about the kind of order to be imposed on the past, they are permitted some latitude as to how restrictively it is to be applied. For Hutton the order to which the past must conform was more or less directly revealed in the processes observable in the present. Charles Lyell, the principal 19th-century advocate of what came to be called "uniformitarianism," insisted that the events of the past could not differ even in magnitude and intensity from those that had actually been encountered in the course of human history. In the 20th century many geologists adopted the less restrictive view that, if warranted by the evidence of particular circumstances, any event that was not forbidden by physical theory could be admitted into their historical accounts.

Ursula Marvin of the Harvard-Smithsonian Center for Astrophysics, Cambridge, Mass., believes, however, that Hutton's and Lyell's restrictive versions of the uniformitarian principle, with its emphasis on the gradual action of familiar processes, still exercises such an influence on some geologists that it is standing in the way of their wholehearted acceptance of the impact of extraterrestrial bodies on the Earth as a significant agent not only of mass extinctions but of geologic change in general. Marvin pointed out that during the past several decades evidence of the importance of impact processes in shaping the Earth's surface had been rapidly accumulating, yet not until 1980—when the late Luis Alvarez and his colleagues published their hypothesis that the impact of an asteroid had caused mass extinctions of plants and animals at the end of the Cretaceous Period (65 million years ago)—had the subject received much attention from the geologic community at large. The impact of external objects with the Earth is consistent with physical theory and is plausible, even to be expected, on the basis of the knowledge of astronomy. But, according to Marvin, because of the extraterrestrial origin and the discontinuous and cataclysmic nature of the phenomena, the theory violates the preference of traditional geologists for gradual, familiar processes. She believes that the phenomena of plate tectonics, on the other hand, being wholly terrestrial, gradual, and even to some extent observable, are consistent with the more restrictive versions of the uniformitarian principle.

Marvin's view that the reluctance of some geologists to accept the importance of impact phenomena as a cause of significant events is the result of historical and methodological rather than substantive factors rests on her conviction that the evidence for these impacts is overwhelming. Kevin McCartney of the University of Maine expressed a somewhat different opinion, at least in regard to mass extinctions. He believes that neither those who advocate asteroid impacts as a cause of mass extinctions nor those who attribute extinctions to other causes such as massive volcanic eruptions have produced wholly convincing evidence to support their views. He suggested that a resolution of the problem may be in the distant future.

The search for the site of the asteroid impact thought to have caused the great extinction at the end of the Cretaceous Period continued to occupy the attention of geologists. Alan Hildebrand and William Boynton of the University of Arizona reported that an analysis of trace elements in material collected at the Cretaceous-Tertiary boundary at localities throughout the world indicated that only a tenth of the material blown into the atmosphere by the impact was derived from continental crust and that, therefore, an oceanic impact site was indicated. They thought that they may have located such a site in the Colombian Basin of the Caribbean Sea. Despite the fact that the impact structure is buried beneath a blanket of sediments more than 2 km thick and has been deformed by the motion of crustal plates, Hildebrand and Boynton were able to estimate that it is 300 km in diameter, more than twice the size of any such structure yet identified on land. Even so, the authors concluded that it is not large enough to account for all of the continental material associated with the impact. They speculated that there may have been almost simultaneous impacts of several asteroids.

The search for impact structures has not been confined to those thought to have been associated with mass extinctions. D.A. Forsyth and his colleagues at the Geological Survey of Canada presented magnetic and gravity data that they interpreted as evidence of the presence of an impact structure beneath the southern part of Lake Huron that may have been formed as late as early Paleozoic time, about 550 million years ago. R.B. Hargraves and his co-workers from Princeton and Stanford universities reported evidence of an impact structure in southwestern Montana of about the same age as the Lake Huron structure.

Mantle plume hypothesis. During the past few years, a significant alternative to asteroid impacts as a cause of mass extinctions has emerged. At the 101st annual meeting of the Geological Society of America (GSA) held in Dallas in November, a session was devoted to "Mantle Plumes and Mass Extinctions." According to the mantle plume hypothesis, masses of material in the deepest part of the Earth's mantle, more than 2,500 km beneath the surface, are heated by the underlying core. The resulting hot, buoyant material periodically rises to the surface through the outer mantle and crust to emerge on the surface as outpourings of immense quantities of lava. One of these episodes, which occurred in Miocene time some 16 million years ago, resulted in the formation of 4.5 million cu km of "flood basalts" on what is now the Columbia River Plateau. The release of CO_2 and sulfides that accompanies such huge outpourings might alter the atmosphere and oceans sufficiently to cause the widespread extinction of plants and animals.

An attractive aspect of the mantle plume hypothesis is that the geologic record and theoretical considerations indicate that lava flooding on such a vast scale may occur with a periodicity of about 25 million years, close to the periodicity of mass extinctions as suggested by David Raup and John Sepkoski of the University of Chicago. Several flood basalts, including an especially large series in India that was formed at the time of the extinction at the end of the Cretaceous Period, are closely correlated with extinctions.

Mass extinctions. James F. Kasting of Pennsylvania State University and his co-workers carried the mass extinction hypothesis to its logical extreme, the obliteration of all life on Earth. In a paper presented at the annual meeting of the American Association for the Advancement of Science held in New Orleans, La., in February, they pointed out that the impact of an object large enough to evaporate all the water in the oceans would have wiped out any life that had appeared up to that time. They speculated that this might have happened more than once during the crucial early history of life between the origin of the Earth and about 3.5 billion years ago.

Although many geologists talk rather casually about mass extinctions, there are lingering questions about how sudden and catastrophic these extinctions were. The preservation of plant and animal remains in the form of fossils is subject to so vast a number of factors that detecting the difference between an extinction that was sudden and one that might have occurred over a period of hundreds of thousands or even millions of years is by no means a simple matter of noting what the fossil record "tells" the scientist. The continuing controversy over the time required for the extinction of the dinosaurs is a case in point. A rare opportunity to assess the effects of one of those contingent factors on the fossil record recently arose quite by chance. Arnold Miller of the University of Cincinnati, Ohio, made several dives to examine the mollusk shells and sediments on the seafloor adjacent to the island of St. Croix in the Virgin Islands before the area was struck by Hurricane Hugo in September 1989. After the hurricane, Miller collected samples to compare with those collected before the storm in an attempt to determine the extent of the disruption of the sediments and their organic contents. Preliminary studies revealed that despite currents generated by the hurricane that were moving as fast as nine knots at a depth of 18 m (60 ft), the effect on the bottom sediments was not pronounced.

Other developments. Most fossils are gathered and deposited in the collections of universities or museums by paleontologists and their associates who are employed by these institutions. There are, however, independent professional collectors, and in 1988 one of these, Stanley Wood, discovered a well-preserved and significant specimen exposed in a stone wall in a farmyard about 24 km west of Edinburgh. The wall had been constructed in the 1830s from rocks dated at 348 million years before the present; they had been obtained in a nearby quarry. As of 1991 the specimen had not been thoroughly studied, but the results of a preliminary examination by Timothy Smithson of the University of Newcastle, England, revealed that it is the remains of a reptile, establishing it as by far the oldest representative of that order yet discovered.

In 1990 geologists continued their tradition of seeking solutions to significant social and economic problems. Progress toward a solution of one of the most pressing of these problems, the disposal of the toxic wastes that are generated in almost every industrial process, was made in a remarkably simple and unexpected way. Arthur Cohen and James

Durig of the University of South Carolina reported that they had achieved promising results in removing radioactive and other toxic materials from water with peat, the fibrous organic material that represents an early stage in the formation of coal. This material, which is found in large quantities throughout the world, apparently has a physical structure that selectively binds the contaminants found in water. The peat is burned, leaving a small residue of ash containing the toxic materials, which can then be easily disposed of. If tests of the effectiveness of peat in removing toxic contaminants from groundwater prove successful, this method may be of great economic significance.

It is reassuring to note that amid all of these developments, interest in the relationship of the Earth sciences to the broader social and cultural milieu has not been neglected and may even have intensified. At the GSA meeting there were not only scientific sessions but also one devoted to "Geoscience and the Arts" and another to "Metageology," which included papers concerning a variety of social and methodological aspects of Earth science.

Anticipating the complex problems that Earth scientists will face in the coming decades, Stanford University established a new academic program entitled Earth Systems. The new program offered both graduate and undergraduate degrees and drew on faculty from biology, engineering, and international studies, as well as from the Earth sciences, in the hope of preparing a new generation of students to consider the Earth as a system rather than as a collection of isolated problems.

—David B. Kitts

Geophysics. The dynamic processes in the Earth's interior manifested themselves at the surface of the planet during the past year in a number of unusual and destructive earthquakes and volcanoes. Appropriately enough, these events ushered in the International Decade for Natural Disaster Reduction (1990–2000), which, as the name implies, will focus intense worldwide attention on the various natural hazards threatening the planet. Foremost among the hazards are earthquakes and volcanoes.

Earthquakes. Of the many earthquakes during 1990, by far the most devastating occurred in northwestern Iran in June near the Caspian Sea. The Manjil earthquake (named after a nearby town) had a surface-wave magnitude of 7.7 and a seismic moment about 10 times that of the destructive Armenian earthquake of 1988. (Seismic moment is proportional to the product of the fault slip and the area of fault rupture; it is thought by many seismologists to be a better measure of overall earthquake size than the magnitude scale introduced by Charles Richter.) The earthquake occurred directly beneath a densely populated and well-developed part of Iran, and the

Collapsed homes in northwestern Iran bear witness to the force of the earthquake that struck the area in June 1990. With a surface-wave magnitude of 7.7 on the Richter scale, the quake killed 40,000–60,000 people in Iran; most of the deaths resulted from the collapse of adobe dwellings.

death toll was estimated at 40,000 to 60,000. Most of the deaths were caused by the collapse of dwellings made from adobe. These structures have notoriously poor resistance to the predominantly sideways motion of earthquake waves. Landslides triggered by the seismic shaking also contributed to the death toll, burying some small villages.

Not all the structures were made of adobe, however. Many modern engineered structures were in the area, including roads, dams, tunnels, power plants, bridges, silos, and water tanks, as well as residential and office buildings. Studies of the damage to such structures provided an excellent opportunity to determine which design and construction principles can stand the test of strong earthquake shaking. To obtain such information, teams of engineers and scientists are routinely dispatched by a number of countries to the sites of almost all major, damaging earthquakes. This was the case for the Iran earthquake. From the U.S. a small team was sent by the Earthquake Engineering Research Institute soon after the earthquake, and their brief report found that in spite of the horrifying death toll, no engineered structure had observable structural damage. There were important lessons for the practice of earthquake engineering, however, the chief of them being that extensive damage to equipment in buildings can be produced by the failure of nonstructural components. For example, heavy walls not involved in the support of the building collapsed at several power plants and toppled onto the main power lines where they exited the building, thus disrupting the distribution of power to the countryside.

According to some observers, the widespread occurrence of liquefaction (the loss of strength of water-saturated sand layers resulting from seismic vibrations) was one of the most significant features of the Manjil earthquake. Regions as far as 80 km from the quake's epicenter suffered damage from vertical

settlement and lateral movement due to liquefaction. There are many susceptible sands in the area, and so, because of the ever present threat of large earthquakes, the possibility of future liquefaction must be given serious consideration when reconstruction and future development there are planned. Even well-engineered and well-built structures can sustain considerable damage if liquefaction occurs in the vicinity of the foundation.

Liquefaction also played a large role in the damage caused by a surface-wave magnitude-7.7 earthquake that ruptured the ground surface on the island of Luzon in the Philippines in July 1990. Several multistory buildings in the vicinity of the coastal town of Dagupan tilted as much as 30° from vertical and subsided into the ground as much as 2 m (6.5 ft). Most of the at least 1,600 deaths occurred when a number of modern structures in the resort city of Baguio collapsed. The cause of the collapses was being investigated by several teams of earthquake engineers from various countries, and their findings will be important in the design of earthquake-resistant structures in earthquake-prone regions. A surprising feature of the quake was the lack of damage attributed to ground shaking in the region of the epicenter. In a number of places the only damage was caused by fault rupture under houses straddling the fault. The lack of vibration damage suggests that the faulting in this region took place smoothly and relatively slowly. Seismograms from stations throughout the world, however, revealed that the overall faulting was quite complex.

From a geophysical point of view, the Luzon earthquake was of interest for several reasons. It occurred on a strike-slip fault—the same type as the San Andreas Fault in California—with well-developed faulting at the surface. The surface exposure of the faulting exceeded 110 km in length, and along that length the average slip was 3 to 4 m (9 to 13

315

ft). The maximum slip was 6 m (20 ft), one of the largest slips along a strike-slip fault observed during this century. The tectonic setting of Luzon is complex, being bounded on both sides by subduction zones (areas in which the edge of one crustal plate is descending below the edge of another), and the occurrence of such a large earthquake in a region between two such zones provides valuable constraining conditions for understanding the tectonics of the area.

A number of unusual earthquakes occurred in 1990 (most of them, coincidentally, in May). An earthquake and two aftershocks occurred in The Sudan within five days of one another (surface-wave magnitude 6.8 to 7.2). These events took place in a relatively aseismic region between several branches of the East African Rift zone, a region of active crustal extension. They were the largest earthquakes known to have occurred in The Sudan and among the largest to occur in Africa during this century. In one of the events the fault slip was horizontal, while the other two produced vertical fault slip in the manner expected for faults in regions in which the crust is spreading apart. The strike-slip event was believed to be along a transform faulting connecting two spreading regions—a continental analogue of a common situation along the mid-ocean ridges.

The earthquakes previously discussed occurred in the upper few tens of kilometers of the Earth's crust (as do most of the earthquakes on the planet). In contrast, several unusual earthquakes occurred at depths of 100 km or more. These events were un-

Lava from the Kilauea Volcano on the island of Hawaii advances across a road in the town of Kalapana. The lava overran much of the town but moved so slowly that the inhabitants had ample time to leave.

usual more for their location than for their depths per se. An earthquake with a body-wave magnitude of 6.1 took place 217 km beneath the Alaska Peninsula, in a region for which no earthquake larger than 5.0 had occurred deeper than 150 km. (Surface waves are not efficiently generated by deep earthquakes, and therefore the magnitudes of such earthquakes are usually computed from the amplitude of waves propagating through the body of the planet.) Two earthquakes with body-wave magnitudes of 5.8 and 6.7 were located 100 km beneath Romania and caused considerable damage near Bucharest. A cluster of earthquakes has occurred there for many years, for reasons not well understood. The area is not a region of present-day subduction, as are those regions beneath which most deep earthquakes occur. The last unusual earthquake took place at a depth of 611 km near the subduction zone off the Kuril Islands and Kamchatka. This zone marks a place where the Pacific Plate is moving under the Eurasian Plate. What made the earthquake unusual was not its depth but the fact that it was 300 km farther from the subduction zone than the previously recorded deep earthquakes associated with the zone. The event may have occurred on a detached piece of subducted lithosphere.

The mechanism of deep earthquakes continued to be a puzzle. The slip in the faulting is similar to that for shallower earthquakes, but the temperatures at depths below about 100 km are too high to allow the brittle fracture of rock that is generally acknowledged to produce shallow earthquakes. Various mechanisms involving phase transformations, frictional heating, or the release of water from minerals have been proposed, but none of the mechanisms can adequately explain all aspects of the spatial and size distribution of deep earthquakes. For better understanding of the mechanisms of such earthquakes, laboratory studies were being conducted using specialized presses and lasers capable of simulating the extreme pressures and temperatures occurring at depths of hundreds of kilometers into the Earth.

Volcanoes. Of interest because of both their hazard to the inhabitants of Earth and the clues they provide to the puzzle of tectonic processes, volcanoes were much in the news during the past year. Eruptions on the eastern rift of Kilauea on the island of Hawaii continued after almost a decade of continuous activity. The lava from these eruptions overran numerous houses and obliterated the small town of Kalapana; at least 120 ha (296 ac) of landmass was added to the island as a result of the lava entering the sea. Fortunately, the eruptions were not the explosive type found along subduction zones (such as the Krakatoa or Mt. St. Helens eruptions), and the slow-moving lava allowed ample time for evacuation of residences. Only one life had been lost to

Steam rises from the Redoubt Volcano in Alaska, which became active in December 1989 after 23 years of quiescence. Seismographic stations on and around the volcano combined with visual observations to provide a warning of the explosive eruption that took place on Jan. 2, 1990.

a volcanic eruption during this century in Hawaii, and that happened to a person trespassing beyond a warning sign. Authorities warn, however, that eruptions on the southwestern rift of Mauna Loa might not be so benign; the topography is steeper, and the lava reaches the sea in hours rather than in days, as was the case for eastern rift eruptions. Substantial residential development has taken place during the past decade in the area of the southwestern rift.

In contrast to the relatively steady eruptions of Kilauea, explosive eruptions occurred in a number of volcanoes around the Pacific Rim. These volcanoes are caused by the melting of material as one tectonic plate is forced beneath another one, and the lava is often more viscous than occurs at "hot spots" such as Hawaii. This more viscous lava can form domes and plugs in the vent and the supply tubes of the volcano. Consequently, internal pressures associated with continuing upward movement of magma in the volcano can lead to catastrophic eruptions when the plugs are forced open.

The eruptions of Redoubt Volcano, a 3,000-m (10,000-ft) mountain about 160 km southwest of Anchorage, were of particular importance. They were interesting more for the success in forecasting them than for the damage they caused. The eruptions involved a series of stages and were well monitored by seismographic stations on and around the volcano. The pre-eruption stage began after 23 years of quiescence and was marked by an intense swarm of seismic events with unusually low-frequency motions (one to three Hertz) in the 23 hours before the vent-clearing eruption on Dec. 14, 1989. Such signals had been detected before eruptions at other similar volcanoes and offered the hope that short-term predictions of eruptions could be made. Indeed, following the December 14 eruption, a stage of dome building characterized by higher frequency seismic waves (5 to 15 Hz) was followed by a reappearance

of the low-frequency events and another explosive eruption on Jan. 2, 1990. The reappearance of the low-frequency swarms of seismic activity, along with the visual observations of a steepening dome in the volcano's throat, prompted a warning of an impending eruption. As a result, personnel were evacuated from an oil terminal at the foot of the mountain before their facility was flooded by debris flows made up of water, ice, and rock fragments (at its peak, the debris flow at about 20 km from the vent had a discharge comparable to that of the Mississippi River).

The ash erupted from Redoubt Volcano caused major disruptions in the air traffic around Anchorage. Soon after the first eruption, an accident was narrowly averted when a commercial jetliner was able to restart its engines after a 12-minute powerless glide. The loss of engine power as a result of flying through ash plumes has occurred about 25 times during the past 15 years and emphasizes the importance of monitoring volcanic eruptions and distinguishing between volcanic plumes and meteorological clouds (the ash is often invisible to aircraft radar and the pilots' vision). Modern satellite surveillance offers much hope that this can be done in a routine and timely basis in the near future. Studies of the Redoubt and other eruptions indicated that the volcanic plumes can be distinguished from regular clouds on the basis of the differences in the spectral composition of the energy radiated from them.

—David M. Boore

Hydrologic sciences

The expansion of low-cost, high-speed computing continued to have a major impact on the way hydrologists approached their science. This was the case across the full spectrum of hydrology—from studies of runoff generation to examination of the link between stream-flow and precipitation patterns to

317

investigations of subsurface flow through soils, unconsolidated sediments, and rock masses. Theoretical studies using computer models also stimulated a new generation of field experiments, as the scope of hydrologic inquiry was effectively no longer limited by a lack of capacity for processing and analyzing large data bases.

Hydrology. The availability of powerful graphics workstations and of software for rapidly quantifying small-scale topographic variability prompted new studies of the mechanisms by which storm rainfall on a catchment leads to runoff in stream channels. The processes involved in generating stream flow are of both scientific interest and practical importance in the management of water resources and the assessment and mitigation of flood risk.

In a 1990 issue of *Reviews of Geophysics,* Eric Wood, Murugesu Sivapalan, and Keith Beven described their progress in achieving a greater understanding of runoff mechanisms. Emphasis was placed on how the spatial variability in the hydrologic properties of the soils and rocks could be synthesized across a range of scales and on how these factors were influencing the ways in which hydrologists were building a new generation of streamflow models. This work was international in scope, with the above authors working at universities in the United States, Australia, and the United Kingdom, respectively. Through the use of interactive graphics, digital elevation models, and high-resolution remote sensing data, it was possible to simulate on the computer the ways by which small-scale variability in catchment topography and soil characteristics influenced storm runoff. From these kinds of studies, it was possible to ask the important question of how hydrologists should average small-scale variability to obtain a model that could be used at the catchment scale to predict storm runoff while at the same time preserving the influence of the complex patterns of runoff on individual segments of a hill slope. Progress in this important area of hydrology was closely tied to advances in computing hardware and software development. Recent and planned large-scale field experiments that coordinated remote sensing data, physical-property measurements, and observations of catchment response to rainfall events were providing the data hydrologists needed to test concepts underlying these new computer models.

The ready access to supercomputers was extending the range of problems that could be investigated in subsurface hydrology. Of particular note in this regard was the progress being made toward understanding solute-transport processes in porous geologic media. Problems that were not computationally feasible even five years earlier could now be considered. Researchers were tackling the problem of modeling, in three dimensions, the simultaneous transport of several different chemical species that are dissolved in the groundwater and that react chemically in a heterogeneous geologic medium.

Researchers were also achieving progress in computer simulation by taking advantage of new algorithms that provided a more efficient solution to the large systems of simultaneous equations that arose during the modeling of three-dimensional, transient problems. In a paper published in *Water Resources Research,* Kerry MacQuarrie, Ed Sudicky, and Emil Frind demonstrated the application of supercomputer technology in solving a problem involving the transport of biodegradable organic contaminants, dissolved oxygen depletion and recharge, and microbial growth. Their findings provided a new perspective on the intimate coupling between the many physical and chemical factors that could influence the fate of man-made contaminants released in the environment. In related developments, three-dimensional visualization of contaminant plumes and their growth through time revealed details of plume geometry that until recently had not been fully appreciated. Exciting opportunities existed in exploring how graphics workstations and real-time visualization could facilitate new insight into hydrologic processes.

Perhaps an even more notable trend than the ready access to supercomputers was the emergence of inexpensive desktop workstations. These machines, costing in the range of several tens of thousands of dollars, approached one-third the speed of supercomputers. They also had large memory capabilities that permitted the manipulation of extensive data sets and large systems of equations. A number of researchers reported that the turnaround time from a simulation on these personal workstations could be shorter than that of a multiuser supercomputer facility. Of course, this did not suggest that the supercomputer had been replaced by the workstation. What was most important was the inexpensive computing power that was in the hands of research hydrologists working in their home institutions.

While easy access to workstations and supercomputers was extending the bounds of hydrologic inquiry, it was becoming increasingly common to find examples of the inappropriate application of model results. This circumstance seemed most prevalent when the models were used to solve engineering problems with a hydrologic component. Two reports released in 1990 by the United States National Research Council (NRC) echoed this concern. One report, entitled "Rethinking High-Level Radioactive Waste Disposal," suggested that in its current form, the U.S. program for deep geologic disposal of high-level radioactive waste was unlikely to succeed. The concept of geologic disposal is to place radioactive waste produced in nuclear power plants into an engineered facility underground, in an area where the local geology and groundwater conditions are suited to containing the radionuclides for tens of thousands of years or longer. However, radionuclides would eventually dissolve in the water contained within the rocks that surrounded the repository and migrate with the groundwater to a discharge location at the ground surface. At the current site being considered by the U.S. (Yucca Mountain in Nevada), questions would have to be asked about how potential long-term climatic variations might change the present-day elevation of the water table in the region and how long it would take for radionuclides dissolved in the groundwater to move from the repository to the ground surface. Because radioactive waste remains hazardous for a long time, these predictions would extend thousands of years into the future.

One of the key concerns raised by the committee of the NRC was that the government's approach to site selection was founded on the assumption that the properties and future behavior of a geologic repository could be determined and specified with a high degree of certainty. In effect, the regulations that had been written to evaluate and judge the acceptability of a site to serve as host for the repository demand more of hydrologic models than could be justified on scientific grounds. The worry was that hydrologic models were being applied incorrectly in that they could not provide accurate predictions of long-term site behavior. The problem was not primarily with the computer models but with the inherent uncertainty in characterizing geologic media and in predicting climatic changes thousands of years into the future. The committee argued that the computer models should be used only as tools for understanding the present characteristics of a site and for exploring possible future behavior, rather than as a yardstick by which a site is judged acceptable or not.

A second report released by the NRC, entitled "Groundwater Models: Scientific and Regulatory Applications," examined how computer models of groundwater flow should be used in addressing legal and regulatory concerns. The report committee, chaired by Frank Schwartz of Ohio State University, considered whether computer models could reasonably be used to assign liability for specific groundwater contamination problems to individual parties and to make regulatory decisions based on long-term prediction. Some of the conclusions reached by the committee were: (1) conceptual limitations and data requirements limit the reliability of groundwater-flow models involving unsaturated media, fractured media, or two or more liquids; (2) the results of mathematical computer models often appear more certain than they really are, and decision makers must be aware of these limitations; (3) computer model results are not a substitute or replacement for sound scientific and engineering judgment; and (4)

as the use of groundwater models has increased, a shortage of qualified staff capable of appropriately applying models has developed. The committee argued for increased government and industry support for research to provide well-controlled field experiments to validate new modeling concepts and guide new model development. They also placed strong emphasis on the need for additional educational resources to meet the severe shortage of qualified personnel in this area.

These reports by the NRC reflected a general consensus in the scientific community that further research was needed in order to develop ways of better using hydrologic models in solving applied problems. Allan Freeze and his coauthors, writing in *Ground Water*, described a framework for using hydrologic models in the decision-making process. During the past decade, advances had been made in understanding how the uncertainty inherent in characterizing a hydrogeologic environment could be used as an input to a computer model in order to quantify the uncertainty associated with a hydrologic prediction. However, relatively less attention had been paid to the question of how the uncertainties in model predictions should be incorporated in management decisions. The authors described a risk-based philosophy that coupled three separate models: a decision model based on a risk-cost-benefit objective function, a simulation model for groundwater flow and transport, and an uncertainty model that accounted for both geologic uncertainty and uncertainty in the hydraulic properties of the medium. To deal with the concerns of model reliability, they promoted a framework whereby computer modeling, field measurements, and risk reduction were evaluated in a sequential procedure.

—Leslie Smith

Oceanography. A wide range of activities took place in oceanography during the past year. Among the most active areas of concern were the relationship between oceans and climate, hydrothermal vents, global ocean circulation, and deep-sea drilling.

Oceans and climate. Attempts to detect the effects of the predicted global warming due to carbon dioxide and other so-called greenhouse gases occupied many oceanographers during the year. The data remained ambiguous, but some tantalizing results were seen. For example, a warming trend was observed in data collected from waters deeper than 400 m (1,310 ft) in the western Mediterranean Sea by oceanographers from the University of Paris. Comparing this information with previous records, they found a trend of continuously increasing temperatures during the past three decades. The deep-water records reflect the averaged evolution of climate conditions at the surface during the winter, when the deep water is formed. Since there are many competing processes in the deep ocean leading to temperature changes, interpretation of these records must be done with care. It is possible, but has not yet been proved, that the temperature trend may be the result of greenhouse-induced local warming.

During the year confirmation was found for one of the key assumptions used in modeling the changing climate. Scientists from the University of Chicago showed that increased water vapor from the ocean that was caused by greenhouse warming itself amplified the warming. Data from ships and buoys in the ocean were used to determine the amount of heat given off in a particular region. Satellite observations were used to show how much of this heat escaped into space and how much was blocked by the greenhouse effect. The scientists found that the greenhouse effect increased significantly with sea-surface temperature, thus confirming the process that is used in the models. The convincing new information contradicted earlier proposals that greenhouse-induced water vapor might diminish rather than amplify global warming.

In general, greenhouse warming is predicted to be stronger in the Arctic than in the lower latitudes and, therefore, should lead to early thinning of the ice and a decrease in its extent. Scientists from the Scott Polar Research Institute in the U.K. announced the results from a 1987 ice-profiling experiment in the Arctic Ocean carried out by submarine. Over a zone extending more than 400 km to the north of Greenland they found evidence of a significant decrease in mean ice thickness compared with a similar measurement in 1976. However, the absence of data in the intervening years and the question of whether the thinning was caused by warming or by ice being blown from the region of measurement by strong winds revealed that it was not yet possible to confirm or deny an effect from global warming in these data.

The processes that lead to global warming are not fully understood, and many of the uncertainties concern biological processes. Biologists from the University of Georgia and the National Oceanic and Atmospheric Administration (NOAA) reported on experiments carried out in the eastern tropical Pacific Ocean on the gas dimethyl sulfide, which produces cloud condensation nuclei and thus affects the climate. Nearly half of the input of this gas from the biosphere to the atmosphere comes from the ocean. The results of the experiments showed that the biological consumption of the gas by organisms in the ocean is more important than physical processes of exchange. The results highlight the importance of the microbial food web in the cycling of this important gas.

Oceanographers from Dalhousie University, Halifax, Nova Scotia, and from the Goddard Space Flight Center, Greenbelt, Md., were able to explain the discrepancy between actual measurements of sea-surface temperatures and models that consistently overestimated them. The absorption of visible light and consequent heating beneath the surface appears to account for the lower temperatures at the surface. The sea-surface temperature is, therefore, sensitive to the optical properties of the upper ocean. Increases in plankton concentration can lead to significant heat being trapped in the upper layers. These data showed the importance of understanding the growth cycles of plankton as part of the interactive ocean-atmosphere system.

The role of the ocean in climate and its effect on global warming continued to be a topic of great interest to policymakers as well as scientists. One important forum was the second World Climate Conference, held in Geneva in October–November and attended by scientists and government officials from around the world. The conference focused attention on the need to reduce uncertainties in climate predictions so that governments would have better information on which to base decisions. Conference recommendations emphasized the need for research to understand how the ocean and the atmosphere interact to cause climate change and also the need for a system for observations of the climate system, including the ocean, so that environmental changes could be adequately monitored as they occurred. Governments were expected to respond with increased support for global observing systems in the atmosphere and ocean.

Camera focuses on sponges growing near a hydrothermal vent on the bottom of Lake Baikal in Siberia. It was the first time that a freshwater vent that supports a diversity of life had been found.

Biological effects of warming. Scientists working in the Caribbean reported that corals in that sea were bleaching; that is, expelling the photosynthetic algae that live within their tissues and provide them with nutrients. While they are bleached, the corals stop growing; if the bleaching continues for periods of months to years, the corals die. It appeared as if the corals were bleaching more extensively than at any other time since a major episode in 1987. The bleaching is correlated with warmer water, and satellite measurements confirmed increased warming of the surface. The bleaching shows the harmful effects of warm waters for some species; many tropical marine organisms have been known to be close to their upper lethal temperature limits, which can be exceeded because of local conditions. The bleaching might be an indicator of global warming.

Hydrothermal vents. Work on hydrothermal vents continued in a number of locations. In studies near Okinawa, Japanese scientists found carbon-dioxide-rich bubbles emerging from the seafloor at a depth of about 1,400 m (4,590 ft). As the bubbles emerged, the gas formed compounds that coalesced to form pipes standing on the sediments. It appeared that this fluid was derived from the same deep magmatic source as dissolved gases in the very hot (320° C; 608° F) hydrothermal solution emitted from a nearby black smoker chimney. It was hoped that these bubbles could be studied to learn more about the genesis and evolution of magma deep within the Earth. The bubbles come from volcanic rock and hydrothermal regions that are much less altered, being beneath the sea, than their terrestrial counterparts.

A joint Soviet-U.S. expedition cosponsored by the U.S. National Geographic Society discovered a hydrothermal vent in the northeastern corner of Lake Baikal in Siberia. This was the first time that a freshwater vent that supports a diversity of life, including fish, sponges, worms, and snails, had been found. The presence of hydrothermal venting could be evidence that the lake floor is slowing spreading, creating a rift valley.

Global ocean circulation. An important aspect of studies currently being carried out was the development of new technology that would allow oceanographers to measure ocean processes on a global scale. The new techniques would be a key element of the global ocean-observing system called for by the second World Climate Conference. Autonomous devices for long-term measurements were being developed to free instruments from the logistic limitations of ships. WCRP began carrying out two major ocean programs that were designed to help in this development.

As part of WCRP's TOGA study, a new generation of satellite-tracked surface-drifting buoys developed at the Scripps Institution of Oceanography completed two years of operation in the tropical Pacific Ocean. The buoys measured properties in the mixed layer and provided information on circulation, eddies, and the balance of heat and mass. New climate-prediction models were using this data together with information from fixed, moored instruments developed by NOAA. The moored instruments were deployed along the equator and reported back in real time the air and sea temperature, winds, and ocean currents.

WCRP's WOCE began its field phase in January 1990 with an expedition across the South Atlantic and the deployment of new autonomous devices for monitoring ocean currents below the surface. Developed at the Scripps Institution of Oceanography, the Autonomous Lagrangian Circulation Explorer (ALACE) is a subsurface float that rises at preset intervals to the surface, where it is located by the ARGOS positioning system carried by the NOAA environmental satellites. Ten ALACEs were deployed at a depth of 700 m (2,300 ft) across the Drake Passage, south of South America, and eight were still working as they moved north and eastward across the South Atlantic Ocean. Also as part of technical developments for WOCE, oceanographers at the Woods Hole (Mass.) Oceanographic Institution developed both an automatic meteorological package that could be used on moorings and on ships and a "fast fish" sampler that would allow more rapid collection of ocean properties from shipboard.

British scientists announced the results of a two-year study of the renewal of the deep water of the world's oceans on the continental slope off East Greenland. Using newly available techniques including Kevlar cable for strength to hold the instruments in place in the strong currents, they found that the flows were remarkably constant and fully consistent with existing theories of how high-latitude heat flux from ocean to atmosphere is balanced by the flow of water from northern basins toward the south.

Gulf Stream studies. The Northwest Atlantic Regional Energetics Experiment (REX), carried out by the U.S. Naval Oceanographic and Atmospheric Research Laboratory, completed its work in 1990. The study involved satellite measurements by the U.S. Navy's Geosat, the application of numerical ocean models, and on-site observations. REX verified and expanded the historical notions of Gulf Stream energetics. A structure consisting of two large circular surface currents was observed, apparently due to the presence of the New England Seamount chain at the seafloor. The experiment demonstrated that the relatively simple vertical structure of ocean density in the northwestern Atlantic allows the use of satellite data to infer vertical profiles of density. On this basis, an operational forecast system was being developed to use these techniques for prediction of ocean conditions in the Gulf Stream region.

The Thomas G. Thompson, *a new research ship owned by the U.S. Office of Naval Research and operated by the University of Washington, was officially launched in July 1990. It was designed to have laboratory space of 390 square meters (4,200 square feet) and accommodations for 30 scientists.*

Indian Ocean studies. The cause of the seasonal reversal of the Somali Current, off the coast of Somalia, has been a subject of speculation for many years. Proposals have ranged from local forcing by the winds, which also reverse during the same period, to remote forcing by events taking place to the east in the Indian Ocean. The problem has been that the observed currents reverse direction before the local winds change. Scientists from the University of South Florida used improved modeling techniques to confirm the remote forcing hypothesis. In the model, disturbances are generated in the interior of the Indian Ocean by winds and then propagate along the equator to the coast, causing the flow to reverse in November and December prior to the onset of local northeasterly winds. The model results agree with observations.

Scientists at the Woods Hole Oceanographic Institution reported results from a set of measurements of temperature, salinity, oxygen, and other physical properties along latitude 32° S in the Indian Ocean. They found a complex pattern of deep flow that reflects an equally complex bottom topography in that region. A series of deep western boundary currents were inferred, each carrying water with characteristics of the North Atlantic Ocean into the Indian Ocean. The data are consistent with a net flow of water from the Pacific Ocean to the Indian Ocean. This net flow is superimposed on a circulation in which water moves from surface to bottom and then returns to surface; this overturning circulation is several times stronger than the flow. The flow pattern implies substantial upwelling of deep and bottom waters to the north. This upwelling of cold, nutrient-rich water could have important effects on both biology and climate.

Coastal studies. Scientists from the U.S. and Brazil announced the first results from a new multidisci-

plinary research program studying the processes occurring at the continental shelf at the mouth of the Amazon. Among the initial findings of the program were observations of large pulses of water and sediment on weekly time scales from the Amazon that could be tracked as far as 1,000 km into the ocean. In addition, iron and manganese cycling was found to be so extensive that it controls the chemistry of the seabed.

Ocean drilling. The international Ocean Drilling Program with the drilling ship *JOIDES Resolution* continued to work in the western Pacific in 1990. The ship was operated by Texas A&M University for the partnership of 19 countries that support the program. (JOIDES is the acronym for Joint Oceanographic Institutions for Deep Earth Sampling.) One of the principal questions addressed during the past year was the response of sedimentation to changes in global climate and ocean dynamics. Drilling on Leg 130, on the Ontong Java Plateau (longitude 160° E on the equator), was able to penetrate the entire sediment cover to basement basalt. The sediment record was used to determine the rate at which sediment is deposited and the temperature of the water back to more than 25 million years ago. Some of the highest rates of sedimentation ever recorded in open ocean sediments were observed at this site. The high rates appear to be correlated with major plate tectonic movements, including phases of mountain building that lead to an increased supply to the ocean of continent-derived materials. Low rates of sedimentation have been correlated with changes in the carbon isotope composition of the ocean, which is the result of an increased difference in productivity between the deep sea and coastal waters. Increased coastal productivity captures a greater share of nutrients for the ocean margins, with the result that sedimentation in the deep sea is decreased.

During Leg 133 drilling took place at the Great Barrier Reef off Australia. The cores that were recovered showed that the reef had responded to at least 24 cycles of global sea-level change during the past one million years. Large changes in sea level destroy the reef, and it appeared to have regenerated at least 20 times during that period. The data also revealed that the reef is only 500,000 to one million years old, considerably younger than the 20 million years previously estimated. This relatively tender age, on a geologic time scale, indicated that the area was not expected to contain exploitable reserves of oil, as some had hoped.

Research vessels. The U.S. oceanographic research vessel the *Maurice Ewing* began its first scientific voyage in July 1990 to explore mid-ocean ridges in the Greenland and Norwegian seas. The 73-m (240-ft) ship, converted with the support of Columbia University, New York City, and the U.S. National Science Foundation to scientific use from a Canadian geophysical exploration vessel, carried a full complement of advanced acoustic and seismic geophysical instrumentation and, in fact, was the first ship in the U.S. academic fleet equipped with a new-generation multibeam sonar system. The new system comprised 59 beams of sound that scan the ocean floor in two directions, determining texture as well as shape.

The new research vessel *Thomas G. Thompson,* owned by the U.S. Office of Naval Research and operated by the University of Washington with support from the National Science Foundation, was officially launched in July 1990. When fully operational, it would be the most modern and capable ship in the U.S. academic fleet. Laboratory space on the ship totaled 390 sq m (4,200 sq ft), and there were accommodations for as many as 30 scientists. The *Thompson* was also equipped with a new-generation multibeam sonar system.

Drilling into the seafloor to collect samples and place devices for long-term monitoring of the ocean had proved so effective that plans were announced by two groups to study the feasibility of building and operating additional scientific drilling ships. Japan's Science and Technology Agency began a feasibility study for an "Earth Observation Ship" that would be similar to the *JOIDES Resolution* and capable of drilling at least four kilometers into the seafloor. Led by a French initiative, the European Communities continued discussions on a research vessel named *Nereis* that would be equipped both for shallow drilling and for extended work with bottom-mounted instruments. Both these ships were expected to be in operation some time before the end of the century and to be available to the international scientific community.

—D. James Baker

Electronics and information sciences

Although the economic slowdown in much of the world during the past year reduced growth in the electronics and information sciences industries, engineers and scientists continued to develop new products and methods of operation. Among them were powerful scientific workstations, new dynamic random-access memory chips, and lightweight "personal-notebook" computers. The war in the Persian Gulf increased the need for military satellite systems.

Communications systems

During past decades engineers and businessmen working in the field of telecommunications were only slightly interested in what was being done by their counterparts in other countries. Telecommunications was very much a national business, with only occasional forays into the international arena. By 1991 this had changed. Countries were interested in the telecommunications of other nations and had come to realize that consistency in operations throughout the world had to be achieved. In other words, there had to be standards.

A second significant change concerned infrastructure. In the early days of the telephone industry, there was essentially one network—at least in the United States. It was called the public switched telephone network (PSTN), and it did everything. There were no synchronous optical networks, no integrated-services digital networks, no personal-communications networks, no intelligent networks. There was simply the PSTN. Every new feature that was suggested for telecommunications was suggested with the PSTN in mind; seldom did anyone think beyond that network. This, of course, also changed. Features and systems and, indeed, total networks that were quite separate from the PSTN were added.

In light of these two basic and profound changes, some of the developments of the past year are reviewed here. Some may be mere cosmetic changes or changes in style, while others may be more substantive.

Fiber optics. In the U.S. the long-distance communications network was well on its way to being converted to fiber optics. A great deal of copper was still in use and would continue to be for a long time, but virtually all new installation was fiber. The major reason for this was the immense capacity of fiber. A single fiber, for instance, was theoretically capable of carrying all the telephone traffic of the U.S. Fiber was also being deployed in submarine cable systems between the U.S. and Europe and to a lesser extent between the U.S. and East Asia.

That left, as a potential application for fiber, the local loop. This loop consisted of two parts: a feeder plant extending service from the local telephone central office to some point of demarcation near an office complex or group of homes; and a distribution plant extending the communications facilities from the demarcation point to the offices or homes.

The question arose as to why fiber should be used for local service. After all, if a fiber—theoretically capable of transmitting hundreds of thousands of conversations—was to be used for only a single conversation, or even two or three conversations, it might not be worth the effort to install it. A splice with copper wire could be accomplished in a matter of seconds, but splicing fiber was not that easy. However, the demand for greater capacity continued to grow. In addition, the demand for television had to be considered. In order to transmit TV signals to a home, either coaxial cable or fiber was needed. Thus, when television was taken into account, fiber had distinct advantages.

One additional question that arose in regard to the use of fiber involved the terminating point of the fiber. Should the fiber extend from the central office all the way to the home, thus requiring one fiber per home, or was there some way the fiber could be terminated short of the home, thus making it possible to share that fiber between several homes? In the U.S. a number of experiments were under way that terminated the fiber short of the home. They were described as "fiber to the curb" because the curb (or a box mounted thereon) was the ultimate destination of the fiber. One further question to be answered concerned the facilities that should be used between the curb and the individual homes. A copper pair was a possibility, but if television was to be carried, then coaxial cable was necessary.

The fiber-to-the-curb approach, although advantageous from the standpoint of providing a minimum number of fibers, presented problems of its own. For instance, how could electricity be provided to the electronic equipment used to convert from fiber to copper? Would the electricity be provided by the local power company? Would there be an electric meter at the terminating point? Or would the power come along a copper pair from the central office? Another possibility was that the electronic devices would be powered by lines extended from the homes, thereby causing subscribers themselves to provide the power. In such a case there would be a problem if one of those homes blew a fuse or tripped a circuit breaker. Backup batteries would have to be provided. There were many questions still to be answered, and a final answer was not likely for several years.

Mobile communications. Some of the most significant advances that had taken place in the field of telecommunications dealt with mobile communications. Cellular radio systems had gained increased popularity throughout much of the world, and the rate of growth of this technology continued to be rapid. The capability of the cellular networks, particularly their ability to locate a subscriber wherever he or she might be and the ability to hand off calls as the subscriber moved from one cell (geographical area) to another, was amazing.

The first cellular systems introduced were analog in nature; each of the communications channels was carried on a particular frequency, and the frequencies were modulated in accordance with the information being transmitted. This was not an acci-

"And, furthermore, if you think for one damn minute, I'm going to put up with your lousy shenanigans . . ."

dent; it was determined that more intelligence could be transmitted by use of this method for a particular expenditure in equipment than by any other method. Also, although the capacity of a particular system was not nearly as great with an analog as with a digital system, it was certainly great enough when the idea was first presented. It was pointed out then that cells could be split and frequencies reused so that capacity would not be a problem.

Soon, however, capacity did become a problem. The growth of mobile communications far exceeded expectations. Consequently, scientists and engineers began trying to find a better way of operating. A lengthy debate on this subject was recently concluded in the U.S. between the proponents of frequency-division multiple-access (FDMA) and time-division multiple-access (TDMA) systems. The TDMA systems, which were digital (the information being transmitted was represented in the form of coded binary digits), had the advantage of increased capacity. It was expected that a cell site using TDMA would be able to handle three or four times as many calls as one using FDMA.

During recent months a group of individuals and companies announced their support for yet a third scheme, a code-division multiple-access (CDMA) system. It employed a technology called spread spectrum that had its origin in military communications. This technology spread out all information over a wide band of frequencies and resulted in a low overall average system power output. Proponents believed that perhaps up to 10 times as many subscribers could be accommodated by a single cell site if CDMA rather than FDMA were used. If the mobile telephones of tomorrow were able to accommodate both analog and digital signals, they would be larger and heavier and more expensive, although few people were predicting just how much larger or heavier or more expensive.

The next generation of mobile systems was named the personal-communications network. In the PCN the cells would likely be smaller, the sets smaller and less expensive, and the requirements for hand-offs greater because of that diminished cell size. The exact role such a network would play had yet to be determined. Skeptics doubted that it would have any significant effect on the world of telecommunications. Proponents suggested that sometime after the turn of the century a person would be assigned a telephone number at birth and that the number would remain with the assignee for life—wherever he or she might live.

Regulation and corporate restructuring. Unquestionably, technology continued to play a most important role in the field of telecommunications, but regulations and changes in corporate organization and enterprises were also important. For instance,

telephone companies throughout the world were being restructured, and their corporate missions were being redefined. In many cases they were embarking on programs quite unrelated to basic telephone service (such as data transmission and voice processing). In several countries these telephone operations—previously an arm of the national government—were being sold to private corporations. Two examples were the telecommunications system of New Zealand—recently purchased by Ameritech and Bell Atlantic Corp. (two of the largest telephone companies in the U.S.)—and the telephone system of Mexico, which was to be sold to a consortium that included Southwestern Bell, another huge U.S. telephone company. Yet another structural change (this time internal to the U.S.) involved the planned merger of Contel Corp. into GTE Corp. The resultant company would be the largest local-exchange telephone firm in the U.S.

—Robert E. Stoffels

Computers and computer science

Early in 1990 IBM Corp., the largest and one of the most conservative computer companies, surprised the industry by announcing a line of scientific workstations that provided significantly more computational power than existing machines. Along with their workstations IBM announced several new technologies, including a larger random-access memory (RAM) chip and faster magnetic disk storage devices. The announcement spurred competition. Several companies followed IBM by reducing prices for their existing workstations or introducing new products of their own.

A scientific or engineering workstation is a computer that is intended for use by an individual scientist or engineer. The workstation is small and quiet enough to fit in a conventional office, yet it provides enough computational resources (processing power, memory, and disk storage) to solve complex scientific or engineering problems. In particular, a workstation includes hardware that performs floating-point computation efficiently, allowing its users to add, subtract, multiply, and divide fractional values.

The idea behind workstations is simple: an engineer or scientist who uses a workstation can choose how to use the computational resources, similar to the ways in which a user controls computational resources on a personal computer. For example, engineers can choose to dedicate their private workstation to the solution of a single problem for an entire day, or they can arrange to work on several problems concurrently. If they arrange to have the workstation solve several problems, the progress made on each problem will be slower. However, because a single user has complete control over the workstation, no other user can interfere with the specified computation.

Of course, a typical scientific workstation costs more than a personal computer, and so workstations can be justified only for users who have complex computational problems that need high speed. It is, however, often less expensive to purchase several scientific workstations than to purchase a high-speed mainframe computer with an equivalent capability.

Because scientific workstations do not include all facilities found in more powerful mainframe computers, they need access to such facilities. For this reason most workstations include hardware and software that allows them to access remote resources across a computer communication network. They use the network connection to access data or programs stored on a remote machine or to invoke computational services available on remote machines.

In addition to special hardware and software for scientific computation, most workstations include a flexible graphics display screen. Such a screen—known as a bit-mapped display—can show text, graphics such as line drawings, and images similar to the pictures that can be displayed on a television screen. Many bit-mapped displays provide color, allowing the user to employ color to highlight parts of a graphic image. An engineer can invoke software that plots data as curves, builds pie charts, or displays three-dimensional figures.

Scientists and engineers use workstations for a variety of tasks, including the solution of equations, other mathematical computations, graphic display of data, and visualization of natural processes. Because a workstation has powerful floating-point hardware and sophisticated software, designers can use it to create realistic scenes that include multiple light sources, shadows, and shading. For example, an engineer can use a workstation to create a color image of an object such as an airplane and then arrange to shade the image to show how it will appear in sunlight. An architect can create scenes that show the exterior or interior views of a building and its surroundings, complete with the shadows that the building will cast at various times of the day.

In addition to complex computations and displays, workstations can perform all the tasks normally accomplished by conventional computers. For example, a workstation can store data bases, operate spreadsheet applications, and run word-processing software that allows a user to prepare documents. From the user's point of view, the integration of all computation into a single workstation allows easy communication among various tasks. For example, it is possible to solve a set of equations and then include the resulting values in a research report without having to move the values to a different computer or type them into the document manually.

The RISC System/6000 series model 530 workstation was introduced by IBM in 1990. Operating at very high speeds, these workstations were able to solve certain problems faster than supercomputers could.

IBM workstations. The new workstations announced by IBM in 1990, known as the RISC System/6000 series (abbreviated RS/6000), provided impressive computational capabilities. The least powerful of these machines, the model 320, provided approximately 27.5 million instructions per second (MIPS), more than twice the speed of most competitors' workstations. The new machine also had impressive floating-point speed; it could compute 8.2 million floating-point operations per second (MFLOPS).

The announcement included several RS/6000 models. The most powerful of the workstations operated at 41 MIPS and had a floating-point capability of approximately 13 MFLOPS. In describing the announcement, industry publications used phrases such as "stunning performance" and "blazing speed." Indeed, its speed of 41 MIPS made the new high-end machine competitive with mainframe computers that cost more than $1 million, and its floating-point speed placed the workstation among supercomputers that cost several million dollars. The speed with which the new machines could access data on disk was equally impressive. In many instances the disk access rate was twice that of competitors' models. Perhaps the most significant aspect of the IBM announcement was price; even though the new workstations performed many times faster than competitors' models, their cost was approximately the same. The least expensive model cost approximately $13,000 and provided a significant improvement in performance per dollar over its nearest competitor.

The performance of the new IBM workstations arose from the technology used in the central processing unit as well as the design used for the input/output (I/O) subsystem. The central processor used a reduced instruction set computer (RISC) chip that operated at extremely high speeds (rates of 20, 25, or 30 MHz, depending on the model). The computer industry in general was shifting from complex instruction set computer (CISC) architectures to RISC architectures, which could operate at higher speeds because the instructions they contained were both few and simple. During the past year RISC designs became an industry standard for scientific workstations.

Processor speed alone is not enough to guarantee a high-performance computer system. The speed at which the system handles input and output (for example, the speed at which it stores data on disk) must match the speed at which the processor computes. IBM achieves high-speed input and output by using its microchannel architecture. The microchannel provides a path between the main memory and peripheral devices through which data can be transferred automatically, leaving the central processing unit free to continue computation while the input and output proceed.

IBM's RS/6000 workstations used the AIX operating system. An operating system comprises the software that controls the computer, manages input and output devices, allocates memory, switches the processor rapidly among all the tasks currently being executed, and provides a command interface for the user. AIX is IBM's version of the UNIX® time-sharing system, a standard throughout the workstation industry. Because they use UNIX, the RS/6000 workstations can interoperate with other vendors' machines. They can share files and command scripts, and users can transport programs between other workstations and the RS/6000 easily.

The IBM workstations also provided support for the X window system, another industry standard. The X window software allows a workstation to have multiple rectangular areas, called windows, on its bit-mapped screen. Each window corresponds to a single computational activity, and the window system allows a user to move from one activity to another quickly and easily. For example, a user can have one window that contains a document-processing activity, while another window contains a spreadsheet. If the need arises to update the spreadsheet while the user is editing the document, the user can suspend work in the document window, move to the spreadsheet window temporarily, and then move back to the document window.

The X window software provides much more flexibility than conventional window systems because it allows each window to connect to an arbitrary computer across a network. For example, if only one computer on the network contains spreadsheet software, a user on a workstation can access the spreadsheet by establishing a window that connects to it. From the user's point of view, windows that display remote computations do not appear or behave differently from windows that contain computations running on the local workstation.

Random-access memory chips. To take advantage of high-speed processors, computer systems must be designed with larger RAM. (RAM, in contrast to read-only memory, permits the recording of new information over previously stored data.) The need for large memories arises because a small memory can prevent a processor (which must wait for data to move into memory) from performing at full speed. Large memories allow processors to operate at full speed because they do not need to wait as often.

Memory building uses dynamic random-access memory (DRAM) chips. While it is possible to build arbitrarily large memories from any size DRAM chip, the size of an individual chip determines how many chips will be needed to form a given memory size. The use of many chips requires large physical dimensions and results in increased heat, necessitating the use of larger, nosier cooling fans.

When IBM announced its new RISC processor chip, the firm also introduced a new DRAM chip that had four megabits of memory on one chip. Previous DRAM chips used throughout the industry contained one megabit per chip, and so the new IBM DRAMs provided a fourfold decrease in the number of chips needed for a workstation memory. Because they needed fewer memory chips, the new IBM machines could accommodate much larger memories in approximately the same physical space as other workstations. For example, while early workstations provided only enough space for one to four megabytes of memory, the largest RS/6000 could accommodate 256 megabytes of memory, more than enough to keep the processor running at full speed. (One byte equals eight bits.)

Other new workstations. The IBM workstation announcement sparked a series of responses by other manufacturers. Most chose to compete by lowering prices on their existing products. Those with new workstation products that were nearly completed announced them quickly; others increased their engineering and development efforts.

Digital Equipment Corp. announced a series of workstations using the name DECstation 5000. Like the IBM announcement, the Digital announcement included several models that covered a wide range of cost and performance. In general, while the new

Digital workstations performed slightly slower than their IBM counterparts, they were significantly faster than the DECstation 3000 series announced in 1989. Digital assured customers that existing software would continue to work on the new models.

Like the IBM machines, the Digital workstations used a RISC processor chip. However, Digital did not design nor did it manufacture the chips. Instead, the firm obtained the chips from MIPS Computer Systems, Inc. Known as the MIPS R3000, the processor chip operated at a speed of 25 MHz.

Other vendors also responded to the IBM announcement by producing higher-speed workstations. Sun Microsystems, Inc., and Hewlett-Packard Co. both made significant improvements in their UNIX-based scientific workstations. Sun Microsystems, once the unquestioned leader in the workstation market and among the first workstation vendors to start using RISC technology, scrambled to catch up after the IBM announcement. The company immediately increased the processor rate on its Sparcstation line of workstations and eventually announced the Sparcstation 2 series. While neither the Sparcstation 1 nor the Sparcstation 2 performed at the same speed as the IBM machines, Sun attempted to retain the loyalty of its former customers by emphasizing its past experience with UNIX workstations as well as the fact that a large set of third-party vendors developed and sold software that operated on the Sun machines.

Labeled the HP 9000, the series of computers introduced by Hewlett-Packard included three models available in both a conventional form and a workstation. The company claimed that the slowest model, the 842S, would operate at nearly 30 MIPS, while the fastest model, the 865S, would operate at more than 50 MIPS. The new machines tripled the speed of existing Hewlett-Packard computers.

Like the high-speed workstations from most other vendors, processors in the new Hewlett-Packard machines employed RISC technology. The firm named its processor design PA-RISC and claimed that the new processors would exhibit the fastest performance of any commercially available computer that ran the UNIX operating system.

In comparison with the workstations announced by IBM, Digital, and Sun Microsystems, the HP computers were expensive. The least expensive cost approximately $80,000, while a high-end system cost more than $140,000. In its announcement Hewlett-Packard emphasized that several vendors would develop and sell software for the new machines.

Unlike vendors that targeted their computers for use as workstations, Hewlett-Packard suggested using its new computers as general-purpose servers. Because they were expensive, the new machines were not practical for individual users. Instead, a site

could purchase one or more of the new high-speed machines and share it among all users. To do so, the site would place the machine on a network and allow other workstations to access it as needed. To help make such access easy, Hewlett-Packard developed a software system called NewWave Access. In addition, HP developed new, large disks that allowed a server to store files for several users.

Future systems. Almost every vendor announced dramatic changes in workstation hardware during the past year. As a result of the higher speeds and increased memory sizes, it was possible to build sophisticated new software systems that would have been impossible only a few years earlier. Thus, industry leaders expected that new software systems using the new machines would be available in the next few years.

—Douglas E. Comer

Electronics

The centrality of technology in general and the electronics industry in particular is manifested by its interdependence with economic, military, and political developments. If the economy slows down, as it did during much of 1990, orders for electronic equipment, for chips, for home entertainment, and for computers all decline.

The political events in Eastern Europe at the end of 1989 and the beginning of 1990 gave rise in the U.S. to speculations about a peace dividend and concomitant reduction in military spending. Indeed, a serious debate began in Congress about the numbers of military dollars that could be saved and put into social programs. However, the invasion of Kuwait by Iraq and the subsequent military buildup of U.S. forces in the Persian Gulf caused Congress to authorize the Grumman Corp. to extend production of its F-14D Tomcat fighter, an aircraft with an abundance of electronics. Thus, it is clear that one must always be aware that the electronics industry is part of a complex worldwide industrial-political-military matrix.

Overview of industry. The future of the industry in the coming year was difficult to predict. While many experts were forecasting a growth of the industry during 1991, no one was predicting the rate of that growth. The recession that occurred during the last quarter of 1990 combined with an already slowing economy and the uncertain effects of the Persian Gulf war to make forecasting a hazardous undertaking.

The uncertain forecast came at the end of a year of modest growth in the industry. Specifically, the U.S. electronics industry experienced a 3.5% growth rate, while that of Japan for the same period was 6.2%. Projected growth rates for the coming year were also modest, and the sporadic growth of some sectors of the industry added to the uncertainty of prediction. For example, computers and consumer electronics grew at healthy rates during the past year, while in other areas of the industry there was little or no growth. An example of the uncertainty for the coming year was the fact that predictions for semiconductor growth ranged from 3 to 15%.

The tentative consensus that seemed to be emerging was that the industry would grow worldwide by 9.5% during 1991 to a level of $635 billion. Computers were expected to increase 12.4% to the $200 billion level, resulting mostly from growth in the sales of workstations. Communications equipment was expected to increase 12–15% to $76 billion, with the greatest growth in Eastern Europe. Consumer electronics were predicted to show only a modest growth rate worldwide; even the brisk sales of camcorders were not expected to boost the growth rate in that sector beyond a 4% rise to $64 billion.

The weakest sector in the industry appeared to be capital equipment. This sector consists of high-cost items such as engineering tools and machines used in the production of semiconductors, test gear, and design-automation tools. Such high-priced items always suffer during a time of recession because investments in those areas decline. The projected growth rate was flat, maintaining that sector of the industry at $20 billion.

In regard to specific countries, the major bright spot in the U.S. was an increase in electronics exports during 1990. Japan had a lackluster year, with corporate profits down 5%. Germany expected a sharp rise in its electronics industry subsequent to and because of its reunification. In particular, its telecommunications and data-processing sectors were expected to grow by 20 and 12%, respectively. The growth rate for the electronics industry in France was expected to be 5%, down from 8% in 1990. Italy, which was 80% dependent on foreign oil, had a more modest anticipated growth rate of 4%. In the U.K. the electronics industry—except for telecommunications equipment—suffered a depression occasioned by a combination of 10% inflation and new personal taxes. The future looked slightly better, with an anticipated growth rate of 2.3% to $45.3 billion.

A huge market potential for personal computers (PCs), measuring in the millions, appeared to exist in the Soviet Union. However, the high price of PCs combined with a lack of money on the part of potential buyers made it impossible to tap that market, at least in the near future.

Semiconductors. In 1983 the U.S. produced 69%, Japan 25%, and the rest of the world 6% of all semiconductors. By 1988 these figures had changed to 51% for the U.S., 40% for Japan, and 9% for the rest of the world. It was projected that by 1993 the figures would read 32% for the U.S., 55% for Japan, and 13% for the rest of the world. In a ranking of semiconductor manufacturers throughout the world during 1989, Nippon Electric of Japan occupied the top position, followed by two more Japanese companies—Toshiba Corp. and Hitachi Ltd. Motorola Inc. ranked fourth, and Texas Instruments Inc. occupied the number six slot. The Intel Corp. was 8th, National Semiconductor 11th, and AT&T 20th. Thus, of the top 20 semiconductor manufacturers in the world, only 5 were American. Twelve of the firms were Japanese.

One problem for the U.S. semiconductor industry was the cost of capital, which prevented U.S. companies from making the needed research and development (R&D) investments. The National Advisory Committee on Semiconductors recommended $1.2 billion for R&D over the next three years, an additional $100 million for Sematech (the manufacturing research consortium), a 50% investment tax credit on purchases of new equipment in the first year after the equipment was introduced, permanent R&D tax credits based on annual R&D expenditures, and a revision of antitrust laws to encourage joint manufacturing ventures.

A somewhat surprising development that took place during the year should help the U.S. semiconductor industry. For the first time ever, the German Ministry of Research and Technology approved a multimillion-dollar contract earmarked as development money to the ITT Semiconductors Group in order to develop key components for Europe's future high-definition television system.

Supercomputers. The U.S. and Japan had both controlled the market for supercomputers and their exports across their national boundaries since 1984. These computers were exported under the strictest controls to some nations, while sales to Eastern Europe, the U.S.S.R., and Israel were prohibited. Exports of these superfast machines were restricted because they can be used in the construction of nuclear weapons. (Sales to Israel were prohibited because that country had not signed the nuclear nonproliferation treaty.) However, the manufacture of both the needed hardware and software for the building and the operation of supercomputers was becoming more widespread, making control of their proliferation more difficult.

Among the most popular chips for the construction of supercomputers was Intel's i860. Its first version was capable of performing 66 million mathematical operations per second. The next generation of the i860 was expected to be capable of performing 100 million such operations per second. By definition, any machine capable of performing that rate of computation is a supercomputer.

The monopoly of this superfast chip was being challenged by a British manufacturer, which planned to produce a chip that ultimately would be capable of 100 million operations per second. In addition, Meiko Scientific Ltd. of England in conjunction with Intel produced a supercomputer that ran these chips parallel and thus could process four billion mathematical operations per second.

The recent spread of supercomputers was not confined to the Western world. Bulgaria produced a supercomputer with a peak speed of 576 million mathematical operations per second; the Soviet Union had a supercomputer in operation capable of one billion mathematical operations per second; and India manufactured a computer with a capacity of 100 million mathematical operations per second.

Personal notebook computers. Both NEC Corp. and Tandy Corp. brought out new notebook computers during the year. The Tandy machine, the 1500 HD, weighed 2.7 kg (6 lb) and was the first to have a 20-megabyte hard drive and a 1.44-megabyte floppy disk for less than $2,000. It was expected to compete directly with Toshiba's T1000XE and the LTE of the Compaq Computer Corp. The V-20 chip used in the computer was capable of handling most typical applications, such as word processing and simple spreadsheets.

NEC originally offered its Ultralite in 1988. While a powerful computer, it lacked a floppy-disk drive and had an inadequate battery system. These drawbacks were eliminated in the new Ultralite 286V. The 2.9-kg (6.5-lb) machine cost $3,999 and appeared in the market during September 1990. Its 80286 chip operated at 12 MHz and was as powerful as any other notebook computer on the market.

Automotive applications. VDO Adolf Schindling AG of Germany developed a "heads up" windshield display that showed the speed of a car and the distance traveled. This display appeared as a projected image 2 to 3 m (7 to 10 ft) in front of the windshield. Together with Volkswagen, VDO placed a prototype of the display into a Volkswagen. The electronic components fit into a small box that could be placed under the dashboard. The unit contained a liquid-crystal display unit with a light source, optical lenses, and deflection mirrors. The mirrors and the lenses projected an image to a green-sensitive reflector embedded in the windshield. The reflector was developed by both Volkswagen and VEGLA GmbH of Aachen, Germany. In addition to the displays of the car's speed and distance traveled, displays alerted the driver to check the car's oil, gas, or water and to have its brake linings adjusted and replaced if necessary.

The Sony Corp. brought a system to market that could determine the location of a car anywhere in the U.S. It combined both loran (a system of long-range navigation) and satellite communications. The car's location was obtained by referencing to various loran beacons. Once that information was obtained, it was transmitted through a roof-mounted antenna to the Geostar satellite, which relayed the data to a Geostar computer in Washington, D.C. From there the information traveled through telephone wires to its final location.

To help drivers stay awake, the Stay Alert Co. developed a lightweight, battery-operated device to be placed near the driver's left foot. The driver activated the device by pressing down firmly when he or she began to feel drowsy. If the pressure was relaxed,

The i860 microprocessor chip, introduced by Intel Corp. in 1990 and seen placed on a human hair, is capable of performing 66 million mathematical operations per second. The second generation of the chip was expected to perform 100 million such operations per second, a speed that defines a supercomputer.

Intel Corporation

The 1500 HD notebook computer, from the Tandy Corp., weighs 2.7 kilograms (6 pounds) and was the first computer of its kind to provide a 20-megabyte hard drive and a 1.44-megabyte floppy disk for less than $2,000.

an alarm would sound to help jar the driver into wakefulness. By pressing the device twice, the driver turned it off.

Consumer products. The products introduced during the past year demonstrated the almost boundless variety to which electronics can be put. For example, a device to be strapped to one's wrist indicated how many calories were burned up by exercising. It also showed distance traveled, the steps that the wearer took per minute, and the average and peak speeds of the wearer's walking or running. Incidentally, it also told time.

A person also could strap a device on the wrist that would reveal exposure to sunlight. Elexis Corp.'s Sundial watch featured an electronic monitor that warned its wearer when it was time to seek some shade. The user fed in information on his or her kind of skin and the protection factor of the suntan lotion used. The monitor then calculated the allowable exposure time. It sounded an alarm when the allotted time was up. It, too, functioned as an ordinary wristwatch.

Light-emitting diode displays measuring 3 × 3.3 × 8.9 cm (1.2 × 1.3 × 3.5 in) began appearing in portable computers and electronic "books." The displays provided an optical image equivalent to a 30-cm (12-in) monitor. It could be hand-held, mounted on a headset in the fashion of the optical lamps that surgeons used, or clipped onto a pair of eyeglasses. It could be driven by a battery. Among the various applications of this relatively simple yet versatile device were a hands-free portable industrial workstation, a monitor that enabled an anesthesiologist to observe vital data while watching a patient, and a paperless pocket facsimile machine.

Often when a CD (compact disc) player did not function properly, the reason was that the lens through which the laser beam must pass was contaminated by dust, dirt, or smoke. To clean that lens, AudioSource marketed what amounts to a programmable dust broom. The device consisted of a digitally encoded compact disc with a built-in brush. When the disc was inserted into the CD player, it issued instructions to the player to align the brush with the laser's lens, at which time the cleaning proceeded. Cleaning stopped when a self-test pronounced the lens to be clean.

The Seiko Corp. produced what it called a "Voice Station Talking Translator," which stored more than 300 useful phrases in read-only memory in the form of a digitized voice. A user would look up the phrase that he or she wanted to have translated from a phrase guide; its code number was then entered into the translator, and the user listened to the correct pronunciation through a single earpiece. The user could then reproduce his or her own pronunciation and have it played back for comparison.

—Franz Monssen

Information systems and services

New information technologies obliged the U.S. government during the past year to review its information-dissemination policies, procedures, and obligations in order to make information available to the public in a useful way. While the Freedom of Information Act was central to federal dissemination policies, more recently the Office of Management and Budget (OMB), acting under the authority of the Paperwork Reduction Act, had become the major information policymaker of the federal government.

In an effort to provide congressional guidance to the OMB, Rep. Robert Wise (Dem., W.Va.) suggested that an effective, efficient, and equitable information dissemination policy should: (1) recognize that the flow of information from the federal government to citizens is essential to the proper operation of the United States as a democratic society; (2) require that electronic data bases maintained by agencies be available to the public in useful electronic formats with adequate software, indexes, and other tools; (3) prohibit the maintenance of monopoly control over public information; (4) supplement and not replace the information-disclosure requirements of the Freedom of Information Act; (5) require agencies to use marginal cost pricing and to provide for fee waivers for public interest disclosures; and (6) require agencies to make public information products, including products in electronic formats, available to depository libraries. In addition, Representative Wise suggested that oversight and enforcement procedures be developed and that an advisory committee on information policy be established.

The U.S. National Aeronautics and Space Administration (NASA) requested an exemption from the provisions of the Freedom of Information Act, similar to the one that the U.S. Department of Defense received a few years earlier, that would allow it to protect information that was subject to export controls and to federally funded research. The exemption was requested for priority areas directly linked to national security and included advanced computer technology applications, engineering, biotechnology, and the applications of lasers in manufacturing. The goal was to ensure that inventions made at research facilities

financed by tax dollars remained the property of the U.S. and that U.S. industry had the initial opportunity to exploit government-sponsored research and development. The withholding authority would provide a mechanism for controlling unwanted transfer of information to potential foreign competitors and adversaries while increasing the value of technology as a commodity in international exchanges. As of early 1991 the Department of Defense was the only government agency that had this authority.

Museums use computers and information technology to entice, educate, and entertain visitors. At the Smithsonian Institution's National Air & Space Museum in Washington, D.C., a computer-controlled robot of the type used in aircraft-manufacturing plants was programmed to make paper airplanes and send them out over the crowds who visited the museum. The Center of Science and Industry in Columbus, Ohio, devised a multimedia blend of video, sound, graphics, and automation to help visitors learn about science and mathematics. At the Roger Williams Park Museum of Natural History in Providence, R.I., life-size exhibits of wildlife specimens set in natural-looking landscapes were automated to allow visitors to interact with the exhibit in such ways that they could request to see, for example, birds in flight, animals gathering food, horseshoe crabs molting, and similar activities. At the Franklin Institute Science Museum and Planetarium in Philadelphia, each visitor was given upon entering a card with a bar code number that could be used to operate a computer workstation and request more information about an exhibit. The workstation, equipped with a touch screen, delivered information

A workstation at the Franklin Institute Science Museum and Planetarium in Philadelphia is one of 42 terminals that can be used by museum visitors to request additional information about exhibits and other aspects of the museum. Six minicomputers and five local area networks are also part of the museum's information system.

at adult, child, or preschool levels in accordance with the screen level selected.

U.S. information systems. The information technology industry in the U.S. grew in revenue during the past decade at an average rate of 9.4%, while the overall economy had an average growth rate of 7.5% per year. The number of data bases also increased and, according to Cuadra/Elsevier, publishers of the *Directory of Online Databases,* there were by 1991 more than 5,000 on-line and CD-ROM (compact disc-read only memory) data bases covering every kind of subject matter imaginable. These data bases were developed by about 2,000 different producers and were offered through more than 600 on-line hosts or gateway services. They were searched by physicians, lawyers, engineers, businesspeople, teachers, students, and anyone else with access to a computer who needed information while seeking solutions to problems.

Health Reference Center prepared a CD-ROM data base of information about health, medical treatments, fitness, and nutrition designed for use by consumers in libraries, hospitals, and patient-education centers. The information was collected from more than 3,000 medical and general-interest publications and was updated monthly. The patient-access module contained background information on illnesses, including their cause, treatment, and prevention, as well as questions to ask a physician. The reference module consisted of either the full text of technical articles or their summaries and excerpts from medical and drug reference books and encyclopedias. The data base was designed to enable virtually anyone to locate, display, and print information relevant to any health-related topic simply by going to a CD-ROM terminal and typing in the desired subject.

The U.S. Department of Health and Human Services built a nationwide data base consisting of physicians and dentists with records of malpractice. This National Practitioner Data Bank was designed to improve the ability of the medical community to police itself and to reduce the likelihood that problem practitioners could avoid detection by moving from one state to another. To ensure confidentiality and security, access to the data base was limited to authorized organizations involved in medical licensing and clinical practice. Physicians and dentists listed in the data base received copies of the reports about themselves and had the opportunity to dispute the accuracy of the report. It was estimated that the data base could receive about 50,000 reports of malpractice per year and that the program could respond to about one million queries per year.

Executive Briefing Service from Western Union Corp. provided a customized gathering of strategic business intelligence from a variety of industrial and financial sources, including trade journals and government reports. Subscribers indicated selected topics of interest, and these sources were regularly searched by computer for relevant information. English-language translations were provided for material that originally appeared in other languages. The week's new information was delivered to the subscriber's facsimile machine or electronic mailbox each Monday morning.

The genome data base at Johns Hopkins University, Baltimore, Md., continued its support of the international effort to map and sequence the human genome by collecting, organizing, and disseminating basic genetic information generated by scientists throughout the world. The data base also contained medical information needed for genetic disease diagnosis and patient care.

International information systems. The 324 million citizens of the European Communities (EC) needed adequate information services to help them communicate and do business together. With nine languages and a variety of information systems, this was not always easy. ECHO, the European Commission Host Organization, created and presented a number of innovative data bases that provided basic information about EC services in all the national languages of the member countries. Users could formulate their requests by simply typing such questions as: Where can I get information on agriculture in Italy? Where do I find out about business opportunities in France? Their questions were interpreted by a natural language computer program and answered by information retrieved from the computer's data base.

Privacy concerns required special protection from abuses that could have resulted from the interlinking and transfer possibilities inherent in computer-based telecommunications systems for a single European market. Recognizing this fact, the Commission of the EC adopted strict conditions for the protection of personal data and information security in both public and private sectors. Individuals were guaranteed the right of access to information concerning themselves and the right to rectify or erase erroneous information. Special protection was provided for sensitive data such as racial origin, religious beliefs, political opinions, trade union membership, health, and sexual behavior. The key issue was the provision of effective and practical security for information held in electronic form for government administrators and the business community without the compromising of the information interests of the public at large.

The Arab Information Network for Terminology, with headquarters in Tunisia, was established to promote a unified Arab terminology for use in the transfer of science and technology as well as cultural and economic activities. Its members consisted of Arab governmental and nongovernmental bodies.

The Soviet Union's Institute of Scientific Information in the Social Sciences (INION) was made responsible for creating and maintaining a data base of abstracts and indexes to articles in social science and humanities journals published in the U.S.S.R. and other socialist countries. Because of the demand in the U.S.S.R. for information on Western European and North American political, social, and economic activities, INION agreed to exchange data with the Research Libraries Group (RLG) in Mountain View, Calif., and the RLG became the repository of INION records in the U.S.

Information science research. The National Endowment for the Humanities awarded funds to the RLG to select and preserve brittle or badly deteriorated material from various library collections that are important for research studies in U.S. history. These documents would be filmed and distributed by the Archives Preservation Microfilming Project over a three-year period.

IBM Corp. gave a multimillion-dollar grant in equipment and programs to Case Western Reserve University, Cleveland, Ohio, to develop a prototype computer-based library information delivery service that would give faculty and students immediate access to written, visual, and audio information at their individual workstations. Initially, the new service would include the university's collection of musical scores and recordings; the medical reference library, containing anatomic drawings, photographs and graphs; and the histological reference library with its collection of biological tissue slides.

The Digital Equipment Corp. provided grants to the University of California and to Pennsylvania State University to support the joining of their on-line bibliographic library catalog systems. The libraries at the two universities served 54 campuses as well as the general public. Using the familiar commands of their own system, faculty, staff, students, and other authorized users would be able to search the holdings of both university libraries, and they would be able to borrow books from each other through standard interlibrary loan procedures.

The National Academy of Science's Committee on National Statistics received a grant to study methods of improving statistical techniques used for analysis in many fields of science. The study was also aimed at upgrading the quality of statistical information on which important basic research and public policy decisions are made.

—Harold Borko

Satellite systems

Earth satellites are grouped into three general classes: communications, Earth observation, and navigation. They are developed, launched, and operated by indi-

Ariane rocket is launched from the space center at Kourou, French Guiana, in August 1990. It placed two telecommunications satellites into orbit.

vidual nations, groups of nations, and private industrial concerns.

The past year was marked by major developments in satellite systems. Expansion of consortia of national, international, and industrial organizations increased services to meet competition. Of particular note was the major increase in the use of military satellite systems after the Aug. 2, 1990, invasion of Kuwait by Iraq. Following the Jan. 15, 1991, deadline whereby the use of force was approved by the United Nations coalition, these systems became vital in the conduct of military operations in the Persian Gulf. The U.S. Air Force stated that information from military intelligence satellites (photo reconnaissance, all-weather radar, missile warning, etc.) was relayed to a central collection point in the United States. Tactical commanders in the field were equipped with small, transportable terminals with access to multiple intelligence sources. This capability allowed commanders to select specific information regarding enemy airlift, air defense, troop movements, etc. In each of the sections below, both civil and military satellite systems are discussed.

Communications satellites. This largest class of satellites continued to grow in size, complexity, and performance. Larger, more powerful transmitters, as well as new experimental systems, were put into orbit by the U.S., Europe, and Japan. The trend toward deregulation of monopolistic government controls was evident, sparking investment and competition by private industry.

Among the developments in communications-satellite technology was the increasing use of very small-aperture terminals (VSATs). The increased power of signals transmitted from orbit allowed the use of smaller receiver antennas. VSAT antennas were about 1.2 m (4 ft) in diameter, compared with diameters of 3–9 m (10–30 ft) typically required for business use. Direct-broadcasting service of commercial television to VSATs for household reception was in use in Europe and Japan. The U.S. National Aeronautics and Space Administration (NASA) began developing ultrasmall-aperture terminals (USATs) at the Jet Propulsion Laboratory, Pasadena, Calif. The first USATs were expected to be about 40 cm (15.7 in) in diameter. According to communications-satellite pioneer Harold A. Rosen, 30,000 VSATs had been installed in the U.S. by 1991. He estimated that several hundred thousand such terminals would be in operation by the end of this decade.

Recent studies identified some 45,000 "passive" (receive-only) VSATs installed worldwide. More complex, "interactive" VSATs sent and received satellite transmissions. Such two-way communications offered industrial firms many opportunities to establish networks for data, voice, and video communications. By 1991 about 35,000 interactive terminals had been installed worldwide.

Although U.S. commercial (as opposed to NASA or military) space launch vehicles had begun operations (Martin Marietta Corp. Titan, General Dynamics Atlas-Centaur, and McDonnell Douglas Corp. Delta II), Arianespace, the 10-year-old French cooperative, held a clear lead in this market by early 1991. In spite of the explosion of Ariane IV on Feb. 22, 1990 (destroying the Japanese Superbird-B telecommunications and BS-2X direct-broadcast satellites), Arianespace's next five launches of telecommunications satellites—extending from July 24, 1990, to Jan. 15, 1991—were successful. Placed in orbit two at a time were: TDS 2 (France), DSS 2 (Germany), Eutelsat II-F1 (European cooperative), Skynet 4 (British Ministry of Defense), SBS 6 and Galaxy 6 (Hughes Communications, U.S.), Satcom C-1 (General Electric American Communications), GStar 4 (GTE Spacenet), Italsat (Italian Space Agency), and Eutelsat II-F2. The total weight of these 10 payloads at launch was 18,148 kg (40,000 lb). Arianespace had contracts to launch 34 satellites during the next three years.

The commercial cooperative International Telecommunications Satellite Organization (Intelsat), composed of 119 member nations, continued to provide telephone, television, telex, facsimile, and digital data services to 170 countries. In 1990 Intelsat operated 15 satellites located in geostationary orbit over the equator. Such satellites, at an orbital altitude of 33,900 km (22,300 mi), traveled at the same angular velocity as the Earth and thus remained constantly over the same place on the Earth.

By 1991 Intelsat's full-time traffic was some 120,000 channels—roughly 700 for international and 600 for domestic service. Three of the new-design Intelsat 6 satellites were launched in 1990. These craft weighed 2,500 kg (5,630 lb) and could relay at least three television channels and 120,000 telephone calls simultaneously. Two of the satellites were successfully placed in geostationary orbit. A third failed because the second stage of the Titan III launch vehicle did not separate from the perigee kick motor and payload. This left the $157 million satellite in an unusable 550-km (340-mi) orbit.

NASA offered to rescue the stranded satellite by sending a manned space shuttle to rendezvous with it and then having the shuttle's crew replace the boost-rocket motor. The cost of such a rescue would be about $100 million. NASA had had previous experience in the repair and return of ailing or inoperative satellites in orbit. One of those "rescued" satellites was Westar 6, recovered by U.S. astronauts in 1984 and refurbished by Hughes Aircraft Co. for Asia Satellite Communications Co., Ltd. (Asia Sat). Renamed Asia Sat 1, the satellite was launched in April 1990 on a Chinese Long March III booster. It was scheduled to provide domestic telecommunications for China, Thailand, Pakistan, and other Asian countries. Two more Intelsat 6 satellites were scheduled for launch by Ariane IV vehicles, in June and October 1991.

A new-design Intelsat "K" vehicle was scheduled to be launched in early 1992. A high-power satellite, it was to be placed over the Atlantic Ocean by an Atlas II-A. Offering specific advantages to international broadcasters in the Atlantic Ocean region, it would provide 32 high-quality television channels that would be available for coverage of the Olympic Games from Barcelona, Spain, and Albertville, France.

The London-based International Maritime Satellite Organization (Inmarsat) was a cooperative charged with the operation of a global satellite system for mobile communications. Member nations in early 1991 totaled 63. In many ways 1990 was a year of major development for Inmarsat. Its satellite system, comprising nine spacecraft, was reconfigured from three to four operating zones, thus providing continuous global coverage, except for the extreme polar regions. The first Inmarsat 2 satellite, with six times the capacity of its predecessors, was launched, and three more were scheduled for launch during 1991. Inmarsat user terminals increased to more than 13,000, with about 10,000 on ships and other maritime applications. The remainder were land-transportable or mobile units. Of particular note was the introduction, in January 1991, of the Inmarsat C terminal. This suitcase-sized unit was able to directly receive and transmit voice and data communications via the nine Inmarsat satellites. Inmarsat C ground stations were operational in Australia and Denmark, and an additional 12 stations were scheduled to open during 1991. One limiting feature of the Inmarsat service was the requirement for international licensing of each mobile unit. A broadcast license had to be obtained in advance from the country in which operation was planned.

In October 1990 Communications Satellite Corp. (Comsat) and Inmarsat jointly initiated satellite communications to the cockpits of the new model Boeing 747-400 aircraft. United Airlines was operating three such aircraft on transpacific routes. Some 12 Gulfstream Aerospace Corp. aircraft were similarly equipped with receiving and transmitting terminals. Current use was for monitoring of onboard aircraft systems, weather data, and fuel consumption. In 1991 Comsat planned to initiate a high-speed data service that would allow airline passengers to make credit-card calls to any Earthbound telephone and to send and receive facsimile messages and data transfers via personal computer from planes flying transoceanic routes.

The use of satellite communications by school districts increased during the past year. An estimated 8,000 schools were using some form of educational material carried by satellites. Satellite-delivered instruction could reach students in remote and isolated areas. In addition, satellites could carry instruction in foreign languages to schools where there were no qualified teachers. A leader in satellite education programs was Oklahoma State University at Stillwater. It offered courses in the German and Russian languages, remedial reading, and advanced calculus. Lessons were broadcast to more than 500 schools via the Westar 4 satellite. The average subscription fee was $2,800 for a year-long class of 10 or more students.

By the end of 1990 the number of transmissions of news programs from the Middle East was establishing new records. Comsat reported more than 220 on a single day. All major networks leased transponders and established ground terminals in Saudi Arabia, Israel, and Jordan. For military operations in the Middle East, the requirement for continuous communications was paramount. Military-communications satellites in use by the U.S. Air Force and U.S. Army were mainly the U.S. Defense Satellite Communications System satellites in geostationary orbit around the Earth. Continuous communications from commanders overseas reported on the progress of operations and processed requests for supplies, personnel, and equipment. Headquarters provided directions and a continual flow of intelligence data. The U.K. Skynet 4 was a similar military-communications satellite supporting United Nations forces.

For its operational communications the U.S. Navy used four Fleet Satellite Communications (FltSatCom) satellites in geostationary orbit. Each of these satellites had 23 ultrahigh-frequency channels. A Navy spokesman stated that one FltSatCom serviced the entire Persian Gulf region.

Earth-observation satellites. This category of applications satellites comprises three general types: meteorological (weather), Earth resources, and military reconnaissance.

Weather satellites. Continuous global weather observations were obtained during the past year from U.S., European Space Agency, Soviet, and Japanese weather satellites in geostationary orbits. Supplementing this capability were the U.S., Soviet, and Chinese satellites in polar orbits. Thus, global coverage of weather patterns and movement was provided continuously.

The U.S. policy was to have two geostationary and two polar-orbiting weather satellites in operation at all times. However, at year's end just one Geostationary Operational Environmental Satellite (GOES 7) was operational, in addition to three National Oceanic and Atmospheric Administration (NOAA) satellites in polar orbit. The next GOES was scheduled for launch in June 1992. On September 3 China launched a second polar-orbiting weather satellite, Feng Yun 2. Images released showed excellent performance.

The U.S. Air Force operated the Defense Meteorological Satellite Program (DMSP). In December a DMSP satellite was launched to join two others in polar orbit. At an orbital altitude of 834 km (518 mi), Earth views were obtained continuously at the same times of day. Images of cloud cover and movement were vital to military commanders in the Middle East. Air operations and weather forecasts were obtained directly from data received by tactical commanders. Knowledge of changing weather conditions would be crucial in the event of chemical warfare, as would foreknowledge of sandstorms and other weather patterns.

Earth-resources satellites. In the U.S. the Earth Observation Satellite Co. (Eosat) continued to manage the Landsat satellite system under contract from NOAA. However, there was stiff competition from multispectral images offered from French and Soviet satellites. Eosat's customers were primarily the U.S. Agriculture, Commerce, and Defense departments.

Images transmitted by Landsats were used to estimate the size and health of crops, map vegetation, locate mineral and oil deposits, and monitor global climatic changes. The spectral images obtained from the Landsat 4 and 5 satellites were limited to a 30-m (100-ft) resolution of surface features. The French and Soviet satellite systems achieved resolutions that were three to five times higher. Furthermore, both countries were developing capabilities to market radar images that could view the Earth through cloud cover approaching optical quality.

Following the Iraqi invasion of Kuwait, the U.S. Defense Mapping Agency utilized both Landsat and French Spot images to update terrain analysis. New roads, buildings, and other features were obtainable through computer enhancement of multispectral imagery.

Military reconnaissance satellites. The prime purpose of this category of satellites is to provide intelligence on movements of troops, tanks, ships, submarines, and missile launch sites. Such satellites record optical and radar images of the Earth. In addition, electronic intelligence satellites monitor emissions of terrestrial and airborne communications and radar systems. Other varieties of reconnaissance satellites record nuclear explosions and detect missile launches by sensing the heat of rocket exhaust plumes.

In early 1991 intelligence analysts believed that at least four U.S. Keyhole-type reconnaissance satellites were operational in orbits that carried them over the Persian Gulf area several times daily. In addition, two imaging satellites (Magnum and Vortex) were in geostationary orbit above the region. Two other types of U.S. reconnaissance satellites, Lacrosse (radar imaging, unaffected by cloud cover) and White Cloud (monitoring ship movement), were operational.

Most Soviet photo reconnaissance consisted mainly of satellites that dropped recoverable film pods of images during two weeks of operation. Another type of Soviet reconnaissance spacecraft remained in orbit for as long as six to eight months, transmitting digital reconnaissance imagery. Considerable orbital altitude control of these Soviet satellites was demonstrated on October 25 when Cosmos 2,102 dropped to an extremely low altitude, 167 km (104 mi) over the Persian Gulf region. On November 2 the satellite was raised to a more normal orbit. After the invasion of Kuwait by Iraq, the Soviets launched more than a dozen military satellites, including four reconnaissance spacecraft.

On November 12 a U.S. Air Force Defense Support Program (DSP) satellite was launched into geostationary orbit. DSP satellites were originally designed to detect intercontinental ballistic missile launches from the U.S.S.R. Despite the relatively short flight duration of most battlefield missiles, Iraqi Scud missiles launched against Saudi Arabia and Israel were detected and tracked, and warnings were delivered to troops manning U.S. Patriot antimissile launchers and to populated targets. The warning time was short, typically 0.5 to 2 minutes. However, this was usually long enough to allow those in the target area to take cover and don gas masks. Data from the DSP satellites were transmitted to computers at Alice Springs, Australia, and U.S. Space Command's Missile Warning Center at Colorado Springs, Colo. Information about the courses and probable impact points of Scud missiles was collected and sent to troop commanders and civil defense personnel in Saudi Arabia and Israel in time for emergency warning alarms.

Navigation satellites. The Global Positioning System (GPS) of the U.S. Department of Defense made significant progress during 1990. Also known as Navstar, this revolutionary navigation system would eventually consist of a constellation of 21 satellites in circular orbit at an altitude of 6,835 km (4,190 mi). By early 1991, 16 satellites were in operation. Additional craft were scheduled to be put into orbit on a 60–90-day schedule by Delta II launch vehicles. GPS was estimated to be 10 times more accurate than the existing U.S. Navy Transit system. With four GPS satellites above the horizon, vertical and horizontal coordinates were provided with accuracies within 16 m (53 ft).

Allied forces in the Middle East relied on the GPS system for precise location information. Receivers were used by troops navigating in the featureless desert and within sealed tanks. The U.S. Army in early 1991 was using 5,000 hand-held GPS receivers, which were reported to be rugged, reliable, and easy to use.

Mazda Motor Corp. of Japan, in a joint venture with Mitsubishi Electric Corp., developed a navigational system using Global Positioning System receivers in conjunction with digitized maps. During the past year about 1,500 units were installed in luxury-line Mazda automobiles.

The Search and Rescue Satellite-Aided (Sarsat) program of U.S. and Soviet Union satellites continued to grow. Some 525,000 distress beacons were in use throughout the world. Both NOAA and the Soviet Nadezhda satellites were in operation to receive and relay emergency position data to ground stations in the U.S., the U.S.S.R., Brazil, Chile, India, Italy, Norway, and the U.K. From 1982 through June 1990 Sarsat provided assistance in the rescue of 1,664 persons in 616 aviation, terrestrial, and marine emergencies.

—F.C. Durant III

See also Feature Articles: PERSONAL COMPUTING IN THE INFORMATION AGE; HOW SUPERCOMPUTERS ARE TRANSFORMING SCIENCE.

Energy

Gulf war. As of early 1991 the war in the Persian Gulf had thrust the world into another of its periodic energy-related crises. It was too early to determine the long-term implications for energy of the rapid completion of the war. However, historical perspective can be provided, and the limits to change can be indicated.

Throughout the 20th century the world's most powerful nations have acted politically to influence world energy supplies. This has involved many different approaches. First, actions have been taken (or avoided) to influence the political structure of the Middle East. The present division of the area into countries was largely produced from the defeated Ottoman Empire by the victors in World War I. Associated with that structuring were decisions about intervention in the internal politics of these new countries. Involvement ranged from making the countries into colonies or protectorates to influencing independent rulers. During the next decades many changes occurred. All vestiges of colonialism vanished, and in many cases there were changes in leadership.

Oil wells burn out of control near Kuwait City in March 1991. Almost all of Kuwait's 1,000 wells were either destroyed or set on fire during the Persian Gulf war. It could take years to cap them all.

AP/Wide World

During this time governments from outside the Middle East tried to influence dealings between oil companies and the countries producing oil. In some cases, such as the U.S. effort to establish a "special relationship" with Saudi Arabia, the dealings were not directly tied to oil policies. At other times the involvement was more direct. Countries tried to influence negotiations and created government-owned oil companies to operate abroad.

A critical, still controversial element of this situation was the participation of the U.S. Department of State in 1971 negotiations between the oil companies and the leading Middle Eastern producers. The State Department supported demands by the producing countries to impose higher taxes on the oil companies. The wisdom of this action inspired considerable debate. Critics, starting with M.A. Adelman of the Massachusetts Institute of Technology, argued that this was an unwise intervention that produced avoidable concessions. The State Department replied that the changes were inevitable and that the department by its action had managed to limit their magnitude.

At the time of the negotiations, Middle Eastern crude oil prices were about $1 per barrel. During the era of controlled increases, a rise to $2 per barrel occurred. This was followed by the rise to approximately $10 in 1973–74. This run-up in prices indicates that the claim that the rises were moderated was true for only a very short time.

Thus, allowing the oil companies to act for themselves would not have been any less successful than was the State Department intervention. This was a prime example of the "narrow" commercial interests of business being more beneficial to oil consumers than the grand strategies of governments. The companies focused on maintaining satisfactory supplies of oil. The State Department was seeking to pursue many inconsistent goals and did not have to pay for the consequences.

A third, contradictory element in policy was the efforts to protect energy industries in the industrialized countries from import competition. These included U.S. policies to protect domestic oil, gas, and coal and the enduring efforts to preserve high-cost coal industries in Western Europe and Japan. By 1991 only The Netherlands had eliminated all coal production, though Belgium and Japan were heading in that direction. Britain was making substantial efforts to reduce its coal industry to a more economic size. By contrast, West Germany remained reluctant to depart from its long-term policy of very slow contraction.

These policies are prime illustrations of the drawbacks of political approaches to economic problems. Defective means were adopted to pursue questionable ends. Even today governments remain unclear about exactly what they expect to achieve in energy. Numerous, inconsistent goals must be reconciled. These include limiting the cost over time of energy to final consumers, meeting demands for environmental protection, responding to protectionist demands of domestic energy producers, and trying to maintain good relations with countries in the Middle East.

Keeping these goals straight is difficult enough. Reconciling them intelligently seems impossible. In particular, calls during crises for decreased dependence on imported oil at best are unsustainable expressions of momentary passions. The costs of reducing imports have proved excessive on reflection. Also, other concerns have arisen to produce indirect incentives to imports. Fears of excess profits inspired restraints on U.S. energy production. For example, U.S. Pres. Richard Nixon publicly favored energy independence but instituted oil price controls. Pres. Gerald Ford signed the bill that continued the controls, and Pres. Jimmy Carter supported more stringent controls over natural gas prices and taxation of domestic oil production. Ford and Carter tried to use complex government regulations on the consumption of energy to produce some reduction of energy consumption and, thus, of imports. Their efficacy was, however, questionable.

Another problem was that increasingly severe environmental restrictions were imposed on U.S. energy production and use. It could be argued that these restrictions were responses to problems more serious than the danger of imports. The validity of that contention has, however, been questioned. The justification for increasingly elaborate air pollution regulations is the subject of some controversy. Also, the severe restrictions on offshore oil and gas drilling discourage an activity with less environmental harm than the shipment of oil from abroad. Large tanker spills are more frequent than serious leaks of offshore oil.

The pursuit of economic goals through political influence has generally proved unworkable. The United States, for example, has concentrated on making oil generally available to all nations rather than especially to the U.S. alone. However, the governments of oil-producing countries generally must seek primarily to advance national interests. They strive to maximize their oil wealth. This, in turn, means selling to the highest bidders, whatever their political relationships.

Whether this is done in a competitive or a monopolistic arrangement is critical for the nature of the outcome. Though consumers would prefer the competitive outcome, government intervention, as prior experience suggests, is not suited to achieving this goal. The governments of consumer countries are, unfortunately, better able to assist monopolization than to foster competition.

Ideally, the U.S. and other Western countries should be moving toward the depoliticization of oil. Much progress was made in that direction during the 1980s. Much of the entanglement with foreign countries was removed. Government intervention in energy in the industrialized countries decreased. The weakening of the Organization of Petroleum Exporting Countries (OPEC) continued.

This trend stopped abruptly, however, with the August 1990 invasion of Kuwait by Iraq. The initial and subsequent actions of Iraq represented a major departure from the patterns that had previously prevailed. Iraq shared the recognition prevalent among oil producers that all policies, including aggression, depended on maintaining oil revenues. Such revenues could be reduced by instability or inability to mount an efficient development program, but they could not be lost.

The long-run implications of the Gulf war for oil and world stability are uncertain. An optimistic vision is that there will be no fundamental changes in either the level or the stability of oil prices. The pessimistic view is that the invasion could inaugurate an era in which wealth acquisition would no longer dominate oil-producing decisions. From an energy point of view, the interesting developments through early 1991 were the ease with which Iraqi and Kuwaiti supplies were replaced and the sharp fall in oil prices once the war started. Supplies from other sources increased substantially.

With the supply increases undertaken, the eventual return of Iraqi and Kuwaiti supplies is likely to set off extensive price declines that will keep oil prices below their early 1990 levels for at least several decades. Thus, another ultimate victim of the war may be the view proclaimed by many that oil prices inevitably would rise in the 1990s.

Policy developments. U.S. environmental restrictions on energy production and use were strengthened in 1990 with the passage of new amendments to the Clean Air Act. The act was passed after Pres. George Bush reversed Pres. Ronald Reagan's opposition to new measures. The massive act (more than 300 pages, compared with about 120 pages for the 1977 amendments) covered such matters as acid rain (sulfur dioxide and nitrogen oxide emissions from burning fossil fuels, particularly coal), auto emissions, and toxic and ozone-depleting chemicals.

Nuclear power remained beleaguered, particularly in the U.S. The last announcement of a new nuclear plant had been made in 1978. Every plant announced from 1974 to 1978 had been canceled, as had a majority of the plants announced from 1971 to 1973. By 1991 only a few of the ordered plants had not yet been completed. At most, these included six units—two in Texas and four ordered by the U.S. government's Tennessee Valley Authority

Energy

(TVA). While the Texas plants clearly would be finished, how many of the TVA units would be opened
remained unclear.

The U.S. remained far ahead of any other single
country in total nuclear generation, though Western
Europe as a whole had somewhat more capacity.
The largest European producer of nuclear power,
France, had by far the highest dependence of any
country on nuclear power for its electricity. U.S.
government forecasts indicated that most of the expansion in Europe would be in France and that the
greatest increase would be in Japan.

Energy consumption. With the appearance of many
new data bases on energy, opportunities arose to
examine more closely what fuels are used for what
purposes in different countries. The Organization for
Economic Cooperation and Development (OECD)
continued to supplement its long-standing reports
on energy use in its 24 members with annual reports
on 87 other countries.

The data for 1988 were combined to provide further indicators of energy patterns. Unlike the United
Nations reports, those from the OECD gave break-
downs of energy consumption by end use. The coverage was not complete, but no important countries

were missing. (The OECD reports together covered
107 countries; the UN reported on about 190. Calculations showed that the countries excluded by the
OECD accounted for less than 0.5% of the total
world use.)

Not surprisingly, large countries dominated energy use. This can be described in several different
ways. About 30 countries accounted for 90% of
world energy use (see Table). More than half of the
total occurred in the U.S., the U.S.S.R., and China.
The 54 countries consuming more than 10 million
metric tons of oil equivalent in 1988 accounted for
about 98% of the total.

Importance as an energy user, however, did not
seem to have a great influence on either the choice of
fuel mix or the importance of at least the three broad
categories of end use—industry, transportation, and
other. The large energy-consuming countries differed greatly from one another in the nature of their
energy use.

What did emerge from the data challenged at least
three often-encountered observations about energy.
First, whatever the reasons were that many leading
industrial countries relied on coal as the primary
fuel in their early development, this pattern was not
being widely imitated by the less developed nations.
Second, despite the frequent claims that their oil
is too valuable to use domestically, OPEC differed
radically in the extent to which member countries
use their gas. Third, heavy reliance on electrifica-
tion was more likely due to substantial hydroelectric
resources or commitment to nuclear power than to
modernization.

Predictably oil was the most heavily and widely
used fuel. Every country reported oil consumption;
this was not true for any other fuel, and about
38% of 1988 fuel use by the 107 countries was
oil. Equally predictably, nuclear was the least used
fuel—24 countries and 5% of the total.

The clearest grouping of countries comprised
those that exported more energy than they consumed
domestically. Typically, these nations relied almost
entirely on oil and gas for their domestic energy.
When oil and gas accounted for less than 90% of the
total, this was almost invariably associated with a 9%
or higher share for hydroelectric power. (Indonesia
was the sole exception; it had a coal share of 7%,
by far the highest coal share for this group, and a
5% hydroelectric share.) Norway was the most exceptional member of this energy-exporting group; it
obtained 58% of its energy from hydroelectric power,
giving it by far the lowest oil-gas share of the group.

All of the OPEC countries belonged to this group.
However, the nations with the largest ratios of exports
to domestic consumption were not OPEC members.
The highest three ratios in 1988 were by nonmem-
bers of OPEC—Brunei, the Congo, and Angola.

Leading Fuel-Consuming Countries, 1988
(Percent share of world consumption)

Country	Total	Coal	Oil	Gas
United States	24.6	20.8	26.8	26.1
U.S.S.R.	17.9	14.3	34.6	14.5
China	8.0	21.8	0.8	3.7
Japan	5.1	3.4	2.4	7.5
West Germany	3.5	3.4	2.8	3.8
Canada	3.2	1.3	3.2	2.6
France	2.7	0.9	1.5	2.8
United Kingdom	2.7	3.0	2.9	2.6
India	2.1	4.1	0.5	1.8
Italy	1.9	0.6	2.1	3.0
Poland	1.7	4.7	0.6	0.6
Brazil	1.6	0.5	0.2	2.0
Mexico	1.4	0.2	1.4	2.5
East Germany	1.2	3.1	0.5	0.6
South Africa	1.2	3.4	0.0	0.4
Spain	1.1	0.7	0.2	1.5
Australia	1.1	1.5	0.8	1.0
Romania	1.0	0.9	2.2	0.7
Czechoslovakia	1.0	2.1	0.5	0.5
South Korea	0.9	1.1	0.2	1.2
Saudi Arabia	0.8	0.0	1.5	1.4
Netherlands, The	0.8	0.4	1.9	0.8
Iran	0.8	0.0	1.0	1.5
Sweden	0.7	0.1	0.0	0.5
Turkey	0.6	0.6	0.1	0.7
Argentina	0.6	0.1	1.2	0.8
Yugoslavia	0.6	0.9	0.4	0.5
Venezuela	0.6	0.0	1.0	0.7
Belgium	0.6	0.4	0.5	0.6
Taiwan	0.5	0.5	0.1	0.7
North Korea	0.5	1.4	0.0	0.1
Indonesia	0.5	0.1	0.5	0.9
Bulgaria	0.5	0.7	0.3	0.4
Total	91.9	96.9	92.7	88.9

Many oil-exporting countries were not heavy gas users. In relative terms, Cameroon with exports five times consumption and no gas use was the most striking case. (Ecuador, with exports double consumption, was the only other country in the group with no reported gas use.) The exporting countries that obtained more energy from oil than from gas included Nigeria, Iraq, Saudi Arabia, Norway, Indonesia, Venezuela, Malaysia, Bolivia, and Iran.

The countries most heavily dependent on oil tended to be fuel poor. None of the 13 nations obtaining more than 90% of their energy from oil was a large-scale exporter. Heavy relative dependence on oil was primarily a sign of limited domestic capability to produce fuel and secondarily of heavy hydrocarbon supplies without an effort to develop the natural gas portion.

Heavy relative reliance on coal was most likely to occur in Communist countries. Six of the 10 countries getting the majority of their 1988 energy from coal had Communist governments. The others were South Africa, Zimbabwe, Hong Kong, and India. A characteristic more universal among these countries was that coal was their most heavily produced fuel. This was true for all but Hong Kong, which chose to rely on imported coal for electricity generation.

Only five countries had enough hydroelectric resources relative to energy consumption to secure the majority of their energy from water. Another seven had hydroelectric shares between 30 and 37%.

Use of nuclear power was confined to some of the largest energy consumers. All 24 of the users of nuclear power in 1988 were among the top 40 consumers of energy. China was by far the largest consumer of energy without nuclear power. It shared with several others the most prevalent characteristic of large consumers without nuclear power—significant domestic energy production. This characteristic applied to Poland, Mexico, Australia, Romania, Saudi Arabia, Iran, Venezuela, North Korea, Indonesia, and Norway. Others among the top 40 without nuclear power were Italy, Brazil, Turkey, Austria, and Egypt. In some of these nations the economics of nuclear power were undoubtedly unattractive. In others, particularly Italy and Austria, antinuclear sentiment had a major influence. For example, Austria decided not to commission a completed reactor. Italy had a modest nuclear program but stopped operating plants during 1987.

Another frequent observation is that energy is used in more processed forms as an economy advances. This observation combines the effects of two distinct developments—increased oil use and increased electricity use. Thus, six countries—Brunei, Paraguay, the United Arab Emirates, Zambia, South Africa, and Malta—lost more than half their energy in pro-

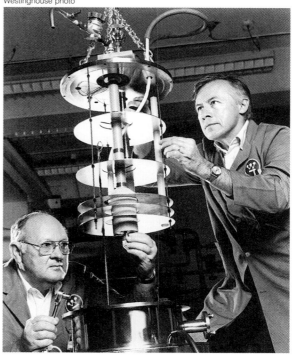

Technicians make connections for a test run of an electrical lead that was later used to set a world record for current (2,000 amperes) carried by a practical high-temperature superconductor.

cessing it. For Brunei and the Emirates this was caused by large losses in gas processing; for Paraguay and Zambia, the heavy importance of waterpower in energy supplies; for South Africa, its commitment to synthesizing oil and gas from coal; for Malta, the major role of fossil-generated electricity. By the nature of their use, hydroelectric and nuclear power involve inputs to electricity. Thus, countries with high hydroelectric or nuclear proportions have high proportions of their energy used to generate electricity. Eight countries—Paraguay, Zambia, Malta, Ghana, Iceland, Norway, Sweden, and Hong Kong—used the majority of their energy to generate electricity. Five—Paraguay, Zambia, Iceland, Norway, and Ghana—obtained the majority of their energy from hydroelectric power. Sweden got the majority from hydroelectric and nuclear power. Malta and Hong Kong were dependent on electricity generated by fossil fuels.

None of the 107 countries had a hydroelectric share in the 40% range; only seven were in the 30% range. The other countries that were heavily dependent on electricity relied mostly on fossil fuels.

Least surprisingly, a markedly above-average share of any sector in final energy use was likely to mean some deficiency in the economy. The 21 countries that had the majority of final energy use in transportation included such nations as the Congo, Lebanon, the United Arab Emirates, Thailand, Bolivia, and Brunei. The 15 countries with the majority of energy use in industry had some more interesting members, such as the U.S.S.R., Taiwan, South Africa, and Luxembourg, but others in that group included North Korea, Bahrain, Burma, Vietnam, China, Bangladesh, and India.

The share of different sectors in energy use shows surprisingly little relationship to the industrialization of a country. Of the ranking by the share of each of the three main categories of users, that by transportation has the clearest pattern. High users for transportation typically were smaller countries. Low transportation shares were usual for Communist and some small industrialized economies.

—Richard L. Gordon

Environment

Three themes permeated environmental news, writing, and research during the past year. First, an extraordinary level of uncertainty was appearing concerning basic facts and theories in a wide range of environmental issues. In many environmental controversies there was a highly visible, dominant position that was widely heralded by the popular media as representing a consensus view of scientists. Not only were such positions often opposed by large numbers of scientists, including some of the most distinguished authorities working in the area, but also, on closer inspection, the positions appeared to be more a product of factors other than carefully designed experiments or detailed analyses of data. Such dominant views often appeared to result from the application of an intradisciplinary, rather than an interdisciplinary, perspective to problems that required the latter. Further, more and more analysts were noting that dominant positions appeared to be influenced strongly by competitive pressures within bureaucracies and among scientists and by a desire to mobilize and galvanize the electorate and government. Thus, ideology that had no objective basis, along with the requirements of politics and the legislative process, was feeding back strongly into the actual content of environmental science.

"Sustainability" was a second theme that achieved new prominence during the year. It was often expressed in connection with energy resources, agriculture, and conservation biology, an emerging new subdiscipline. Third, a surprisingly large number of authors focused on the role of government in environmental affairs. In a variety of fields, analysts were arguing that government policies and legislation were not based on sound science, were not well thought out, and were highly wasteful of tax income.

Problems with basic information. A theme appearing throughout the environmental literature during the year was that the particular problem under discussion would worsen in the future because of human population growth, especially in Third World countries. Population in the industrialized nations was expected to grow very little or even decline slightly during the next three decades. Thus, the expectation of population growth in the world as a whole was actually an expectation of vigorous growth in Third World countries or in the Third World demographic groups within the industrialized nations.

In connection with this situation, some prominent ecologists pointed out that AIDS (acquired immune deficiency syndrome) could substantially slow the growth of Third World populations. Zimbabwe could be used to illustrate the contrast between two points of view on likely Third World population growth. The 1990 *Statistical Abstract of the United States* gives 10,480,000 as Zimbabwe's projected 1990 population and 13,770,000 as the projected total in the year 2000, representing a growth rate of 2.8% a year. However, the number of AIDS cases in Zimbabwe jumped from 119 in 1987 to 9,000 in September 1990. An unpublished analysis by Zimbabwe's Central Statistical Office estimated that the nation's future population eventually would be more than halved by the epidemic, from a potential 18 million in 2017 to only 8 million, its approximate 1982 number. According to eyewitness accounts in many Third World countries, the likely impact of AIDS would be the same as in Zimbabwe, and world population growth would be only a distant memory within three decades.

The key point in this discussion was that the way a problem appears is altered dramatically when one shifts from an intradisciplinary to an interdisciplinary perspective. In this case a demographic projection was strongly modified when epidemiology was included among the factors believed to be regulating birthrates and death rates.

Energy reserves were a second factor basic to the discussion of all other environmental issues. From acid rain to climate change, much of the projected effect of these phenomena depended on the global consumption rate of fossil fuels. The responses to the problem of increased consumption varied throughout the world. Vienna, for example, responded by making heroic efforts to entice commuters out of their cars. Construction of a fourth subway line was nearing completion, and peak rush-hour service on major lines was one train every three minutes; in addition, high-speed train service was increasing on many suburban lines. In the San Francisco Bay area, by contrast, high-speed rail service was much less frequent; the bulk of commuter transportation was by one person per car, and traffic congestion

342

was becoming perceptibly worse every six months for about 65 km (40 mi) in all directions from San Francisco. There was an astonishing difference between metropolitan Vienna and the San Francisco Bay region in the time required for commuting long distances to work. No new rail lines were under construction in the latter. There was a simple explanation for this continuing commitment to a remarkably energy-wasteful mode of transportation in the U.S. As James MacKenzie of the World Resources Institute pointed out, constant-dollar U.S. gasoline prices in 1990 were about the lowest they had been in 40 years. Life in Vienna would be disrupted far less should there be a sudden global energy-price increase.

Attempting to determine the truth about the global greenhouse warming issue was still difficult in 1990 and early 1991. Headlines on Jan. 10, 1991, announced that two studies ranked 1990 as the warmest year throughout the world since climate measurements began. This coincided with news that the most up-to-date estimates of the losses to the California fruit and vegetable farmers because of record cold weather in December would be at least $700 million. North Americans would be reminded of the unprecedented cold throughout the U.S. Southwest in December whenever they paid for fresh fruit and vegetables during the next year.

Several examples illustrated the difficulty of determining climate trends. On August 12 a science documentary, "The Greenhouse Conspiracy," was shown on British television. The *Financial Times* said of the program that producer Hilary Lawson had set out to test the four pillars on which the theory of global warming rests and showed that not one could be relied on. It was demonstrated that the popular perceptions were opposite to reality; for example, in Missouri the "greenhouse year" of 1988 was colder than the long-term average rather than 1.2° C (2.2° F) above average, as most people had come to believe. The program demonstrated that evidence that the Earth is warming was weak, that proof that carbon dioxide in the air was the primary cause of such warming was nonexistent, that the ability of computer climate models to project changes far in the future was nonexistent, and that the physics underlying such models and projections was still wide open to debate.

Two scientific papers illustrated the technical problems involved in assessing the degree of climate change through history. F.J.M. Rietmeijer showed that the ash from a volcanic eruption in Mexico persisted in the atmosphere for at least three years. This suggested the need to correct for this phenomenon when using satellites to measure global sea-surface temperatures since the ash-filled air would affect such measurements. There appeared to be a belief among some scientists that moving from a low-technology system of measurement to a high-technology system would decrease problems with bias. As this paper indicated, it might instead increase the possible sources of error. All other things being equal, it would appear to be cheaper and less vulnerable to error to make measurements of sea-surface temperature at the ocean surface rather than far up in space, where the radiation being measured has to pass though a deep column of air that may contain its own impurities.

Reports from various large networks of weather stations indicated that the world had become warmer in recent decades or in the last century. Many scientists, however, conducted careful analyses of the reliability of the estimated trends and concluded that, for various reasons, it was extremely difficult to detect any trend at all. To illustrate, in 1990 R.C. Balling and S.B. Idso conducted a careful investigation of five different measures of the trend in air temperature in Arizona during the past 50 years. One historical time series was from a station in the Grand Canyon, and the other four were obtained from networks of stations. All five of these data sets had been previously deemed to be of high quality, free from various types of measurement error and

The old and the new meet in Vienna, where a fourth subway was being built next to historic St. Stephen's Cathedral. City planners hoped that the new line would reduce traffic congestion and air pollution.

bias, and supposedly in need of only minimal adjustments prior to use for assessing the direction and magnitude of climate trends. During this period the benchmark station showed a drop in air temperature of 1.364° C (2.455° F); two of the other sets showed drops of 0.110° C (0.198° F) and 0.192° C (0.346° F); and the other two showed increases of 0.075° C (0.135° F) and 0.008° C (0.014° F). These discrepancies are particularly startling if one reads about the care with which the data for each set were selected and the number of stations included. If research done with this care could produce opposite answers about the direction of the trend, one must question the meaningfulness of the studies that purport to give reliable results on the magnitude of increase or decrease.

Perhaps the most controversial environmental issue of all during the past year was acid rain. Indeed, the intensity of this controversy had been too great to conceal; it was covered in national magazines and on network television, and there could be no doubt that reputable people held diametrically opposed views. In 1980 the U.S. Congress commissioned the National Acid Precipitation Assessment Project, a 10-year, $500 million study on acid rain. The study employed 700 experts on water, soil, agriculture, and the atmosphere and produced a 28-volume report. The study found almost no damage from acid rain to crops or forests and only very weak causal connections to acidity in lakes, most of which were acidic in preindustrial times. In spite of this and apparently unaware of the existence of the 28 volumes, Congress voted in May 1990 for a $7 billion-a-year "cleanup" of acid rain. As one respected environmentalist put it recently, this was a landmark piece of environmental legislation for which costs might exceed benefits by a wide margin. The irony in this situation is that many scientists had known for years much that is in the 28 volumes; the massive study simply provided more proof of the correctness of many earlier studies.

Another environmental controversy that surfaced during the year concerned the health effects of low levels of radiation. Sarah C. Darby and Richard Doll found that the risk of contracting lung cancer when there is a low level of exposure for a long period is greater relative to what one would expect from higher levels of exposure over shorter periods. The significance of this finding is that one should not decide that there is some very low level of radiation below which the environment can be considered "safe." This subject was explored in great detail by John Gofman in a major new statistical analysis of data on 91,231 survivors of the atomic bombs that were dropped during World War II on the Japanese cities of Hiroshima and Nagasaki. He concluded that the risk from acute low-dose and slow low-dose ex-

posures to radiation is up to 30 times higher than the estimates arrived at in two official reports on the same data. Gofman challenged the dominant views that low doses and dose rates of radiation may be completely safe and that there may even be a positive net benefit to human health from low-dose exposure to radiation.

The public health implications of Gofman's findings are important. How the medical effects of low levels of radiation are evaluated might generate policies that could result in cancer being inflicted on a hundred million or more humans. Gofman's work was remarkable for the completeness of the exposition as to how he arrived at his results and why he differed with other analyses. A theme that appeared in his work ran through much of the material reviewed during the year: political considerations were feeding back into the actual content of scientific theory in a way that would ultimately be damaging to the credibility of science and scientists in the eyes of the public. For example, Gofman showed how data bases had been altered in a way that changed the conclusions drawn from them.

Sustainability. During the past year sustainability in agriculture was the subject of much research. An article by Wes Jackson of the Land Institute in Salina, Kan., was illustrative. Rather than dealing with problems in agriculture here and now, the Land Institute takes a long view, reexamining the correctness of the agricultural grand strategies of the past 10,000 years. This long backward look helped institute scientists consider corrective measures that might be appropriate for a long time into the future. Putting it differently, the Land Institute is not simply concerned about correcting problems of agriculture that have surfaced since World War II, such as the excessive dependence on fossil-fuel inputs (pesticides, herbicides, fertilizers). Rather, they also ask if the dependence on monoculture based on annuals (wheat, corn, and rice, for example) is wise or should be replaced by polyculture based on perennials. An interesting feature of their thinking is that they learn by comparing the systemic features of native prairie with those of ordinary grain-crop landscapes, such as corn or wheat. Against a very long-term perspective, one notices these differences. Nutrients are constantly running off to the sea from the sloping fields of crops, whereas native prairie draws nutrients from parent rock material or subsoil while bathing them with the chemicals produced by living organisms. In short, agriculture gradually drains soil of its nutrients, whereas native prairie gradually builds soil. Also, native prairie consists of many perennial plant species. This tends to check the growth of insect pests and plant pathogens. Thus, outbreaks of pests, blight, or rust, so common in agriculture, are rare in native prairie.

This type of observation raises the question as to whether agriculture based on monoculture using annual plants should be replaced by one based on polyculture using a mixture of perennials. Stimulated by such a line of thought, the Land Institute undertook a search of the literature to discover candidate plant species for a new approach to agriculture. The goal was to discover perennials with both annual and long-term seed yield that would be economically competitive with the seed yields of such traditional agricultural species as wheat. Also, they cultivated 300 species of winter-hardy perennial herbaceous species. Efforts gradually focused on five species, together with a hybrid of their making.

The researchers thoroughly investigated the seed yields of candidate species, the field conditions associated with these yields, and the protein content of the seeds. One discovery was that when there was no program of breeding to select for high-yield strains, seed protein yields were below those of standard crop species. Thus, in order to be productively competitive, the wild species would have to undergo the same long-term breeding programs that increased the productivity of wheat, corn, rice, and the other modern crop species. The question then arose as to whether herbaceous perennialism and high seed yield could be combined in a single plant. One measure useful for the comparison is the harvest index, defined as the ratio of seed or fruit weight to the aboveground weight of the plant. For wild senna this ratio was 0.31, comparable to the average of low-yielding strains of crop species but only 77% of the harvest index of high-yielding wheat, 64% of high-yielding corn, and 54% of high-yielding rice. A second question was whether perennial polycultures could outyield perennial monocultures. Experiments were conducted with two-species and three-species mixes (bicultures and tricultures). For at least one of the species, plants adjacent to other species produced more flowers and seeds than plants growing next to their own species. Other questions being explored included testing of "domestic prairie" ecosystems to see if they sponsor their own nitrogen fertility and tests to see if perennial polyculture could adequately control pests. Obviously, the exploration of all possible aspects of all such issues requires a massive program of experimentation. Vulnerability to plant diseases, competition from weeds, and attacks by insect pests all require separate programs of research. Also, in addition to the requirement for testing all possible combinations of prospective crop species being grown together, many procedural issues must be explored. For example, how far apart should rows of seeds be planted to obtain the best results?

Sustainability is the central issue of conservation biology. During the past year there was a major effort to get this field on a sound scientific footing. To illustrate the type of reasoning used to make

Crude oil released in January 1991 from Kuwait into the Persian Gulf during the Gulf war washes ashore at Khafji in northern Saudi Arabia (below) and coats the feathers of a cormorant (right). The Iraqis poured an estimated 500,000–3 million barrels of oil into the Gulf by opening the pumps at a supertanker loading dock off the coast of Kuwait and releasing oil from several Kuwaiti tankers.

Photos, AP/Wide World

Wes Jackson, director of the Land Institute in Salina, Kansas, and a leader of the sustainability in agriculture movement (see text), stands next to sorghum in a greenhouse at the institute. He is trying to develop a winter-hardy sorghum.

educated guesses about rates of species extinction, a recent paper by E.O. Wilson of Harvard University is revealing. He assumes that half the species in tropical forests are distributed in such a way that the rate of species extinction is 0.5 multiplied by the annual proportion of the forests being destroyed. Approximately 76,000 sq km (29,340 sq mi), or 0.007, of the total tropical forest is being destroyed each year. Wilson estimated that about five million species of organisms are confined to the tropical rain forests. The annual rate of species extinction is therefore about 0.5×5 million $\times 0.007$, or approximately 17,500 species per year.

A major scientific issue was emerging in conservation biology. It centered on whether a plan for ensuring the survival of a diverse array of species should be devised in terms of a static model of how species interact with their food organisms or a dynamic model. In a static model one would assume that the species to be maintained could be confined indefinitely in a park reserved for them and that they would survive forever. In a dynamic model it would be assumed that the optimal strategy for maintaining diversity of a community of species would be to allow the large carnivores and herbivores to migrate. They would deplete food supplies at one site and then migrate to a second site and deplete food supplies there. Such movement would occur repeatedly until eventually the species would migrate back to the first site and repeat the process.

Several arguments support the dynamic approach. First, if species of great destructive potential, such as crown-of-thorns starfish or elephants, are confined to one site, they will simply wipe it out and markedly decrease both productivity and species diversity there. In addition, both theory and actual field observations suggest that when a destructive species depletes the food supplies at a site and then moves on, this fosters an explosive renewal of both productivity and diversity at the first site after they move away. During the year, David Western noted that the areas outside of eastern African wildlife parks have as rich and diverse a fauna as are in the parks. His observations indicated that wildlife seems to survive and thrive in free competition with livestock. High elephant concentrations in parks lead to the transformation of woodlands to grasslands, which in turn support hot fires that further inhibit woodland regeneration. Woodland regeneration is fostered if the elephants are not enclosed behind a fence but are free to migrate to another area once they have depleted a local plant community. Conservation biologists certainly need the collection and analyses of a great deal of data to resolve this issue of static versus dynamic models.

Solar-powered detoxification system in New Mexico consists of a trough of parabolic mirrors that concentrate sunlight on a long glass tube within the trough. Contaminated water and titanium dioxide are pumped through the tube, where the titanium dioxide acts as a catalyst that speeds up the reaction of the water with ultraviolet energy in the sunlight. Hydroxyl radicals and peroxide ions created by this reaction attack the organic contaminants in the water and break them down into environmentally safe components.

Ideology, politics, government, and the environment. During the past year the issue of government's role in the environment often arose. Derrick Exner, Richard Thompson, and Sharon Thompson pointed out that corn-intensive rotations were least profitable without the federal feed-grain program and that under the program they became the most profitable rotations. Thus, a government program designed to support corn prices had, in fact, encouraged the production of corn. C.B. Flora noted that without government intervention that, in turn, would drive down corn prices, farmers must plant at least half their base area in crops included in government price-support programs in order to maintain full price-support eligibility. This penalizes farmers who use crop rotations that extend for three years or more and forces farmers to abandon six-year rotations, which build soil. It also forces farmers to increase their use of agrichemicals and fertilizers, because the greater the crop production per unit area, the more price support will be received. In short, government policies to prop up commodity prices not only lead to overproduction but are also environmentally damaging and lead to long-term soil degradation.

In reviewing the history of the U.S. Environmental Protection Agency, M.K. Landy, M.J. Roberts, and S.R. Thomas produced one of the year's most exhaustive and revealing analyses of environmental problems. Their findings go far to explain why ideology, politics, and the dynamics of government are having a strong, harmful impact on environmental policy and, ultimately, on environmental sciences. In regard to government structure and dynamics, it has become a punishing task to convert a draft piece of legislation to law during a two-year session of Congress. Two features of the legislative-hearing process can halt the progress of a proposed piece of legislation. The first is lengthy debate. Accordingly, sponsors often seek to avoid any complexity that might invite debate in the draft legislation; such complexity often, however, is necessary to reflect reality. The second potential pitfall is that too many congressional committees might hold hearings on the proposed legislation. This simply increases the number of legislators with whom the sponsors must conduct negotiations in order to enact the bill into law. Furthermore, in order to create a constituency that will support enactment of the legislation, the sponsors must simplify and select data so as to dramatize the seriousness of the problem.

These types of considerations feed back, first, onto the strategy for passing the legislation into law. Key conceptual ambiguities must be kept unresolved. Crucial strategic decisions must be avoided. One must create a sense of crisis and promote an alarmist tone. In some cases these considerations might even damage the science that purportedly establishes the need for the new legislation. For example, the governor of New York established a blue-ribbon scientific panel to examine the reports that supposedly demonstrated the severity of the pollution at the Love Canal toxic chemicals waste-disposal site. Their conclusion contained this language: "The design, implementation, and release of the EPA chromosome study has not only damaged the credibility of science but exacerbated any future attempts to determine whether and to what degree the health of the Love Canal residents has been affected." This language appears to make clear that political considerations can feed back into science in a way that is damaging to the scientific enterprise, which ideally should involve only the rigorous, strong inferential testing of scientific hypotheses against data. The need to galvanize and mobilize constituencies and then get draft legislation enacted into law is leading to a kind of science in which hypotheses appear to have been tested but in fact have been the subject of experiments or data analyses that allow for only the desired answer.

—Kenneth E.F. Watt
See also Feature Article: SOLVING THE TRASH CRISIS.

Food and agriculture

Agriculture worldwide was affected by the decline in economic activity that began in 1990 and continued into 1991. The decline reflected lower growth in the developed countries and production contractions in Eastern Europe. Inflation also contributed to the slowed growth pattern, influenced by fluctuating petroleum prices. Only Latin America showed substantial growth—an increase of almost two percentage points—between 1989 and 1991. In the United States the Food, Agriculture, Conservation and Trade Act of 1990 (commonly called the Farm Bill) strengthened the role of science and education while making major changes in U.S. food-aid programs.

Agriculture

U.S. agricultural exports fell for the first time since 1986; values declined by more than $1 billion, while export volume dropped 6%, mainly because of a decline in grain exports. The lower world grain trade reflected larger harvests by nations that traditionally were grain importers. U.S. corn exports were affected by a predicted decline of more than a third in Soviet corn imports. Higher world wheat production resulted in sharply lower wheat prices. Poultry (including turkeys and ducks) now accounted for an estimated 32% of world use of formulated feed. Large-scale adoption of mechanical feeders boosted world egg production.

U.S. Farm Bill. The annual budget resolution approved by Congress set the stage for the 1990 farm policy debate. The 1989 deficit-reduction package called for $91.4 million in spending cuts for agricultural programs. Early in 1990 legislators began introducing bills to replace the Food Security Act of 1985. Along with its usual task of revising and developing policies to maintain the economic health of U.S. agriculture, Congress had to take into account budgetary concerns, a continued shift to more market-oriented policies, and the need to maintain U.S. leverage during the latest round of multinational trade negotiations. Federal outlays for farm programs had declined steadily from the 1986 peak, but the burgeoning deficit put strong pressure on Congress to reduce federal spending in all areas, including farm programs. Cost-cutting measures included reducing target prices further, realigning target prices to reflect production costs, and allowing farmers more flexibility in deciding what to plant. Congress also addressed the relationship between the Federal Crop Insurance program and emerging disaster-aid legislation. Markets for new farm products, environmental concerns, and food-safety issues figured prominently in the farm-policy debates.

The Farm Bill included five major initiatives that responded directly to consumer concerns over food safety and nutrition, a strong environmental push to protect water quality and natural resources, and the need to enhance U.S. agricultural competitiveness. Although the U.S. Department of Agriculture (USDA) has been addressing an ever increasing

Protesting efforts by the General Agreement on Tariffs and Trade (GATT) to cut agricultural price supports, thousands of European farmers march outside GATT headquarters in Geneva in November 1990.

AP/Wide World

array of topics, it was directed to consider the environment, nutrition, water quality, and economic competitiveness when awarding research grants. The legislation authorized a 10-fold funding increase for research on sustainable agriculture, aimed at helping farmers find production methods that require less use of chemicals. It also authorized the establishment of an Alternative Agricultural Research and Commercialization Center to develop new nonfood, nonfeed products from agricultural commodities.

After two decades of level funding for research, the Farm Bill increased the authorization for competitive research grants. Under the umbrella of a national research initiative, the authorization was raised to $500 million per year over five years for competitive grants in six high-priority research areas: plant systems; animal systems; nutrition, food quality, and health; natural resources and the environment; engineering products and processes, including new uses and new products; and markets, trade, and policy. Receiving special attention would be multidisciplinary research teams, new investigators, and faculty from small and midsize academic institutions that had not been very successful in obtaining competitive grants in the past.

Trade. In December 1990 a protracted round of international food disputes ended with no winners. The backdrop was the Uruguay round of negotiations under the General Agreement on Tariffs and Trade (GATT). There had been seven previous GATT sessions, beginning in 1947. The latest round of GATT talks, aimed at reducing barriers to trade in products and services, began in 1986 and focused on agriculture, although questions regarding services, intellectual property, and investments were also debated. A major stumbling block was the question of whether price supports to farmers result in an unfair distortion of international trade in agricultural products.

U.S. officials argued that under the European Communities (EC) common agricultural policy (CAP), high price supports resulted in "force-fed" high yields; the CAP, combined with the EC's variable import levels, often kept competing farm goods out of European markets. The U.S., which also has a farm price support program, proposed a reduction in tariffs, the phasing out of export subsidies and trade-distorting internal policies tied to farm production, and the establishment of scientifically based sanitary standards to prevent food safety from being used as an excuse to bar foreign products.

The EC counteroffers were seen as totally inadequate by the U.S. and the members of the so-called Cairns Group of nations (Australia, Canada, New Zealand, and several South American countries). Although the Uruguay round was scheduled to end in 1990, the talks continued in the new year. However, the outlook was not bright.

Food safety. As U.S. consumers have become more knowledgeable about scientific issues, their interest in food safety has increased dramatically. Nowhere has this been more evident than in the areas of pesticides and food additives. While consumers cite these as the greatest threats to human health emanating from the food supply, however, scientists rank them at the bottom of their list of concerns. Data from the Institute of Food Technology show that scientists rank threats to human health from the food supply in the following order: (1) microbial infections and poisoning; (2) nutrition/malnutrition; (3) naturally occurring and induced toxic agents; (4) chemical and physical contaminants; (5) pesticides; and (6) food additives. The ranking is generally supported by most other major scientific groups, although some do not include nutrition and malnutrition.

Disease-causing microorganisms in improperly handled and inadequately processed foods and feeds are a constant threat. Research was under way to determine the routes, modes, and amounts of toxic substances and harmful microorganisms transmitted through the food chain. New processing technologies and distribution techniques that would ensure microbiological safety were being developed and evaluated, as were rapid-detection methods and control techniques to detect and stop the spread of food-borne illnesses. Characterization of microorganisms newly implicated in food-borne disease outbreaks was part of the ongoing program.

Naturally occurring toxins in foods represent a little-recognized health threat. Current research was aimed at identifying such toxins, their occurrence, and how they act. A significant effort was being expended on research to prevent or eliminate mycotoxins, produced by molds, from feed and food supplies. Research also was aimed at identifying induced toxins formed during processing and cooking or through genetic manipulation of plant materials. Finally, agricultural researchers were studying the safety of additives intentionally introduced into food products and the prevalence and effects on human health of incidental additives. More reliable and faster methods for detecting trace quantities of pesticides were being developed.

One example of ongoing food-safety research involved poultry and poultry products. Public fear of contracting food poisoning as the result of eating salmonella-infected chicken and eggs was growing, but studies showed that salmonella in chicken and eggs would present little risk if the food products were handled properly and cooked thoroughly. Even so, scientists at the University of Arkansas Agricultural Experiment Station were working on methods that would greatly reduce or eliminate salmonella and other bacteria in water used to process raw poultry.

Researchers at the Agricultural Experiment Station at the University of Wisconsin-Madison produced a new test that dramatically improves the ability to monitor aflatoxin, a naturally occurring carcinogen, in milk and grain. Aflatoxin, a potent cause of liver cancer, occurs frequently in corn and peanuts in certain parts of the United States. In drought years it can be a major problem nationwide. Regulators must spend a great deal of time and effort screening grains for aflatoxin, but the new test, an enzyme-linked immunosorbent assay, promised to make the screening process faster and more accurate than was possible with earlier methods.

Genome mapping projects. Genetic improvement of plants and animals offers one of the most cost-effective and environmentally sound methods of enhancing the ability to produce food and fiber. It can improve efficiency and productivity, increase tolerance of the plants and animals to chemical, physical, and environmental stresses, and strengthen resistance to common pests and diseases. However, scientists must understand the molecular and cellular processes of plants and animals and the nature of inheritance before they can translate these processes into desired characteristics.

An important step in this process is systematically mapping the genes responsible for producing the critical functional characteristics of plants and animals. Scientists want to know which genes affect which characteristics and where they are located. To find out, scientists were focusing on a type of genetic analysis called restriction fragment length polymorphism, which would allow them to detect the unique genetic fingerprints that serve as markers for certain characteristics. Scientists were also looking closely at quantitative trait loci, those multiple genes affecting economically important characteristics. Using enzymes, scientists cut DNA (deoxyribonucleic acid), the basic genetic material of plants and animals, into fragments of different lengths, each containing different genes. DNA probes then can be used to determine if a specific gene is present in a fragment. Once an association has been made between a specific fragment and a specific gene, selections of desired genes can be made.

The mapping processes used by agricultural scientists are similar to those of the National Institutes of Health's five-year human genome mapping project. Unlike that project, however, the agricultural scientists would map not the entire genetic makeup of a plant or animal but only those portions with economic significance. The first systematic national funding for plant genome mapping appeared in the USDA's budget for fiscal 1991. There was no similar funding for animal work, but scientists had banded together to create their own informal network for sharing information and locating funding.

Sunflowers high in oleic acid have been bred to supply the vegetable oils necessary for making biodegradable plastics. Possible uses for these plastics include moistureproof packaging, such as bottles and cable insulation.

Working with plants, scientists could already trace complicated genetic traits such as disease resistance. Eventually they hoped to be able to produce desired characteristics in a wide variety of plants quickly, accurately, and economically. Animal scientists hoped that by mid-1992 they would have mapped most of the major genetic traits they were seeking. Both

An inexpensive coating for fresh fruits and vegetables retards ripening without harming quality. Consisting of an emulsifier added to a vegetable-oil coating, it allows them to be stored at room temperature.

groups stressed that the information they were gathering and the ability to use it had to be passed on to agricultural producers if it was to provide the major benefits they hoped for. This would not be accomplished quickly or easily without nationally focused research programs.

New products. A small U.S. firm and a large Japanese manufacturer received exclusive licenses for development of ski clothing and other sportswear made from fabrics that respond to changes in temperature.

In a process developed by scientists at the USDA's New Orleans, La., laboratory, the thermal fabrics are treated with polyethylene glycol or with compounds known as plastic crystals. In laboratory tests the fabrics absorbed and stored heat when the temperature rose and released it when the temperature dropped. The amount of heat the treated material stored and released depended on the type of fabric and the kind and amount of chemicals used. Several U.S. and Canadian companies were interested in licensing the technology for use in carpets, footwear, automobile interiors, and fabrics for agricultural applications.

An aseptic yogurt that would keep on a pantry shelf for up to six months was on the drawing boards at the Agricultural Experiment Station at Utah State University. Scientists reported that their research had clearly demonstrated that ultrafiltering low-fat or skim milk to 12.5% milk solids, followed by ultrahigh-temperature processing before adding the yogurt cultures, results in a yogurt superior to conventionally prepared products. The heat treatment effectively reduces competitive organisms, so the yogurt cultures can ferment the milk with little or no competition. The liquid does not separate from the solids over a 21-day period, and refrigerated shelf life is extended. The next step would be development of a yogurt that requires no refrigeration.

With USDA researchers already making plastic from cornstarch, other biodegradable plastics were not far behind. Using a new process, scientists at the Battelle Institute in Frankfurt, Germany, produced biodegradable plastics from vegetable oils. In the process, the fatty acids are linked almost unchanged to the polymer chains constituting the plastic. Experiments showed that thermoplastics created in this way could be processed by conventional methods. Polymers with nontearing, rubberlike properties also could be produced. Possible uses for the new plastic include moistureproof packing materials, such as bottles and cable insulation. Vegetable oils that have a high oleic acid content are particularly suitable for use in this process. A new, high-oleic sunflower that thrives under German climatic conditions was bred specifically to supply the requisite raw materials.

Other developments. An edible, inexpensive coating for fresh fruit and vegetables that retards ripening without reducing quality and can be applied easily was reported by USDA researchers. At a federal laboratory in Florida, researchers added an emulsifier to a commercially available vegetable-oil coating. With the emulsifier, which disperses fat globules in water, the new coating increased the shelf life of tomatoes, carambola (starfruit), and oranges. Scientists at the University of Idaho suggested that pregnancy-specific protein B may play a critical role in preventing immunorejection of an embryo by the maternal system. If this protein could be used in therapeutic situations, dairy farmers could save millions of dollars per year now lost as a result of embryonic deaths. University of Massachusetts researchers were developing a procedure for efficiently producing large numbers of genetically identical mammals using nuclear transplantation. The researchers increased the efficiency of cloning rabbit embryos by 50% and noted that the procedure could be used with other farm animals as well.

—John Patrick Jordan

Nutrition

The Dietary Guidelines issued by the secretary of agriculture and the secretary of health and human services represent the U.S. government's principal statement of nutritional advice. The third edition of the Guidelines, issued in 1990, was considered by many to be "clearer and more diet-oriented" than earlier versions. Recommendations for healthful eating were more specific, while some former prohibitions had been changed to "use in moderation." Also, appropriate body weight was defined more realistically by taking body composition and build into account. However, the bottom line remained the same: a varied diet rather than a single food or supplement is needed to supply the more than 40 nutrients that are essential for health.

The major points emphasized in the Guidelines are: eat a variety of foods; maintain a healthy weight; choose a diet low in fat, especially saturated fat and cholesterol; choose plenty of vegetables, fruits, and grain products; use sugars, salt, and sodium compounds in moderation when preparing foods; and consume alcoholic beverages in moderation. The daily diet should include 3–4 servings of vegetables; 2–4 of fruits; 6–11 of grains (breads, cereals, rice, pasta); 2–3 of milk, yogurt, and cheese; and 2–3 of meat, poultry, fish, dry beans and peas, eggs, and nuts. Servings are defined in household measures; for example, a serving of vegetables equals one cup of raw vegetables, as in salad, or one-half cup cooked.

The nine nutritional authorities who designed the Guidelines agreed that "food alone cannot make you healthy." Good health also depends on heredity, environment, general health care, and life-style.

Food labels. The American Institute of Nutrition and other nutrition-oriented professional organizations approved a Position Statement on Food Labeling, which was forwarded to the U.S. Food and Drug Administration (FDA). The statement includes recommendations on the contents of nutrition labels, disease-specific label claims, and definitions of such terms as *low-fat* and *reduced-fat*.

With prepared "heat and eat" food products becoming increasingly popular, informative labeling, legible enough to be read easily by consumers—including the elderly—in a food store, is a necessity. It was generally agreed that the labels should specify the amount of nutrients per unit weight, volume, or specified serving size and also that the listed components should include salt, leavening agents, and other additives that many people cannot tolerate. A major need in the U.S. was harmonization of the labeling policies of the FDA, the USDA, and the Federal Trade Commission.

Special needs of the elderly. A study of nearly 1,500 males aged 65 and over in the Honolulu Heart Program found that higher levels of blood cholesterol correlated with a higher risk of heart disease. The scientists who conducted the study recommended cholesterol-lowering treatment for those found to have high cholesterol levels, including men under 65. Such treatment could involve diet, medication, appropriate exercise, or some combination of those options.

Mature and elderly persons often resist drastic changes in their food and eating habits. Attempts to enforce such changes may seriously endanger the already fragile health of such persons, especially if they are part of an overall adjustment to an institutional environment. Life for the elderly is more pleasant when dietary practices and eating habits continue to reflect the customs and culture of a lifetime.

An elderly woman eats dessert at a restaurant. Although changes in diet are often recommended for older people because of their blood cholesterol levels, many resist extensive changes in their eating habits.

Smart snacking. As the traditional three-meals-a-day pattern increasingly gives way to one of many small meals or "snacks," the nutritional quality of the snacks has become a matter of concern to dietitians. The typical between-meal snack has tended to be high in sugar, salt, and fat, consisting of such foods as candy, cookies, crackers, nuts, and chips. The newsletter of the American Institute for Cancer Research pointed out that these "quickie" foods could be made to supply proteins, minerals, vitamins, and fiber comparable to a small meal. By improving the nutritional quality of its products, the vending machine industry could make a substantial contribution to the health and well-being of a large segment of the population. It was estimated that many young people obtain a third or more of their daily calorie supply from vending-machine snacks.

Hunger. For some years, the conquest of hunger in the U.S. has been a subject of concern to educators in the area of human nutrition, especially dietitians whose field includes the dietary practices of women in the childbearing years. The problem of hunger in America was targeted in 1969, when Pres. Richard Nixon called a White House Conference on Food, Nutrition, and Health. The conference consisted of a cross-section of nutritionists, physicians, industrialists, farmers, and many others. Over 1,800 recommendations were made, designed "to eliminate hunger in the U.S. for all time."

A follow-up conference in 1979 reported that 1,600 of the recommendations had been put into effect. Some 22 million people had been brought into the Food Stamp Program, and participation in the school lunch and breakfast and the meals-on-wheels programs had tripled. The conclusion was that hunger as a social phenomenon in the U.S. had to all intents and purposes disappeared and that the pledge to eliminate hunger had been realized.

Jean Mayer, the president of Tufts University, Medford, Mass., who had chaired the National Council on Hunger and Malnutrition when he was on the nutrition faculty of Harvard University, believed this assessment was overly optimistic. In the early 1980s, he pointed out, "close to $12 billion was cut from the food programs at the same time that the cost of food increased enormously." At least partly because of his efforts, Congress reinstated $8 billion in the 1982–84 session, but recent efforts to balance the budget once again brought the food programs under threat.

Mayer especially criticized cuts in the WIC program (for women, infants, and children). Other considerations aside, such cuts are not cost effective. Many studies have documented the better growth and health status of babies whose mothers were well nourished during pregnancy. WIC costs $35 per woman, while intensive care for a deficient infant may cost more than $1,000 a day. Mayer believed that "WIC should be made an entitlement." He also endorsed full funding for the Food Stamp Program, which reaches more children than the school lunch program and which he considered superior to commodity-distribution plans because it does not differentiate between kinds of food for the rich and the poor.

Food for the troops. With the deployment of U.S. troops to the Persian Gulf region beginning in late 1990, the desire of citizens to "do something" for the troops often found expression in the sending of food. However, Sue Templin, supervisor of the USDA's Meat and Poultry Hotline, urged that the troops receive "food presents and not food problems."

The USDA, food scientists, the military, and the U.S. Postal Service joined forces to compile a list of dos and don'ts for overseas food packages. First among the don'ts were foods that require refrigeration, including all fresh foods that would normally be under refrigeration at home. Canned foods were also on the don't list because cans may become dented or corroded, allowing the contents to become contaminated. Moist foods such as cakes and cookies are subject to mold growth, and fragile items such as cookies may be reduced to crumbs by the time they arrive. Similarly, candies with cream or chocolate centers may liquefy. In general, all perishable foods are at risk. It was also noted that Muslim religious customs forbid all pork products and those with alcohol (*e.g.,* brandied fruits). Foods that survive shipment best are dried or baked and preferably commercially packaged. They include dried fruits, canned mints, nuts, fruit drink mixes, and tins of popcorn.

—Mina Lamb

Sidney Harris

Life sciences

Environmental concerns pervaded much of the past year's advances and topical issues in the life sciences, which ranged from the use of microorganisms to degrade toxic wastes, to studies of the effect of increased ultraviolet light on crop plants, to expressions of distress over declining numbers of amphibians, bears, and sharks. New discoveries included a monkey called the black-faced lion tamarin and a 20-million-year-old fossil leaf that yielded intact genetic material. Molecular biologists identified the gene whose mutant form leads to the disease known as neurofibromatosis and probed how that mutation upsets the processing of chemical signals in the cell.

Botany

Steady progress in botany during the past year continued to reveal interesting information about plants and their environments. A number of noteworthy findings emerged from studies involving genetics, leaf function, the effect of the environment, and forestry.

Genetics. Edward M. Golenberg, then at the University of California at Riverside, and associates reported their analysis of DNA from a *Magnolia* leaf approximately 20 million years old. That genetic material from such an old fossil could be identified is remarkable and required special conditions of fossilization, which left the leaf still green and unmineralized. The leaf was found in the Clarkia deposits, 9 m (30 ft) of fine, unoxidized clay shales formed under a lake near present-day Moscow, Idaho. The researchers carefully split open some of the shale to reveal the fossil, immediately ground the fossil material into a fine powder, and extracted the DNA. They used a recently developed amplification technique called the polymerase chain reaction to isolate a segment containing the chloroplast gene *rbc*L. Determination of the sequence of nucleotide bases—the essence of the genetic code—in the segment showed that it differed by only 17 bases out of a total of 820 from the corresponding DNA of modern *Magnolia*.

The conditions of preservation were such that some of the DNA in the leaf's chloroplasts remained undamaged by oxidation of the usually susceptible parts of its structure. It was thought likely that the leaf had fallen directly into the lake and had come to rest in cold water that was undisturbed, low in oxygen, and rich in organic sediments. The investigators predicted that the ability to compare the DNA of closely related fossil and modern species would allow the determination of mutation rates. In fact, it might offer a way to test models for evolutionary relationships among species and for the geographic distribution of species.

The father of genetics, Gregor Mendel, described the relationship of genes controlling seven different phenotypes, or observable traits, in garden peas (*Pisum sativum*). For each trait there were two alternatives, which Mendel called dominant and recessive and which correspond to two different forms of the controlling gene. One of his phenotypes was the texture of the seeds: smooth (dominant) or wrinkled (recessive). More than a century later, in 1990, a group of researchers from the John Innes Institute, Norwich, England, reported discovering at least part of the molecular explanation for the difference in texture. Madan K. Bhattacharyya and his associates were able to clone the DNA from both the dominant (R) and the recessive (r) forms of the gene and to determine the proteins for which they code. Pea plants that receive an r gene from each parent, and thus have no copy of the R gene, produce a mutant form of an enzyme, starch-branching enzyme I (SBEI), which results in a defect in starch synthesis in the pea seed and a consequent high sugar content. Although other differences are present, the high sugar content is interesting in that it accounts for the wrinkling in the rr plants. Higher sugar content ensures higher water content in the developing seed, which wrinkles when the water is lost in the drying of the seed. The difference in the r gene proved to be an interruption in the base sequence of the normal R gene in the form of an extra piece of DNA about 800 bases long—a so-called transposable element similar to those known in other plants, such as maize (corn).

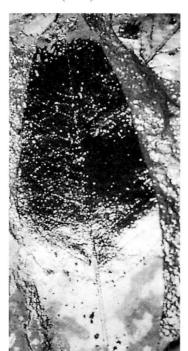

A fossil magnolia leaf, still green after spending 20 million years in water-saturated shale formed under an ancient lake, yielded intact DNA. The genetic material was identified as a chloroplast gene that codes for part of an important enzyme.

E.M. Golenberg of Wayne State University, Detroit, Mich., and D.E. Giannasi of the University of Georgia, Athens

Growth in plants is affected by many environmental factors. One of the most intriguing growth responses is to touch stimuli. A small plant called *Arabidopsis thaliana* responds to water spray, sub-irrigation, wind, touch, wounding, or darkness by developing leaf petioles (stems) and bolts (flowering stalks) that are shorter than normal. Such responses, called thigmomorphogenesis, seem to be influenced by the presence of at least four touch-induced (TCH) genes, according to a report by Janet Braam and Ronald W. Davis of Stanford University. Although the relationship of the environmental stimulation to control of the genes remained to be learned, the genes were found to be activated within 10 minutes of stimulation and appeared to code for a substance called calmodulin. Calmodulin and other proteins, in turn, bind calcium ions, which may be involved in a number of metabolic process that result in the altered growth after touch stimulation.

Leaves. Fulton Fisher of Simon Fraser University, Burnaby, B.C., invented a mechanical leaf, which he named PHYLLUS, to study leaf movements. One discovery emerging from the work concerned the commonly observed turning of leaves to expose their broad surface fully to sunlight. It is the reception of blue light by special and precisely placed cells that induces this movement. Stimulation of the cells, which contain blue-light-sensitive granules, initiates the movement of hormones in such a way that the leaf turns until all the cells are illuminated equally. The hormones promote the lengthening of cells in part of the leaf in order to effect the tilting.

Mayapple *(Podophyllum peltatum),* a common woodland plant of the eastern U.S., was studied by two Indiana University researchers to learn more about the relationships between leaf senescence and plant metabolism. In August, at the annual meeting of the American Institute of Biological Sciences in Richmond, Va., Ying Lu and Maxine A. Watson reported observations over a two-year period in which they noted that leaves survived 8–14 days longer in sexually reproducing plants. Apparently, the longer period of photosynthesis gained by longer-lasting leaves supplies energy related to a number of associated events: sexual reproduction, fruit production, development of large rhizomes (underground plant stems), and sexual reproduction the following year. Since leaf senescence provides for some recovery of nutrients by the plants, such recovery is delayed by the extended period of photosynthesis. Whatever the nutrient recovery accomplishes, its delay is part of the trade-off related to sexual reproduction in the mayapple.

Botanists have long observed that leaves growing in shade differ from those growing in full sunlight. Shade leaves are often thinner, broader, and greener than sunlight leaves, even on the same tree. The differences had been assumed to make the shade leaves more efficient under lower light intensities. David W. Lee of Florida International University and his associates demonstrated how internal structure relates to function in examples of tropical-forest species. Thirteen shade-adapted species were compared with 12 sun-adapted ones. It was found that the arrangement of internal cell layers corresponds to the adaptation. Leaves of dicotyledons (the larger of the two great groups of flowering plants) tend to have two different cell layers within. The upper one, called the palisade layer, is made of cells that tend to be columnar (longer than wide) and are packed together. The lower one, called the spongy layer, tends to be made of more spherical cells with considerable air space separating them. In shade-adapted leaves, the palisade cells have dimensions that are more equal and a dense layer of chloroplasts to capture the available light. Sun-adapted leaves have longer palisade cells, which result in a less dense arrangement of chloroplasts; the centers of the cells have no chloroplasts at all, allowing light to penetrate more easily to the spongy layer. The researchers found certain pioneering species to be exceptions to this pattern. Since these species grow under less crowded conditions, they may flourish in the direct sunlight with a shade-adapted type of structure because sunlight reaches the more exposed undersurfaces of leaves.

Environmental effects. Concern with the possibility of future changes to the global environment has encouraged botanists to experiment with the effects of such changes on plants. Of particular interest are effects due to thinning of the atmospheric ozone layer, to general atmospheric warming (enhanced greenhouse effect), and to air pollution resulting in acid rain.

Depletion of the ozone layer will permit greater exposure at the Earth's surface to ultraviolet (UV) light from the Sun. To ascertain whether increased UV exposure would enhance the likelihood of infection by disease organisms, Ann B. Orth and her associates of the University of Maryland, College Park, treated cucumber plants in a greenhouse. They subjected three cucumber (*Cucumis sativus*) cultivars to a daily dose of biologically effective ultraviolet-B (UV-B, 280–320-nanometer) radiation in an unshaded greenhouse before infection, after infection, or both. As the infective agent they used one of two fungi, *Colletotrichum lagenarium* (which causes anthracnose) or *Cladosporium cucumerinum* (which causes scab), and analyzed for disease development. The three cucumber strains were Poinsette and Calypso Hybrid (both normally disease resistant) and Straight-8 (disease susceptible). Straight-8 plants that had been exposed before infection to UV-B for one to seven days developed more severe

Thomas Bartholin

Wibjörn Karlén of the University of Stockholm samples a disk from the stump of a Scots pine in Sweden as part of efforts to construct a continuous tree-ring record of summer temperatures in Fennoscandia from AD 500 to the present.

infections of both diseases than did unexposed control plants. Both resistant cultivars, Poinsette and Calypso Hybrid, developed more severe anthracnose in cotyledons than did controls when previously exposed to UV-B. For all plants, treatment both with higher concentration of fungal spores and with UV-B radiation resulted in enhanced severity of disease. Other variations of outcome were recorded, leading to the preliminary indication that the effects of UV-B radiation on disease development in cucumber vary depending on cultivar, timing and duration of UV-B exposure, level of exposure to the disease agents, and plant age.

Scientists do not agree on the extent to which global warming is taking place because it has been difficult to sort out the evidence for general trends from that for short-term and local trends. Botanists have used tree-ring studies to gather evidence for climatic change in the past and to gain some insight into ways of predicting present trends. Again, there have been problems in distinguishing tree-ring variations that are due to other than long-range climatic factors. A large group of European investigators reported a technique for reanalyzing tree-ring data from Fennoscandia (Finland, Norway, Denmark, and Sweden) that attempts to factor out the short-term and nonclimatic effects on tree-ring

growth. K.R. Briffa of the University of East Anglia, Norwich, England, and associates studied ring-width data collected on Scots pine *(Pinus sylvestris)* that represents a continuous history since AD 500. Among a number of conclusions was their prediction that summer temperatures in northern Fennoscandia will show an upward trend of about 0.9–1.5° C (1.6–2.7° F) over the next 40 years. They suggested that it will not be possible to detect, with confidence, global warming until the year 2030.

Forestry. Although the war in Vietnam ended in 1975, the Vietnamese have continued to suffer from its effects. During the war defoliation destroyed thousands of hectares (a hectare equals 2.47 ac) of forest. Afterward the degradation was extended by overcutting of the forest for postwar reconstruction, exploitation by industry and new settlement, shifting cultivation practices, and firewood. Although hampered by insufficient government funding, efforts to establish tree farms have gone forward at three levels: individually owned plots of about six hectares, larger areas operated by village cooperatives, and still larger areas run as government forestry units. In all cases tree farmers have set their own production levels and have sold their products on the free market. Since the land is now depleted and forest products are not yet in great production, innovative measures are needed. Practicing agroforestry (raising row crops together with young trees) and providing housing for farmers in villages are two ways by which the country can couple forestry with food production while yet protecting the land. Foreign investment is being sought to help Vietnam get its forests to the necessary productive stages.

Foresters in the U.S.S.R. have been looking to their American counterparts for ideas for developing Soviet forests. While the Soviet forest service is gradually shifting efforts away from what others have criticized as overutilization of timber, it is seeking ways to increase forest productivity from the present 30%. The amount of timber involved is great, since the U.S.S.R. possesses more than a quarter of the world's forests—36 trillion bd-ft of timber, mainly in Siberia and the Far East. Present emphasis is on accumulation of information about important forest characteristics and problems. In a recently initiated joint Soviet-U.S. effort, four northern forest sites, two in each country, were chosen for intensive ecological study. A simulation model would be constructed from the accumulated data and would be used to predict effects of possible global warming on the northern forests, to forecast economic effects of forest practice, and to test strategies for planting and harvest practices.

New programs to encourage tree planting throughout the world have been started, particularly in the U.S. For example, Global ReLeaf, introduced by the

American Forestry Association in 1988, has gained support from a variety of community and corporate groups; financial support for 1990 has been estimated at $10 million. Following the massive damage in 1989 from Hurricane Hugo in Puerto Rico and the Carolinas, Global ReLeaf personnel have joined in the effort to reforest more than 538,000 ha, where estimated damage included 6.7 billion bd-ft of timber and 20 million cords of pulpwood. Extensive replanting of urban trees also has been undertaken.

Other developments. Gardeners and farmers remove weeds from gardens and fields because the weeds compete with crop plants for nutrients, water, and sunlight. Francisco J. Rosado-May and colleagues of the University of California at Santa Cruz noted that in apparent contradiction of this reasoning, farmers in Mexico allow certain weeds to coexist with their maize crop. A common weed, *Bidens pilosa,* is permitted to grow beginning about 15 days after the crop plants emerge. Then the weeds are cut back every month until harvest. Although it is true that uncontrolled weed growth would seriously decrease crop yield, the controlled weed-growth technique actually benefits the crop. It was found that the weed's roots produce compounds that inhibit certain fungi and nematodes that harm maize. Field trials in the U.S. with other weeds produced similar results, according to the researchers.

Recent concern about the fate of giant pandas and their reliance in the wild on bamboo has renewed interest in the plant. During its lifetime bamboo produces flowers only once, between 12 and 120 years of age, and then dies at the end of the fruiting period. Because local populations of the plant all flower at the same time, whole populations may die about the same time after reproducing, causing sudden food shortages for local panda populations. R.S. Nadgauda and associates of the National Chemical Laboratory, Pune, India, have been working on methods to produce bamboo seed annually. Recently they succeeded in raising fruiting shoots of three species (*Bambusa arundinacea, Dendrocalamus brandisii,* and *D. strictus*) in the laboratory and look to their technique to provide material for experiments to understand better the life history of bamboo and to provide seed when production techniques are developed.

Foraging is an activity usually attributed to animals, but Colleen K. Kelly, studying at the University of Oxford, suggested that some plants also forage. She reported her research on the behavior of dodder, *Cuscata subinclusa,* a parasite on other plants. Dodder is rootless, nearly leafless, and completely dependent on its host, upon which it climbs throughout the growing season. On reaching the host plant, dodder forms one or more loops around the stem of the host and proceeds to grow tiny peglike branches

into its phloem tissue to secure nutrients. Kelly discovered that dodder will "choose" certain hosts over others, probably as a response to stimulation by certain chemical differences in bark substances. When germinating from seed or sprouting from previous year's growth, dodder shoots produce greatest growth on those host plants that are "recognized" as being able to provide maximum nutrients. The largest dodder plants are most capable of surviving to the following year and providing shoots to repeat the parasitic processes. These new plants are more likely to flower and set seed than new plants germinating from seed.

Plants play an essential role in traditional medicine throughout the world. For centuries properties of certain native plants have been exploited to promote various forms of healing. Such rich and fascinating traditions are of interest to modern medical researchers who search for new biologically active compounds. They are also interesting to historical botanists, who study the relationships of plants and people. Kelly Kindscher of the University of Kansas studied the traditions of 20 tribes of North American Plains Indians, finding that they had developed medicines from at least 165 prairie plants. He reported at the annual meeting of the Society of Ethnobiology, held in March 1990 at Arizona State University, Tempe, that botanists must change their assumption that Plains Indians found their herbal remedies in the wooded parts of the prairie. He also stated his belief that the plants used in traditional medicine should be more fully investigated worldwide for their value to modern medicine.

—Albert J. Smith

Microbiology

Bacteria and simple eukaryotic microbes such as fungi are the most biochemically diverse group of organisms on Earth. Some of them thrive in environments that would be lethal to plants and animals; for example, geothermal springs, where the water temperature is close to boiling, or the sediments of swamps, which can be devoid of oxygen. These microorganisms perform a vast array of biochemical reactions whose potential uses to human beings are likely to be enormous. Those uses, many of which were explored during the past year, include but are by no means restricted to the destruction of hazardous waste, the development of novel medical and agricultural products, and the production of energy.

Bioremediation. Bioremediation is the use of biological or biotechnological means to halt or reverse degradation of the environment. Currently most efforts have centered on the use of bacteria to convert toxic industrial waste into nontoxic compounds. Naturally occurring microorganisms already have de-

Rectangular bioremediation test plot on an oil-fouled Alaskan beach contrasts sharply with its surroundings. Some weeks earlier, in the summer of 1989, the plot had been sprayed with fertilizer to enhance microbial degradation of the oil.

graded a small but significant portion of the 1989 *Exxon Valdez* oil spill in Alaskan waters and, given enough time, probably could cleanse the shorelines. Such organisms exploit the crude petroleum as a source of carbon and actually grow and increase their numbers while removing the oil. By extrapolation one could easily imagine vast numbers of bacteria effectively degrading major spills of toxic waste to harmless and less visible compounds.

Biological cleanup of hazardous waste is generally recognized as the most cost-efficient means of purifying the Earth of the industrial pollutants that have accumulated over the years. Small-scale experiments in the 1980s have been enormously successful. Large-scale projects in the early 1990s are expected to involve more than 76,000 cu m (100,000 cu yd) of contaminated soil and to cost upwards of $5 million. Georgia Gulf and Georgia-Pacific corporations recently completed a one-hectare (2.5-ac) bacterial bioremediation project in Plaquemine, La., in which two types of *Pseudomonas putida* and one species of *Acinetobacter* degraded the toxic aromatic compound phenol to carbon dioxide in about 80 days.

A typical bioremediation project works in the following manner: After a waste dump is located, the toxic chemical components are identified. Then bacterial species are identified that grow on the toxic substances and convert them into harmless compounds. The bacteria accomplish this feat of transformation by means of a series of enzymes, which change one chemical into another. From the chemical conversions they often derive energy for use in their growth processes. After enough chemical conversions have occurred, the starting molecule generally is changed to a much smaller and less toxic form, such as carbon dioxide. By 1991 a large variety of such bacteria were available, and others were being routinely isolated.

Not surprisingly, the best place to find such bacteria is the toxic-waste site itself. Bacteria that are useful in bioremediation tend to thrive at such sites because they are resistant to the toxic effects of the pollutants. Sometimes a single microbial species can accomplish the entire series of chemical conversions, but often several species are necessary to assure complete remediation, particularly if the toxic compound has a complex chemical structure. When an appropriate mixture of bacteria has been identified, large numbers are grown in the laboratory, concentrated, and shipped to the contaminated site. The microbial cocktail is mixed with the contaminated material along with organic nitrates and phosphates to enhance bacterial growth. The bioremediation project is monitored periodically to determine how fast the toxic compounds are being degraded. A typical project lasts from several months to one year. What happens to the introduced microbes after the toxic compounds disappear from the area? Although it is not possible to remove these bacteria selectively from the soil, their numbers decline when the toxic compound is depleted, and with time they are replaced by indigenous species.

The U.S. government has invested in the development of bioremediation technology and will continue to do so. In the early 1990s the Department of Energy's Microbiology of Subsurface Environments Program supported a number of research projects designed to improve the technology. Such research includes isolating unusual types of bacteria that degrade toxic waste for which there is currently no remediation, determining the biochemical pathways involved in the degradation process, and operating small-scale experimental projects.

One day it may be possible to apply the technology to the remediation of mining areas, which often remain devoid of plant life for many years owing to the toxic effects of metal-containing ore tailings. Bacteria can concentrate rare metals from dilute solutions; the most well-understood examples involve the acquisition of iron by means of siderophores, molecules that specifically attach to iron. Bacteria also are able to convert toxic forms of a metal such as mercury into nontoxic forms, an ability that may be useful in the cleanup of mining operations.

Novel microbial compounds. Plants and plant extracts have been used to treat human disease for thousands of years, but only recently have bacteria and fungi been exploited for their useful metabolites. Microbes have metabolic pathways that produce compounds having remarkably diverse chemical structures. These compounds are called secondary metabolites because they are not essential to the growth of the producing organism; in most cases, their roles are unknown. Historically the most beneficial of the secondary metabolites are the antibiotics, which have been used to treat disease for about 50 years. Antibiotics, however, are not the only microbial products that have attracted research interest. Others also have applications as therapeutic agents and are being marketed.

Bacterial products hold great promise in several important areas. One is that of immunomodulation, which involves stimulating or suppressing an individual's immune system. Immunostimulation is beneficial in restoring an impaired immune system, whereas immunosuppression is useful in preventing an immune system from rejecting an organ transplant. Cyclosporin, a compound produced by certain filamentous fungi, has been used since the late 1970s to suppress immune rejection in patients who have received organ transplants. Unfortunately, the drug has some severe side effects, which limit its utility. Recently a variety of other immunomodulators were discovered, particularly from bacteria of the genus *Streptomyces*. One, an immunosuppressive drug known by the code number FK-506, proved just as effective as cyclosporin in human clinical trials and had fewer short-term side effects. In addition to their therapeutic applications, such compounds should be useful to researchers studying how the immune system works.

A second emerging application for microbial products is enzyme inhibition. Microbial products that inhibit cholesterol synthesis in humans and other organisms (*e.g.*, livestock) or the formation of dental plaque have recently been identified. Dental plaque is composed of bacteria as well as organic and inorganic compounds. One of the bacterial components is *Streptococcus mutans*, which causes tooth decay by dissolving the enamel surface of the tooth. Mutastein, a glycoprotein (sugar-protein compound) produced by the fungus *Aspergillus terreus*, inhibits the synthesis by *S. mutans* of an extracellular compound that promotes attachment of the bacterium to the tooth surface. In 1990 mutastein was in commercial use as a prophylactic agent for tooth decay.

A third group of microbial products with potential therapeutic value are receptor agonists or antagonists, chemicals that bind to a hormone receptor and either enhance or inhibit its function. For example, oxytocin is a pituitary hormone that regulates uterine contraction and lactation. The bacterium *Streptomyces silvensis* produces a compound that has been found in laboratory experiments to inhibit oxytocin-induced contraction of rat uteri and thus may be useful in delaying premature labor in humans. A fourth group of products are antineoplastic drugs, which prevent proliferation of certain types of cancer cells. Many of them, such as adriamycin, suppress the activity of protein kinase C, an enzyme involved in cell proliferation. A fifth group of products are those that inhibit the growth of certain insects or plants,

a function that makes them useful in agriculture. Long exploited commercially as a crop insecticide, *Bacillus thuringiensis* produces proteins which kill the insect larvae that eat plant material coated with this bacterium. Apparently, insects that develop resistance to one type of *B. thuringiensis* insecticidal protein remain sensitive to others, offering hope that these proteins will remain useful for many years to come in controlling crop pests.

Once a microbial compound with useful properties has been discovered, it is purified and its chemical structure determined. Then chemists devise ways to make subtle changes in the chemical structure in order to improve its potency, spectrum of activity, specificity, or oral absorption. Second- and third-generation products created in this manner often have improved activity-to-toxicity ratios. Although all these steps are critical to the development of such compounds, the most difficult and expensive step in the process is the identification of the initial active compound from microorganisms. During the past year it became apparent that only a few of the bacterial species in aquatic and soil ecosystems have been identified. Apparently, conventional techniques for culturing such microorganisms fail to allow the growth of the majority of them. For instance, the myxobacteria, which were virtually ignored in initial searches for antibiotic-producing bacteria because of culturing difficulties, appear to have a wealth of secondary metabolites that inhibit the growth of disease-causing microorganisms and viruses. Compounds useful in the treatment of such fatal diseases as AIDS undoubtedly exist in the microbial world and await discovery and exploitation.

Energy production. During 1990 the price of crude oil rose because of political events in the Middle East. In the future, as the cost of crude oil continues to increase for various reasons and as the oil supply diminishes, industry will be forced to develop alternate means of producing energy. Given the consequences, humans have been remarkably remiss in developing alternate energy sources. There are many ways to generate energy by physical means; for example, solar collectors, hydroelectric plants, and nuclear power plants. One way of using bacteria to provide an alternate energy source is in the production of the flammable gas methane from agricultural waste. Cellulose, by far the most abundant carbohydrate available from plant biomass, is synthesized at an estimated rate of 40 billion tons per year. Conversion of even a small portion of that total to methane would provide a considerable energy source. Such a conversion process occurs naturally in the rumen of cows through the concerted effort of a variety of different microorganisms.

The first step in the conversion process is the breakdown of cellulose into the glucose molecules that compose it, a complicated task that requires many different cellulose-degrading enzymes known as cellulases. Certain fungi and bacteria secrete a variety of cellulases that act together to hydrolyze cellulose to glucose. Next, the glucose is oxidized to carbon dioxide. Finally, bacteria known as methanogens convert carbon dioxide to methane. Microbial methane generation is inhibited by oxygen and occurs only under anaerobic (oxygen-devoid) conditions such as those in the rumen of a cow or the deep sediments of a swamp. By means of anaerobic cellulose-degrading bacteria, it may be possible to perform the whole process of methane production from cellulose in anaerobic vessels.

At the present time the production of methane from agricultural waste is limited by the expense of the technology, and development incentives are stifled by the relatively cheap cost of crude oil. The recent increases in oil prices should help revive interest in alternate approaches to fuel production and may provide capital for continued research in cellulose-to-methane conversion.

—Lawrence J. Shimkets

Molecular biology

Of the myriad advances in molecular biology during the past year, three have been chosen for detailed description: identification of the gene involved in the disease neurofibromatosis and its relationship to the molecular mechanism of intracellular signal transduction; a method for detecting and amplifying RNA molecules with desired properties; and the three-dimensional structure of phospholipases, proteins that do chemistry at an oil-water interface.

Genetics of neurofibromatosis. Quantum jumps in understanding the molecular basis of human diseases now happen regularly. In 1990 the disease in the news was neurofibromatosis (NF), which affects about one in 3,500 individuals of all ethnic groups. Owing to mutation in a gene called NF1, affected individuals usually display café-au-lait (pale brown) spots on the skin as well as neurofibromas, tumors of peripheral nerve tissue. Although all cells of the body carry the same NF1 gene, the disease is manifest principally in cells of the peripheral nervous system. The NF1 gene was identified as the result of intensive work of two large teams, one headed by Ray White at

the University of Utah School of Medicine and the other led by Francis Collins at the University of Michigan. The race for discovery of the gene was described fully in major newspapers. In this article the focus is on the subsequent analysis of the NF1 gene product and its possible role in the cell.

The NF1 gene is immense, covering more than 130,000 nucleotide pairs of human chromosome 17. The part of the gene that encodes the NF1 protein contains at least 7,455 nucleotide pairs; the remainder is organized in 11 or more long stretches of interrupting sections called introns, some of which encode other proteins. In many cases, determining the nucleotide sequence of a gene, which allows the deduction of the amino acid sequence of the protein product of the gene, fails to provide a clue to the function of the protein. In the case of the NF1 gene product, however, comparison of its amino acid sequence with all the sequences of known proteins stored in the protein-sequence data base at Los Alamos (N.M.) National Laboratory revealed a similarity of part of the NF1 protein with two families of known proteins: IRA proteins of yeast and GAP proteins of mammalian cells. IRA stands for "inhibitory regulator of RAS," and GAP stands for "GTPase activating protein." Both IRA and GAP proteins regulate the activity of an intracellular signal-transducing protein called RAS by stimulating the ability of RAS to convert a compound, guanosine triphosphate (GTP), that is bound to it to guanosine diphosphate (GDP; *see* Figure 1). (RAS accomplishes the conversion to GDP by splitting off a phosphate group from GTP by means of hydrolysis. Proteins that can do this are said to have GTPase activity.) The RAS-GTP complex promotes certain cellular activities, as described below, while the RAS-GDP complex is inactive.

Recent experiments involving a collaboration between White's laboratory and that of Fuyuhiko Tamanoi at the University of Chicago showed that the NF1 protein is indeed a GAP protein. Among other things, it was demonstrated that a purified NF1 protein fragment stimulates the GTPase activity of RAS protein in the test tube. The GTPase activity of certain mutant forms of the RAS protein cannot be stimulated by IRA or GAP proteins; these mutants cannot be stimulated by NF1 either. Tamanoi showed further that both GAP and NF1 interact at the same domain of the RAS protein. Similar con-

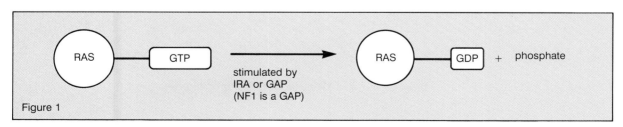

Figure 1

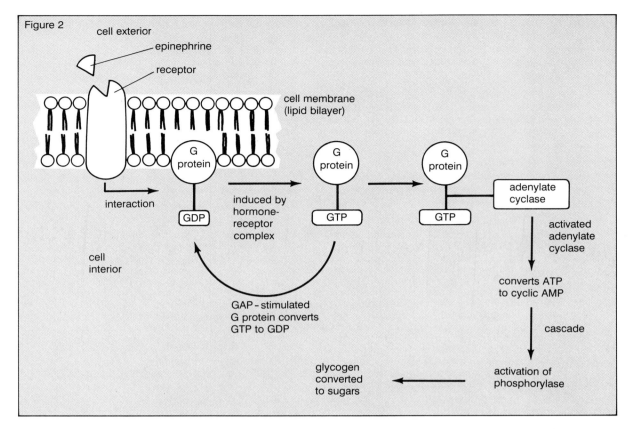

Figure 2

clusions were reached by Collins and another group. To understand the significance of these results, it will be useful to review some of the features of the mechanisms by which cells process chemical and physical signals from the outside world.

Signal processing employs several different biochemical pathways, but most of them include a type of intermediary compound called G protein. The role of G protein in signal transduction can be illustrated by following the process by which the hormone epinephrine (adrenaline) induces the breakdown of the carbohydrate glycogen stored in liver cells (see Figure 2). First, epinephrine carried to the liver by the bloodstream binds to receptor protein embedded in the liver cell membrane. The binding results in a change in structure of the part of the receptor protein that protrudes into the cell. Nearby, in the membrane, is the G protein, which is bound to a molecule of GDP. The hormone-receptor complex interacts with the G-protein–GDP complex (which is inert), causing the GDP to dissociate and be replaced by GTP. The G-protein–GTP complex then binds to, and activates, the enzyme adenylate cyclase, which converts the compound adenosine triphosphate (ATP) to cyclic adenosine monophosphate (cyclic AMP). The latter compound, called a "second messenger," in turn initiates a cascade of

reactions that eventually activates the enzyme phosphorylase, which breaks down glycogen into simpler sugars. In this system and many others, the G protein functions as a signal transducer and amplifier, continuing to stimulate adenylate cyclase as long as the compound to which it is bound remains GTP. The G protein, like RAS, is a GTPase; over the course of a few minutes it splits its bound GTP to give GDP and phosphate. The resulting G-protein–GDP complex is unable to activate adenylate cyclase; it has returned to the state in which it is ready to receive another signal from a hormone-receptor complex. It should be noted that the regulatory features of this system require that GTP be converted to GDP. If it were not, the system would be locked in the "on" position all the time. In the example above, the liver would be unable to store glycogen because phosphorylase would be activated continuously, whether or not the cells were stimulated by epinephrine.

Returning to the RAS protein, one notes first that it is a G protein, binding GTP and converting it to GDP when stimulated by IRA proteins of yeast or GAP proteins of mammalian cells. Mutant forms of RAS protein were discovered first as the products of genes in tumor-forming viruses. The name, in fact, comes from the rat sarcoma virus in which the gene, named *ras*, was discovered. As with other viral oncogenes, related cellular *ras* genes were subsequently isolated, and then, to complete the picture, RAS-encoding genes were isolated from human tumors. Comparison of the nucleotide sequences of normal and tumor-forming RAS-protein genes showed single nucleotide changes in one of two positions. Each of these changes affected the GTP-binding site of the RAS protein, reducing its ability to convert its bound GTP to GDP even when stimulated by IRA or GAP proteins. Thus, the RAS protein is a regulatory G protein that, when mutated, is locked in the "on" position. In this case, the result is uncontrolled cell proliferation, or tumor growth.

How does RAS function as a signal-transducing protein? Like the other G proteins, RAS is normally bound to the cell membrane. It appears to be brought into play by the interaction of a protein growth factor, such as platelet-derived growth factor (PDGF), with its membrane-spanning receptor. The activated RAS protein, with its bound GTP, even initiates a cascade that leads to cell growth. The components of this cascade remain to be identified; they could include adenylate cyclase and the cyclins and protein kinases that control the cell-division cycle. With regard to neurofibromatosis, it seems likely that the disease is due to a mutation of NF1 such that this GAP protein loses its ability to stimulate RAS to convert its bound GTP. The unchecked RAS-GTP complex then continues to stimulate cell proliferation. Whether NF1 plays this role uniquely in cells of the peripheral nervous system and whether this role is not taken by other GAP proteins in these cells are questions for the future.

The description above outlines how mutation in a gene encoding the RAS protein or in a gene encoding a protein that regulates RAS, such as NF1, can lead to tumor growth. Other human afflictions result from acute damage to G proteins by bacterial toxins. One of the best studied is cholera. The cholera organism produces a protein toxin that modifies one of the G proteins in cells that line the human gut. The modified G protein activates adenylate cyclase continuously in these cells, resulting in loss of water from the cells. This effect manifests itself in the severe diarrhea and dehydration that characterize cholera. Notwithstanding the misery produced by the disease, the toxin has provided a useful tool for understanding the way G proteins work.

Phospholipases. Another family of toxins, the phospholipases, function differently. Lengthy study of their structure came to fruition in 1990 with the determination of the three-dimensional structures of the phospholipases from cobra venom and from bee venom.

Phospholipids are the basic building blocks of the double-layered membranes that surround cells. These membranes are impermeable to most chemical compounds. Traffic in and out of cells is controlled by proteins embedded in the membranes, examples of which include the hormone receptors and growth factor receptors mentioned above. A phospholipid molecule is constructed from four elements: the three-carbon molecule glycerol, one phosphate group, two molecules of long-chain fatty acids, and a basic group such as choline, ethanolamine, or serine attached to the phosphate (*see* Figure 3). Cell membranes are bilayers of these phospholipids, with the hydrophobic (water-avoiding) fatty acid chains pointing toward the interior of the membrane and the hydrophilic (water-seeking) phosphate groups with their associated choline on the outside, where they face the watery medium outside and inside the cell.

The phospholipid components of membranes have to be "biodegradable" in the sense that as cells die, the membranes are recycled. Moreover, the fatty acid components can be damaged by oxygen and have to be repaired (by removal and replacement) to maintain the cell's integrity. Consequently, phospholipases, enzymes that cut apart, or cleave, phospholipid molecules at various bonds, are normal components of the body, serving a repair role as well as participating in the generation of a second messenger, called arachidonic acid, in some types of cells. Phospholipases occur in four classes, differing in the bond whose cleavage they catalyze. Phospholipase A_1 cleaves the fatty acid near carbon 1 of the glycerol backbone; phospholipase A_2 cleaves the fatty acid near carbon 2; and phospholipases C and D cleave on either side of the phosphorus atom in the phosphate. The toxic components of snake and bee venoms are phospholipase A_2 (PLA_2) enzymes.

Generalized structural formula for a phospholipid molecule identifies the specific bond cleaved by each of four different classes of phospholipases: A_1, A_2, C, and D.

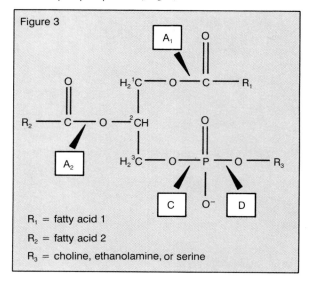

Figure 3

R_1 = fatty acid 1
R_2 = fatty acid 2
R_3 = choline, ethanolamine, or serine

These proteins cause trouble in two ways. First, they split the fatty acid from the 2 position of the phospholipid backbone, which destroys the membrane bilayer. Second, the product of this reaction, 1-acyl phosphatidylcholine, also called lysolecithin, is a powerful detergent that lyses, or breaks down, red blood cells.

Interest in the phospholipases from a molecular viewpoint stemmed from a mystifying feature: the enzymes are water soluble, yet their preferred substrate (the molecules whose reaction they catalyze; *i.e.*, phospholipids) is aggregated in an intact membrane rather than dispersed in a watery medium. Why is this so? The answer was provided by the structure of cobra venom and bee venom PLA$_2$, complexed to an inhibitor and determined to high resolution by means of X-ray diffraction methods by a team headed by Paul Sigler at Yale University.

Phospholipase structure has been investigated for many years. Indeed, the first crystal structure for a PLA$_2$ enzyme, from bovine pancreas, was determined in the early 1980s by Jan Drenth and co-workers in The Netherlands. The features of that structure, in fact, enabled the structure of the cobra venom enzyme to be determined because the two

are so similar. As of 1991, the amino acid sequences of more than 50 different PLA$_2$ enzymes had been determined. Comparison of the sequences indicates which parts have been conserved throughout the evolution of the protein family and therefore are likely to participate in PLA$_2$ function. The bee venom enzyme belongs to a different sequence family, and much of its three-dimensional structure is different from that of the cobra venom enzyme. Nevertheless, the part that binds and cleaves phospholipid can be superimposed on the corresponding part of the cobra venom PLA$_2$. The net result of the new information is a plausible model that explains how PLA$_2$ can cleave phospholipids without a change in the structure of its own polypeptide backbone and why it requires a phospholipid substrate that is aggregated rather than dispersed.

One of the fascinating details of the model is the way in which the PLA$_2$ molecule is thought to interact with the cell membrane's lipid bilayer (*see* Figure 4). The part of the enzyme labeled "interfacial surface" sits on the bilayer in such a way that its "hydrophobic channel" precisely covers one phospholipid molecule in the bilayer, providing a nonaqueous environment for that molecule to dif-

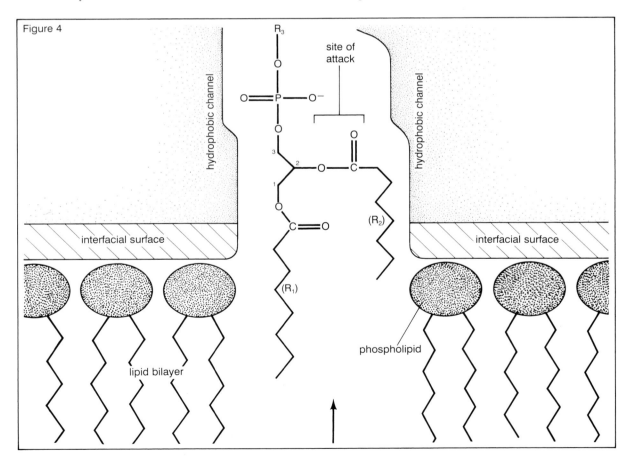

Figure 4

fuse upward. Once in the enzyme's channel, the phospholipid is bound to a calcium ion and certain amino acids forming the channel wall, where cleavage of the fatty acid from the phospholipid can occur. This elegant model accounts neatly for one of the great puzzles of biochemistry. Essentially, PLA_2 never deals with the problem of how to get its substrate to come out and play in the water. Instead, it covers the membrane with an umbrella and allows the substrate to keep dry while it diffuses up into the catalytic pocket.

Directed evolution of RNA molecules. During the past year researchers continued to find new ways to exploit the awesome power of the polymerase chain reaction (PCR), which in a few hours can amplify the nucleotide sequence of a single DNA molecule to produce enough of the sequence for detailed diagnostic purposes (see *1991 Yearbook of Science and the Future* Year in Review: LIFE SCIENCES: *Molecular biology*). The guardians of remnants of Abraham Lincoln's hair, for example, were considering a proposal to examine its DNA, by means of the PCR, to determine whether Lincoln had a genetic condition called Marfan's disease. Among more practical applications, however, was a new method for the rapid, directed evolution of nucleic acid molecules capable of binding a particular target molecule. Devised by Craig Tuerk and Larry Gold of the University of Colorado, the method is called SELEX, for "systematic evolution of ligands by exponential enrichment." A related procedure was developed by A.D. Ellington and J.W. Szostak of the Massachusetts General Hospital, Boston.

Many of the critical steps in gene expression require specific binding of proteins to nucleic acids: RNA polymerase's recognition of the start signals for transcription of DNA into messenger RNA, the binding of messenger RNA to ribosomes, and so on. For scientists to discover the rules governing these interactions, sometimes it is sufficient to compare the nucleotide sequences of many different examples. For example, comparison of the nucleotide sequences preceding the start site for transcription of many bacterial genes led to the conclusion that two short sequences located within 40 nucleotides of the site comprise the best, or strongest, "promoter" for the initiation of transcription. If one were interested in a protein-nucleic acid interaction that is unique, however, the conventional approach would be to change, by mutation, each of the nucleotides in the suspected region of interaction one by one and then determine the consequence for the interaction. This process can take a very long time, and the result will give information only for single nucleotide changes. As designed, such an experiment gives no clue to alternate paths that evolution of the interaction might have taken.

Tuerk and Gold changed the conventional approach completely. They were interested in a small RNA loop in a regulatory sequence, occurring in a virus, to which a particular protein binds. First, using a mixture of nucleotides, they synthesized a mixture of more than 65,000 RNA molecules that had every possible eight-nucleotide sequence in the loop region. They then passed the mixture through a filter medium to which the protein had been affixed, washed away every RNA molecule that bound loosely, stripped off the ones that bound tightly, reverse-transcribed them to DNA, amplified them using the PCR, and finally transcribed the amplified DNA back to RNA. After they had repeated this procedure several times, they examined what they had netted. Their catch consisted mainly of two molecules: one had the sequence of the viral RNA molecule already known. The second molecule differed from the first at four nucleotide positions out of eight. Such a result is remarkable in several ways. The alternate structure would never have been found by systematic one-by-one replacement of nucleotides in the original sequence. The affinity of the mutant sequence for the protein is nearly the same as that of the wild type; it thus represents an alternate path that evolution could have taken. However, because four nucleotide changes are required and the single-change intermediates do not bind the protein, it is not possible today for evolution to get from the sequence in the virus to the alternate sequence.

The SELEX method, in principle, should work to select an RNA molecule that binds to any desired target molecule. For example, RNA molecules having particular enzymic or inhibitory properties might be selected in this way. Tuerk and Gold concluded their paper with the statement that SELEX could "provide unpredictable and unimaginable molecular configurations of nucleic acids and proteins with any number of targeted functions."

—Robert Haselkorn

Zoology

Considerable excitement in zoology during the past year was provided by discoveries of new primate species, contrary finds in evolution, fascinating "digs" in paleontology, concerns for endangered species, and culturing of brain cells. Unfortunately, the excitement was tempered by continuing world problems developing from pollution, the threat of global warming, mismanagement of natural resources, loss of wildlife habitats, and the lack of human concern for nature. Particularly distressing was the lengthening list of vanishing species, among which were amphibians, bears, and sharks.

Paleobiology. With a length of 12 m (40 ft), *Tyrannosaurus rex* was the largest carnivorous dinosaur.

To complement its size, the king of dinosaurs had large hind legs and a powerful, massive jaw filled with banana-sized flesh-cutting teeth. Scientists envision *T. rex* as the most fearsome animal that ever trod upon the Earth. Nevertheless, its meter-long (three-foot-long) forelimbs always have appeared small and feeble compared with the whole animal, and paleontologists have never agreed about the function of the structures. Possible answers were recently gleaned from well-preserved tyrannosaur fossils obtained from sites near Bozeman, Mont. Pieces of *T. rex*, including a complete forelimb, were studied by Matt B. Smith at Montana State University's Museum of the Rockies, Bozeman, and by Kenneth Carpenter of the Denver (Colo.) Museum of Natural History.

By examining the forelimb bones and measuring the diameters of tendon attachment scars, the scientists determined the muscle mass and the stationary force that could have been produced by such forelimbs. The latter figure was calculated to be about 193 kg (426 lb) or 10 times that produced by a human bicep—certainly not indicative of feeble limbs. Furthermore, from observations of digits, carpals, and metacarpals of the forelimb, Smith and Carpenter described two claws that faced away from each other and thus could not clasp in the manner of the human thumb and index finger. They concluded that the claws were capable of penetrating animal flesh and may have functioned for killing prey or perhaps picking up dead animals, but they probably were not involved in capturing prey.

Discovery of dinosaur embryos is so rare that, according to Phillip J. Currie of the Tyrrell Museum of Paleontology, Drumheller, Alta., only six species had been documented. Thus, the finding of the embryo of a seventh dinosaur species 135 million to 150 million years old was indeed an event. While working through materials obtained from the fossil-rich Morrison Formation near Uravan, Colo., a geology student, Rodney D. Scheetz of Brigham Young University, Provo, Utah, discovered the embryo of a dryosaur (*Dryosaurus altus*), a 3.7-m (12-ft) gazelle-like herbivorous dinosaur. The 30-cm (12-in) embryo appeared to be well developed and possessed at least two baby teeth, indicating that hatching was near. In 1991 Scheetz planned to collect more materials at the same site, which was believed to have been a nesting area for a herd of dryosaurs. He hoped to contribute to knowledge of embryology and family life in dinosaurs, topics about which little information currently existed.

Primates. The discovery of a new species of primate and the rediscovery of one believed extinct stirred the world of primate biology. The new species, the black-faced lion tamarin (*Leontopithecus caissara*), is the fourth known species of lion tamarin, some of the rarest and most endangered primates

AP/Wide World

A new species of monkey, the black-faced lion tamarin, was discovered on the island of Superagui off the heavily populated coast of southern Brazil.

in the world. It was found by Maria Lúcia Lorini and Vanessa Guerra Persson of the Capão da Imbuia Natural History Museum, Curitiba, Brazil, on Superagui, a 14,200-ha (35,000-ac) island located 250 km (155 mi) south of São Paulo. The black-faced lion tamarin is a squirrel-like monkey with a golden body and a black face. The colorful lion tamarins exist only in remnant forests of eastern Brazil and are endangered because of encroaching civilization. Dante Martins Teixeira of the National Museum in Rio de Janeiro planned an expedition to learn more about the new species and was encouraging the Brazilian government to extend the national park boundary on Superagui to include the habitat of the black-faced lion tamarin before it was destroyed by commercial ventures.

The hairy-eared dwarf lemur (*Allocebus trichotis*) is a prosimian, one of the two major groups of primates. Previously thought extinct, the species was found alive and described by Bernard Meier of Ruhr University, Bochum, Germany, and by Roland Albigniac, UN Development Program/Unesco, Antananarivo, Madagascar. On his third expedition Meier located, captured, and photographed a single live specimen in a remote rain forest in northeastern Madagascar. Later two pairs were trapped and observed by Albigniac.

Russell Mittermeier, president of Conservation International, Washington, D.C., regarded the rediscovery as important because the tiny, brown, mouselike lemur, with a 12.7-cm (5-in) body and 17.8-cm (7-in) tail, is one of the smallest known primates and the only species in its genus. Until this find it had never been seen alive by any scientist, all previous information having come from preserved specimens. As a result, its basic biology (nutrition, behavior, social organization, and reproduction) was unknown. The scientists expressed hope that the discovery would focus attention on the primate and on preserving the forests where it lives. In 1990 the Malagasy government was considering protection of the last patches of Madagascar's virgin rain forests.

Amphibian decline. Most amphibians lead a two-staged life, first developing as aquatic tadpoles and then maturing into semiterrestrial creatures such as frogs and salamanders. These animals readily absorb chemicals (*e.g.*, acids, pesticides, and organic compounds) through their skin from either water or soil and so are regarded as excellent ecological barometers of the health of the environment.

Because recent reports indicated that amphibian populations were dropping in many parts of the world, a panel of experts met at the University of California at Irvine in February 1990 to discuss the problem and seek explanations. Among those attending was David Wake, director of the Museum of Vertebrate Zoology of the University of California at Berkeley, who reported that numerous species of amphibians were rapidly disappearing in the Americas, Europe, Asia, Africa, and Australia. Wake stated, "[Amphibians] were here when the dinosaurs were here, and [they] survived the age of mammals. They are tough survivors. If they're checking out now, I think it is significant." Stanley Rand of the Smithsonian Tropical Research Institute reported that between 1979 and 1982 at the University of São Paulo's field station at Boracea, Brazil, 6 of 30 common species of frogs had disappeared and 7 had experienced major declines. According to Michael J. Tyler of the University of Adelaide, Australia, serious population declines in 20 of Australia's estimated 194 frog species had occurred since the early 1980s. Two species had disappeared completely, including the gastric brooding frog (*Rheobatrachus silus*) identified by Tyler in

the early 1970s. In the Rocky Mountains of Colorado and Wyoming, Paul S. Corn of the U.S. Fish and Wildlife Service reported difficulty in finding the boreal toads that once had been so common "you had to kick them out of the way as you were walking down the trail."

The experts agreed that a worldwide decline of amphibians was occurring, but factors causing the phenomenon were not known. Although the usual reasons such as loss of habitats, stocking of predatory fish, industrial wastes, and "11-year-olds playing catch with gel masses of eggs" were suspected, many declines were occurring in pristine areas and other favorite collecting sites of herpetologists. Possibly, acid rain and snow (which hold airborne pesticides and other toxic substances) may be having a significant effect. It was concluded that long-term studies needed to be carried out and should consider, among other things, environmental chemistry, population surveys, and the pathology and toxicology of dead animals.

Other imperiled species. As a result of careful management, cooperation between various state and federal groups, tough regulations by the U.S. Fish and Wildlife Service, and banning of the insecticide DDT, the population of the American bald eagle (*Haliaetus leucocephalus*) is increasing. The species likely will soon be removed from the endangered list and placed on the threatened list. The upgrading will not reduce federal protection of the bald eagle but will allow wildlife officials to remove healthy birds from the wild for exhibition and educational purposes. According to the National Wildlife Federation, about 2,600 nesting pairs of bald eagles were reported in the contiguous 48 states in 1989, a figure considerably above the 400 nesting pairs reported in 1960. To reestablish the population, numerous

Previously thought extinct, the hairy-eared dwarf lemur was found living in a remote rain forest in northern Madagascar. Until the recent find, the mouse-sized prosimian had never been seen alive by any scientist.

The grizzly (above) and other brown bears constitute one of several bear species whose global populations were recently reported to be declining. Among the causes cited were poaching and loss of habitat to human activities.

bald eagles were captured in Alaska and Canada and successfully reintroduced to most regions of the contiguous U.S. A point of importance in this story is that an endangered species, with considerable help, has successfully recovered and should not be left on the endangered list. Of the approximately 450 endangered species of plants and animals in the U.S., fewer than 20 have been reclassified as threatened, the last being the American alligator in 1987.

Concern for declining animal populations should begin early and not wait until extinction is a distinct possibility. Two major animal groups that are showing definite declines in global populations are bears and sharks. The plight of bears was reported in a monograph by Christopher Servheen of the U.S. Fish and Wildlife Service, Missoula, Mont. He wrote that bears are being killed or are losing their habitats to human settlement, agriculture, and industry. In addition, bears throughout their range have become the target of poachers engaged in illicit trade with China, Japan, and South Korea, where such items as bear claws and bear gallbladders are believed to have special powers and thus are in high demand. Since in the public eye most bear species are not members of the charismatic megafauna (elephants, tigers, wolves, rhinoceroses, and other large animals that attract most of the attention) and are somewhat solitary in behavior, their decline has not stirred much interest. Of the world's eight species—black, brown, sun, sloth, panda, polar, spectacled, and Asiatic black—only the populations of black and polar bears seem reasonably stable. Servheen believed that major efforts should be made to protect bears and to save quality environments for them.

Sharks may not seem like animals whose population declines should cause concern, but these denizens of the deep are the top carnivores of the ocean. Severe reduction of their numbers will allow other animal populations to mushroom, leading to imbalance in marine food chains. Although recreational shark fishing has been common, commercial exploitation of sharks has undergone a significant rise in the 1980s. Shark steaks and fin soup, unfortunately, are now common restaurant fare. Fins are obtained by a practice called finning, in which sharks are caught, the fins cut off, and the bleeding carcasses thrown in the water. Roughly 16 million kg (34 million lb) of sharks are slaughtered annually in this manner. In response to the problem, the National Oceanic and Atmospheric Administration proposed a plan that would limit the numbers of sharks taken by commercial interests in U.S. waters along the Atlantic coast.

Ecology. In 1982 P.R. Zimmerman and co-workers of the National Center for Atmospheric Research, Boulder, Colo., reported that termites emit about 150 trillion g (330 billion lb) of methane gas each year, or about 30% of the total methane released into the environment. Methane is considered a "greenhouse gas"; it absorbs heat in the form of infrared radiation and so contributes to the global warming of the atmosphere via an enhanced greenhouse effect. The scientists suggested that increased termite populations were responsible for a major part of the currently detected rise in atmospheric methane and thus could seriously affect the environment.

To reexamine the suggestion, a team of American and Australian scientists collected data from field studies of mounds of five species of Australian termites from various sites in Queensland. In addition, detailed studies were performed on mounds of one species (*Coptotermes lacteus*) located in the Boola Boola State Forest southeast of Melbourne. The six-year study was carried out by M. Aslam K. Khalil and R.A. Rasmussen at the Institute of Atmospheric Sciences, Oregon Graduate Center, Beaverton, and Australian colleagues J.R.J. French of the Commonwealth Scientific and Industrial Research Organization, Division of Forest and Forest Projects, Highett, Victoria, and J.A. Holt, Division of Soils, Townville, Queensland. The scientists measured methane gas release by placing stainless steel domes over the termite mounds, collecting the gases in stainless steel flasks, and analyzing the gases (for methane, carbon dioxide, chloroform, and other organic compounds) with standard gas chromatographic techniques. Combining these data with estimates of the world termite population and the biomass that the termites consume each year, they calculated that the termites' contribution of methane to the environment was at most 4% of the global annual emission. Rather than blaming termites, these investigators believed that the increasing numbers of rice fields, where methane-producing bacteria thrive, and of cattle and sheep, which generate methane in their digestive tracts, may be major reasons for methane buildup.

An ecosystem is a complex of many populations of living organisms interacting together with the nonliving environment in a particular unit of space. The burning and devastation of tropical forests are slowly destroying the tropical ecosystems. In the past decade the devastation of coral reefs has been having a similar effect on the marine ecosystems to which they belong. Coral reefs are found in low-nutrient tropical and subtropical ocean waters and are the haven for countless forms of life. As coral reefs disappear, so do the forms dependent on the reefs for habitat and food. The reefs are being destroyed by vessel groundings, pollution, sewage runoff, predation by the crown-of-thorns starfish, deforestation and associated runoff, viral disease, loss of algae-eating sea urchins, hurricanes, dynamiting of the water for fish, coral mining, coral collecting, and recreational activities. Yet another, more insidious event presently affecting the reef ecosystem is coral "bleaching." Each chunk of coral comprises individual polyps, which capture and feed on plankton. A great deal of food for each polyp, however, comes from pigmented algal cells that live in the animal's tissues and that give reefs their various hues. The algal cells are capable of photosynthesis and produce by-products, which the coral uses for energy.

According to Ernest H. Williams, Jr., and Lucy Bunkley-Williams of the University of Puerto Rico, abnormally warm water temperatures are causing the death and loss of the algal cells, resulting in patches of coral that become white, or bleached. Long-term bleaching will result in starvation of the coral, destruction of the reef, and the eventual death of all reef-dependent organisms. Coral bleaching has been observed for many years but not nearly as extensively as it has since the late 1980s. It has been reported in the Florida Keys, the Caribbean, Australia's Great Barrier Reef, and areas near Hawaii and Okinawa. The cellular mechanism responsible for bleaching is not presently understood but, as theorized by Peter Glynn of the University of Miami, Fla., may be due to depletion of the energy reserves of the coral polyps caused by rapidly photosynthesizing algal cells. Another theory, put forth by Ian Sandeman of the University of Trent, Ont., involves overproduction of oxygen by the algal cells; the oxygen forms peroxides, substances toxic to both the algae and the polyps.

Animal behavior. The wandering albatross (*Diomedea exulans*) is the largest seabird, having a wingspan reaching 3.4 m (11 ft). It skims over the ocean surface foraging for squid, fish, and other marine animals. During the breeding season, the bird forages and returns to its mate to feed the young. Because of the low altitude at which it flies and the long distances covered, the path that the albatross takes had been impossible to follow. Using satellite telemetry, however, two French researchers successfully tracked them and found that they can fly as far as 15,200 km (9,445 mi) on a foraging flight and can cover daytime flight distances of up to 936 km (582 mi) at speeds as high as 80 km (50 mi) per hour. Pierre Jouventin and Henri Weimerskirch of the National Center for Scientific Research, Beauvoir, France, attached 180-g (6.3-oz) radio transmitters to each of six different male birds from a colony on Possession Island in the Crozet Islands, a French possession located in the southwestern Indian Ocean. The birds were followed by two satellites and were found to be actively flying day and night, resting only for short periods. Foraging trips lasted 2–33 days before the albatrosses returned to the nest, at which time they were caught and transmitters removed. As with so many other interesting animals, the wandering albatross is an endangered species, and this study is critical to its conservation.

Animals have evolved many ways of discouraging predators. Some also have joined with other species in complex relationships from which one or both benefit. In 1990 an unusual association was described between an amphipod and a pteropod inhabiting the waters of McMurdo Sound in Antarctica. A plankton-feeding fish, *Pagothenia borchgrevinki*, readily consumes the tiny shrimplike amphipod *Hyperiella dilatata* but avoids the tinier, thimblelike pteropod *Clione limacina*, the latter presumably being a chemically noxious organism. To take advantage of this chemical protection, the amphipod kidnaps a pteropod and carries it around piggyback. This behavior was observed by James B. McClintock of the University of Alabama at Birmingham and John Janssen of Loyola University, Chicago. By placing amphipod-pteropod pairs in aquariums, the biologists observed that fish sampling the duo always spit them out. They believed that their work provided the first documentation of an invertebrate increasing its chances for survival by capturing and carrying another species that gives chemical protection to both.

Vertebrate evolution. To discover fossils of the oldest tetrapod (four-limbed) vertebrates is exciting, but to find out that they were polydactylous (possessed more than the normal five digits) is truly revolutionary. In examining fossils of the two earliest known amphibians, Michael I. Coates and Jennifer A. Clack of the University Museum of Zoology, University of Cambridge, discovered the multiple digits. *Icthyostega* had seven digits on the hindlimb, and *Acanthostega* had eight digits on the forelimb. The fossils were located in an Upper Devonian deposit (360 million years old) by a Cambridge-Copenhagen expedition to Greenland in 1987. The discoveries complement the earlier finding of the only other De-

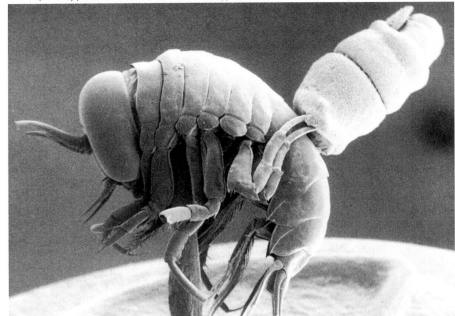

The shrimplike amphipod Hyperiella dilatata *of Antarctic waters was found to capture the smaller pteropod* Clione limacina *and carry it on its back as protection. Although the amphipod is normally defenseless, the pteropod apparently produces a chemical that makes both organisms distasteful to predatory fish.*

vonian tetrapod limb, that of the six-digit *Tulerpeton*, by O.A. Lebedev in the Soviet Union. They are not only interesting scientifically but also contrary to the traditional view held by many paleontologists and modern developmental biologists that the primitive ancestors of present tetrapods had the traditional five digits. Coates and Clack rejected that view and proposed that Devonian amphibians were just as likely to have six, seven, or eight digits, an idea that supports a recently proposed model by Neil H. Shubin and Pere Alberch that digit numbers were flexible and unspecified.

Neurobiology. For neurophysiologists the continuous culturing of a human cell line of cerebral cortical neurons (brain cells) had long been a goal. Success always had been limited by cells that either did not divide or did not survive culture conditions. From research reported by Gabriele V. Ronnett, Lynda D. Hester, Jeffrey S. Nye, Karen Connors, and Solomon H. Snyder of John Hopkins University School of Medicine, Baltimore, Md., such a cell line appeared to have been established. Immature human brain cells were removed from an 18-month-old patient with unilateral megalencephaly, a disorder associated with enlargement of the brain. The cells were placed in specially prepared solutions and, although most died, a few were found to survive and to proliferate. From these, two cell lines were maintained in culture for more than 19 months. When samples of the immature brain cells were removed from culture and exposed to various nerve growth factors, they specialized into mature brain cells having typical numerous long processes and branches. As further

proof that they had become mature brain cells, tests demonstrated the presence of specific neurotransmitters, the chemical messengers used by brain cells to communicate with each other. Several neurotransmitters, including somatostatin, glutamate, and cholecystokinin-8, were detected.

The study has important implications in neurobiology, fetal research, and the treatment of such afflictions as Alzheimer's disease and Parkinson's disease. As stated by Snyder, many advantages exist with the new system: neurobiologists will have cells with which to study development and differentiation; pharmacologists can design drugs for specific diseases; and existence of the cell lines may eliminate the need for obtaining immature brain cells from aborted fetuses to treat brain diseases. In addition, the cell lines possibly could be genetically engineered—for example, by inserting a gene responsible for secretion of the neurotransmitter dopamine, a chemical lacking in individuals suffering from Parkinson's disease. The engineered cells could then be implanted in the proper region of the patient's brain, where they would differentiate into specialized cells and secrete dopamine.

—George G. Brown

See also Feature Articles: Bats: Fragile Masters of the Night; Biotechnology for the '90s; Invader from the South: The Africanized "Killer" Bee; Masqueraders of the Plant World; Nature's Detectives: Biological Pollution Monitors; Preservation a Piece at a Time: The Captive Breeding and Reintroduction of Wildlife; Space: A New Laboratory for Biologists.

Materials sciences

Ceramics

Significant progress was made in several major areas of ceramics research during the past year. Of particular note was the synthesis of diamonds that exhibited the highest thermal conductivity ever reported for any solid material.

Structural ceramics. Efforts continued in the development of materials resistant to catastrophic failure under mechanical load. These toughened ceramics show promise for a range of structural applications, including automotive parts, gas turbine engine components, and space vehicle structures. The approach to designing such materials typically incorporates microscopic features that serve either to stop the propagation of a crack or to force the crack along a more tortuous path. When these features are incorporated, additional mechanical energy must be expended to fracture the material.

Kyocera Corp., Kyoto, Japan, developed a silicon nitride material that maintains impressive levels of strength and toughness to temperatures as high as 1,400° C (2,552° F). The toughness is derived from the presence of whiskerlike grains (microscopic crystallites resembling needles) that are formed in the material during processing. Cracks must propagate around these grains, making fracture more difficult. Flexural strength (resistance to fracture under bending load) approaching 700 MPa and fracture toughness of 8 MPa m$^{1/2}$ were reported. (Fracture toughness is a measure of the size of a flaw a material can tolerate before failing catastrophically under load. Ceramics typically have fracture toughness values of 1–6 MPa m$^{1/2}$, while metals exhibit values of 25 MPa m$^{1/2}$ or higher.) Resistance to both thermal shock and oxidation were said to be excellent.

The material can be fabricated to complex shapes by traditional methodologies such as slip casting (the pouring of liquid suspensions of particulates into porous plaster molds). These shaped components are then densified by gas pressure sintering (the application of heat in a pressurized gaseous environment). The microstructure and properties of the material can be tailored through the choice of starting constituents and processing parameters. Of particular importance is the purity of the silicon nitride powder and the nature of the densification additives employed. As of 1991, sintered silicon nitride was used for turbocharger rotors and held great promise as the material that would facilitate the development of ceramic automotive gas turbine engines.

The Carborundum Co., Niagara Falls, N.Y., developed a tough silicon carbide that had potential for structural application in severe environments. Current nonstructural uses of silicon carbide exploit its resistance to wear and chemical inertness. The new Carborundum material promised improved toughness, resistance to chipping, and strength for structural applications. It exhibited very fine equiaxed grains (microscopic crystallites of similar dimension in all directions) of 1–2 μm (micrometers) size. Fracture toughness up to 10 MPa m$^{1/2}$ and flexural strength of 910 MPa were measured at room temperature, and the material retained good properties up to 1,400° C. Cracks propagated along the boundaries between the individual grains. This behavior has a direct bearing on the enhanced toughness and may be related to the presence of an yttrium aluminate second phase along some grain boundaries and at the junctions where three grains meet.

Reference: Kyocera's brochure "Enter the New Stone Age"

Prototype automotive engine parts are made of sintered silicon nitride, which maintains high levels of strength and toughness at temperatures up to 1,400° C (2,552° F). The toughness is provided by whiskerlike grains (microscopic crystals resembling needles) that are formed in the material during processing.

Courtesy, Sociètè Europèene de Propulsion

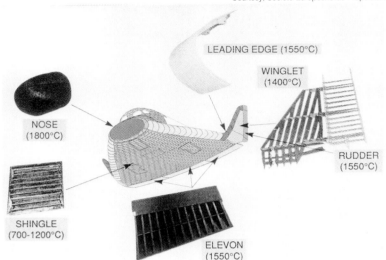

LEADING EDGE (1550°C)

WINGLET (1400°C)

NOSE (1800°C)

RUDDER (1550°C)

SHINGLE (700-1200°C)

ELEVON (1550°C)

Parts for the European space shuttle Hermes, except for the nose cap, are made of silicon carbide that is reinforced with carbon fibers. Toughness and resistance to high temperatures and oxidation are properties of this material.

The greatest increases in toughness can be achieved by reinforcing a ceramic with continuous fibers (long strands of manufactured fiber). With an appropriate choice of matrix, fiber, and the interface between them, cracks can be diverted along the fiber-matrix interface. This results in significant capability to accumulate damage on a local scale without failing. In fact, the response under load of such a fiber-reinforced ceramic composite often resembles that of a metal. Although the material remains brittle, it exhibits a pseudoplasticity and very high degree of toughness.

This desirable behavior was being exploited by the Société Européenne de Propulsion (SEP) of France in the design and fabrication of fiber-reinforced ceramic composite components for a variety of systems, including the European shuttlecraft, the Hermes. Prototype parts made of silicon carbide that contained layers of carbon fiber cloth showed great promise for these applications. Such materials exhibit flexural strength of 500 MPa and tensile strength (the greatest longitudinal stress that a substance can bear without tearing apart) of 350 MPa at room temperature, with good property retention to as high as 1,500° C (2,732° F) in air. Oxidation resistance is provided in part by the silicon carbide matrix and in part by a special coating.

Both thermal protective and structural components for the Hermes, including underbody shingles (insulative tile face sheets), wing leading edges, and elevons (maneuverable flaps at the rear of the wings), were made and tested in prototype form. In one case, samples of the material were subjected to temperatures and stress equivalent to what would be encountered during 15 Hermes missions. The test caused the material to lose only a small amount of tensile strength. In another test a full-size wing

leading edge panel was subjected to combined thermal and structural loads in a solar furnace in Spain. This facility permitted exposure to extremely high temperatures and very rapid heating and cooling cycles. The test panel experienced 12 excursions to 1,550° C (2,822° F) and 2 excursions to 1,700° C (3,092° F). Posttest analysis indicated a weight loss of approximately 1.8% and good residual mechanical properties. These results were in close agreement with tests on laboratory-scale samples and boded well for the ultimate use of these materials on the Hermes space vehicle.

Ceramic fibers. For composite applications requiring high-temperature service for hundreds or even thousands of hours, it is desirable to use a reinforcing fiber less prone to oxidation than is carbon fiber. Unfortunately, as of 1991 no such fibers on the commercial market were oxidatively stable and able to maintain mechanical properties much above 1,100°–1,200° C (2,012°–2,192° F). During the past year, however, U.S. companies produced three new fibers with the potential to fill this need, as described below.

Saphikon Inc., Milford, N.H., developed to preproduction status a sapphire (single-crystal aluminum oxide) filament made by edge-defined film-fed growth. In this process, molten alumina is drawn through a capillary die, and the solidified rod is collected on a spool to form a continuous fiber. The diameter is typically 125 μm. Reasonable strength (about 700 MPa) and excellent creep resistance can be maintained to as high as 1,500° C. (Creep is permanent dimensional change in a body while subjected to a constant mechanical load.)

Carborundum reported significant progress on silicon carbide fibers made by sintering filaments spun from a particulate-loaded molten thermoplastic polymer. This mixture is extruded through a multihole plate, called a spinneret, to form the fibers, which are then heated to burn out the polymer and sinter the silicon carbide particulates. The resulting fiber has a nominal diameter of 50 μm, grain size of 3–4 μm, and density of 3.15 g per cc. The typical tensile strength of 1,050 MPa is maintained to 1,550° C, and very good creep resistance was reported at 1,400° C.

Dow Corning Corp., Midland, Mich., successfully processed fine-diameter silicon carbide fibers spun from an organosilicon precursor polymer. After extrusion through the spinneret, the fibers are cured (connecting parallel polymer chains) to maintain shape and heat-treated to convert the precursor to a ceramic. The microstructure exhibits 0.5 μm grains at a density of 3.2 g per cc. Fiber diameter is about 10 μm, and room-temperature tensile strength of 2,660 MPa was reported. The fiber maintains this property after 12-hour exposures in inert atmospheres to temperatures as high as 1,800° C (3,272° F) and loses only 25% of that property value after similar exposure in air at 1,370° C (2,498° F).

Two polycrystalline aluminum oxide fibers were also developed during the past year. Though likely to be limited by creep to service temperatures below 1,200° C, both were expected to be used as composite reinforcements. The first, from the Mitsui Mining Co., Tokyo, is produced from a particulate-loaded spinning solution and in 1991 was commercially available. The second, produced by 3M Corp., St. Paul, Minn., is spun from a polymeric precursor solution and by 1991 had reached preproduction status. Both fibers have fine diameters (about 10 μm) and exhibit excellent room-temperature mechanical properties.

Diamonds. Considerable research during the past few years has been directed at making diamond thin films by using chemical vapor deposition (CVD) and ion beam techniques. These films are of practical interest because of their electrical behavior, thermal conductivity, and resistance to wear.

Naturally occurring diamond contains 1% of the heavy carbon isotope ^{13}C, the balance being [12]C. Though the thermal conductivity of diamond is extremely high, prior theoretical work indicated that elimination of the ^{13}C isotopic "impurity" should enhance the conductivity. To what degree such enhancement is theoretically possible has been the matter of some debate and controversy. During the past year researchers at General Electric Co.'s Research and Development Center, Schenectady, N.Y., succeeded in making diamond single crystals that were isotopically almost pure and then measured their thermal properties. Isotopically enriched diamond sheet was the source material for the crystals. The sheet was prepared by CVD using enriched (99.9% [12]C) methane. (This polycrystalline sheet

exhibited the same thermal conductivity as CVD diamond sheet made from methane containing 1% [13]C.) The enriched sheet was crushed and powdered and used for the high-temperature, high-pressure growth of the almost isotopically pure (99.9% [12]C) single crystals. The crystals had the highest room-temperature thermal conductivity of any solid. This new material was expected to be a candidate for numerous applications where extraction of heat is a critical limiting factor.

—Allan P. Katz

Metallurgy

Electroplasticity. Electroplasticity is an unusual phenomenon wherein applied voltages alter the deformation behavior of some metals. In some cases the strength, fracture behavior, and rate of crystal growth are all influenced by the application of electricity to the material.

Current passing through a metal under an applied potential is a well-understood phenomenon. Normally the applied potential, or voltage, causes electrons to migrate through the conducting material. The rate of migration of such charged particles is called the current. The relationship between current and voltage changes as the resistance of the particular object is changed. Both the thickness and length of material and the type of material over which the voltage is applied determine the resistance. Using a longer wire of the same diameter or changing materials from copper to iron increases the resistance, whereas enlarging the diameter of a wire decreases it. The specific resistance—resistivity to the motion of electrons—is greater in iron than in copper. Thus, the same voltage produces less current if a copper wire is replaced with an otherwise identical wire made of iron.

In addition, atomic impurities in metal wires usually increase the resistance. An application of this principle is the use of special iron alloys for electrical resistance burners on kitchen stoves. Called Nichrome (80% nickel and 20% chromium alloys), they have high resistances and demonstrate the phenomenon of resistance heating, the generation of heat by electric conductors carrying current. The replacement of nickel atoms by different-sized chromium atoms in this alloy causes the increased resistance.

Another interaction between electricity and metals is the increase in the density of defects in metals as a result of cold working, which is the deformation of a metal below the annealing temperature in order to cause permanent strain hardening—increased hardness and tensile strength. For example, a soft wire bent repeatedly usually becomes harder when bent back and forth. The hardening is caused by an increase in the number of defects called dislocations in the material. Dislocations are linear defects in atomic stacking, which, in small numbers, enable plastic deformation of many materials. On the other hand, existence of a very large number of dislocations tips the scale in the other direction and makes deformation more difficult. Large levels of working (such as bending the wire) produce high densities of dislocations.

By increasing the dislocation density, one increases the resistance of a wire to the passage of current. Thus, bending a section of a soft wire back and forth can increase its resistance. The increase in resistance of a wire containing many dislocations is due to the errors in atomic stacking caused by dislocations. Rather than passing from atom to atom in an orderly fashion, as can occur in perfect crystals, the electrons must overcome a greater set of obstacles to get through dislocated crystals. The elimination of dislocations as obstacles to electrons is one of the reasons perfect crystals of silicon are grown for electronic applications.

Just as dislocations can interfere with the passage of electricity through a wire, the phenomenon of electroplasticity is a circumstance wherein electricity interferes with the mobility of dislocations. The dislocations that move and form within deforming metals are essential for ductility to occur in crystalline materials. One common analogy used for dislocation motion is that of the process used in moving a large rug. Grabbing the rug from one end and pulling it requires a large instantaneous force to overcome the friction between the rug and the floor. A less intensive effort for moving the rug is to create a wrinkle at one end and push the wrinkle across the rug. The wrinkle serves as the local dislocation of the rug, which enables motion of the rug without a need to enlist a large crew of workers to move it. It is the effect on motion of these wrinkles or dislocations by an applied voltage that causes electroplasticity.

In a recent review in *JOM* (September 1990), Hans Conrad and coauthors summarized the effects of electron motion on the movement dislocations and, correspondingly, the strength and ductility of some metals. The concept of electrons interfering with the fundamental deformation mechanisms of crystalline solids was first suggested in 1963 by two Soviets, Troitskiy and Likhtman. They demonstrated that the resistance to plastic deformation, called the flow stress, was reduced when electrons were directed along the slip planes in zinc single crystals. To perform their experiments Troitskiy and Likhtman sent electrons along particular slip directions while subjecting the material to a tensile test (calibrated pulling apart of the material). The dislocations that move in particular slip directions apparently do so at smaller applied forces while electrons are moving in the same directions. When similar current pulses were applied in other directions, the force needed to deform the zinc single crystals was higher. Subsequent investigations by other scientists demonstrated that the slipping of crystal planes past one another via the motion of dislocations is enhanced by an apparent electron wind force along the slip planes and by another, smaller secondary component that causes at least some reduction in crystal strength any time a potential is applied. A good analogy for the electron wind force might be that of an airplane flying with a tail wind.

Work at North Carolina State University by Conrad and co-workers demonstrated the electroplastic effect in a large number of pure metals at low homologous temperatures. Low homologous temperatures are considered by metallurgists to be temperatures that are less than half of the melting temperature of a metal on a temperature scale in which absolute zero, 0 K, equals $-273.15°$ C ($-459.67°$ F). At higher homologous temperatures the deformation of most metals is dominated by a phenomenon called creep, which usually involves a smaller contribution of dislocations to plastic deformation.

Apparent electroplastic effects were also observed in high-temperature deformation of metals and alloys. The most dramatic example is the effect of electric fields on fracture during large-scale deformation of a typical aircraft aluminum alloy, usually designated as alloy 7475. The electroplastic effect on this alloy is a reduction in the formation and growth of cracks during hot working (deformation at high rates and temperatures wherein strain hardening cannot occur). Such an effect has potential for practical application by enhancing the high-temperature formability of these alloys.

The major limitations of high-temperature forming operations are tearing or cavitation (the opening of holes in a material on a microscopic scale). Any reduction in these processes will be beneficial to industry. An additional drawback to high-temperature operations is their need to consume large amounts of energy.

The fundamental attributes of electroplastic effects are not well understood. It is not even certain that all of the electroplastic effects observed in different metals and under different conditions are demonstrations of the same basic processes.

Simulated bird damage for jet engines. Two scientists from Howmet Corp., Greenwich, Conn., a leading high-temperature metal alloys company, reported in *JOM* (May 1990) on a new test for recreating the same type of impact damage caused by the ingestion of birds into jet engines. Previous tests had involved the firing of artificial birds made of gelatin from a pneumatic cannon at rotating, engine-ready fan blades. Candidate materials had to be fabricated into complete engine assemblies. Then the simulated birds were shot with increasing velocities at these assemblies. The assemblies were then ranked by their resistance to the bird impacts.

The new test was an attempt to reduce the cost of the current program. Rather than subject a completed set of turbofan blades to impact, a simpler, less expensive turbine blade-shape would be subjected to impact by a swinging pendulum. The hammer attached to the pendulum was designed to re-create the same type of load transfer experienced with the bird-impact simulator. Experimental comparisons of the new test to simulated bird tests conducted at Wright-Patterson Air Force Base, Ohio, on the same materials revealed comparable test performances. New tests of this type should enable enhanced material screening, thus allowing for lower costs and quicker qualification times for jet-engine materials.

Several standards were available for the simulation of impact damage by birds. One American Society for Testing Materials standard, ASTM No. F330-89, regarding bird windshield damage, specified the bird, the bird-launch procedure, and the bird launcher itself. Of most interest were the bird specifications, which noted that the bird could be wild or domestic as long as it weighed 1.8 kg (4 lb). Because chickens are readily available and usually are about the desired weight, freshly killed or specially prepared and thawed frozen chickens were considered to be optimal choices.

To protect the bird during launching, a mesh sheath would be used to keep the bird intact while it was projected through the air. Obviously, the use of synthetic birds made of pouches containing gelatin seems more neat and easy; however, the goals of the investigators included simulation of realistic conditions. The birds were fired by a compressed gas cannon. For verification of speed, most systems used a series of light-beam sensors to measure the bird's velocity.

—Keith J. Bowman

Mathematics

Outstanding developments in mathematics during the past year included resolution of a long-outstanding conjecture on shortest networks, a significant advance in the emerging field of chaotic dynamics, and faster algorithms (step-by-step procedures) for factoring integers and triangulating polygons. Also, mathematicians seemed poised on the brink of finally solving a famous problem in sphere-packing. At their quadrennial international congress in Kyoto, Japan, mathematicians honored the best of their young colleagues with Fields Medals, the mathematical equivalents of Nobel Prizes.

Shortest networks. Many practical problems in transportation and communications involve routing traffic among points in a network. It is often desirable to minimize the total length of all the links between pairs of points. Such a situation arises, for example, in selecting the site for the hub of a "hub-and-spoke" system of distribution, used by airlines and trucking firms. Given a number of points and possible links between pairs of them, a network without cycles in which each point can be reached from every other is a "spanning tree"; one with the least overall length is a "minimal" spanning tree. It is easy to determine a minimal spanning tree even for a large number of points and interconnections.

Managers know that they can sometimes do even better. Rather than simply using existing facilities, they often can reduce the total length of connections by adding one or more new points to the network (Figure 1). In the case of the U.S. interstate highway system, which was designed to connect the country's urban areas, economies were realized by the addition of junctions of highways at some rural locations; for instance, I-90 and I-94 meet in western Wisconsin, and I-76 and I-80 meet at the corner where Colorado tucks under Nebraska.

Mathematicians call such added points "Steiner points," after the 19th-century mathematician Jakob Steiner, who investigated minimal networks. The shortest network that interconnects all the original points, with added points allowed, is called a "minimal Steiner tree." For n original points, at most $n-2$ points need to be added, each of which is connected to three other points.

How much can be saved by adding Steiner points to a minimal spanning tree? In 1968 Henry O. Pollak and Edgar Gilbert of AT&T Bell Laboratories conjectured that the greatest possible improvement is to reduce the total length by a factor of $1-\sqrt{3/2} \approx 13.4\%$, which is exactly the amount of improvement in the simplest possible case, shown in Figure 1.

During the past year another AT&T Bell Laboratories scientist, Frank Hwang, together with Ding-Zhu Du (Ting-chu Tu), visiting Princeton University from Beijing (Peking), finally proved this conjecture, using analytic optimization techniques. AT&T's interest in the problem resulted from the need to minimize cabling and routing in long-distance telephone networks.

Finding Steiner points for a network is one of a class of problems referred to as "NP-complete" (where "NP" stands for "nondeterministic polynomial-time"). For such problems the amount of time needed for any known algorithm to compute a solution for n points grows faster than any polynomial in n (such as n^2 or n^3); with more than just a handful of points, it is computationally infeasible to determine

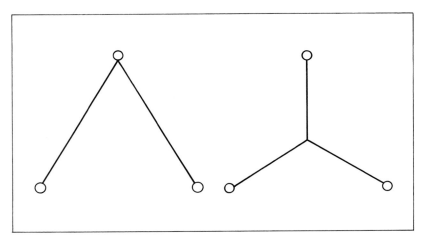

Figure 1. Minimal spanning tree (right) is a network in which each point can be reached from every other with the least overall length. A minimal Steiner tree (far right) is the shortest network that interconnects all the original points with added points allowed (see text).

where Steiner points should be added. The new result provides the welcome assurance that an easy-to-find minimal spanning tree is almost as good as an elusive minimal Steiner tree.

Chaos reigns. Chaos, in the mathematical sense, was spreading. Mathematical chaos—the unexpected behavior of systems described by what appear to be simple and straightforward equations—was used to interpret business cycles, bird flock movement, earthquakes, and childhood epidemics.

To some extent the applications have outstripped the foundations of the subject. For example, the family of dynamical systems known as the "Hénon attractor" (Figure 2) has long been a favorite model for the dynamics of chaos. Although the behavior

Figure 2. The "Hénon attractor" is a useful model for the dynamics of chaos. The figure shows a plot of 100,000 points, for which the coordinates of the next point (x_{n+1}, y_{n+1}) are determined from the previous point (x_n, y_n) by the rule $x_{n+1} = 1 + y_n - Ax_n^2, y_n + 1 = Bx_n$. The plot is for the values $A = 1.4$ and $B = 0.3$. The starting point is $(x_0, y_0) = (0,0)$; with any starting point, the resulting plot tends toward the figure shown.

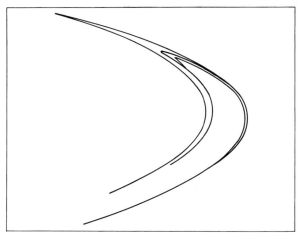

looks chaotic, until the past year no one had proved that it is. Lennart Carleson and Michael Benedicks of the Royal Institute of Technology, Stockholm, demonstrated that the dynamics is chaotic for some of the members of the family and even more intricate than computer images suggest. Mathematicians expect the result to be extended to cover the entire family of the Hénon attractor.

Progress in factoring. There are no known efficient algorithms for factoring an integer into primes, but mathematicians have been unable to quash the possibility that there might be one that they have not yet discovered. Contemporary cryptography depends heavily on the hopes that there are not any and that progress in factoring will continue to be slow.

By distributing the effort over more than 1,000 computers working for two months, mathematicians during the past year managed to factor $2^{2^9} + 1 = 2^{512} + 1$, an integer of 155 digits. It had been known already that 2,424,833 is a divisor, but the divisors of the remaining 148-digit quotient had been unknown. It was only at the end of 1988 that mathematicians had managed to factor the first 100-digit integer whose factorization had not been known previously. In 1970 the limits of factoring were about 40 digits; in 1980 they reached approximately 50 digits.

The significance of the new achievement is that many contemporary cryptographic schemes (but not the U.S. commercial Data Encryption Standard) rely on the difficulty of factoring integers that are about 150 digits long. Although the factoring of the 155-digit number used a new algorithm, called the "number field sieve," which took advantage of the special form of the number, researchers expect eventually to extend its benefits to most factoring problems.

The number that was factored is described as F_9, the 9th *Fermat number*, after Pierre de Fermat, a 17th-century lawyer whose hobby was number theory. On the basis of the primality of the first four of numbers of the form $2^{2^n} + 1$—5, 17, 257, and 65,-

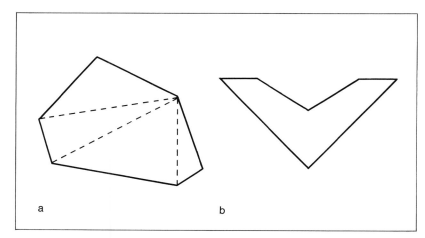

Figure 3. Triangulation of polygons is essential to achievement of computer representations of curves and surfaces. For a convex polygon (a), this is accomplished by picking any vertex and drawing line segments from it to each other vertex. For a nonconvex polygon (b), the problem is more difficult. A procedure that decomposes the polygon into trapezoids and then converts the trapezoidal decomposition into a triangulation is the fastest method yet devised.

537—Fermat conjectured that all of them are prime. Leonhard Euler, using modular arithmetic, found in 1732 that F_5 is divisible by 641. Since then, F_6, F_7, and F_8 have been factored. Factoring the next number in the family, F_{10}, with 309 digits, was beyond the capability of mathematicians in 1991.

Triangulation of polygons. Cutting up a planar polygon into triangles lies at the heart of computer representations of curves and surfaces. As computer graphics uses polygons with more and more sides to approximate curves, and as surfaces are dissected into ever finer meshes of triangular elements, it has become important to be able to "triangulate" a polygon as efficiently as possible. For a convex polygon, one in which a line segment between any two interior points lies entirely inside the polygon, triangulation is simple: one need only pick any vertex and draw line segments from it to each other vertex, forming a kind of fan (Figure 3a). Nonconvex polygons present a greater challenge (Figure 3b).

A computer represents a polygon by a listing of its vertices. Each vertex is represented as a pair of coordinates, and vertices that are connected by an edge are consecutive in the list (with the first and last also understood to have an edge between them). The computer does not have a picture or any inherent geometrical insight, as a person might; the triangulation method needs to be general enough to handle all polygons efficiently.

A simple algorithm is to start with any pair of connected vertices and search through the remaining vertices for a third that will form a triangle, checking to be sure that the triangle lies entirely inside the polygon. Then one should consider an edge that extends from one of the vertices of this triangle to a vertex outside the triangle and search through the list again, checking for a vertex that will form a triangle with those two. This procedure should be repeated until the polygon is broken into triangles. Both on average and in the worst case, this algorithm requires a number of checks for triangle formation that is proportional to the square of the number of vertices. For polygons with few vertices, this is not a bad algorithm, but the situation quickly becomes unacceptable for large numbers of vertices.

During the past decade mathematicians have devised faster algorithms. A breakthrough occurred in 1990 when Bernard Chazelle of Princeton University invented one that requires a number of operations proportional only to the number of vertices. His algorithm first decomposes the polygon into trapezoids in a very careful way and then converts the trapezoidal decomposition into a triangulation. Chazelle's algorithm is too complicated for practical use except on polygons with a huge number of sides, but he and other mathematicians expect that his ideas will lead to further insights and even better algorithms.

Packing spheres. During the year, mathematicians were waiting to see details of an announced proof that packing spheres the way oranges or cannonballs are stacked, with each fitting into the space between three in the layer below, is the most efficient packing, achieving the most spheres per unit volume. Johannes Kepler in 1611 had conjectured this. During the 19th century Carl Gauss proved that the packing in question is the most efficient among packings in which the centers of the spheres form a regular, or lattice, pattern in space. What has been unknown is whether some sort of irregular packing might do better—as can be the case in higher dimensions.

The one-dimensional analogue of a sphere is a line segment, and adjacent line segments can cover an entire line, giving a packing that is 100% efficient. The two-dimensional analogue is a circle; circles most efficiently cover the plane when placed in a hexagonal arrangement with each surrounded by six others. The proportion of the plane that is covered is $\pi/2\sqrt{3} \approx 91\%$. That no irregular arrangement of circles does better was not proved until the 20th century.

The face-centered cubic lattice packing of spheres in three dimensions covers a portion $\pi/\sqrt{18} \approx 74.05\%$ of space. Mathematicians have been inching toward proving that this is the best packing by gradually lowering the upper limit for the best packing, which they have known since 1988 cannot be any more than 77.84% efficient. It may be many months before mathematicians can resolve whether all the intricate details of the latest attack on the problem are correct.

Although the main interest in sphere-packing in three dimensions stems from the amazing difficulty of solving a problem so simple to state, lattice packings in higher dimensions have practical applications in communications systems. For these applications efficient lattice packings are desired, sometimes in thousands of dimensions. In 1990 Noam Elkies of Harvard University and Tetsuji Shioda of Rikkyo University, Tokyo, independently discovered the most efficient lattice packings in dimensions greater than 24. Elkies derived them from elliptic curves, which had also led in the recent past to new algorithms for factoring integers, and Shioda found them while working on what are known as Fermat surfaces. The elliptic curve method leads to all the best packings in dimensions up through 24, but in very high dimensions the packings it produces are not the most efficient known.

Milestones. An International Congress of Mathematicians was held in Kyoto in August 1990. Fields Medals are awarded every four years to between two and four mathematicians under the age of 40. The four winners in 1990 were Vladimir G. Drinfeld (Institute for Low Temperature Physics and Engineering, Kharkov, U.S.S.R.), Vaughan F.R. Jones (University of California at Berkeley), Shigefumi Mori (Research Institute of Mathematical Sciences of Kyoto University), and Edward Witten (Institute for Advanced Study, Princeton, N.J.). Drinfeld's achievements were in the field of quantum groups, a branch of mathematical physics. Jones discovered a new polynomial for distinguishing knots, which has been applied to sort DNA (deoxyribonucleic acid) by the types of knotting involved. Mori extended the classification theory of algebraic surfaces in three dimensions. Witten was a major developer of the theory that the universe is made up not of fundamental particles but of tiny strings.

Three of the U.S. National Medals of Science awarded in 1990 went to mathematicians: George F. Carrier, Stephen C. Kleene, and John McCarthy. Carrier applied mathematical modeling to problems of engineering and geophysics; Kleene contributed to mathematical logic by helping found the theory of recursion and effective computability; and McCarthy made numerous contributions to computer science, including inventing the LISP programming language, developing the idea of time-sharing computers, and defining the field of artificial intelligence.

The U.S. team placed third in the International Mathematical Olympiad in Beijing, a contest for high-school students in mathematical problem solving. The host team from China placed first, followed by the Soviet Union.

—Paul J. Campbell

Medical sciences

For the first time, medical researchers during the past year attempted to treat cancer and an immune-deficiency disease with gene therapy. Results of long-term studies confirmed that the risk of heart attacks could be reduced by stopping smoking, losing weight, and lowering blood pressure and blood cholesterol levels. Dentists found that ultrasound provided more comfortable root canal treatment than had previous methods, and veterinarians were considering ways to deal with the rapidly growing numbers of pet birds.

General medicine

Major advances were made during the past year in understanding the genetics of cancer, the development of heart disease, the molecular cause of diabetes, how cells age, and how to treat various diseases.

Heart disease. The "Model T" of artificial hearts, the Jarvik heart, lost the approval of the U.S. Food and Drug Administration (FDA) during the past year, preventing its manufacturer from selling the $22,000 device in the U.S. The first artificial heart had been placed in a Seattle dentist in 1982; more than 150 other people subsequently received similar fist-sized electric pumps. The Jarvik heart required a tether from the patient's chest cavity to an external air compressor. The FDA cited poor manufacturing practices as the reason for dropping its approval, and the agency was also concerned about infections and strokes. The manufacturer, Symbion Inc. of Tempe, Ariz., planned to continue marketing the device outside the U.S.

Ten-year data on the extensive Multiple Risk Factor Intervention Trial (MRFIT) were received, and the results confirmed what earlier data had suggested: men who stopped smoking, lowered their saturated fat and cholesterol intake, and lost weight reduced their risk of a heart attack. More than 6,400 men adopted the healthier life-style and enjoyed a 24% lower rate of death from heart attacks than did a similar-sized group who continued living their lives as usual.

While no similar studies were done on women, researchers from the Brigham and Women's Hospital,

Boston, and the Harvard Medical School concluded that women can help their hearts by shedding excess weight. Their conclusion was based on results from the Nurses' Health Study, an epidemiological survey of nearly 116,000 nurses who were 30 to 55 years of age in 1976. Among the findings were the following: women who had gained more than 10 kg (22 lb) since the age of 18 had a risk of heart attack approximately double that of women whose weight was stable (with a change of less than 3 kg [7 lb]); mildly to moderately overweight women had an 80% higher risk of heart disease than lean women; and 70% of the heart attacks in obese women could be blamed on their body size.

A Vitamin A precursor called beta carotene (found naturally in carrots, green leafy vegetables, and many fruits) earned acclaim for slowing the seemingly inexorable progression of hardening of the arteries, atherosclerosis. In a Harvard University study of 333 male physicians who already were suffering heart pain or other signs of atherosclerosis, those men taking 50-mg doses of beta carotene had only half the number of strokes and heart attacks than those who did not take beta carotene. That does not mean that taking beta carotene pills is enough to stave off heart disease; the study was done in men who already had symptoms, and no one knew whether beta carotene could prevent heart disease.

Another vitamin may protect the hearts of patients undergoing coronary artery bypass surgery. Canadian scientists from the University of Toronto found that administering Vitamin E to patients before bypass surgery protected them from some of the metabolic damage caused by the heart stoppage required for such surgery.

Parkinson's disease. Following up on earlier experiments in which fetal brain tissue was transplanted into the brains of people with Parkinson's disease, Swedish researchers from University Hospital in Lund, along with British colleagues, described the progress of a patient with Parkinson's disease who in 1989 had received implants of fetal brain cells. His severe tremors and rigidity had not responded well to dopamine, a precursor to a chemical lacking in people with Parkinson's disease. Following the fetal cell surgery, the physicians reported, the implanted cells survived and pumped out the needed chemical. Physicians were less optimistic about the future of a procedure that involves transplanting dopamine-producing cells from a patient's own adrenal gland to the brain, a surgery pioneered in Mexico City. Numerous surgical attempts to achieve this in the U.S. and Canada yielded only mediocre results.

Paradoxically, turning off one section of the brain may help Parkinson's patients. Researchers at Johns Hopkins University, Baltimore, Md., injected a nerve-killing substance into the brains of two monkeys

Michael Harrison cuddles Blake Schultz, on whom he had operated when the child was a 24-week-old fetus. Involving the repair of a diaphragmatic hernia, this was the first major surgery performed on a fetus in utero.

with artificially induced Parkinson's disease. Within minutes the monkeys, who had been almost catatonic, were able to move about. The targeted section of the brain is one suspected of being overactive in Parkinson's.

Aging. Scientists were drawing nearer to understanding the exact controls of aging, at least in worms and laboratory-grown tissue. A University of Colorado geneticist altered a single gene on a tiny roundworm, *Caenorhabditis elegans*, and increased the worm's life span from about 22 days to about 37 days in one strain and 57 days in another. American Red Cross workers extended the life span of human endothelial cells. These cells normally divide 20 to 60 times in a test tube. However, when the Red Cross scientists bathed the cells in a chemical that blocked the production of a substance promoting cell growth and differentiation, the cells went through as many as 140 cell doublings.

Human growth hormone increased strength and endurance in men over 60, according to the Medical College of Wisconsin. The scientists who conducted the study quickly cautioned, however, that the drug may prove to have significant side effects that make the treatment not worthwhile. After six months the 12 men who took the drug had grown thicker, more youthful skin. They had lost nearly 15% of their body fat and had increased their lean body mass by almost 9%. In addition, X-rays showed that their muscles and organs had grown larger. British researchers gave human growth hormone to children who had normal levels of the hormone but were very short and found that the drug had a potentially harmful effect on the children's metabolism.

Transplants. An attempt to use an artificial lung failed, but in another case a mother successfully donated a piece of her lung to her 12-year-old daughter. In the first case, physicians at LDS (Latter-day Saints) Hospital in Salt Lake City, Utah, placed a bundle of hundreds of hair's-width tubes in the chest of a 16-year-old girl suffering from severe respiratory distress syndrome. However, she died 4½ days later. Stanford University Medical School doctors had better luck using lung tissue from a living donor, apparently the first time that such a procedure had been tried. They removed one-third of the right lung of a 45-year-old Utah woman and implanted it in her 12-year-old daughter, who had bronchopulmonary dysplasia.

Physicians at Loyola University Medical Center, Maywood, Ill., demonstrated that OKT3, a powerful immune-suppressing chemical employed to prevent implant recipients from rejecting their new organs, could induce a serious immune system disorder. Other immune suppressors commonly used in transplant recipients had also been shown to cause potentially life-threatening side effects. However, early studies suggested that FK 506, a substance under development by a Japanese pharmaceutical company, might be able to prevent rejection without any untoward side effects.

Genetics. On the same day, two separate groups of scientists—from the University of Michigan and the University of Utah—reported the discovery of the gene that causes neurofibromatosis. The gene is extremely large and became the second gene known to have other genes embedded within it, in this case three. Neurofibromatosis is an inherited condition that may cause only such mild symptoms as tannish spots on the skin. However, it can also cause learning disabilities or spark the growth of bulky and recurring skin tumors. One person in 4,000 shows some effects of the disease. Just one month after publishing details of the discovery of the gene, the Utah researchers announced that they had determined the protein that the aberrant gene manufactures; it is similar, if not identical, to a protein that plays a role in causing cancer. Genes were also found for several other diseases, including spinal muscular atrophy, which affects one in 10,000 babies throughout the world, often resulting in death.

Researchers from the U.S. National Institutes of Health (NIH) in Bethesda, Md., conducted what might have been the first approved test of gene therapy. They removed white blood cells from a child with an immune deficiency, infected the cells with a weakened virus that carried the healthy, needed gene, and injected the cells back into the child. The FDA gave the same researchers permission to try gene therapy for cancer, and they went ahead in early 1991. This time they added the gene for a tumor-fighting protein—tumor necrosis factor—to the white blood cells of people with malignant melanoma, a deadly form of skin cancer. They hoped that the cells would travel to the cancer and excrete the chemical.

While the NIH scientists implanted the virus in cells that had first been removed from the body, University of Michigan scientists announced that they had developed a surgical technique to perform a gene transplantation. They blocked off a section of a pig's artery and injected a virus that had first been loaded up with a marker gene. The test gene then showed up only in artery cells, not in any other parts of the pig. The researchers believed that the technique could be useful in providing therapeutic proteins to treat heart disease and cancer.

An initial report of a gene associated with alcoholism, received with some cynicism by the medical community, was quickly discredited by other researchers. The initial report, not the first to connect a gene with alcoholism, came from the University of Texas at San Antonio and the University of California at Los Angeles. Scientists at those institutions studied 70 brain samples. They found the same gene in 77% of the alcoholics and failed to find it in 72% of the nonalcoholics, leading them to conclude that the gene predisposed its bearer to alcoholism. Six months later National Institute on Alcohol Abuse and Alcoholism researchers announced that their studies of 40 alcoholics showed that the gene was no more prevalent among alcoholics than among the general public.

University of California at San Diego researchers added to the evidence that some genes actively protect against cancer. Faults in such genes had already been blamed for some cases of retinoblastoma, colon cancer, and other cancers. The researchers worked with the retinoblastoma gene, which, when absent or abnormal, causes an eye tumor. When they put a normal copy of the retinoblastoma gene into human prostate cancer cells and injected them into mice, the cells caused much smaller tumors than did cells that had not received a normal copy of the gene. This finding suggested that the retinoblastoma gene might also be involved in prostate cancer and that discovering a way to restore normal copies of this gene could be a way to treat that disease.

Mark and Crispina Calvert are shown with their son, Christopher, after a superior court judge ruled in October 1990 that the woman who had carried the Calvert's fertilized embryo to term had no legal right to custody of the child.

Following the discovery that some colon and breast cancers are caused by a genetic flaw in a gene that controls growth, Johns Hopkins University scientists returned cancer cells to normalcy by inserting a copy of the normal gene, called p53, into the cells. Putting normal genes into colon cancer cells in a human afflicted with the disease was not practical with current knowledge. However, scientists hoped to build on the research by determining what the gene produces and whether they could use that gene product to treat colon cancer. Massachusetts General Hospital investigators reported that that same p53 gene also is to blame for Li-Fraumeni syndrome, a rare condition of inherited cancer of various organs. And University of California at Berkeley and University of Utah investigators each identified genes that may predispose bearers to breast cancer.

Once again, scientists believed that they had figured out what makes a man male. British scientists pinpointed a segment of the Y chromosome by studying males who had two copies of the X chromosome (normally a hallmark of females). Scientists assumed that the sex-determining region must lie in a tiny part of the Y chromosome carried on one of the X chromosomes of the double-X men. Another group of British researchers followed the activation of specific genes in mice and found one in particular that began working at exactly the time that the mouse embryo embarked on the road to being a male or female. U.S. and Canadian researchers also identified a female mouse that carried an X and a Y gene but was missing that part of the Y chromosome that they believed carried the sex-determining gene. Other researchers, however, cautioned that it may take more than one gene to create a male.

AIDS. Researchers from Columbia University, New York City, and Harvard University independently determined the precise shape of a molecule that sits on the surface of white blood cells and provides a docking site for the human immunodeficiency virus (HIV), which causes AIDS (acquired immune deficiency syndrome). They published their results in the same issue of the British science journal *Nature*. X-ray crystallography revealed that the molecule takes the shape of a cigar, with a ridge and channel at its tip where the virus presumably docks.

Also during the year several new drugs were developed. Among them were two that block the enzyme that the virus uses to insert itself into the genetic material of human cells. The testing of these drugs began in Europe and the U.S. Among the other treatments under evaluation were a drug activated by light and a natural stimulator of the immune system. Meanwhile, trials of vaccines in noninfected as well as infected individuals continued.

Other AIDS research led to new insights into related conditions. Epidemiological studies suggested that Kaposi's sarcoma, a cancer that appears in people with AIDS and in older men of Mediterranean descent, may have been caused in people with AIDS by a sexually transmitted infectious organism. As evidence for this, Kaposi's sarcoma was far more common among homosexuals with AIDS than in intravenous drug users with AIDS. In addition, a New York University Medical Center dermatologist reported a handful of cases of homosexuals with Kaposi's sarcoma who were not infected with HIV. A scientist from the Armed Forces Institute of Pathology, Washington, D.C., identified what he believed to be a new organism in people with AIDS; he also found it in the blood of AIDS-free people who had mysteriously died after suffering a fever and swollen lymph nodes.

Cancer. Red meat was given a red flag by Harvard University researchers, who studied the incidence of colon cancer in nearly 89,000 women. They found that the more red meat a woman eats, the more likely she is to get colon cancer.

Another Harvard University study showed that women who use estrogen to offset the effects of menopause place themselves at a slightly higher risk of breast cancer. How that balances out against the protection estrogen offers had yet to be determined.

Pregnancy. Israeli doctors from Chaim Sheba Medical Center and Tel Aviv University showed that fresh embryos are most desirable for implantations. In an in vitro fertilization program, the implantation rate was significantly higher in women who received fresh embryos (24%), compared with those who received frozen and thawed embryos (7.7%). Moreover, only 16% of the women who received frozen and thawed embryos became pregnant, compared with 37% of the women who received fresh embryos.

Scientists from several hospitals successfully transferred a heart surgery tool to the field of obstetrics. For years heart surgeons had been threading thin balloons into narrowed arteries of the heart. They then inflated the balloons to widen the artery. The obstetrical surgeons reported that balloons can also be used to unstop blocked fallopian tubes, the cause of much infertility. They were able to open a tube in 71 of 77 women, allowing eggs to make the vital passage between the ovary and the uterus.

It may be the age of the egg rather than a woman's age that determines whether she can became pregnant. University of Southern California researchers reported that they had been able to induce pregnancy by means of embryo transfers in five of seven women over the age of 40, all of whom were incapable of producing viable eggs. Like much reproductive research, this work raised a number of ethical and practical questions—for example, can older women safely carry a pregnancy to term?

The German government passed one of the world's strictest fertility ethics laws. The national legislature prohibited a woman from carrying the egg of another woman and banned research on human embryos. U.S. courts faced the issue as well. A California court ruled that a surrogate mother had no rights to a child she bore, and a Tennessee court granted joint custody of seven frozen embryos to the now-divorced "parents."

Treatments. A multitude of potential treatments and cures were announced during the past year. All required evaluation on far larger groups of people to determine whether they were truly effective and whether they would have any serious side effects.

NIH workers announced that 7 of 10 people with sickle-cell anemia responded well to hydroxyurea. The drug apparently turns on a gene unused since before birth; it is a special fetal gene that manufactures hemoglobin, a vital oxygen-carrying protein in blood. The adult hemoglobin gene in sickle-cell sufferers is aberrant; activating the fetal gene produces a new and healthy supply of hemoglobin.

A high blood pressure treatment might prove helpful in people with cystic fibrosis, a common genetic ailment of Caucasians marked by thick mucous buildup in the lungs. The drug, amiloride, loosened the mucus and significantly slowed the typical loss of lung function in 14 people under treatment at the University of North Carolina at Chapel Hill.

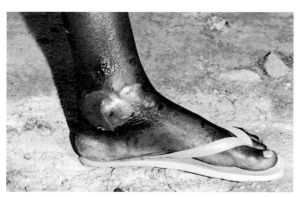

Blister grows on the skin of a Nigerian suffering from guinea worm disease (above). At the right, a woman in Nigeria pours drinking water through a nylon filter developed by the Du Pont Co. to catch the worm larvae that cause the disease.

Photos, E.I. du Pont de Nemours & Co.

Etidronate, a drug marketed for a rare brittle bone disease, performed well against osteoporosis (a decrease in bone mass that results in fragility of bones). It reduced the fracture rate by more than half in tests on more than 400 women at seven U.S. medical centers.

A Massachusetts General Hospital research team determined that warfarin, an anticlotting drug, could prevent 60,000 strokes a year in the U.S. The drug was tried in 212 people who had heart flutter. Over an average 2.2 years in the study, only two of the subjects suffered a stroke. However, 13 of 208 patients with the same condition who did not receive warfarin had strokes.

The World Health Organization announced the discovery of a treatment for sleeping sickness, a condition that afflicted hundreds of thousands of Africans each year. Untreated, it was invariably fatal. With the current treatment, which required a month of intravenous doses, 5% of the recipients die. The new drug had fewer side effects and had brought comatose people back to life.

E.I. du Pont de Nemours & Co. offered hope to African nations beset by guinea worm disease. In this ailment victims swallow worm larvae with their drinking water, and the worms grow in their bodies, travel to the skin, and induce a painful blister before they finally crawl out. The Delaware company promised to provide free nylon filters that remove the larvae from the water.

The news was discouraging for antimalarial treatments. Researchers from the Uniformed Services University of Health Sciences, Bethesda, Md., gave antimalaria drugs to mice and then deliberately infected them with one of two types of tropical viruses. The mice got sicker more rapidly and suffered more than did mice that did not receive the antimalarial agents. The antimalarials probably suppressed the immune system and, if the results were repeated in experiments on primates, this could bode ill for people who live in malaria-rife areas who are also threatened by viruses such as HIV.

Aspirin, which in the past few years had garnered praise as a preventive for heart disease and stroke in men, was shown by New York researchers to boost the effects of alcohol enough to affect driving ability. The researchers gave five men alcohol with or without two extra-strength aspirin and found their blood alcohol levels were 34% higher with the aspirin.

Diabetes. Scientists gathered more evidence implicating amylin, a protein discovered in 1987, in diabetes. Rats secrete amylin after eating, suggesting that it may be involved in glucose metabolism—a process that does not operate normally in diabetes. Rats given amylin needed less glucose to maintain their blood sugar levels, and amylin injections boosted rats' blood sugar.

U.S. and Danish researchers made a discovery that could lead to an early-warning system for diabetes. They proved that an enzyme found in very small quantities in people about to become diabetic is identical to an enzyme that appears in much larger quantities in the brain. With this richer source available, researchers may finally be able to purify the protein and learn more about how it works.

Vaccines. Yale University scientists protected mice from Lyme disease by injecting them with a bioengineered version of a protein that sits on the Lyme disease bacterium's surface. Mice that did not receive the vaccine were affected with the symptoms of Lyme disease.

A new approach to vaccine technology may lie in the field of ceramics. University of California at Los Angeles researchers were working on attaching vaccine proteins to tiny ceramic crystals. They hoped that tying the proteins to the crystals would ensure the identification of the vaccines by the immune system, which could then begin producing antibodies to fight the vaccine and the disease associated with it.

—Joanne Silberner

Dentistry

The U.S. government and the American Dental Association (ADA) during the past year pondered two of the crucial issues confronting the dental profession as the 21st century approached: possible personnel shortages and the scope of dental research. Though some forecasts suggested a possible shortage of dentists in the not-too-distant future, ADA economist Kent Nash rejected such notions. "The fact that the nation's production of dentists has slowed significantly does not alone imply that we must face an impending shortage of dental services," he said. Dentistry's capacity to treat patients was utilized in 1990 at an estimated 63%. By holding this capacity at that level and assuming patient visits increase at a fixed rate of 2.5% a year, the utilization rate would climb to about 81% in 10 years. Capacity would also be boosted by new technology and improved treatment techniques, according to Nash.

Dental research in the 1990s will no longer be dominated by tooth decay and periodontal (gum) disease but will span a range of genetic, autoimmune, and other diseases from AIDS to xerostomia (dry mouth), according to a 10-year research plan released by the National Institute of Dental Research (NIDR). The blueprint, developed in consultation with the ADA and other professional dental organizations, placed special attention on the oral health needs of older Americans and of adults in high-risk groups. Goals included eliminating toothlessness in future generations and helping individuals who have compromised their oral health because of neglect.

Ultrasound and root-canal therapy. Ultrasound was making root-canal treatment more comfortable and less stressful for patients because it clears, disinfects, and prepares the root canal for filling more effectively than the tractional file technique, Howard Martin of Georgetown University, Washington, D.C., told the ADA annual meeting. Endodontics, or root-canal therapy, removes injured or infected pulp (nerve) tissue from inside a tooth. Effective endodontic treatment can save a tooth from extraction. With traditional treatment an opening is drilled into the root canal, and a small, thin file is inserted into the canal to remove all debris. The canal is then disinfected and shaped in preparation for the filling material used to strengthen the tooth. Ultrasound endodontics, which uses high-frequency sound waves, is done with just one handpiece and can take only half as long as the traditional procedure.

"The ultrasonic pulsating waves that vibrate the tooth pulp also stir and destroy bacteria," Martin explained. "Through research, we found that ultrasound could be used to disinfect the canal walls. But we were pleasantly surprised when we discovered the sound waves also could be used to shape and prepare the canal walls." With the use of ultrasound many root-canal procedures can be accomplished in one visit.

Type A personalities and TM. Driven and goal-oriented individuals are prime candidates for TM (temporomandibular) joint disorders, according to Ronald Auvenshine of the University of Texas. Tension headaches, ringing in the ears, dizziness, and aches of the neck and shoulder all can signal TM—jaw hinge joint—disorders, which affect about 10 million people in the U.S. The problems occur when the chewing muscles do not work together properly with the TM joint. Factors such as clenching or grinding of the teeth (bruxism) are often the cause, as are arthritis and injuries from accidents.

"Dentists are beginning to recognize the earlier signs of TM disorder before it advances into the chronic pain syndrome. It is vital for the dental practitioner to be keenly aware of the relationship between the syndrome and the actual internal problems of the joint. Diagnostic procedures must incorporate palpation of the muscle, listening to joint sounds, and checking range of motion of the joint," Auvenshine noted. For people with mild cases, treatment could consist of eliminating spasms and pain by applying moist heat to the face, using prescribed muscle relaxants or other medications, massaging the muscles, eating soft foods, and using bite plates or splints to eliminate bruxism. More aggressive treatment might require counseling or biofeedback training to reduce stress or orthodontics to adjust the way in which teeth fit together. In severe cases surgery might be necessary.

Dental implants. Increasingly versatile dental implants support crowns, bridges, and full-mouth restorations that span the upper and lower jaws, replacing partial or full dentures for some patients. Patients with implant-supported restorations discovered that they could chew better with a fixed, stable device than with a removable denture, said Clarence Lindquist, an oral and maxillofacial surgeon. For certain patients greater comfort and improved appearance were potential benefits of implants that were monitored for more than 25 years. Not all patients are candidates for implants, said Lindquist, who had placed implants in patients ranging in age from 15 to the mid-80s.

Since 1982 Lindquist and his colleagues had placed more than 2,000 osseointegrated implants—those in which bone tissue bonds to the implant—with a success rate of 90%. The two-step procedure involves surgical insertion of a titanium cylinder into the patient's jawbone, performed under local anesthesia. Titanium is used because of its compatibility with natural bone. During the four-to-six-month healing process, the bone must be given time to adhere to the implant, and this bonding must occur for the treatment to be effective. In the next step the top part of the cylinder is connected to the implant above the jawbone to allow for placement of a restoration, completing the link of bone to implant to restoration. Replacement teeth attached to the implant are formed of the same material used for conventional bridges and dentures—porcelain, acrylic resin, and various metals. The end result is a permanently anchored, natural-looking restoration that functions in the same way as natural teeth.

Harvard University School of Dental Medicine researchers also reported progress with implants. Paul Schnitman told the annual meeting of the International Association for Dental Research that, in a carefully controlled clinical trial conducted over five years, blade-implant-supported bridges demonstrated safety, effectiveness, and patient satisfaction. Blade implants, like the titanium cylinders, are surgically inserted into the jawbone and become anchored to the surrounding bone, similar to a natural tooth. The blade implant can support tooth replacements or bridges through a post that protrudes through the gum tissue into the mouth and to which the bridge is attached. A cantilever bridge is anchored to existing teeth on one end and extends, unsupported, toward the back of the mouth. During the five-year period, Schnitman and his team regularly monitored the durability and mobility of both types of bridge and their supports as well as the health of the surrounding gums and bone tissues. Although results showed that the cantilever bridge was more mobile than the implant-supported bridge, patients felt more comfortable and more secure with the latter.

At the same meeting, researchers from the Texas Health Science Center in San Antonio also reported a 94% success rate with 130 blade implants. Of this number only eight implants failed when attachment to the bone was not achieved. No patient, however, experienced failure of all implants that had been installed. Even with one or two successful implants, the denture remained firmly in place.

Electrosurgery and stress. A technique that is precise, fast, and comparatively unstressful to patients was finding its way into an increasing number of dental offices in the U.S. and Europe. Called electrosurgery, it utilizes a safe, easy-to-use "electronic scalpel" instead of a regular scalpel for gum surgery and other soft-tissue procedures. The scalpel generates an electric current that is guided by the dentist through oral tissue.

"Unlike a regular scalpel, electrosurgery can be used without applying pressure to the patient's gum and nearly diminishes any bleeding," said William McGrannahan. "By containing or stopping bleeding, dentists can perform procedures with a clear operating field, providing greater visibility and precision. In addition, it expedites the treatment process and gets the patient out of the dental chair earlier than does the use of a regular scalpel, which can be more cumbersome," he explained. "With a regular scalpel, a dentist must use various types of blades to get around certain corners, curves and hard-to-reach places. With electrosurgery, one or two electrodes will get the job done."

Gum disease. New diagnostic approaches were revealing a lower-than-expected prevalence of periodontal (gum) disease, according to Roy Page, a researcher at the University of Washington School of Dentistry. The traditional probe used to detect and measure periodontal pockets, the space between teeth and gums, was joined by an expanded assortment of diagnostic tools. A diagnostic kit to pinpoint certain molecules in gum fluids that indicate the presence of periodontal disease was recently approved by the U.S. Food and Drug Administration and was expected to make its way into dental offices shortly. DNA probes to identify specific bacteria that cause periodontal disease were also being developed. They were expected to provide early identification of persons at risk for gum disease.

New statistics placed the prevalence of periodontitis, advanced gum disease, at less than 5–10% of U.S. working adults aged 18–65 and gingivitis, the easily curable early stage of periodontal disease, at about 40% of adults under 65. "Some things we thought we knew about periodontal disease are turning out to be untrue," said Page. "Until the 1980s we thought that there were only two kinds of periodontal disease, but now it's accepted that there are five major categories of this disorder, some with sub-groups. With many types of periodontal disease, the mode of treatment will be different."

Periodontists also were finding that some types of gum disease, especially the one commonly seen in young people, tend to run in families. Another new development was the distinction between "disease-active and disease-inactive" periodontal pockets. Most pockets are disease inactive most of the time, and episodes of disease activity are infrequent in most people. To what extent this knowledge would have a direct impact on the rationale for periodontal therapy was uncertain.

Dental anxiety. Researchers at the National Institute of Dental Research in Bethesda, Md., reported a new approach for relieving anxiety in patients undergoing dental extractions that offers many benefits over traditional methods. Instead of using intravenous sedation to reduce apprehension during dental surgery, patients now can take a pill that has the same effect. In one of the first studies to evaluate the effectiveness of giving the drug triazolam, a derivative of valium, orally, Raymond Dionne, Kenneth Hargreaves, and Eliezer Kaufman looked at 75 patients undergoing extraction of wisdom teeth. Their study showed that the drug provided patients with anxiety relief just as effective as that achieved with intravenous valium, commonly used by dentists during tooth extractions. Patients were divided into study groups, testing the oral drug against intravenous valium, nitrous oxide, inhaled nitrous oxide gas plus triazolam, and an oral placebo plus oxygen. All patients were monitored during extractions, postoperatively, and 24 hours later.

All subjects reported an increase in anxiety during the extractions, although the groups that received triazolam and intravenous valium reported the least amount. Nitrous oxide alone did not alleviate anxiety, although the combination of nitrous oxide gas and triazolam was similar to use of triazolam alone. Significantly, patients in the triazolam group experienced a faster mental and physical recovery than the group that received intravenous valium.

Chewing gum and cavities. Researchers at Indiana University School of Dentistry found that chewing sugarless gum for 10 minutes after eating sugar- and starch-laden foods such as granola bars, corn chips, pretzels, chocolate bars, and cream-filled cupcakes significantly reduced the acid levels of plaque between teeth. Reducing plaque decreases the development of tooth decay.

Researchers first tested plaque levels in five adults who ate junk food. After the subjects chewed gum for 10 minutes, plaque levels were checked again. The potential for tooth decay apparently decreased by an average of 72% after patients chewed gum, the researchers said. "If you chew sugarless gum for 10 minutes after you eat a snack, you would probably help protect yourself against tooth decay," said John Brown of the Academy of General Dentistry. He cautioned, however, that such practice must be used in conjunction with other preventive measures, such as regular brushing, flossing, and visits to the dental office.

—Lou Joseph

Veterinary medicine

The National Veterinary Education Program of the Pew Charitable Trusts in 1990 awarded grants totaling more than $2 million to U.S. veterinary colleges for development of programs to strengthen the study of veterinary medicine in preparation for the challenges of the 21st century. Several of the grants involved multi-institutional consortia that addressed food-animal-production issues (seven colleges), cooperative programs in aquatic pathobiology (six colleges), interinstitutional programs for faculty development and for student recruitment and admission (three colleges), and interinstitutional instruction in wildlife health (two colleges). Grants to individual colleges promoted programs for alternative careers, companion-animal-population management, assessment of minority attitudes toward veterinary medicine, and interdisciplinary training in food safety.

Also established during the year as a component of the Pew program was the North American Strategic Veterinary Education Task Force. Members of the task force were from veterinary schools and colleges in the U.S. and Canada, veterinary science departments, and the American Veterinary Medical Association (AVMA). At its first meeting the task force sought to identify issues of national and international importance to veterinary medicine and to pursue those issues by establishing action groups from among the membership. They included communication of ideas among colleges, faculty development, student development, public and social issues, and curriculum. An additional challenge to the task force by its own membership was formulation of the model veterinary graduate for the 21st century.

Students. Total veterinary student enrollment in 1989–90 in the U.S. was 8,456 and in Canada 1,158. In West Germany about 5,960 students were studying veterinary medicine, while in the U.K. there were about 1,645 and in Australia about 1,300. Women continued to outnumber men in U.S. colleges (59 to 41%) and in Canadian colleges (61 to 39%). In West Germany more than 60% of the students were women, and in the U.K. the total was about 50%.

Applications to U.S. veterinary colleges increased in 1990 after having declined continuously during the previous decade. A particularly large increase in overseas applicants occurred at U.K. veterinary schools during the past two years. The newest Canadian veterinary college, the Atlantic Veterinary College at the University of Prince Edward Island, became fully accredited in April 1990 and graduated its first class in May 1990.

The recommendation of the Riley Committee in the U.K. that the number of British veterinary schools be reduced was controversial and unpopular in the veterinary community. This recommendation was criticized for being based on an incomplete analysis of veterinary supply-and-demand information. To better assess veterinary manpower needs in the U.K., a committee chaired by Ewan Page, vice-chancellor of the University of Reading, England, was established and examined the demand for veterinary graduates in private practice, government service, research and education, and animal welfare. An average shortfall of graduates of 18% in 1995 and 22% in 2000 was projected for the U.K. by consultants to the committee. The committee suggested that veterinarians from other nations be encouraged

A woman veterinarian (right) examines a cat in a veterinary hospital in Georgia. Assisting her is a veterinary technician, also a woman. In 1990 women outnumbered men 59 to 41% in U.S. veterinary schools.

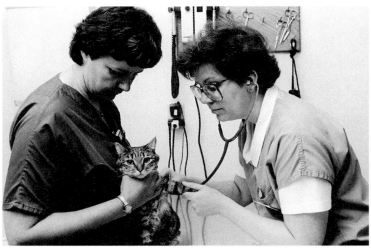

John Leone

Military dog handler takes his dog out on patrol in the desert during the Persian Gulf crisis. Desert conditions were particularly stressful to dogs because their bodies do not dissipate heat efficiently. In addition, airborne sand caused respiratory and eye problems, and scorpion stings were a frequent hazard.

to immigrate to Britain as a short-term solution to the shortage.

The British government's response to the Page Committee's report was favorable except that it did not agree to provide additional funds for implementing the recommendation that the number of students accepted be increased from the current 335 to at least 400. As an alternate approach to funding, the committee recommended increasing student fees.

Specialization. Specialization was increasing in veterinary medicine. Veterinary specialists are members of one or more colleges or boards that require specific training in a particular specialty and passage of a certification examination for acceptance to membership. Specialization may be oriented to a biological system, such as ophthalmology; to a discipline, such as radiology; or to a specific category, such as zoo animals. While veterinary colleges had been the primary location of specialists since the first two specialty organizations were approved by the AVMA in 1951, the current trend in employment of specialists was toward private practice. The American Association of Feline Practice was organizing an Academy of Feline Medicine, which might evolve into a specialty college. Opportunities for specialty training in feline medicine took a major step forward with the establishment of the first U.S. residency training program in this field at the Ohio State University College of Veterinary Medicine.

A petition for organization of the American College of Avian Medicine and Surgery was under consideration. This specialty would emphasize pet bird care. The pet bird population in the U.S. was expected to equal that of dogs and cats within the next 10 years.

Plans were also in progress to petition in 1991 for provisional recognition of the American College of Veterinary Informatics. The informatics discipline incorporates information science and engineering with computer technology to support and enhance veterinary teaching and research and both the man-

agement and the medical components of practice. The integration of personal computers with digital videodisc technology provides veterinary students with valuable learning experiences in disciplines such as pathology and surgery. Videodisc technology enables the storage of many thousands of color images (of a diseased kidney, for example) that can be retrieved by a computer almost instantly and displayed as a near-lifelike simulation. Student interaction with such simulations was expected not only to promote improved learning but also to ease the transition from preclinical to clinical sciences.

A University of California veterinary surgeon was involved in the application of robotic technology to orthopedic surgery. A robotic system was used in a successful total hip-replacement operation in a dog. The value of this system is the marked improvement in precision of placement of the prosthesis.

Veterinary medicine in the Third World. World food production was not growing at the same rate as the population. Veterinarians have an important role in improving the food supply, particularly in less developed countries by means of assistance with livestock production, animal product distribution, and control of animal diseases. While some of this assistance could be accomplished through research on improved drug-delivery systems for tropical climates and conduct of genetic studies on disease resistance, important assistance was being provided within the less developed countries. The Volunteer Partner Program worked with the Peace Corps to provide veterinary assistance in Morocco. The veterinarians spent about one year in villages and cities in Morocco, where they instituted herd health programs, made improvements in meat-inspection programs, and helped with government disease-eradication programs. Some of the villages had never had local veterinary services. One U.S. veterinarian noted that he had diagnosed diseases he only read about as a veterinary student.

Military veterinarians were filling important roles in animal-disease-control programs throughout the world. Veterinarians in the Department of Veterinary Medicine at the U.S. Armed Forces Research Institute of Medical Sciences in Bangkok, Thailand, were helping evaluate a new, rapid diagnostic test for anthrax in an effort to control that disease in Thailand.

In addition to research, military veterinarians were involved in ensuring a safe food supply for soldiers and military working dogs and in providing veterinary care for the dogs. These activities were important components of the Persian Gulf war. Desert conditions are especially stressful to dogs. A dog's body does not dissipate heat efficiently, and overheating can easily occur. Panting to control overheating results in rapid dehydration. A combination of heat and airborne sand has caused upper respiratory irritation and eye problems, and the dogs were also susceptible to the stings of scorpions commonly found in the desert of Saudi Arabia. Exercising the dogs at night and providing them with a special high-energy diet helped maintain them in top condition for fulfilling their military responsibilities for patrol and security duties and detection of concealed explosives.

When a Maryland veterinarian was called to reservist duty in the invasion of Panama, a special committee of the Maryland Veterinary Medical Association made arrangements to keep his clinic in operation while he was away. Similar support was offered by fellow veterinarians as reservists were called to serve in the Gulf war.

—John M. Bowen

First photograph released from the partially completed Keck Telescope in Hawaii, taken Nov. 24, 1990, is a mosaic of four successive exposures of the spiral galaxy NGC 1232, approximately 65 million light-years away.

Optical engineering

During the past year the visible semiconductor laser diode replaced many of the functions for the venerable helium-neon laser, disk cameras disappeared, and optical storage finally began to catch up with magnetic storage. In astronomy the Keck Telescope became partially operational, but the Hubble Space Telescope was limited by a mistake in optical testing that was the most expensive single error ever made in optical engineering. Some advances were made in fiber optics for communications, and some potential realizations of optical computers were demonstrated.

The mainstay of the low-power laser market for more than 25 years had been the familiar red helium-neon laser. During the past year, however, the number of such lasers that were manufactured decreased drastically owing to their replacement by visible red semiconductor lasers that were designed into new products. With this concept a five-milliwatt laser could be included in a semiconductor measuring only a few millimeters on a side; the package would contain all the electronic drive circuitry for

the laser and could be sold for only a few dollars. The efficiency of such lasers made lightweight products with batteries quite practical. Because no gas discharge was involved, the lifetime was virtually unlimited, producing even more economies. By 1991 almost all new laser products, such as scanners, laser printers, and pointing devices, were beginning to use these new devices.

Erasable and rewritable optical data storage disks with one gigabyte (one billion bytes) of storage space became available from several suppliers, and the market for these devices finally began to grow, fueled by the seemingly insatiable demand of computer users for more memory. The CD-ROM (compact disc-read only memory) began to grow in practical importance. The cost of manufacturing a CD-ROM disc was about the same as that of an audio compact disc, and so distribution of computer programs, documentation, and catalogs was quite cost-effective. Some models of computers were being sold with built-in CD-ROM drives, with the system software supplied on these inexpensive and easily replaceable disks. These were signs that the long period of development was over and that optical memory products would be widely available.

Clever industrial applications of lasers continued to be made. One of those that became implemented in 1990 was three-dimensional optical lithography. In this process a mold or prototype part can be fabricated directly from a computer-generated data base by use of a laser to scan a rotating bath of photosensitive plastic. Wherever the scanned laser beam intersects the surface, the plastic polymerizes and forms a hard surface; a full three-dimensional part is then built up by slowly lowering the level of the fluid in the bath as the laser defines the surface shape. This process provides a very inexpensive method of producing a test or prototype part since there is a direct transfer from design to prototype.

Material cutting and modification using high-power lasers was a growth business, with YAG (yttrium-aluminum-garnet) lasers the most commonly used sources. The introduction of a 25-w laser diode array promised to have a significant effect on the industry, and the compact nature of such a source made new configurations of machining and cutting tools possible.

While there continued to be growth in the area of optical systems in general, the military market began to sag considerably. This generated some trouble for an actively growing industry based on the application of infrared detectors. While the production capability for infrared imaging array detectors became established during the past year, the market for these greatly diminished. The market for visible detector arrays, however, continued to expand as video cameras and electronic still cameras sold well.

An impressive achievement in astronomical optics occurred in late summer when the 10-m-diameter Keck Telescope, under construction in Hawaii, began to provide images from the central portion of the array of segments forming the primary mirror. Engineering of the 8-m telescopes from the European Southern Observatory was begun, and trial castings leading to the pouring of the first 8-m blanks were planned for early 1991.

The most disconcerting news in optical engineering in many years was the discovery of a basic manufacturing error in the Hubble Space Telescope that limited the basic capability of the telescope to approximately the same resolution as that of a ground-based telescope. While clever image processing extended the capability to the point at which perhaps 80% of the scientific goals for the observatory would be attained, the telescope remained an embarrassingly flawed instrument that could be only partially repaired by astronauts on a space shuttle visit in 1993.

The problem was first identified from examination of the early pictures relayed from the telescope. Analysis showed that the image was afflicted with a large amount of spherical aberration, which meant that each star image was about 10 times the diameter it would have been had the telescope optics

been made properly. The U.S. National Aeronautics and Space Administration (NASA) convened a panel to examine the problem. The panel determined that the 2.4-m-diameter primary mirror had been fabricated with the wrong surface shape. This at first seemed to be difficult to explain, since the mirror surface shape had been tested during fabrication in 1981 by the use of one of the most sophisticated interferometers and optical test arrangements ever built. The investigative panel determined that the error was due to a 1.3-mm mistake in setting the spacing of a small compensating lens in the testing optics when those optics were assembled in 1981. This mistake in spacing resulted from an error in interpreting the position of an image returned from an erroneously located defining aperture placed on the end of a measuring rod; the image was believed by the test engineers to determine the spacing of the components of the test optics to an accuracy of less than 0.001 mm.

Several opportunities existed for observing the consequences of this error during the test process, and test data that could have revealed the error actually existed in 1981. However, all of the error indications were ignored by the project engineers in the mistaken belief that all test steps had been carried out perfectly. Thus, the $2 billion telescope system remained significantly flawed. The result would be a costly repair mission that would undoubtedly limit the ability to spend money on other aspects of the space astronomy program.

Back on the Earth's surface, several other problems were resolved. Eastman Kodak Co. discontin-

Minolta Maxxum 8000i, a highly automated 35-mm single-lens reflex, features computer-chip-controlled autofocus, a choice of exposure control modes, and a "creative expansion card" system capable of adding such special operating features as flash bracketing or fantasy effects.

Courtesy, Minolta Camera Co.

ued the manufacture of its miniature disk camera line. While film for existing cameras would continue to be sold, this marked the end of one of the most innovative steps ever made in compact still photography. Public acceptance was marginal, even with the great convenience of the camera. The winner in the photographic format competition was the automated 35-mm camera. It defeated the disk camera because the larger format image provided significantly better image quality. The number of clever innovations in automated cameras at all price ranges continued to expand, with full automation that included focusing, exposure setting, and even motion stabilization being provided.

Other areas of optical technology also produced interesting accomplishments. Transmission of data at rates equivalent to 300,000 separate simultaneous telephone conversations over a single 118-km (73-mi)-long optical fiber was demonstrated and shown to be practical. In biology the microscopic rearrangement of cell structures using laser "tweezers" to detach and reattach parts of a molecule was demonstrated. Surgery for removing lesions under the skin without physical penetration of the skin was carried out by the use of lasers that were transmitted by the skin and then absorbed by the lesion. New laser wavelengths permitted the tailoring of the

An engineer at Bell Laboratories inspects a rudimentary model of an all-optical digital computer. The packaging of a useful large-scale optical computer in a small space was not expected until the late 1990s.

© Yoav Levy—Phototake

wavelength to the specific surgical procedure to be performed.

A promising application of lasers to refractive correction of the eye was demonstrated several times but had not obtained Food and Drug Administration (FDA) approval for general use in the U.S., although some applications overseas had occurred. The process uses ultraviolet light from a laser to change the shape of the surface of the cornea in a form determined by a computer and measuring instrument, thus correcting visual defects in the eye. Questions remained about both the possibility of damage to the eye tissue and the length of time that the change in the eye structure would be maintained. Therefore, as of 1991 the procedure remained experimental.

Other developments included a demonstration of a rudimentary form of an all-optical digital computer by Bell Laboratories. This computer occupied an entire laboratory table and had less computation power than a small pocket calculator, but the principle and the speed of operation were confirmed. However, packaging a useful large-scale optical computer into a small space might not be accomplished before the late 1990s.

Several laboratories demonstrated somewhat more practical approaches to optical interconnections within electronic computers, as well as very high-speed direct optical switching devices for fiber-optic communication systems. Practical passive couplers for fiber optics were available, but active coupling components would eliminate the need to convert from light to electronic signals in order to process the signals being carried on optical fibers. During the year there were demonstrations of direct light amplification and switching, with the probability of practical product implementation in the next two years.

The future for optics appeared to be bright, with emphasis on photonic and electro-optical applications, such as video systems and communications. The use of optics in industrial processes in which laser light interacts with materials continued to increase. Imaging devices, both visible and infrared, expanded in applications. However, much of the vitality of the industry worldwide had been oriented toward military applications. The end of the cold war and the subsequent reduction of defense budgets limited much of this research and development. During the Persian Gulf war lasers were used with considerable success as target indicators. The major activity for the next year was expected to be in commercial and consumer applications. Such developments as high-speed semiconductor diode lasers provided an opportunity for the application of many of the traditional as well as the new and innovative optical processes in a cost-effective manner.

—Robert R. Shannon

Physics

Advances in seeing, understanding, and exploiting the microscopic and submicroscopic worlds of matter ranked high on the list of achievements in physics during the past year. Important biological molecules and chemical processes were imaged, the internal structure of protons and neutrons in the atomic nucleus was clarified, the long-unresolved "solar neutrino problem" came a few steps closer to solution, and a simple way of fabricating solids with dramatically modified electromagnetic behavior was demonstrated.

General developments

During the past year advances in scanning tunneling microscopy and its variants allowed scientists to image atoms, molecules (including the DNA helix), and important chemical and biochemical processes and to gain experience in manipulating individual atoms. Work progressed on a new category of materials—called nanophase materials—that offered properties and processing characteristics unlike those of conventional metals and ceramics. A developing theory, self-organized criticality, promised insights into phenomena as diverse as avalanches, current fluctuations in electronic components, and the spread of forest fires.

Scanning tunneling microscopy. The 1986 Nobel Prize for Physics went to Gerd Binnig and Heinrich Rohrer of the IBM Zürich (Switz.) Research Laboratory for their invention of the scanning tunneling microscope (STM), which allows individual atoms on the surface of an electrically conducting sample to be imaged. In subsequent years variations on the basic STM design permitted the study of not just surface topography but also the nature of chemical bonds and magnetic properties of surface layers of atoms. In the past year more advances were made in the imaging of macromolecules and biomolecules and in the use of the STM and related devices to actually push atoms around on a substrate.

In the basic STM configuration a very sharp needle probe, perhaps only a few atoms wide at the tip, is brought within nanometers or angstroms (billionths to ten-billionths of a meter) of a sample. If the probe and sample are close enough, a "tunneling" current (subject to a small applied voltage) will flow between them. The size of the current is sensitive to the gap between tip and sample. Thus, by carefully scanning the probe across the sample surface using delicate piezoelectric controls and by measuring the tunneling current, or rather by measuring the adjustments needed to maintain a constant current, scientists can build up a three-dimensional map of the sample topography with atomic-scale resolution.

In an STM variant called the atomic force microscope (AFM), it is the force, rather than the current, between the probe and sample that is measured. The probe of an AFM is often a small diamond tip mounted on a sensitive spring or cantilever mechanism, whose motions can be monitored and converted into a measurement of force. Using AFM techniques, a team of scientists at the University of California at Santa Barbara led by Paul K. Hansma recently imaged, as it occurred, the polymerization of fibrin, an important clotting agent in the blood. In another study Hansma, A.A. Gewirth of the University of Illinois at Urbana-Champaign, and co-workers made AFM images during the process in which a layer of copper atoms was electroplated onto gold. Such atomic-resolution electrochemistry will be particularly important for the study and design of fuel cells and sensors.

Because the STM depends on the flow of an electric current, it has some trouble imaging nonconducting samples. Nevertheless, in the past year a group at the California Institute of Technology led by John D. Baldeschwieler published atomic-resolution images of DNA made with the STM. The pictures, which show clearly the double-helix structure of DNA, provide a magnification of 25 million. The sample was placed on a graphite substrate and in ultrahigh vacuum.

Some scientists have exploited the fact that STM or STM-like probes can push, or drag, atoms or molecules under observation. In 1990 Donald M. Eigler and Erhard K. Schweizer at the IBM Almaden

Atomic force microscope image made after the electroplating of a gold crystal surface with copper reveals the atomic arrangement of the first layer of copper atoms (top layer) deposited on the gold atom substrate (bottom layer).

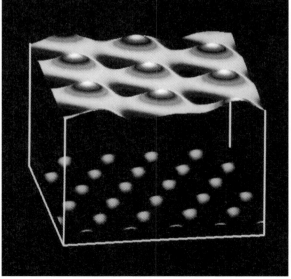

S. Manne, P.K. Hansma, J. Massie, V.B. Elings, and A.A. Gewirth

Research Center, San Jose, Calif., used an STM probe to move xenon atoms on a nickel surface and thus spell out the letters *IBM*. This achievement represented the first time individual atoms had ever been deliberately positioned in a pattern. Eigler was able not only to drag atoms across a substrate but also to pick them up with the probe and later put them down somewhere else. By bringing together two or more specific atoms in this way, Eigler hopes one day to study a completely controlled chemical reaction.

Another group at the IBM Almaden center used an STM with a gold tip to deposit hills of gold as small as 10 nm (nanometers) wide and 2 nm high. Although these "structures" (the small hills contain perhaps thousands of atoms) are not as small as Eigler's single atoms, the conditions in this case were much more favorable: the gold-tipped STM operated in room-temperature air rather than at low temperatures or at high vacuum. Furthermore, the gold tip did not wear out as had been the case in many other STM applications. (See *Condensed-matter physics*, below.)

At IBM's Thomas J. Watson Research Center, Yorktown Heights, N.Y., Mark McCord used an STM to decompose $Fe(CO)_5$ molecules in such a way that tiny deposits, 20 nm across by 80 nm high, were formed. These deposits are approximately 50% iron, and they may have uses as tiny magnets.

Finally, in another application of STM technology, ballistic electron emission microscopy (BEEM), electrons emitted from the probe with sufficient energy are able to penetrate a sample consisting of a thin metal film and, beneath it, a thin semiconductor layer. The measured current provides information about atomic details of the metal-semiconductor boundary, which should help in the design of electronic devices. Using an even higher voltage than was needed to image the boundary layer, scientists at Cornell University, Ithaca, N.Y., found that they could inscribe lines (only 8.5 nm wide) in the boundary layer without disturbing the outer surface of the metal layer above.

Nanostructured materials. New kinds of materials can now be assembled from grains having sizes as small as nanometers or less. The materials, sometimes referred to as nanophase materials or cluster-assembled materials, often possess properties and processing characteristics that differ from those of conventional materials made from coarser grains. For example, scientists at Argonne (Ill.) National Laboratory and Northwestern University, Evanston, Ill., showed recently that nanophase copper and palladium, assembled from grains five to seven nanometers in size, are harder and stronger than their conventional counterparts by a factor of five. As of early 1991, single-phase metals and ceramics

had received the most attention, but more complex materials may soon be studied as well.

The synthesis of nanostructured materials, based on a method first suggested by H. Gleiter of the University of Saarbrücken, Germany, is carried out in a vacuum chamber that, after being evacuated, is filled with a high-purity gas, either an inert gas like helium or a reactive gas if a ceramic compound is to be assembled. Typically, metal atoms (or the component atoms of the ceramic) are evaporated from a heated source; the atoms move through the gas and then condense and collect on a fingerlike projection chilled from within by liquid nitrogen. The tiny nano-sized clusters that form are scraped off and later compacted into pellets. Other synthesis techniques exist; chemists have been able to grow clusters in solution or inside powdered glasses, but in such cases there is less control over the size of the resultant clusters. In the gas-condensation approach the grain size can be controlled by varying the evaporation rate or by changing the gas type or pressure.

An interesting feature of the small clusters is that a significant fraction of the constituent atoms (30–60% for five-nanometer grains) will be part of the cluster surface, a fact of interest to scientists because it may offer a new way of studying the physics of condensed matter, particularly "quantum size effects." Also, the clusters' small sizes may facilitate the creation of materials having special properties. Cluster size, for instance, has a large influence on physical properties, whether the clusters are studied in the form of a powder or assembled into a bulk material. Louis Brus at AT&T Bell Laboratories, Murray Hill, N.J., created a series of powders—each of them made from cadmium and selenium atoms but each with a different cluster size—in a wide spectrum of colors. One powder, for example, consisting of five-nanometer clusters that contain perhaps only 3,000 atoms each, has a red color. The powder consisting of 3.5-nm clusters, each containing only 1,000 atoms, has a green color.

Electron microscopy can be used to study the structure of larger clusters, but this direct approach cannot be used for smaller, nano-sized clusters. Moreover, it has been difficult to characterize the structure of such small clusters with methods like scanning tunneling microscopy without altering the structure in the process. Therefore, other methods must be sought. Stephen J. Riley at Argonne has observed the chemical activity of small nickel clusters with fewer than 200 atoms in order to probe their structure, while Brus has used optical properties to characterize the structure of small clusters.

Argonne scientists Richard W. Siegel and his colleagues have studied assemblages of clusters. They discovered, as mentioned above, that copper assembled from small grains is much harder and stronger than conventional copper. The reason is that dislocations—defects in the crystal structure that can lead to deformation and fracture—are more easily frustrated in a nanocrystalline environment than in one made up of large crystals. If assembly from clusters makes deformation more difficult in metals, it seems to make deformation, and hence ductility, easier in ceramics (*e.g.*, by a factor of four for titanium dioxide, TiO_2), which are usually brittle and hard to work. In addition to being more ductile, nanophase TiO_2 can be sintered at a temperature some 400° to 600° C (720° to 1,080° F) lower than in the conventional processing method.

Self-organized criticality. Self-organized criticality is the name for the tendency in some large interactive systems to evolve toward a critical state in which a minor event can lead to a chain reaction of events or catastrophe. To take a common example, the addition of a single grain of sand to a sandpile may initiate avalanches of all different sizes. Following the avalanche, the addition of more grains will cause the pile to reorganize itself in such a way that it will exist perpetually in a critical state of marginal stability; the pile will become vulnerable to further avalanches. According to Per Bak, a scientist at Brookhaven National Laboratory, Upton, N.Y., the global properties of such systems can be understood not by studying parts of the system but only by looking for relations and connections at all levels.

Bak's study of self-organized criticality began with his work on "flicker noise." Many systems in nature exhibit this phenomenon. For example, the fluctuations of certain measurable quantities such as the luminosity of stars, the electrical current through a resistor, or the flow of a river over time may appear to be no more than random variations. Actually, however, the fluctuations are observed to obey a power law: the likelihood of fluctuations of a certain size is inversely proportional to the size raised to some power. Bak and others believe that flicker noise may arise from the superposition of interactions that take place within the system over a variety of time and distance scales. In other words, a fluctuation now will depend in some way on fluctuations in the past.

The theory of self-organized criticality, exemplified by Bak's predictions about sandpiles, recently was put to experimental test. Glenn A. Held of IBM's Watson Research Center, using a balance sensitive to the presence of single sand grains, carefully dropped grains one at a time (occasional avalanches carried sand off the balance and were registered as a loss of mass of the pile as a whole) while monitoring the likelihood of avalanches of different sizes. A plot of the mass of the pile as a function of the number of grains dropped (one experimental run used 35,000 grains) proved to have a fractal shape; the plot resembled itself at several levels of mag-

nification. This result suggested that connections between avalanches of many different sizes and at different periods were at work. Held's experimental results, at least for small sandpiles (scale-invariant behavior was not evident for large sandpiles), agreed with Bak's numerical simulations conducted three years earlier.

The year also produced an interesting convergence of experimental observations and computer simulations in the study of earthquake faults. Decades earlier U.S. seismologists Beno Gutenberg and Charles Richter (after whom the Richter scale of earthquake magnitude is named) showed that the probability of earthquakes that dissipate an energy E is proportional to E raised to a certain power. In 1990 Jean Carlson and James Langer of the Institute for Theoretical Physics at the University of California at Santa Barbara carried out computer simulations of earthquakes using blocks (which could slip or stick) connected by springs to represent the connected parts of a fault line. Their results exhibited the characteristic power-law behavior.

According to Bak, "fractal structures and flicker noise are the spatial and temporal fingerprints, respectively, of self-organized criticality." He has looked for such hints, with some success, in a number of complex systems, including snow avalanches, fluid turbulence, the spread of forest fires, and even the performance of a market economy.

—Phillip F. Schewe

High-energy physics

Over the past few years, the so-called standard model of elementary particles and their interactions has continued to gain support from progressively more sophisticated and precise experiments, although, at the same time, there have remained outstanding, unresolved questions. The standard model identifies quarks and leptons as the fundamental constituents of all matter and categorizes their interactions as occurring through a small set of fundamental forces, or fields, each mediated by one or more particular field particles, or field quanta. Thus, as shown in Table I (p. 392), there are now known to be three generations or families of quarks and leptons, each generation consisting of a negatively charged lepton and a neutral, possibly massless lepton called a neutrino together with a pair of quarks, one having an electric charge of $-\frac{1}{3}$ ($\frac{1}{3}$ the charge of an ordinary, negatively charged electron) and the other a charge of $+\frac{2}{3}$. The quarks are the constituents of nuclear matter (protons and neutrons) and of the many mesons that have been discovered; they account for most of the mass of normal matter.

Although the tau neutrino has not yet been detected, indirect evidence for it is very strong. On the

Table I. Properties of Quarks and Leptons

| Generation | Leptons | | Quarks | |
	Charge − 1	Neutral	Charge + ⅔	Charge − ⅓
1	electron (0.51)	electron neutrino	up quark, u (~340)	down quark, d (~340)
2	muon (106)	muon neutrino	charmed quark, c (1,550)	strange quark, s (~510)
3	tau (1,784)	tau neutrino	top quark, t (>95,000)	bottom quark, b (4,720)

All charges are in units of the electron's charge (− 1). Masses, shown in parentheses, are in millions of electron volts (MeV); the masses of the neutrinos are consistent with zero. The tau neutrino and the top quark have not yet been observed.

other hand, the top quark has not yet been seen even indirectly. All of these particles, both quarks and leptons, have an intrinsic angular momentum, or spin, of ½ in units of Planck's constant. For each quark or lepton, there is a corresponding antiquark or antilepton, having the same mass but opposite in certain other properties (*e.g.*, electric charge or spin). The quarks appear constrained to be bound to other quarks or antiquarks to form particles (proton, neutrons, and other baryons or mesons) of integral electric charge.

Quarks and leptons interact through the forces identified in Table II. The field quanta that mediate the forces are all of integral spin (one unit of Planck's constant for all save the graviton, which may have two units) and are called bosons, as they obey statistical rules that were first understood by S.N. Bose and Albert Einstein decades ago. It is now understood that the weak and electromagnetic forces are in fact "low-energy" manifestations of a single electroweak interaction. A major reason for the "weakness" of the weak interaction is the very large masses of its field quanta, the $W^\pm$ and Z^0 intermediate vector bosons.

Table II. The Basic Forces or Interactions of Physics

Force	Field particle and rest mass	Strength relative to strong force at 10^{-13} cm distance	Particles that experience force
electromagnetic	γ (photon); 0	10^{-2}	all electrically charged particles; all quarks and charged leptons
weak	$W^\pm$; 80.6 GeV Z^0; 91.16 GeV	10^{-13}	all particles
strong	g (gluon); 0	1	quarks and hadrons (particles composed of quarks)
gravitational	G (graviton)	10^{-38}	all particles with mass

The electromagnetic and weak forces are now understood as special cases of a more general electroweak interaction. The graviton has not yet been experimentally observed.

Much of the progress in understanding elementary particles over the past two years has come through the exploitation of three remarkable new particle accelerator facilities: the Tevatron proton-antiproton collider at the Fermi National Accelerator Laboratory (Fermilab) near Chicago, the electron-positron Stanford Linear Collider (SLC) in California, and the Large Electron-Positron (LEP) colliding-beam facility at CERN (European Laboratory for Particle Physics), near Geneva. Recent findings from these laboratories are summarized below.

Tevatron results. The Fermilab Tevatron provides head-on collisions between protons and antiprotons (the antimatter counterpart of protons), each particle having an energy of 900 GeV (billion electron volts), or 1.8 TeV (trillion electron volts) in the center of mass of a two-particle collision. When the effects of special relativity are taken into account, this energy is equivalent to a proton with almost two million billion electron volts of energy striking a proton at rest. A large detector called the Collider Detector at Fermilab (CDF) has been used to collect data on these collisions.

Some of the more interesting results to emerge concern the nature of quark-quark collisions. The standard model argues that the forces between quarks at very small distances should behave much like the electromagnetic force; *i.e.*, they should behave as a force field obeying the inverse square law. One early important experiment in electromagnetic scattering was that of Ernest Rutherford in 1911, wherein alpha particles (the positively charged nuclei of helium) were scattered on gold foil, and the resulting angular distributions of the deflected alpha particles provided convincing proof that each gold atom consists of a small, dense, positively charged nucleus surrounded by a cloud of electrons.

The Tevatron data showed that proton-antiproton collisions often resulted in two energetic jets of particles (mesons) emerging from the collisions nearly back-to-back. It had been known that quarks cannot be produced free of other quarks at "large" distances (*i.e.*, much larger than the diameter of a nucleus). When a quark is given enough energy to free it, it appears instead as a jet of mesons, the extra energy being invested in the creation of quark-antiquark pairs. The Tevatron jets thus were easily identified as the visible product of energetic quarks, and the events with two back-to-back jets were interpreted as the result of a quark of the proton having scattered against an antiquark of the antiproton. The resulting angular distributions were in fact remarkably similar to those Rutherford had seen in his classic experiment almost 80 years earlier. And, in the spirit of Rutherford's precedent, the data were interpreted as not only confirming the quantitative predictions of the standard model of the strong interaction of quarks (known as quantum chromodynamics) but also setting limits on the finite size of the quarks. From the results the quarks are still consistent with being point particles; there was no evidence that they have any finite extent.

It is noteworthy that the 1990 Nobel Prize for Physics was awarded to three physicists, Jerome Friedman and Henry Kendall of the Massachusetts Institute of Technology and Richard Taylor of Stanford University (*see* SCIENTISTS OF THE YEAR), for experiments at Stanford from 1967 to 1973 that first demonstrated, by means of inelastic scattering of electrons on protons, that the proton consists of quarks. In that experiment the quarks (there also manifested as jets of mesons) were found to be much smaller than the proton, although the upper limits set for their size were crude compared with those from the newer Tevatron results.

At Fermilab a primary objective has been the search for the top quark. Because the standard model defines quite well the particle's expected properties, with the conspicuous exception of mass, experimenters have known what to look for. By 1991 only the lower limit to the mass of the top quark had been set; from the latest data the mass must be at least 95 GeV (more than 100 times the rest mass of the proton). Physicists strongly suspected that the mass is less than 200 GeV, and members of the Fermilab group were confident that they would find the top quark in future experiments at the Tevatron.

Other Tevatron results gave improved measurements of the masses of the W and Z bosons and related parameters of the standard model.

Electron-positron collider results. Since 1989 the Stanford Linear Collider and CERN's LEP facility have provided exceptional data on the nature of physics accessible through the production and decay of the Z^0 boson. At both facilities physicists have operated experiments in which the final state of the colliding electrons and positrons (the antimatter counterpart of electrons) had an energy in the vicinity of the mass of the Z, or about 91 GeV. At CERN each of four different experiments has recorded hundreds of thousands of Z events, from which a wealth of physics has been extracted. Perhaps the most significant result (described in detail in the

An immense electromagnet, the largest ever constructed for particle physics research, surrounds the L3 detector at CERN's LEP collider. Observation of Z boson decays at the L3 have helped set limits on the number of generations of particles.

1991 Yearbook of Science and the Future Year in Review: PHYSICS: *High-energy physics*) is the fixing of the limit on the number of neutrino types—and, hence, of the number of generations of elementary particles—to the three already known. Since in the standard model each generation includes a neutrino, the limit of three neutrino types is interpreted to mean that there are no more than three generations of quarks and leptons. The caveats are that a very massive neutrino (having a rest mass of tens of GeV) could have been missed or that a neutrino exists that does not behave in a manner predicted by the standard model.

Other results from the LEP experiments include a refined determination of the values of the weak-interaction coupling constants; *i.e.*, the parameters that determine the rates of nuclear and particle reactions that proceed via the neutral weak interactions (in which no net change of electric charge occurs). The LEP data improved the precision on these constants by about two orders of magnitude over previous results.

Negative results. An important contribution from the new facilities was the collection of negative results that set limits on the existence of other postulated particles. One outstanding question in particle physics concerns the ratio of the masses of the different elementary particles. Why, for example, should the mass of the muon be 210 times that of an electron and the mass of the tau lepton about 17 times that of the muon? A theoretical mechanism proposed to answer this question predicts the existence of a new particle, dubbed the Higgs particle (after Scottish physicist Peter Higgs, who proposed it). The Higgs particle could have almost any mass up to perhaps 1 TeV, and its properties should be predictable. Careful searches were made at LEP for the Higgs within the energy range accessible there, but no trace of the Higgs appeared over a mass range from zero to about 40 GeV.

Other postulated particles were sought unsuccessfully. For example, it has been proposed that there may be a so-called supersymmetric set of particles: particles having integral spins (as opposed to the half-integral spins of all known particles) and interacting through a corresponding set of half-integral-spin field quanta. Again, there is no prediction as to the masses of any of these particles, but their properties otherwise are calculable. Recent searches at CERN ruled out the existence of any supersymmetric particles that have masses less than about 40 GeV. It was also possible to rule out, for example, excited states of the electron and muon as well as a number of other exotic theoretical suggestions not otherwise experimentally excluded.

Over the next few years, the energy of the LEP collider will be increased to the threshold for producing pairs of W bosons. This goal will allow further refinements to the parameters of the standard model and broaden the search horizon for the Higgs and other unobserved particles.

Unresolved problems. Although it now appears more firmly established that the fundamental particles of the universe all fall within the three generations already known, physicists do not understand why, nor do they understand theoretically why the particles have the masses they do. The discovery of the Higgs, if it happens, will be a most valuable event, for it should be a sort of Rosetta Stone of particle physics. On the other hand, if Higgs particles having masses up to about 1 TeV are ruled out, physicists then will be without a clue in understanding the "whys" of the observed set of particles, their masses, and other properties.

So far, all experimental results are consistent with the concept of quarks as point particles and as "fundamental" or indivisible entities (in the sense that the ancient Greeks used the term *atom*). There is no proof of this, however. Indeed, self-consistent theoretical models have been proposed suggesting that the six quarks are made up in turn of a smaller number of yet more fundamental objects. Only future experiments at higher energies will decide this question.

Furthermore, physicists have come to expect surprises. When in the past they crossed new energy thresholds, it was their frequent experience to find totally unanticipated phenomena. Of the most important discoveries made with high-energy particle accelerators in the past 30 years, about a dozen were total surprises, while only a couple were predicted.

Questions that tie in high-energy physics with cosmology and astrophysics continue to challenge human understanding. For instance, it is generally believed that most of the mass of the universe so far has been unobserved. This mass could be in the form of small, weakly luminous stars or dark planetary bodies (perhaps similar to the planet Jupiter) filling the galaxies, or it could be in the form of subatomic particles; *e.g.*, weakly interacting massive particles (WIMPs), neutrinos with mass (see *Nuclear physics,* below), magnetic monopoles, or other exotic, yet undiscovered entities. Astrophysicists and particle physicists continue to search for evidence of such particles in astronomical observations, in data collected from terrestrial detectors set up to record particles arriving from space, and in high-energy collisions at particle accelerator laboratories.

Future accelerators. High energies play two roles in particle physics. First, in order to produce more massive particles, it is necessary to provide energies sufficient to create them within the constraints of the laws of relativity. Second, high energies make possible collisions having a high momentum transfer, which in turn allows physicists to probe smaller distances within the constraints of the uncertainty principle of quantum theory (see *Nuclear physics,* below). For both reasons particle physicists have exploited progressively higher energies over the past 50 years.

Two facilities under construction in 1990 should open new horizons in the near future. In Hamburg, Germany, a colliding-beam accelerator nearing completion will bring together 30-GeV electrons and 800-GeV protons and so extend the class of experiments begun by Friedman, Kendall, and Taylor to much higher energies than have been explored to date. This effort is an example of the second reason for higher energies: the desire to probe ever smaller distances. The facility, named HERA, will include two detectors, each built and operated by a large international collaboration. In the Soviet Union at Protvino, near Moscow, a 3-TeV proton accelerator/collider facility (UNK) was being built to extend the energy of experiments of the kind so far undertaken at the Tevatron.

The most ambitious project launched to date is the Superconducting Super Collider (SSC), presently in its early stages of construction near Dallas, Texas. It will bring together two beams of 20-TeV protons head on, making available 40 TeV in the collision center of mass. Among other things, either the Higgs particle will be found at these energies, or the standard model will break down. Meanwhile, physicists at the CERN laboratory are designing a Large Hadron Collider (LHC), which will use the LEP tunnel to house two proton accelerators, each of 8 TeV, in order to produce collisions with a total energy of 16 TeV. As with the SSC, the goal of the LHC is to test the standard model to the breaking point, to seek the Higgs particle, to find or rule out other postulated particles—and, of course, to discover the unexpected.

—Lawrence W. Jones

Nuclear physics

Dramatic progress in understanding many aspects of the diverse field of nuclear physics took place during the past year. Experiments with very high-energy protons impinging on nuclear targets helped physicists refine their theoretical picture of the way in which the distribution of quarks and antiquarks in a neutron or proton is modified when that particle is part of an atomic nucleus. In low-energy nuclear-structure physics, an old puzzle regarding the existence of particular surface vibrations in deformed nuclei was resolved. In another illustration of the diversity of nuclear research, particle detectors making use of the nuclei of a large quantity of the metallic element gallium measured the flux of neutrinos coming from the Sun. The measurements shed light on a fundamental problem in elementary particle physics; namely, whether one kind of neutrino can transform into another.

Quarks and antiquarks in nuclei. Although the atomic nucleus has been an object of study for more than 50 years, there remain a number of critical questions concerning the origin of nuclear forces, the extent to which nuclei can be described as an assembly of independently moving nucleons (neutrons and protons), and the role played by the elementary constituents of nucleons; *i.e.*, the quarks. The internal structure of neutrons and protons cannot be neglected, since the distance between nucleons in a nucleus is about 1.7 femtometers (millionths of a billionth of a meter), comparable to the diameter of a nucleon.

Over the past two decades, the development of the underlying quark theory of strong interactions (quantum chromodynamics, or QCD) and the study of particle interactions in which a large momentum is transferred to a target nucleus by an incident lepton (electron or muon) have greatly enlarged the understanding of the quark structure of the nucleon. Recently there has been dramatic progress in probing the distribution of quarks and antiquarks (the antimatter counterparts of quarks) in nuclei. The European Muon Collaboration, an international collaboration of scientists working at CERN (European Laboratory for Particle Physics) near Geneva, first reported a difference between the structure functions of heavy and light nuclei, as observed with high-energy muons. In the framework of QCD, these structure functions indicate the manner in which the momenta (speeds) of quarks are distributed in the nucleus. It was determined that quark distribution in heavy nuclei differs from that in deuterium, an isotope of hydrogen whose nucleus is made up of only one proton and one neutron. The difference can be attributed to the tighter binding of the nucleons in heavier nuclei.

In the past year new results on the behavior of quarks in nuclei became available from the analysis of interactions of high-energy protons with nuclear targets. In an experiment at the Fermi National Accelerator Laboratory (Fermilab), Batavia, Ill., a beam of protons was accelerated to an energy of 800 GeV (billion electron volts) and directed onto nuclear targets of deuterium, carbon, calcium, iron, and tungsten. The interaction of a proton with a nucleus leads to the production of a pair of leptons, namely the negatively charged muon (μ^-) and its positively charged antiparticle (μ^+). At the level of quarks, this interaction consists of a quark (from the proton) and its corresponding antiquark (from the target nucleus) coming together and annihilating into a photon, a quantum of the electromagnetic field. The photon then dissociates into the $\mu^-\mu^+$ pair. Thus, the observation of $\mu^-\mu^+$ pair production from proton-bombarded nuclear targets is able to shed light on the distribution of antiquarks in the nucleus. In the experiment at Fermilab, physicists saw almost no dependence of the production of $\mu^-\mu^+$ pairs on the type of nuclear target. This observed result in turn implies that modification of the momenta of antiquarks due to the presence of surrounding nucleons is rather small.

In the simplest theoretical approach, the antiquarks in nuclei are pictured as being bound up in mesons, such as the pion, which mediate the strong interaction between the nucleons. These mesons form a cloud surrounding a nucleon in the nucleus. The clouds are deformed when many nucleons are present, an effect that leads to a predicted modification of the antiquark distribution. This model has been ruled out by the Fermilab data. A second approach is the quark-cluster model, in which the nucleus is viewed as a collection of essentially free nucleons, plus some component of multiquark clusters (six quarks, nine quarks, and so on) formed in a region where the nucleons overlap. This model also seems inconsistent with the data since it leads to the prediction of a significant, and unobserved, enhancement of the number of antiquarks in the nucleus. A third approach, which has proved approximately consistent with experiment, is the "scaling" model. In this case the antiquark momentum distribution in the nucleus is related to that measured for an isolated nucleon by a change of scale of the momentum imparted to the nucleus by the incident proton. The understanding of the scaling hypothesis in terms of the emission of gluons, the quanta of QCD that are analogous to photons, is still not complete, and intense theoretical studies of such processes in nuclei are continuing.

Collective and single-particle behavior in nuclei. Physical systems composed of a number of individual "particles" often display diverse modes of excitation.

395

It is sometimes possible to interpret the behavior of such systems in terms of the motions of the individual particles, while in other cases the system exhibits a correlated collective behavior such as a rotation or vibration of the entire entity or the movement of surface waves around it. In many systems of physical interest, such as solids, the number of particles participating in collective motions is effectively infinite. By contrast, atomic nuclei, with their finite numbers of constituents, offer a unique "laboratory" in which the interplay of collective and single-particle (quantal) states can be studied. The number of nucleons actively involved in the nuclear motion is often quite small, on the order of 10–20. In such systems the Pauli exclusion principle plays an important role, prohibiting two nucleons from occupying the same quantum state.

One of the most telling signatures of the interplay of single-particle and collective motion occurs in the study of "multiphonon" vibrational states in nuclei. Both atomic and nuclear systems can exhibit collective motions characterized as surface vibrations, or phonons. In solids, multiple vibrations can be piled on top of one another essentially at will. In nuclei, however, the finite number of particles and the Pauli exclusion principle have long been thought to impede significantly the creation of such modes. Indeed, for three decades a long-standing issue in the study of the collective behavior of atomic nuclei has been whether multiphonon vibrational excitations could exist in nuclei that are nonspherical. Since most nuclei are nonspherical or deformed, the question is of considerable importance; hence, the issue pervades the study of low-energy nuclear structure. Some theoretical approaches allow such collective multiphonon states to exist, whereas others predict that the vibrations will be totally fragmented.

The difficulty of observing such nuclear states and determining their properties precluded an empirical answer to the question until the appearance of a powerful new method known as the gamma-ray-induced Doppler (GRID) technique. The technique was pioneered at the Institut Laue-Langevin (ILL), Grenoble, France, and applied to the determination of the lifetimes of a number of nuclear excitations. Determination of lifetimes by Doppler techniques relies on observation of the decay of a nucleus while it is in flight. In the GRID technique the nuclear motion is induced by the recoil of a nucleus following its emission of a gamma ray (a very high-energy photon). In contrast to normal Doppler applications, the recoil energies are extremely small (a few electron volts); therefore, extraordinarily sensitive techniques are required. Recently a sophisticated GRID-based instrument was developed as a joint project of ILL and the U.S. National Institute of Standards and Technology, Gaithersburg, Md. In a collaboration involving ILL, Brookhaven National Laboratory, Upton, N.Y., and other institutions, the first definitive evidence for the existence of multiphonon vibrations in deformed nuclei was detected with this instrument in an experiment on the nucleus erbium-168. The results confirmed the predictions of nuclear models in which such collective excitations remain intact. The new measurements greatly clarified the question of how the development of highly correlated collective motions in deformed nuclei is affected by the Pauli principle.

Neutrinos from the Sun. Weakly interacting particles called neutrinos are formed by fusion processes in the interior of the Sun. In the standard model of elementary particles, neutrinos come in three types, the electron neutrino, the muon neutrino, and the tau neutrino, which are associated with the electron, muon, and tau lepton, respectively (see *High-energy physics,* above). Hints that neutrinos may oscillate, *i.e.,* that neutrinos of one type transform to those of another type, have motivated a number of experiments aimed at detecting the oscillations. These experiments use neutrino beams from medium- and high-energy particle accelerators and nuclear reactors.

Decades ago the idea had been proposed to use nuclear targets to detect the neutrino flux from the Sun. The nuclear process involved in detecting neutrinos is the inverse of ordinary nuclear beta decay; namely, interaction of an electron neutrino with a nucleus results in the transformation of a nuclear neutron into a proton accompanied by the emission of an electron. In the 1960s measurements with a target of chlorine-37 (17 protons, 20 neutrons), which when it captures a neutrino transforms to radioactive argon-37 (18 protons, 19 neutrons), were started in the Homestake Gold Mine in South Dakota. The observed capture rate for neutrinos reaching the Earth, averaged over the period 1970–88, is about two solar neutrino units (SNUs, a customary measure of solar-neutrino flux). By contrast, the predicted rate based on the standard model for solar-energy generation is almost eight SNUs. This deficit of neutrino detections, recently corroborated by the Kamiokande II experiment in Japan, is called the solar neutrino problem.

The Homestake experiment is mostly sensitive to higher energy electron neutrinos, whose rate of production depends sensitively on the temperature in the interior of the Sun. However, more than 90% of solar neutrinos are produced by proton-proton fusion, and these lie below the energy threshold of the Homestake and Kamiokande experiments. Recently two detectors sensitive to lower energy neutrinos were constructed, using gallium-71 (31 protons, 40 neutrons) as the nuclear target. After neutrino capture, the produced germanium-71 (32 protons, 39 neutrons) is chemically extracted from the gallium and measured. The standard solar model predicts a neutrino capture rate of about 132 SNUs. The new experiments are called SAGE (Soviet-American Gallium Experiment) and GALLEX (Gallium Experiment for Solar Neutrino Detection). SAGE is situated in the Soviet Union near Baksan in the northern Caucasus, while GALLEX is located in the Gran Sasso Tunnel in northern Italy. The first SAGE results, announced in 1990, suggested a neutrino capture rate considerably lower than predicted, an indication that the solar neutrino problem also applies to neutrinos resulting from proton-proton fusion.

An attractive theoretical solution to the problem of the missing neutrinos has been provided by the Mikheyev-Smirnov-Wolfenstein (MSW) effect (named after the scientists who developed the idea in the 1980s), which allows for the transformation of one neutrino species into another during the passage of neutrinos through the high concentration of electrons in the Sun's interior. According to standard electroweak theory (which encompasses descriptions of both the electromagnetic and weak forces), the unique characteristics that help distinguish the electron neutrino from the muon neutrino and tau neutrino allow it to interact in a special way with negatively charged electrons. This so-called charged-current interaction, which is proportional to the density of electrons through which the neutrino passes, becomes extremely pronounced within the electron-rich solar medium, resulting in the transformation of a large fraction of electron neutrinos to other types and a consequent reduction in the number of electron neutrinos detected on the Earth. Muon neutrinos and tau neutrinos do not react with the nuclear targets of the detectors and so do not contribute to the measured rate of neutrino capture.

Although neutrinos generally have been regarded as having zero mass, for them to oscillate among

Seven tons of gallium, which is a liquid above 30° C (86° F), rest in a tank located under a mountain in the northern Caucasus. The metal element forms the heart of the SAGE experiment's solar neutrino detector.

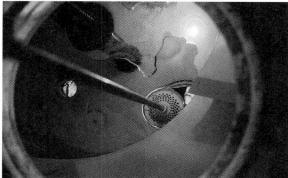

Los Alamos National Laboratory

types requires that they have at least a tiny mass. Moreover, the probability that electron neutrinos will survive unchanged during their passage through the gas of electrons in the Sun—and hence the neutrino capture rate measured on the Earth—depends in part on the size of the mass difference between the electron neutrino and the muon neutrino. Thus, if the very low capture rate seen in the SAGE experiment is confirmed by GALLEX, physicists will have essentially unambiguous proof of the existence of neutrino oscillations and of the presence of a small but finite mass difference between neutrino species. This result would be of fundamental importance for particle physics, astrophysics, and cosmology.

—Carl B. Dover

Condensed-matter physics

Condensed-matter physics, the largest and perhaps the most diverse part of physics, experienced considerable progress during the past year. Advances ranged from discoveries of a fundamental nature to those having potential practical applications. Selected highlights include the fabrication of dielectric structures to create photonic band gaps and thus modify dramatically the electromagnetic spectrum in a medium, simulations from first principles of the properties of materials by means of quantum Monte Carlo techniques, and the development of the scanning tunneling microscope as a solid-state emission source for the direct depositing of nanometer-size structures.

Photonic band structure. A well-known fact in wave mechanics is that waves do propagate through periodic barriers, although their dispersion relation (frequency ω versus propagation wave vector $\mathbf{k}$) may be significantly modified from that for waves traveling through a homogeneous medium. An important example of this principle is the extended electron states in crystalline materials. In crystals, because of the periodic lattice potential, electronic states are allowed only in certain energy ranges, with gaps separating the allowed bands of states. The energy of the electron, $E_{n\mathbf{k}}$, is given by the electron energy band structure in which n is an index labeling the bands. The existence of band gaps together with the Pauli exclusion principle explains why certain materials are metals whereas others are semiconductors and insulators.

The same principle applies to electromagnetic waves, *e.g.*, light or radio waves, in a periodic dielectric medium. (Dielectric materials are insulators or poor electrical conductors.) Under the appropriate conditions, it is possible to create large gaps in the electromagnetic spectrum forbidding the existence of photons in those frequency ranges. In the case of electrons, the electronic band gap is crucial in determining the transport, electronic, and optical properties of semiconductors. Likewise, it is expected that the existence of a photonic band gap would fundamentally modify the electromagnetic properties and the interaction of radiation with matter in a medium. As has been advocated by Eli Yablonovitch of Bell Communications Research Inc. (Bellcore), Livingston, N.J., potential applications for such dielectric structures are numerous. Over the frequency range of the gap, the medium represents a noiseless environment in terms of electromagnetic radiation. For example, it is possible to suppress the radiative decay of excited atoms or other entities embedded in such material if the decay frequency is in a photonic band gap.

The two main challenges in this field have been to demonstrate experimentally (1) the existence of a full three-dimensional photonic band gap in some type of dielectric structure and (2) that such structures may be amenable to practical microfabrication. In the past few years, attempts to produce photonic band gap structures have been concerned mostly with creating regions of contrasting dielectric constants (or refractive indexes) by cutting away at a dielectric material using precision machine tools. These structures typically have consisted of closed-packed arrays of dielectric spheres or spherical voids having dimensions of several millimeters (a millimeter is about $\frac{1}{25}$ in) and dielectric-constant differences in a ratio of about 3:1. For structures arranged in the face-centered-cubic lattice, gaps in the electromagnetic spectrum in the range of 1–20 gigahertz (GHz; billions of cycles per second) were observed for most propagating directions but not all directions. This incompleteness leads to having only a "pseudo gap"; that is, the spectrum of the material has a region of low density of states rather than a completely forbidden frequency gap. Theoretical calculations done independently by K. Ming Leung and Yi-San Liu of Polytechnic University, Brooklyn, N.Y., Ze Zhang and Sashi Satpathy of the University of Missouri at Columbia, and Kai-Ming Ho, Che-ting Chan, and Costas M. Soukoulis of Ames Laboratory, Iowa State University, showed that the vanishing of the gap along certain propagating directions is a consequence of the high symmetry of having dielectric spheres in a face-centered-cubic lattice. Further calculations by Ho, Chan, and Soukoulis demonstrated that less symmetrical structures (*e.g.*, dielectric spheres arranged in the diamond lattice structure) do give rise to a full photonic band gap, and the gap exists for refractive-index contrasts as low as 2.

Experimental fabrication of a dielectric structure having a full photonic band gap was achieved by Yablonovitch, Thomas J. Gmitter, and Leung in work at Bellcore. The new structure is created simply by boring three sets of holes 35.26° from the vertical

into the top surface of a solid slab of dielectric material (*see* Figure 1). In such a structure the dielectric "atoms" are nonspherical and thus permit a full photon band gap instead of a pseudo gap. Although the experimental structure, created by direct mechanical drilling with a real drill bit into a low-loss dielectric material, has its photonic band gap in the microwave region, the process appears amenable to reactive-ion-etching techniques, which would be able to create structures having photonic band gaps at optical wavelengths. This advance would be significant because many potential applications exist in the optical regime. For example, the inhibition of spontaneous emission of frequencies in such photonic gaps has been suggested as a way to enhance the performance of semiconductor lasers and other quantum electronic devices. The absence of vacuum fluctuations in the photonic gap will likely lead to new physical phenomena. In early 1991 the field was at a rapidly developing stage, and it appeared that the applications of photonic band gaps to situations of great physical interest could soon be possible.

Numerical simulations of the properties of materials. It has been a long-sought goal of condensed-

Figure 1. Diagram depicts an experimental method of fabricating a face-centered-cubic dielectric structure having a full photonic band gap. Guided by a mask, a drill bit bores each hole three times at the angles shown.

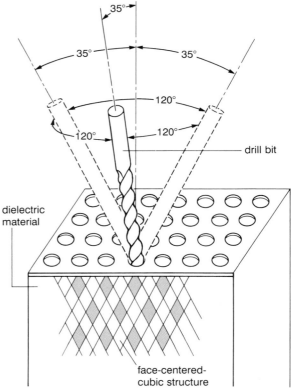

Adapted from information obtained from Eli Yablonovitch, Thomas J. Gmitter, and K. Ming Leung of Bellcore

matter theorists to predict the properties of real materials from first principles using only information about their constituent atoms. A major limitation in calculating the properties of solids accurately has been the inadequate treatment of the strong electron-electron interaction effects arising from the Coulomb force between the electrons. The traditional approach to a solution has been to reduce the many-electron problem to one of a self-consistent field scheme that involves solving only for the energy and wave function of a single electron moving in the mean field of the other electrons. By far, the most successful and commonly used method of this type is the local-density functional approach (LDA). In LDA the many-electron interactions are replaced by a simplified potential that depends only on the local electron density. The LDA has been applied to a wide range of materials with much success in obtaining some of the ground-state properties, among them the structural and vibrational properties, electron-phonon and phonon-phonon interaction parameters, and structural phase transitions. The LDA and other similar methods, however, have failed to yield, from first principles, accurate binding energies for solids and, in many cases, the correct magnetic and related properties of materials having highly correlated electrons.

Another way to calculate materials properties is to employ directly the many-body wave function, which depends on the position of all the electrons in the system. Correlation effects that arise from the correlated motions of the electrons can be built into the wave function explicitly instead of being treated in an average fashion as in the one-electron methods. In the correlated wave function approach, such physical quantities as binding energies are given by integrals of 3N dimensions, in which N is the number of electrons in the system. Because a macroscopic sample of material contains on the order of 10^{22} electrons, this approach had been used in the past only for model solid-state systems that employed simplifying approximations to the particle interactions and the evaluations of physical properties.

Recent advances now have made it possible to simulate numerically from first principles the properties of real crystals such as those of silicon using correlated wave functions. In work by Stephen B. Fahy, Xuewen Wang, and Steven G. Louie of the University of California at Berkeley, the material is simulated using a small volume with periodic boundary condition (*i.e.*, the volume is repeated indefinitely in space to avoid surface effects) containing up to several hundred electrons. The approach employs a many-electron wave function of the form of a determinant of single-particle wave functions (thus satisfying the Pauli exclusion principle) multiplying a symmetrical correlation function that includes a one-

body and two-body correlation term. The ground-state energy and wave function are determined using the variational principle that the energy of a system is at a minimum for the ground state. The exact Coulomb interaction between electrons is retained, and the multidimensional space integrals are evaluated using a Monte Carlo sampling scheme. The approach makes use of the important fact that LDA calculations yield excellent electron charge density and single-particle wave functions and that electron correlations are mostly two-body in nature, which may be described quite accurately using several variational parameters. Another important technical advance in the calculations is the use of ab initio pseudopotentials, which combines the nucleus and the core electrons into one entity and thus eliminates from the problem the large fluctuations in energy associated with the core electrons. These considerations make the approach practical, for the first time, for crystals consisting of elements heavier than helium (atomic number 2).

The quantum Monte Carlo simulations have given first-principles cohesive energies—obtained with the atomic number and the symmetry of the crystal structure as the only input to the calculation—for real materials at an unprecedented level of accuracy. Highly accurate results for structural properties have also been obtained. In addition, since the many-electron wave function is known, the method gives important information on a number of physical properties that are not accessible to standard one-electron theories. For example, the electron pair correlation function, which describes the correlation between motion of an electron and that of the nearby electrons, is directly obtainable from the simulations. This development promises to open an exciting new avenue for studying the electronic properties of materials.

Scanning tunneling microscope. There has been tremendous progress in the development and applications of the scanning tunneling microscope (STM) since its invention in the early 1980s. The device has made possible direct determination of the surface structure of materials on an atomic scale by means of the monitoring of tunneling current between the sample and a sharp probe tip maintained typically several angstroms (Å; ten-billionths of a meter) above. Achievements have ranged from the detailed mapping of the structural and electronic properties of surfaces to that of "seeing" the atomic structure of DNA and other organic molecules. Furthermore, the STM technique has stimulated development of a host of related techniques, including atomic force microscopy, magnetic force microscopy, near-field scanning optical microscopy, and scanning capacitance microscopy.

A recent development of considerable fundamental and technological potential is the experimental

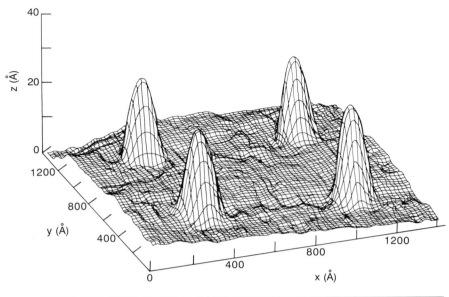

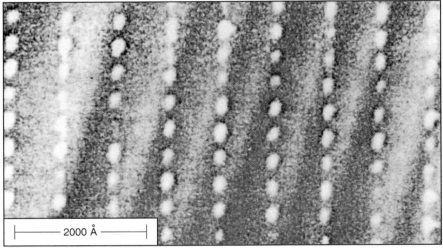

Figure 2. A perspective plot (top) created from STM data details the dimensions of four gold mounds deposited by the STM on a gold surface. An STM image (bottom) shows about 90 such mounds aligned in rows on a stepped gold surface.

H.J. Mamin, P.H. Guethner, and D. Rugar of IBM Almaden Research Center, San Jose, Calif.

demonstration by H. Jonathon Mamin, Peter H. Guethner, and Dan Rugar of the IBM Almaden Research Center, San Jose, Calif., that the STM tip can be used as a miniature solid-state emission source for the direct deposit of nanometer-size structures on surfaces (a nanometer is a billionth of a meter). They showed that when a gold STM tip was scanned across a surface in air, application of a short voltage pulse of several volts to the tip resulted in deposition of a small mound of gold atoms. The mounds were typically about 100–200 Å across at the base and 20–30 Å high. Figure 2 shows a perspective plot of the dimensions of the gold mounds and the image of an array of about 90 mounds created on a stepped gold surface. The emission mechanism is believed to be field evaporation, whereby atoms are ionized and ejected from a tip owing to the action of a high elec-

tric field. In the case of the STM tip, the emission process is enhanced by the closeness of the substrate to the tip, and thus only a small voltage is required.

The emission process was found to be both reproducible and fast. Several thousand nanometer-size features were created on a gold surface with no apparent degradation of the tip's ability to emit atoms. The new technique thus may find eventual use in the large-scale industrial fabrication of nanometer-size structures or in fundamental studies of the physical properties of nanometer-size objects. (See *General developments*, above.)

—Steven G. Louie

See also Feature Articles: CLUSTERS: STRANGE BITS OF MATTER; HOW SUPERCOMPUTERS ARE TRANSFORMING SCIENCE; SCIENCE'S "INTELLECTUAL HOTEL": THE INSTITUTE FOR ADVANCED STUDY.

Psychology

The past year marked the death of Burrhus Frederic Skinner, professor emeritus at Harvard University (*see* Year in Review: OBITUARIES). Called "the greatest contemporary psychologist" by Raymond Fowler, editor of the *American Psychologist,* Skinner died at the age of 86, barely one week after having delivered a final address at the annual meeting of the American Psychological Association (APA) in Boston. In a dramatic presentation the physically frail but intellectually unimpaired Skinner captivated an overflow audience. At the Boston meetings he also received a "citation for outstanding lifetime contribution to psychology," the first such award ever granted by the nearly century-old association.

Skinner developed the principles of operant conditioning. Briefly, they claim that an organism's behavior is shaped by the consequences of that behavior. In the main, these determinants are positive and negative "reinforcements." Throughout his career Skinner emphasized the importance of using positive reinforcements, such as praise, rather than negative ones, such as punishment. His influence in educational and mental health programs was largely due to this emphasis. In an illuminating interview on National Public Radio's "All Things Considered" less than a month before his death, Skinner described himself as "a locus in which a lot of very lucky accidents have come together to make me productive." His last essay, on which his convention address was based, was finally completed the night before he died. The paper attempted to integrate what he saw as the three major influences on human organisms—genes, behavior, and culture.

Cognitive psychology. In reviewing his long-term experimental investigation of the "dynamic operations of thought systems," Yale University psychologist William McGuire demonstrated how research on inner events of the sort that Skinner, as a radical behaviorist, believed existed but were not scientifically meaningful could be operationally based and empirically investigated. This providing of a viable counterpart to Skinnerian or other more clearly behavioral research was a good example of the healthy diversity of contemporary conceptual and empirical psychology.

Although McGuire's work was generally regarded as dealing with attitude change, he considered that feature more as a vehicle to the manipulation of thought systems than as an objective. Focusing on two empirically determined major dimensions—desirability and likelihood—of what he called "core events," McGuire manipulated and measured both these dimensions and their antecedents and consequences. For example, he used eight core events, all with mid-scale desirability and likelihood ratings

according to data from prestudies (for example, that in the future most shopping will be done by means of home computer terminals). As an independent (manipulated) variable, discrepantly high, moderate, low, or no "expert norms"—experimenter-derived, or made-up, values, intended to influence the subjects' judgments—were given the subjects (128 introductory psychology students). The norms were counterbalanced over the eight events. The subjects then free-associated on four of the events, one for each of the four norms used (high, low, moderate, or none). Three minutes were allowed for each subject to write all the thoughts that occurred about each event. The free associations were analyzed for content by judges into 15 categories (such as desirable or undesirable antecedents that would make the event more or less likely; and desirable or undesirable consequences made more or less likely by the event).

The results of the experiments were interpreted by McGuire as substantially in accordance with predictions. The manipulation of the alleged expert norms was successful as measured by the subjects' raised or lowered ratings on desirability and likelihood, compared with earlier pre-experimental ratings and with other later ratings in which no norms were involved.

This brief, oversimplified description of McGuire's research program does not do justice to its full scope but should impart something of its essential nature. McGuire's plans for future research entailed more fully quantitative formulations than had been thus far used. Whether this kind of manipulation and measurement of thought systems and their organization would ultimately prove to be effective in predicting future behaviors, in apparent contradiction to Skinner's contention and his general anticognition stance, remained to be seen.

Personality and social psychology. A provocative developmental account of social relationships between the sexes was offered by Stanford University psychology professor Eleanor E. Maccoby, a longtime student of sex differences. Reviewing changes since the publication of her landmark 1974 book, *The Psychology of Sex Differences,* Maccoby observed that "there are still some replicable sex differences, of moderate magnitude, in performance on tests of mathematical and spatial abilities [favoring males], although sex differences in verbal abilities [favoring females] have faded." She noted, however, some very important new results. In the main these were related to the inclusion in the studies of a social variable, in contrast to the simpler individual-differences approach formerly used exclusively. When the social composition of a dyad (pair) or a larger group was considered, important, durable, and developmentally persistent sex differences emerged.

These new results may be summarized in the statement that children in all cultural settings prefer same-sex playmates from at least three years of age and that subsequent sexual interactions depend on two fundamental factors that are first evident in preschool. In Maccoby's summary, "The first is the rough-and-tumble play characteristic of boys and their orientation toward issues of competition and dominance [which] appear to be somewhat aversive to most girls. The second factor of importance is that girls find it difficult to influence boys."

Maccoby hypothesized that girls as young as 33 months begin to avoid unresponsive playmates, mainly boys. She reviewed the growing developmental literature on intersex interactions and the relationships of each sex with adults (for example, it had been shown that the tendency of girls to stay closer than boys to adults occurs only in mixed-sex social situations). Although many of these observations were familiar to perceptive teachers and parents, the wealth of carefully controlled and systematically collected information that was rapidly emerging from studies of this kind should be helpful to all persons intimately engaged in social situations with children and adolescents.

A second development in the social-personality sphere that occurred during the past year was the suggestion of a new interpretation of the earlier research by Stanley Milgram on obedience to authority. In his mid-1970s research, Milgram found a remarkably high degree of compliance in subjects who, as supposed "teachers," were instructed by the experimenter to administer increasingly severe electric shocks to other ("learner") subjects (actually confederates of the experimenter) as punishments for errors in a word-association setting. When the supposed recipient of the shock began to show distress, even demanding that the shock be stopped, the "teacher" was placed in conflict. That conflict was intensified when the experimenter insisted that the shock was not really harmful and had to be continued. (No shock was actually used.) Under these conditions approximately two-thirds of the subjects continued to administer the supposed shock up to the highest levels. Milgram's interpretation of this unexpected and, in his own words, "unsavory" result was that the fully compliant subject regarded himself or herself simply as an instrument or agent of the experimenter, an authority figure, and so could not be held responsible for the apparently harmful actions.

During the past year a new counterintuitive interpretation was advanced by Moti Nissani of Wayne State University, Detroit, Michigan. The interpretation was based solely on a number of recent experiments in which subjects were asked to evaluate a new industrial manual. Before the evaluation they were given four hours of firsthand experience to familiarize them with the procedures described in the manual. In the course of this training experience,

they had to deal with a faulty formula concerning the computation of the volume of a sphere. They were also given an actual sphere and asked to measure its volume first by using the formula and then by filling the sphere with water and then transferring the water to another container in which it was directly measured. The key question in the experiment was to what extent the subjects would reject the false formula when they evaluated the manual. Such a rejection would mean accepting the evidence of their senses (the direct measure that differed from the computed value) rather than the legitimacy of the manual.

Finding the formula faulty proved to be extremely difficult; not a single subject in the first experiments absolutely rejected the clearly faulty formula or refused to continue to use it in subsequent work. Moreover, no substantial differences in results were later found, even when all of the subjects were Ph.D.'s in natural science employed as research assistants in universities, when a second sphere was introduced to facilitate faulty-formula rejection, or when the faulty formula was made to refer to another type of receptacle (such as an ellipse).

Nissani concluded that transitions from one belief system to another are much more difficult than might be assumed; in this case the transition was from the manual-evaluation procedure, in which adequacy of the text rather than accuracy of the basic formulas was considered to be the task, to one in which the fundamental components of the manual were themselves under investigation. Nissani, therefore, suggested that a similar interpretation might well be applied to the Milgram obedience results.

Developmental psychology. A number of ingenious measurement techniques were recently used on problems of cognitive development in young children. During the past year two new techniques were emphasized. Renëe Baillargeon of the University of Illinois demonstrated an unsuspected level of simple reasoning ability in infants as young as $3\frac{1}{2}$ months. Using visual tasks rather than the manual tasks employed by Jean Piaget, she found, in contrast to Piaget, that very young infants can differentiate between possible and impossible events. Her measure was the amount of time that the infants spent in looking at the events. In a study with infants, a box was placed either on top of tracks on which a toy rolled behind a screen or in front of or in back of the tracks. The infants spent more time looking at the impossible event—in this case the toy seemingly moving through the box—compared with the possible event—the box not on track. Baillargeon suggested that in this task, as in a number of other ones in which similar results were obtained, the infants were "surprised" to see the "impossible" event and therefore spent more time looking at it.

In another series of experiments with infants, Carolyn Rovee-Collier and colleagues at Rutgers, the State University of New Jersey, found a high degree of specificity, or dependence upon context, in memory. Their measure was the amount of kicking that occurs when a ribbon is tied to an infant's ankle and also to a mobile placed over the crib. Typically two to three times as much kicking occurred as had in baseline measurements (ribbon not tied to mobile).

Rovee-Collier found that memories of the linkage between kicking and movements of the mobile were readily forgotten, especially if more than a single element of the stimulus situation was changed. Older infants showed more retention after relatively long test intervals, such as two or three weeks, but they tended to be more dependent on exact maintenance of the context. The researchers also found that both three- and six-month-old infants could learn to respond in a novel context if they were appropriately trained in different contexts.

Memory. Implicit memory continued to be the hottest topic in memory research. Work on this subject had accelerated at an unprecedented rate during the past decade. Evidence of the enthusiasm for it was seen in the introductory comment in the recently published *Implicit Memory: Theoretical Issues* that "present developments are wildly exciting and highly significant."

Implicit memory is demonstrated by tasks that require the subject to make some kind of more or less natural response, such as completing a word on the basis of a fragmentary stimulus (only some letters provided), whereas explicit memory tasks require the subjects to "declare" what was learned (recall test) or to select a learned item from a set of alternatives (recognition test). The most impressive research result was the marked discontinuity between these two types of memory. For example, in amnesic patients explicit or declarative memory is absent, which, of course, accounts for their amnesic classification; however, in these patients there is not any marked loss of implicit-memory performance. Also, young children and elderly adults show little, if any, deficit in implicit learning but are substantially inferior to older children and young adults on practically all measures of explicit memory.

One interpretation of this difference is that implicit memory does not require the elaborate processing that is characteristic of explicit memory tasks. Such processing requires considerable effort.

A relatively high level of research activity also occurred in the neuropsychological investigation of memory phenomena. In one especially suggestive investigation, University of Virginia psychologist Paul Gold and his associates found a strong beneficial effect on memory from increasing the level of blood glucose circulation. In one experiment subjects aged 62 to 84 years performed a memory test after drinking saccharine-sweetened lemonade and then performed the same test after drinking glucose-sweetened lemonade. These researchers reported a 30 to 40% increase in declarative-memory performance after the subjects had drunk the glucose-sweetened lemonade. The usual decline in performance with increasing age in this kind of memory test was eliminated. Three other, as yet unpublished, studies were said to show the same results.

Gold was careful to note that no improvement in the normal memory ability of young adults had yet been achieved by this treatment and also that attention and short-term-memory tests did not reveal any improvement in the older subjects. The results nonetheless offered promise of the eventual solution of certain facets of the complex problem of the neuropsychological basis of memory, at least pointing one direction in which more definitive studies could proceed.

Behavior and health. In September the U.S. Department of Health and Human Services released what promised to be a landmark document, "Healthy People 2000," an overview of the national health promotion and disease prevention objectives. One of the main themes of this report was that much preventable illness was due to human behavior rather than strictly physical factors and that efforts to reduce health risks, therefore, had to address behavioral problems.

Psychology would have a major role in this effort. The APA was closely involved in the consortium of health leaders that worked on the report for two years and would no doubt be actively involved in further efforts.

One interesting and promising example of how psychology can contribute to this program was described at the APA Boston meetings. Funded by the National Cancer Institute, this project attempted to guide consumers in the direction of healthier diets (mainly, more fiber and less fat). Using social-learning theory and positive feedback for incremental behavior changes, Virginia Polytechnic Institute and State University psychologist Richard Winett designed the first experiment, which took place in three supermarkets in two Virginia cities. Three hundred shoppers put their Social Security numbers and their intended purchases into a computer and then later recorded their actual purchases. They went through this procedure once each week and sent in their shopping receipts. For seven weeks data were obtained, with the shoppers merely entering their intended purchases and submitting their receipts.

After seven weeks a control group continued this procedure for an additional eight weeks, while an experimental group of subjects as they proceeded through the market was shown a series of videos

Richard Winett, Virginia Polytechnic Institute and State University

A shopper at a Virginia supermarket uses a computer to record intended and actual purchases, part of an experiment that attempted to guide consumers toward having healthier diets.

describing nutritionally sound foods. In both the eight-week test period and in a three-week follow-up test five weeks later, the experimental group bought more high-fiber grains and cereals and more low-fat foods than did the control group.

Improvements on the experimental design and execution of this kind of direct-intervention program were being planned. Among the improvements under consideration were the simplification of the videos so as to appeal to less-educated shoppers and the offering of redeemable coupons for the purchase of the healthier foods.

—Melvin H. Marx

International Developments. Recent changes in Europe involving the tearing down the Berlin Wall and the democratization of many nations behind what was formerly the iron curtain were warmly welcomed by Western nations. The changes had important implications for psychology. Greater independence of Eastern European nations and the

completion of the single European market by 1992 was facilitating the movement of psychologists from one country to another and was thereby encouraging the exchange of information necessary to promote the rapidly expanding discipline of psychology. Research and the views of psychologists in only a few nations had long dominated developments in the discipline and practice of psychology, which were now being opened up to the contributions of many more nations.

In the less developed countries the tendency to specialize within psychology was being questioned. Specialization results in a fragmentation of psychological knowledge rather than holistic models of behavior, which many believed were more relevant to the challenge of tackling large-scale social problems.

Western nations had responded to these developments by setting up exchange programs, such as the Visiting Scholars Scheme of the British Psychological Society to establish scholarships for students from Eastern European and less developed nations to visit the U.K. Elsewhere, the American Psychological Association extended a well-organized program whereby scientific journals could be donated to such recipients as the libraries of universities in less developed countries. In Germany exchange programs were introduced that would send West German psychologists to East Germany for hands-on training and also East German psychologists to West Germany to be trained in new skills.

In many countries, such as Norway and the U.K., where ethical codes of conduct were part of the standards for those who were licensed to practice psychology or to use particular titles, such as Chartered Psychologist in the United Kingdom, efforts were made to develop common ethical principles for practice. The European Federation of Professional Psychologists Associations set up a multinational working party on ethical codes. Within this context searching questions were being asked about the need to develop multicultural ethical guidelines that would accept the importance of the cultural differences studied by psychologists for many years. For instance, not all cultures shared the same definition of public and private information. Therefore, rules of confidentiality might have to be interpreted in accordance with a client's culture, or else a well-intentioned psychologist might cause harm by disclosing information considered public when the client might consider the same information private.

The increasing contact between psychologists of all nations heightened the value of resolutions such as that passed in November 1989, when the General Assembly of the United Nations adopted the first international treaty on children's rights based on established psychological principles that regard a child as an individual with "evolving capacities." Resolutions of this nature underpinned other international initiatives, such as the program of the World Health Organization's Division of Mental Health that was developing a series of clinical learning modules to teach medical students about psychological aspects of health care in clinical practice and in community-oriented projects.

In July 1990 more than 2,000 applied psychologists met in Kyoto, Japan, to attend the 22nd international congress of the International Association of Applied Psychology, which had members in more than 80 countries. At the congress 131 symposia were held. They dealt with such topics as organizational psychology, educational and school psychology, gerontology, health psychology, economic psychology, social psychology, ergonomics, traffic psychology, and psychology and law. All symposia included presentations by psychologists from at least two countries.

—Colin V. Newman

Space exploration

An active year in space included several manned missions in U.S. space shuttle orbiters, flights by Soviet cosmonauts to their space station, and probes of Venus and the Moon. A probe to the Sun was launched in October.

Manned flight

The U.S. space program experienced one of its most difficult years in 1990, as leaks grounded the space shuttle for several months and budget and design problems forced a redesign of the proposed space station. Those difficulties (and the unrelated manufacturing fault in the Hubble Space Telescope) prompted the government on July 16 to direct the National Aeronautics and Space Administration (NASA) to form an outside panel that would examine NASA's management structure and advise on how best to organize it for large programs. The Advisory Committee on the Future of the U.S. Space Program, as it was known, recommended that the shuttle be used only for those missions that required a human presence. The committee, chaired by Norman Augustine, also recommended that the space station have a rescue vehicle attached and that plans to send humans back to the Moon and Mars be paced by technology development and not adhere to an artificial schedule. Some weeks later NASA formed an internal Synthesis Group under former astronaut Thomas Stafford to analyze space exploration options.

Space shuttle. NASA managed three space shuttle missions before hydrogen leaks in two shuttles grounded the fleet for several weeks, cutting the

agency's 1990 flight plan in half from 10 to 5. First, on STS-32 (January 9–20), *Columbia* brought back the Long Duration Exposure Facility (LDEF), launched in 1984 on a nine-month mission that was extended by various schedule problems and the *Challenger* tragedy. LDEF carried samples of window materials, module coatings, fiber optics, and tomato seeds, as well as cosmic-ray detectors and cosmic dust traps. NASA was under pressure to rescue LDEF because its orbit was decaying and reentry was expected in the spring of 1990. The facility was retrieved January 12 after *Columbia* deployed a U.S. Navy communications satellite. The mission—crewed by commander Dan Brandenstein, pilot James D. Wetherbee, and mission specialists Marsha Ivins, Bonnie J. Dunbar, and G. David Low—also set a new duration record for the shuttle of 10 days 21 hours.

Atlantis (STS-36, February 28–March 4) launched a secret U.S. Department of Defense satellite called AFP-731 that was believed to be the first of a new generation of advanced, digital imaging systems. *Atlantis* also carried a "phantom head," a human skull fitted with detectors to help study the effects of radiation on the human brain. The mission was crewed by commander John Creighton, pilot John Casper, and mission specialists David Hilmers, Richard Mullane, and Pierre Thuot. Soon after deployment, the photo spy satellite was rumored to have failed and reentered the atmosphere, although later reports disputed this.

Discovery (STS-31, April 24–29) deployed the Hubble Space Telescope on the highest Earth-orbit mission, 618 km (384 mi), flown by human astronauts. *Discovery* was crewed by commander Loren Shriver, pilot Charles Bolden, and mission specialists Bruce McCandless, Kathy Sullivan, and Steven Hawley. During deployment of the telescope, one of its solar panels refused to open fully, and Sullivan and McCandless moved from standby to final preparations for a space walk to open the panel manually. At the last moment, however, it finally became unstuck. Deployment and release of the Hubble proceeded without further incident. Weeks later, however, it was discovered that the 2.4-m reflector telescope could not be properly focused because its mirror had been ground to an incorrect shape in the early 1980s. The problem—spherical aberration—was to be corrected by a shuttle maintenance mission already scheduled for 1993. At that time astronauts would install a camera with corrected optics and a module with mirrors that would compensate for the problem. (*See* Year in Review: OPTICAL ENGINEERING.)

Hydrogen leaks in the shuttle appeared during preparations to launch the Astro-1 Spacelab mission aboard *Columbia* (STS-35). For their fuel the shuttle main engines use liquid hydrogen; because hydrogen is the lightest and smallest element, liquid hydrogen

NASA

Discovery *shuttle is launched from the Kennedy Space Center in Florida on April 24, 1990. The craft achieved the highest altitude—618 kilometers (384 miles)—of any Earth-orbit mission flown by human astronauts and also deployed the Hubble Space Telescope.*

can seep through seals and materials that are "solid" to other fluids. During propellant loading on May 29, sensors in *Columbia*'s engine compartment detected excessive levels of liquid hydrogen, and the launch was postponed. *Columbia* eventually had to be rolled back to the vehicle assembly building so that it could be separated from the external tank and its seals inspected. Engineers decided that crushed glass beads in the seal were the cause and certified *Columbia* as ready for a September 1 launch. That was postponed to September 6 by the failure of an electronics box on one of the telescopes in the payload bay, and then to September 18 when another leak appeared. NASA finally removed *Columbia* from the launch pad again and thoroughly inspected and retested the shuttle; a successful propellant loading was finally achieved on October 30.

Meanwhile, an unrelated hydrogen leak delayed the classified military mission (STS-38) of *Atlantis* from July to November. Following *Columbia*'s problem, NASA ran a precautionary tanking test on *Atlantis* on June 29. This revealed a leak, and *Atlantis* also had to be removed from the launch pad for inspection and retest. The entire shuttle fleet was briefly grounded until *Atlantis* was cleared for launch in October. Then its spy satellite cargo developed a problem, causing yet another delay. The nature of the satellite was not revealed by the Department of Defense, though it was believed to be a photo reconnaissance craft that was expected to supply information for the multinational forces in the Persian Gulf crisis. *Atlantis* was finally launched on November 15 and landed at Kennedy Space Center at Cape

Canaveral, Fla., on November 20 after 4 days 22 hours. The flight marked the end of the secret shuttle missions because most classified payloads were to be transferred to unmanned launchers.

Leak problems also put pressure on NASA to launch Ulysses, the international solar polar mission, in October or postpone it another 13 months. The STS-41 mission by *Discovery* was crewed by commander Richard Richards, pilot Robert Cabana, and mission specialists William Shepherd, Bruce Melnick, and Thomas Akers. After a brief delay for weather and a minor engineering problem, *Discovery* lifted off safely on October 6 and deployed Ulysses and its three-stage booster six hours later. A legal challenge to block the mission, because the probe uses a plutonium power source, was denied by a federal court. The mission ended on October 10.

The last mission of 1990 was STS-35 (December 2–10). The *Columbia* shuttle carried Astro-1, which consisted of a battery of four telescopes, three designed to observe the stars in ultraviolet light and one to observe in X-rays. The 10-day mission was crewed by commander Vance Brand, pilot Guy Gardner, mission specialists Robert Parker, John Lounge, and Jeffrey Hoffman, and payload specialists Ron Parise and Samuel Durrance. Soon after launch the crew encountered a series of technical problems that hindered their ability to make observations. First, they had difficulty in locking onto guide stars so that the instrument pointing system could aim the ultraviolet telescopes at their targets (the X-ray telescopes were controlled differently). Then, when they overheated, the two control consoles in the aft flight deck of

406

the shuttle both suffered electrical short circuits and failed at separate times. (A buildup of lint and dust in the air-cooling system was blamed for the failures after the mission.) Mission controllers at Johnson Space Center, Houston, Texas, took over direct operation of the telescopes while the astronauts aimed them manually with a joystick. Initially, the astronauts could gather data for only a few seconds, as compared with plans to observe for half an hour, but in time they became proficient. By the end of the mission, Astro-1 had accomplished 400 observations of 135 targets (200 targets had been planned). As well as observing stars and galaxies in portions of the ultraviolet spectrum that had not been studied previously, Astro-1 observed Comet Levy and the planet Jupiter and confirmed that interstellar dust consists primarily of graphite grains. Two reflights of the Astro observatory were canceled early in 1991 because of budget problems.

Looking to the future, a unique industry team offered a design for the National Aerospace Plane (NASP), a vehicle that would take off from a runway like a jetliner, rocket into and out of space like a shuttle, and land again like a jetliner. A decision was expected in 1993 as to whether to build the X-30, a flying test version of the NASP. In a different vein, the Strategic Defense Initiative Organization started studies of a smaller single-stage-to-orbit (SSTO) vehicle that would carry a crew of two on a four-day mission.

An orbital rescue demonstration was planned for the second flight of the Soviet Union's *Buran* ("bliz-

Gamma Ray Observatory (GRO) remains in the grasp of the space shuttle Atlantis *in April 1991. A space walk to manually extend the GRO's jammed antenna boom was necessary before it could be released into orbit.*

NASA

zard"), tentatively set for 1991. *Buran* had made only one flight (two orbits of the Earth in 1988) previously. The second mission was to be unmanned during launch and landing but would attempt a rendezvous and docking with the *Mir* space station.

Space stations. The Soviets' *Mir* space station program moved ahead and added a major module that enlarged it to match the Skylab station flown by the U.S. in 1973. Aleksandr Viktorenko and Aleksandr Serebrov, launched on Sept. 5, 1989, aboard the Soyuz TM-8 spacecraft, returned to Earth on Feb. 19, 1990, after a five-month stay aboard *Mir*. On February 1 and 5 they conducted two space walks to test a "space bike," a backpack that allows cosmonauts to maneuver freely in space. On one test Viktorenko flew almost 46 m (150 ft) away from *Mir* while remaining tethered to the station (*Mir* cannot maneuver to retrieve an astronaut).

Serebrov and Viktorenko were replaced by cosmonauts Anatoly Solovyov and Aleksandr Balandin, launched on February 11 aboard Soyuz TM-9. Solovyov and Balandin conducted two space walks during their stay. On July 17 they repaired torn insulation on their Soyuz spacecraft. The space walk lasted longer than planned, and the two cosmonauts almost ran out of oxygen. When they tried to return through the airlock, they found that the hatch could not be closed—the hinges had been bent when the hatch was opened before the airlock was completely vented—and they had to use an emergency airlock. On July 26 they tried unsuccessfully to repair the hatch, although they could close it by using brute force. Their return to Earth was delayed to allow a second space walk to complete repairs and retrieve tools left outside. They were replaced by Gennaidy Manakov and Gennaidy Strekalov, launched aboard Soyuz TM-10 on August 1.

Materials processing was among the chief activities for the crews, with the Soviets claiming that they produced electronics and biomedical crystals worth several million dollars. The Kristall materials module was launched to *Mir* on May 31. Problems with thrusters delayed its docking with *Mir* for several days into June. Addition of the module increased the station's volume by a third and its weight to 82,800 kg (182,600 lb), the heaviest satellite ever. The Soviets also introduced a modified version of the unmanned Progress supply craft to return materials samples. On November 28 Progress M5, launched on September 27, undocked from *Mir* and fired rockets to reenter the atmosphere. Before entry, it detached a small capsule that safely carried materials samples back to Earth. Such a system allows scientists on Earth to analyze space samples sooner than if they waited for crews to return.

On October 29 cosmonauts Manakov and Strekalov performed a space walk in another futile effort to

Soyuz TM-10 spacecraft is launched by the Soviet Union on Aug. 1, 1990. It carried Gennaidy Manakov and Gennaidy Strekalov to the Soviet space station Mir, where the two later performed a space walk to repair an airlock hatch.

repair the airlock hatch. The two returned to Earth after being replaced by Viktor Afanasyev and Musa Manarov, who were launched aboard Soyuz TM-11 on December 2; they were to remain aboard *Mir* until May. Also launched on Soyuz TM-11 was Japanese reporter Toyohiro Akiyama, the first journalist in space. Tokyo Broadcast System paid some $12 million for the flight. While in space he broadcast observations about the environment and assisted with biological experiments. He returned with the Soyuz TM-10 crew on December 10.

The veteran Salyut 7 space station, which had been host to a number of successful Soviet space missions, reentered the Earth's atmosphere in February 1991. Salyut 7 had not been used since 1986.

The program to develop a U.S. space station continued to encounter problems. In March NASA engineers determined that the station would start breaking down before it was even finished. An intensive analysis by astronaut William Fisher and engineer Charles D. Price revealed that more than 2,000 man-hours of space walks would be needed each year to maintain the space station almost from the start of operations. The study led to a redesign effort to bring many elements "inside" the station's pressure modules, where repairs would be easier. At the direction of the U.S. Congress, a strong redesign effort was initiated. Options included limiting assembly flights to no more than four per year and eliminating external payloads such as solar telescopes and cosmic dust collectors. Materials and life sciences would remain as the primary goals of the station's science research.

Astronauts. The first female pilot candidate was among 23 new astronaut candidates that NASA began training in July. The 11 pilot candidates were Maj. Kenneth D. Cockrell, Maj. Eileen Collins, Capt. William G. Gregory, Maj. James D. Halsell, Maj. James J. Precourt, Capt. Richard A. Searfoss, and Maj. Terrence W. Wilcutt; Wilcutt was in the Marine Corps, and the others were in the Air Force. The 12 mission specialist candidates were Lieut. Comdr. Daniel Bursch (U.S. Navy), Leroy Chiao, Maj. Michael R.U. Clifford (U.S. Army), Bernard Harris, Capt. Susan J. Helms (U.S. Air Force); Thomas D. Jones, Maj. William S. McArthur, Jr. (U.S. Army), James H. Newman, Ellen Ochoa, Ronald M. Sega, Capt. Nancy J. Sherlock (U.S. Army), Donald A. Thomas, Janice E. Voss, Capt. Carl E. Walz (U.S. Air Force), Peter J.K. Wisoff, and David A. Wolf.

Two veteran astronauts, Robert L. ("Hoot") Gibson and David M. Walker, were grounded for violating flight rules. Former astronaut Ron Evans, who was the command module pilot on the Apollo 17 mission in 1972, died on April 7. Bob Springer and William Fisher resigned from the astronaut corps to pursue careers in the private sector.

The European Space Agency (ESA) began the selection of its first astronaut corps to support planned work aboard space stations and its own Hermes shuttlecraft in the 1990s and beyond. A total of 10 astronauts were to be selected from nominees forwarded by the ESA's 12 member nations.

Space probes

Planetary exploration experienced its busiest year in a decade. A total of seven instrument-laden spacecraft operated from the innermost reaches of the solar system to its farthest boundaries.

Venus. The first spacecraft to visit Venus was actually making just a quick stop on its way to Jupiter. The Galileo spacecraft zipped past Venus at an altitude of 16,110 km (10,010 mi) on Feb. 9, 1990, and used the planet's gravitational pull to boost its speed and redirect it toward the Earth for two more gravity assists that would send it toward Jupiter in 1996. Because no rockets were available with enough power to send Galileo directly to Jupiter, it had to gather the extra energy by three gravity assists at Venus and

Earth. The accuracy was so great that Galileo came within five kilometers (three miles) of its predicted closest approach to Venus. Because of the accuracy of Galileo's guidance, engineers expected that they would be able to complete all 10 encounters with Jupiter's moons.

During the encounter Galileo took 81 pictures of Venus and collected other data. These were to be transmitted after the spacecraft flew past the Earth in December. Galileo also observed plasmas flowing at much higher velocities than anyone had expected in what should have been a more "placid" interplanetary environment.

The Magellan spacecraft, launched before Galileo in 1989 by NASA, arrived at Venus on August 10 to start a 243-day mission of mapping the planet's surface by radar. After a nearly uneventful 16-month journey to the planet (which involved 1½ orbits of the Sun), Magellan fired a small solid-propellant rocket motor to slow itself into orbit around Venus. Excellent radar images were soon returned, and then Magellan shut down and was out of contact for 14 hours until it was heard intermittently as it searched for Earth in its "safe mode." Contact was lost and regained at least five times for various reasons. Some events were believed to be software or static electricity problems. One was caused by a programming error that omitted crucial blank spaces, prompting Magellan's onboard computer to go into safe mode. Nevertheless, by early January nearly half the planet had been mapped by Magellan's radar.

Impact crater on Venus is revealed in a radar image obtained from the space probe Magellan. The kidney shape of the crater is unusual and may have been caused by several almost simultaneous impacts.

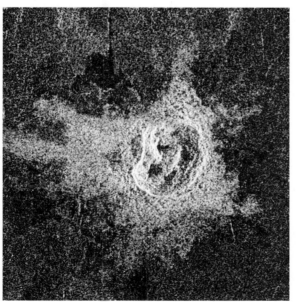

JPL

Because Venus is completely enshrouded in a thick, acidic atmosphere, its surface can be seen only through direct travel to it or by the use of radar to penetrate to the surface. (Indeed, the clouds themselves are featureless except in ultraviolet light.) Magellan used a combination of radar altimeters and synthetic aperture radar (SAR) to map the surface with a clarity approaching that of high-altitude photographs. Altimeters simply measure the time that it takes a radio energy pulse to return from the surface of the planet directly below the spacecraft. SAR scans a narrow radar beam through a large angle to the side. The combination of return time, strength, and other factors allows a computer to build an image that resembles a photograph of the surface. However, the image actually shows radar brightness (rough areas will be darker than flat areas)—not light brightness as the human eye would see it—that accurately depicts geologic structures. For additional information on Magellan, *see* Year in Review: ASTRONOMY.

Earth and Moon. The year started with Japan launching the first probe to the Moon since 1976. The Muses-A spacecraft was launched on Jan. 24, 1990, into an elliptical Earth orbit that took it within 16,000 km (10,000 mi) of the Moon in March. At that time a small subsatellite was injected into lunar orbit.

Galileo became the first interplanetary mission to the Earth when it flew by on December 8 and took a series of pictures of the Earth and Moon. Galileo used the Earth to make the second of three planned gravity assists on its way to Jupiter. The spacecraft flew by the Earth at an altitude of just 955 km (593 mi) above the southwestern Atlantic Ocean. Among Galileo's accomplishments during the flyby was the taking of a series of pictures of the Earth every minute for a day to make a unique time-lapse motion picture of the Earth's weather. For these and other pictures Galileo used a high-resolution, solid-state camera that takes full-color pictures with more than three times the detail of conventional TV cameras. Spectral instruments also detected the presence of nitrous oxide, methane, and oxygen in the Earth's atmosphere. These chemicals would not last long in a dead environment, thus suggesting that life could be detected indirectly from space.

Images of the Moon by Galileo confirmed the presence of the South Pole-Aitken Basin, which scientists had long only suspected because no mission had ever provided a clear view of the south pole. A clear view of the eastern limb provided detail of the 1,900-km (1,180-mi)-wide Aitken Basin. Spectral data suggested that the basin was caused by an impact that dug up the Moon's iron-rich mantle. Galileo's next flyby was scheduled to be the asteroid Gaspra in October 1991.

The Soviet Union announced that in 1992 it planned to launch Lunar Prospector, a spacecraft being developed by the Space Studies Institute in Princeton, N.J. On its one-year mission it was to carry three instruments to map minerals in the lunar surface and measure the Moon's magnetic field. A nonprofit corporation was being established to raise money to pay for the launch.

Mars. The Soviet Union moved ahead with plans for its Mars '94 project to orbit two spacecraft around the planet and place two landers on the surface; one would carry a balloon system to carry instruments across the surface, and the other would drop two penetrators into the surface for geologic studies.

After landing on the surface, each lander would release a helium-filled balloon that would carry atmospheric instruments and cameras to study the planet from an altitude of 300 m (10,000 ft). A weighted line trailed by the balloons would keep them from rising too high as more of the weight was lifted. The balloon-borne instruments would also analyze the surface when the balloon's gas cooled and the balloon descended each night. The balloon system was being developed and supplied by the Planetary Society in the U.S. Launch was set for October 1994, and arrival at Mars was planned for August 1995. Operation was to be guaranteed for one Martian year (687 days) after arrival.

Outer planets. The first "family portrait" of the solar system was taken Feb. 13, 1990, by Voyager 1 as its camera was used for the last time, at a distance of 5.9 billion km (3.7 billion mi) from the Sun. The mosaic of 60 images covered the entire solar system and all of the planets except Mercury (too close to the Sun), Mars (obscured by the Sun), and Pluto (too faint). NASA anticipated that the camera would be damaged in taking the picture because the long exposure for the inner solar system would burn out part of the picture tube as it stared at the Sun. Voyager 1, launched in 1977, was expected to continue sending data as the craft reached interstellar space in the early 21st century. Voyager 2 continued to send data on interplanetary space but was not in a position to take a similar picture of the planets.

Pioneer 11, launched April 5, 1973, became the latest of the outer planet probes to leave the solar system. It was on a slower trajectory than the two Voyagers and Pioneer 10, all boosted by encounters with two or more planets; Pioneer 11 flew only past Jupiter. The probe's mission might be ending, though, because of communications problems. It would not receive commands for about two weeks, and NASA had to draw on time allocated to the Magellan mission before it finally switched to sending mostly engineering data. If the problem remained unresolved, the spacecraft would then be ignored. Pioneer 10, meanwhile, reached the remarkable distance of 50 astronomical units (7,490,000,000 km) from the Earth (one astronomical unit equals the distance from the Sun to the Earth). Its communications were expected to last until the year 2000. By early 1991 it took 14 hours for a signal to reach Earth from the spacecraft.

Planning continued for the Cassini/Huygens mission to explore Saturn and its large moon, Titan. NASA would supply the Cassini orbiter, and ESA would provide the Huygens probe. In November NASA selected 62 investigations to analyze the structure and composition of Saturn's atmosphere and the physical properties of the rings and to map several of the moons and moonlets within the rings.

The mission was named after two 17th-century scientists—Jean Dominique Cassini, who discovered what was once thought to be a major gap within Saturn's rings, and Christiaan Huygens, who discovered the true shape of Saturn's rings; launch was set for 1994. After gravity-assists at the Earth and Jupiter, the two spacecraft would arrive at Saturn in 2002. Huygens would be carried on the Cassini spacecraft, which was scheduled to orbit Saturn 30 times after the probe was released.

Sun. While Galileo was touring the inner solar system to reach Jupiter, the Ulysses probe was launched by the STS-41 space shuttle mission to Jupiter in order to tour the Sun. Ulysses was the international solar polar mission developed by ESA to fly over the poles of the Sun, which could not be seen from Earth. An immense amount of energy is needed to rotate a probe's orbit 90° from the plane

Ulysses probe travels toward the Sun at a record 54,959 kilometers per hour (34,150 miles per hour) after being deployed by the shuttle Discovery on Oct. 6, 1990. The mission of the probe was to fly over the poles of the Sun.

NASA

of the Earth's orbit. However, it takes less energy to reach Jupiter and make a hairpin gravity-assist turn that will pitch the probe above the Earth's plane.

A three-stage rocket that boosted the probe from Earth orbit after deployment from the shuttle sent Ulysses speeding at a record 54,959 km/h (34,150 mph), the fastest man-made departure from the Earth (greater speeds had been achieved in planetary encounters). A few hours into the mission, however, Ulysses developed a control problem. As the probe rotated and exposed different sides of a rear-pointing antenna to the Sun, the boom expanded and contracted, causing a slight wobble in the spacecraft's spin. Such a wobble could endanger Ulysses' ability to point precisely at the Earth as it flew over the poles of the Sun. Engineers concluded that a damper built into the spacecraft could handle the wobble, which should be of lesser magnitude when Ulysses was farther from the Sun. After flying past Jupiter in early 1992, Ulysses would sail under the Sun's south pole in June 1994 and over its north pole in February 1995. All other instruments and systems aboard Ulysses were activated and operating as planned, according to ESA.

Comets. The Giotto probe, which flew through the tail of Halley's Comet in 1986, was awakened from hibernation for a second comet encounter with Grigg-Skjellerup in 1992. On July 2 the spacecraft flew past Earth on a gravity-assist maneuver to target it for the flyby.

When Giotto, built and launched by ESA and European manufacturers, encountered Halley's Comet, dust particles from the comet's tail blinded Giotto's camera but left other instruments intact. Grigg-Skjellerup appeared to be less active than Halley, and so the contrasting measurements were expected to be of great value, especially with regard to dust–gas ratios, plasma science, and solar wind-comet interactions. The data were also expected to help in designing the Comet Rendezvous/Asteroid Flyby (CRAF) and Rosetta missions.

—Dave Dooling

See also Feature Articles: BALLOONING FOR SCIENCE; SPACE: A NEW LABORATORY FOR BIOLOGISTS.

Transportation

While a steadily declining national economy in the U.S. during the past year tended to put a damper on new high-cost, innovative technological advances, the relatively rapid payback from administrative automation continued to stimulate the use of electronic data interchange (EDI), including automated paperwork and bar coding on transport equipment. The U.S. Customs Service, for example, reported that one-third of all import freight entries were being processed by computers. It said that shipping manifests on 84% of the dollar value of all imports were filed electronically, 71% of all traffic was cleared on consolidated reports, and 29% of all tariff payments were made electronically. These tasks were handled by four high-speed computers. So-called line-release imports (highly repetitive shipments by low-risk importers with reliable performance and cargo security records) could move rapidly through checkpoints—30 seconds for trucks crossing the Canadian border—through the use of bar-coded invoices that fed data needed by Customs into its computers.

The use on transport equipment of small bar codes containing shipment data (identification of contents, shipper and customer, destination and origin points, etc.) that could be picked up by hand-held laser scanners for immediate computer analysis might be increased significantly. Symbol Technologies, Inc., of Bohemia, N.Y., announced the development of a new high-capacity, two-dimensional bar code only 6.35 × 6.35 cm (2.5 × 2.5 in) in size but able to store up to 3,000 bits of data, all of which could be read and decoded on site with a simple scanner without relying on a hookup to a larger computer system. Symbol claimed that its new bar code could store not only data now shown on normal bar codes but also details such as handling instructions and regulations (as for hazardous materials being shipped). The small size of the code allowed small packages to be labeled, thus providing both carriers and warehouses with data covering an entire shipping manifest and a full set of instructions for both transit and storage.

IBM Corp. won the coveted Malcolm Baldrige Quality Award for its development and manufacture of the AS/400 family of relatively inexpensive computers and hard disks that opened the door for small transport companies to capitalize on the benefits of EDI. The AS/400 systems were described as affordable, easy-to-use, reliable, flexible, and backed by strong customer servicing. Users included both small and midsize steamship lines, shipping agents, and truckers. One shipping agent said that he used the computer to track more than 30,000 pieces of equipment and process 5,400 bills of lading per month.

Air transport. The U.S. Congress passed into law the nation's first aviation noise policy, which directed the Department of Transportation to phase out all excessively noisy (known as Stage 2) aircraft operating to and from U.S. airports. The final deadline was Dec. 31, 1999, with an airline given to Dec. 31, 2003, if 85% of its fleet is converted by that deadline. U.S. airlines favored such legislation because they had invested heavily in new transports equipped with noise suppressors that allowed them to meet U.S. Environmental Protection Agency standards, yet they had to compete with many Stage 2 foreign transports exempted from those standards.

The twin-engine, widebody B-777 was introduced by the Boeing Co. during the past year. The jet airliner accommodates 360–390 passengers.

As an incentive to persuade airports to ease noise restrictions during the phaseout period, the new law allowed them to impose a $3-per-head departure tax on outgoing passengers; however, revenues from this tax had to be used to help finance new and improved airport facilities.

A major potential benefit cited for developing the General Electric Co. unducted fan engine—fuel savings of 25–40% compared with current turbofan engines—proved insufficient to retain enough airline interest. Despite promising results with this advanced propeller-type engine on test flights of a Boeing 727 and McDonnell Douglas MD-80, plus the latter company's testing of a Pratt & Whitney-Allison propfan engine, all such programs were dropped. The primary reason given was low fuel prices, which reportedly would have to increase to $2 a gallon to generate a savings. While prices rose sharply because of the war in the Persian Gulf, they remained well below the $2 level, and the higher price was not considered to be long term. Other problems cited were the high risk in using variable-pitch fan blades and counterrotating turbines.

The first of a new family of air transports, the Boeing Co.'s twin-engine, widebody B-777, was launched following a firm order by United Airlines for 34 of the planes—at a cost per plane of about $100 million—with options for 34 more. The 360–390-passenger jet transport was described as a virtually new concept rather than an updated derivative of the B-767 twinjet. The advanced features included quieter engines, an optional folding wing to increase airport ramp utilization, a long-range version to transport 300–320 passengers on transoceanic flights, and a variety of fuselage versions to fit different markets.

United Airlines also ordered 30 four-engine, advanced B-747-400s, with options for 30 more. Thus, United's combined 777 and 747 firm order totaled $11 billion, or $22 billion with options. The 747-400F all-freighter version was regarded as a plane of the future for the rapidly growing air-cargo market, especially on long international routes. It was designed to hold 135,000 kg (300,000 lb)—36,000 kg (80,000 lb) more than the largest commercial freighter now in operation—fly farther than any other commercial freighter on a single load of fuel, and require only a two-person crew. Boeing earlier had obtained 12 firm orders for the 747-400F from four airlines, but heavy Boeing air-transport orders delayed the first delivery date to late 1993.

The high cost of the 747-400F—possibly more than $200 million apiece at delivery time—stimulated many orders for converted, older 747s or other passenger transports to accommodate the expected continued growth in air cargo. Some air-cargo carriers expressed concern about being able to utilize economically the huge capacity of the 747-400F, preferring to use the smaller, converted planes.

The U.S. Federal Aviation Administration (FAA) certified the McDonnell Douglas MD-11 trijet transport, clearing the way to begin deliveries to three airlines. The new transport could carry from 250 to 405 passengers, in different configurations, and fly more than 12,550 km (1 km = 0.62 mi) in a 323-passenger, international version. Its extensive automation included computerized controllers that operated hydraulic, electrical, and fuel systems—in parallel rather than series so that pilot changes adjusted all systems simultaneously. Each system was operated by two computers and could be reverted to manual operation if necessary.

Airbus Industrie of France, concerned about two crashes of its highly automated, twin-engine, widebody A320, announced plans to build into its computers safeguards to counter crew overconfidence—a factor cited in both instances. One example was to install a feature to ensure that the aircraft had sufficient automatic thrust settings in normal, as well as unusual, landing approaches.

British Aerospace and France's Aérospatiale began a joint three-year study of the technical and economic feasibility of a second-generation supersonic transport (SST) to follow the Concorde. Among the goals for such an aircraft, in comparison with the Concorde, would be much lower noise levels, reduced nitrogen-oxide emissions, a 20–25% improvement in aircraft structure efficiency, and a 30% gain in aerodynamic performance. The $10 million study would benefit from advanced supersonic research already under way in both companies. Preliminary analysis envisioned a $10 billion overall cost for development and production, with a decision to produce in 1995 and entry into service by 2005. The cruising speed (2–2.2 times the speed of sound) was expected to be the same or slightly faster than the Concorde's (2.05), and it would use the same ground and terminal facilities as the Concorde. A much longer range could sharply reduce times on long-haul routes (London–Tokyo from 13 to 7 hours). The new SST would weigh 50% more than the Concorde and be 50% longer; it would carry more than twice as many passengers (275–300). Unfortunately, the two firms did not believe that they could solve the sonic-boom problem sufficiently to permit supersonic speeds over land.

An international group of five aircraft manufacturers (Boeing, McDonnell Douglas, Deutsche Airbus, British Aerospace, and Aérospatiale) in a related but separate SST program joined to explore basic issues that would have to be resolved for development of a new SST. Boeing believed that one key to success

would be the use of light but very strong structural materials able to remain thermally stable at peak temperatures near 204.4° C (400° F) in supersonic cruise flight and to retain their stability for a 25-year service life. The company believed that polymeric composites appeared to have an advantage over metallic systems, claiming that such materials could save up to 67,500 kg (150,000 lb) of structural weight.

The FAA began implementation of the first stage of an automated terminal area system developed by the U.S. National Aeronautics and Space Administration as a means of increasing airline landings at airports. The computers' software helped air traffic controllers optimize the spacing and sequencing of incoming aircraft for landing approaches, with initial contacts about 200 nautical miles from the airport. Subsequent stages of the system were to provide more refined cruise and descent clearance and final approach spacing. The software package would require extensive testing before full implementation, which could take up to 10 years and cost $100 million before final development.

Highway transport. Despite the serious lag in the U.S. development of a "smart" motor-vehicle/highway system as compared with such efforts in Europe and Japan, the gap might soon be narrowed. To help coordinate the U.S. effort, the Highway Users Federation in Washington, D.C., announced the creation of IVHS America, the Intelligent Vehicle Highway Society of America. Its goal was to develop "safer, more economical, energy efficient, and environmentally sound highways." Four basic elements would make up the IVHS program: Advanced Transportation Management Systems, with computers controlling the timing of traffic lights to facilitate traffic flow as measured by roadway sensors; Advanced Driver

Artist's drawing reveals a 300-seat transpacific supersonic airliner. Designed by British Aerospace, it would fly at 2–2.2 times the speed of sound.

Information Systems, with an on-board data and communication system to enable drivers to receive continuous updates of traffic conditions directly affecting them, along with information on how to avoid upcoming roadblocks; Advanced Vehicle Control Systems, with automatic vehicle speed control that would use on-board radar capable of measuring distances from other vehicles or obstacles and of braking or stopping the vehicle to avoid a collision, unless overridden by the driver; and Heavy Vehicle and Commercial Operations Systems, with similar collision-avoidance technology, plus the use of on-board computers and roadside sensors to provide en-route data to computer centers on the locations, weights, and cargoes of trucks and the identifications of their drivers.

For automobiles, a joint federal-state-General Motors Corp. test project using 25 Oldsmobiles was started along a 16-km stretch of the Santa Monica (Calif.) Freeway. Installed in the cars were computer screens that displayed maps of the highway being used and alternate routes ahead. The drivers also received direct audio alerts from the Smart Traffic Center.

For trucks, both U.S. and Canadian trucking groups, with help from 16 U.S. states, approved a test project of an automatic truck identification and monitoring system. It would use 34 truck weighing stations and ports-of-entry sites, including some in British Columbia, since many of them already had basic computer-monitoring systems in place. The overall program would involve U.S. Interstate Highways 5 and 10 running through western states from Canada to Texas. Transponders placed on the test trucks would feed data to roadside readers for transmittal to central computers for analysis and storage. Three objectives were initially being sought: automatic vehicle identification and location, weights of trucks, and vehicle classification. A long-range goal was to promote standardization in truck licensing, registrations, permits, and taxes. The system should also make the tracking of trucks hauling hazardous materials easier, as well as facilitate the clearance of trucks though weigh stations and ports of entry.

Extensive road testing of buses and trucks using alternate fuels resulted in negative reactions from carriers. The California Trucking Association reported that alternates to diesel fuel in heavy-duty trucks, used in order to meet that state's tough emission standards, were impractical and probably ineffective, citing reasons such as higher cost, lack of fueling facilities, and the toxicity of such alternates as methanol. Seattle (Wash.) Metro ended its methanol bus program ahead of schedule, blaming high costs and lack of technology to make it equal to diesel fuel. It cited numerous failures of pistons and other parts on the 10 buses that were fueled by methanol, which resulted in a continual need for high-cost replacements.

Roadway Express, Inc., on the other hand, announced that it would start a one-year road test of 10 heavy-duty trucks fueled by liquefied natural gas (LNG). Six of them would be new trucks fitted with medium-duty, 200-hp General Motors Corp. cast-block engines with spark ignition. Other alternate fuels were considered but were rejected as too toxic for handling and as possible contaminants of groundwater. Roadway also planned to seek ways to store LNG along its extensive routes for use in fueling its thousands of trucks if LNG was found to be practical.

A report by the Transportation Research Board of the U.S. National Research Council concluded that the use of large trucks equipped with additional axles and double tires (to spread the gross truck weight over more axles) could permit such trucks to use highways and inflict about 40% less wear on them than the smaller trucks they would replace. If adopted nationally, the report claimed, highway wear from trucks would be reduced by 19%. Offsetting this, in part, would be higher bridge costs, which were associated with gross vehicle weights. Trucking groups generally favored such an approach but questioned broad industry utilization because of the substantially higher capital investment. Railroads opposed them because they feared sizable traffic and revenue losses.

Pipeline transport. A new dual-coating system was selected by Mobil Oil Corp. for leak prevention on a pipeline moving heavy crude oil from the San Joaquin Valley in central California to southern Los Angeles, a distance of about 240 km across desert and rough terrain and with exposure to severe weather conditions. Because the oil must be heated to about 85° C (180° F) in order to flow, a special coating is required for protecting the pipeline from corrosion. Following a two-year test program, Mobil selected the two-part coating process. The bottom coat, developed by Valspar Inc. of Ontario, is an epoxy that makes a strong bond to steel but is otherwise substandard for wear. The top layer, manufactured by Du Pont Canada Inc., is made of polypropylene, which keeps out moisture and is able to withstand the tough environmental conditions and high temperatures. The process requires that the polypropylene top layer be applied immediately after the bottom epoxy. The resulting bond provides protection of the pipe both mechanically and electrically. If an environmental-impact study proved favorable, the dual system was planned for use in Nigeria, a hostile environment with high temperatures.

A pipeline industry report on various ways to recondition or rehabilitate steel pipelines and provide long-term anticorrosion protection—in compliance

Workers on the Channel Tunnel celebrate their arrival in Folkestone on the coast of England on Nov. 20, 1990. Their breakthrough completed the land-tunneling phase of the project, designed to join England and France.

with U.S. Department of Transportation safety regulations—gave high marks to the use of polyethylene butyl rubber adhesive tape. One of several methods of applying this material quickly and efficiently was to use a line travel machine that moves along an exposed pipeline needing repair and performs the following tasks: removes the old coating with special knives, cleans the surface with brushes, primes the pipe's surface, and applies the tape. The use of polyethylene tape ensures high electrical resistance and long-term chemical stability.

A highly innovative sulfur pipeline was scheduled for construction by Shell Caroline in the southwestern Alberta foothills—a project to start in the fall of 1991 and to be completed by the end of 1992. The sulfur would be moved in warm liquid form from a holding tank through a specially treated, heated pipeline to a sulfur-forming facility 40 km away for conversion to spherical pellets for shipment by CP Rail of Quebec to markets. The buried system would consist of a pipe 20 cm (8 in) in diameter to carry the liquid sulfur; this pipe would be set inside a pipeline 25 cm (10 in) in diameter that would enclose heated water to maintain the liquid sulfur at a constant temperature. The outer pipeline would be encased in 10 cm (4 in) of foam insulation surrounded by a water barrier wrap of impervious material. The water in the line would be heated by five gas-fired heaters located along the right-of-way at eight-kilometer intervals. Leaks would be detected by spotting water in the sulfur, which would move under less pressure than the water. If successful, the system could handle 4,000–4,500 long tons of sulfur a day.

Railroad transportation. Growing congestion on the highways and airways in the U.S. stimulated interest in building high-speed rail passenger systems along a number of high-density routes between cities (San Francisco–Los Angeles; Miami–Orlando–Tampa, Fla.; Atlanta–Savannah, Ga.; Cincinnati–Cleveland, Ohio; Minneapolis, Minn.–Milwaukee, Wis.–Chicago; Pittsburgh–Harrisburg, Pa.; and Washington–New York–Boston). As of 1991 the last route was the only one that had near high-speed rail service, with a top speed of 200 km/h on portions of the Washington–New York segment. Increasing the speed on the highly curved New York–Boston section would require costly track realignment or banking, or the use of special trains built to tilt around the curves.

For intercity routes such as the above, rail-on-rail technology appeared to be the best choice, based on the experience and plans of European nations—despite the technological progress with magnetically levitated (Maglev) trains in both Germany and Japan. One goal of European cooperation was to develop a huge high-speed (over 240 km/h) rail network linking all 12 European Communities nations plus Austria and Switzerland. Completion of the new rail tunnel under the English Channel, which was scheduled to open in 1993, would further expand this network.

France alone announced plans to expand its TGV (train à grande vitesse) passenger-train network from 3,444 km in 1991 to 10,980 km over the next 25 years, at a cost of $37.8 billion. The second-generation technology of TGV trains currently in service provided quiet and comfortable passenger service at top operating speeds of 293 km/h. The French na-

France's high-speed passenger train, the TGV, in May 1990 achieved a record speed of 515 kilometers per hour (320 miles per hour) during a test run with 40 persons on board near Vendôme, France.

tional railroad, the Société Nationale des Chemins de Fer, and an industrial group led by GEC-Alsthom launched a $106.3 million research program to develop a third-generation TGV system able to cruise at over 349 km/h and be compatible with the different electrical power systems used by other European railroads.

In the U.S. the Maglev train received a big boost when the Federal Railroad Administration (FRA) announced results of a study claiming that such trains were already technologically feasible and, on some high-density intercity routes, possibly economically feasible. The FRA was to receive $10 million to make further analyses, the goal being to skip over the European and Japanese lead in high-speed, rail-on-rail technology. An initial 400-km/h Maglev demonstration line extending 21.7 km between the Orlando International Airport and Disney World in Florida was being planned as a cooperative federal-state-developer test. The Bechtel Corp. submitted a proposal to the California-Nevada Super Speed Train Commission for a $5 billion, 480-km/h Maglev

train. Bechtel claimed that the train could divert more than 1.5 billion vehicle kilometers from air and highway travel along the congested Los Angeles–Las Vegas (Nev.) corridor.

In contrast to the glowing potentials cited for Maglev passenger trains, a transport adviser to the Commission of the European Communities listed several reasons why high-speed, rail-on-rail trains were the better choice. At speeds above 240 km/h, air drag, and not rolling resistance, is the major force to be overcome; thus, the economical operating speed of both types of train would be virtually the same, as would energy consumption. The top speed of a German Maglev was 435 km/h, and it was 517 km/h for a small, unmanned Japanese Maglev, as compared with the record 515 km/h by a demonstration TGV with 40 persons on board. Unknown were the effects of strong energetic fields on Maglev trains, whose investment cost was much higher. The noise factor was not significantly different because the cause for both was primarily air turbulence at high speeds. Finally, the TGV had proved that such service could be profitable.

In regard to the rail-freight field, U.S. railroads reported such technological developments as an improvement in the safe handling and transport of hazardous materials through use of double-shelf couplers and head shields on all pressure tank cars, the use of thermal insulation, protective skids shielding bottom outlets, and X-ray inspection of welds on tank cars. An articulated "Super Hopper" grain car was developed during the past year by the Santa Fe Railway Co. and Thrall Car Manufacturing Co. The aluminum-covered hoppers could carry approximately 30% more lading than a similar-length standard train; thus, a train 1,664 m (5,491 ft) long with 34 five-unit new cars would have the same capacity as one with 120 standard jumbo hoppers 2,182 m (7,200 ft) long. The capacity was increased largely by the use of shorter, articulated connectors that reduced the space between hoppers and by the addition of height to the cars.

The CSX Corp. and the New York Air Brake Co. agreed to develop "technologically advanced integrated transportation equipment that could dramatically expand the market for intermodal service." They said that the new equipment would be made up of continuous elements rather than distinct locomotives and cars, each element consisting of a 300-m (1,000-ft) slack-free, articulated platform joined at each end by a control cab to enable the unit to move in either direction. Such equipment could handle containers of any size and in any configuration; it would also feature a center loading deck allowing direct loading onto the platform (thus eliminating the need for cranes or auxiliary ramps). An on-board computer would monitor the operations.

Launching of a railroad antiderailment vehicle was announced by the Association of American Railroads, which called it "the most sophisticated research vehicle of its kind and the only one in North America." The vehicle featured a retractable set of wheels mounted underneath its center that was used to apply various types of loads to the track and measure the response. The wheel-set was equipped with computer-controlled, electrohydraulic actuators that could apply forces of up to 50,000 kg (110,000 lb) to the track. It could simulate track conditions and load factors that might cause derailments, so that railroads could determine causes. It could also apply forces that might cause track shifting or spreading, thus determining reasons why wheel flanges climb rails.

Water transport. Ten of the world's largest ocean shipping lines—which included mostly British, but also European and U.S. lines—agreed to work cooperatively to speed up their use of EDI. They formed a new Ediship Service, which took effect in January 1991, to transmit simple, standardized EDI messages covering ship bookings, transport orders, ship contract status reports, schedule changes, shipping charges, and responses. The joint effort was considered practical following a long delay by European lines in adopting EDI because of disagreements on standardized computer networks and software. That roadblock appeared to have been removed by the United Nations when it supported an international standard EDI approach for transport rules in the worldwide shipping trade. The new service would first be used by British exporters and importers and then, if successful, would be extended to continental European and North American shippers.

Sea-Land Service Inc. and American President Lines stepped up their high-tech race to implement automatic equipment identification systems for electronic tracking of both containers and truck trailers as soon as an international standardized system was adopted. The U.S. Maritime Administration was sponsoring the effort. The technology used radio-frequency identification to track transport equipment and cargo as it moved past strategically placed monitors that could read, via radio waves, data encoded on transponder tags on the passing equipment that identified it and its location. The Sea-Land tests were carried out in Alaska because of its rugged environmental conditions; and the carrier claimed virtual 100% success on tracking thousands of Anchorage-bound trailers and containers.

The U.S. Congress passed a law that, in part, required, on a phased-in basis, tankers entering U.S. ports to contain double bottoms. This action resulted from public concern about environmental destruction caused by the *Exxon Valdez* grounding and oil spill in Alaska's Prince William Sound in 1989.

While all new tankers would require double bottoms, older vessels would be given time for conversion or removal from U.S. service. In addition to increased safety, another benefit cited was the extra protection given to double-bottom tankers because the high-tensile steel used in new tankers was more susceptible to corrosion.

The need for rapid and voluminous sea lift of military cargo to the Persian Gulf stepped up the demand by the U.S. Department of Defense for new, fast ships that were both commercially viable and suitable for military use. Seaworthy System, Inc., of Essex, Conn., proposed a highly flexible design. It would be a hatchless, dual-speed, diesel-electric, multipurpose vessel that could carry the equivalent of 2,300 6-m (20-ft) containers in a commercial configuration but could be quickly transformed for military sea-lift use into a heavy-lift vessel or a roll-on/off vessel with more than 1.45 ha (3.6 ac) of deck space. The conversions, it was claimed, could be made in 24 to 48 hours.

American Commercial Barge Line Co., the largest U.S. inland waterway carrier, announced that it planned to build its first towboat since 1981. The design called for a 7,200-hp, twin-screw boat, 53 m (175 ft) long and 15 m (50 ft) wide, at a cost of more than $5 million. Its construction was scheduled to start in late 1991 and be completed by mid-1992. The boat would use German engines which burn an inexpensive heavy fuel blend that can cut operating costs.

A large catamaran, built by International Catamarans of Tasmania, Australia, and sold to Sea Containers Ltd. for ferry service across the English Channel, made a record-breaking crossing of the North Atlantic, shortening the record of 3 days 8 hours 31 minutes set in 1986 by the *Virgin Atlantic Challenger II*. Australian shipyards called this a further boost to their successful efforts to capture a major share of the world's specialized ship market as a result of their claimed "renaissance of design and construction of recreational boats, small naval patrol craft, and state-of-the-art ferries."

—Frank A. Smith

U.S. science policy

When scientists learned the details of the budget Pres. George Bush presented to Congress on Jan. 29, 1990, for the 1991 fiscal year, they were delighted but stunned. During his campaign Bush promised to reduce budget deficits not by raising taxes but by cutting domestic spending. Yet here was a document that proposed significant increases in federal spending for nearly every scientific discipline. How, scientists wondered, would the president and Congress ever find other programs to cut that would make such welcome increases possible?

They did not. However, after a titanic series of budget battles, President Bush gave up his campaign promise of no new taxes, the Democrat-controlled Congress agreed to some domestic spending restraint, and by the time the 1991 budget was finally law—more than one month after the October 1 start of the fiscal year—the promised increases for science remained largely intact. Some major initiatives, including the space station and the Superconducting Super Collider (SSC), were slowed, and others, such as the Human Exploration Initiative that was to lay the groundwork for manned missions to the Moon and Mars, were canceled. Most science agencies, however, enjoyed increases above the rate of inflation, and a few, such as the National Institutes of Health (NIH) and the Alcohol, Drug Abuse, and Mental Health Administration, fared significantly better.

Despite the apparent good news, individual scientists spent an unusually large amount of time trying to convince Congress and the Bush administration that they were in the midst of a crisis. This paradoxical situation arose for several reasons. First, the number of scientists was growing faster than the money that was available to support them. Second, the cost of doing research was accelerating much faster than inflation. The days when breakthroughs could be expected from a lone researcher working at the bench with a Bunsen burner and a few Erlenmeyer flasks were long gone, scientists argued.

Nowhere was the paradox more acutely visible than at the NIH. As the agency responsible for supporting most of the biomedical research in the country, the NIH had seen its budgets grow steadily throughout the 1980s. By 1990 the total had reached $7.6 billion, and the administration was proposing to raise that figure to $7.9 billion for 1991. While the dollars were going up, however, the number of new grants awarded to individual scientists was going down. In 1988 the NIH awarded nearly 6,500 grants to researchers competing for new awards. In 1990 that number slipped to just 4,600. Young scientists with no track record were finding it increasingly difficult to take the first step on the research ladder, and more seasoned scientists were getting praise for their research efforts but no money to continue them. Upset and confused, biomedical scientists took their case to Congress, insisting that without more support the best and brightest young people would abandon scientific careers, and the United States would falter in yet another area where it once was the envy of the world.

Congress took note. The House of Representatives Appropriations Committee recommended that the NIH receive $8.3 billion in 1991 ($400 million

more than the Bush administration's request), but it also informed the NIH that the agency was largely to blame for the anxiety that scientists were suffering. In a report accompanying its appropriation bill, the committee described how the NIH had bitten off more than it could chew by promising scientists more money for longer periods of time without having the resources to make good on those promises. The report told the NIH to use the budget it would receive to award 6,000 new grants every year, each lasting four years, in order to arrive at a steady pool of 24,000 total grants. With these parameters, the report insisted, and greater attention to the cost of individual grants, the NIH could avoid throwing researchers into a panic. By year's end the NIH was working out the details of complying with Congress' wishes, but the agency warned the committee that even though the budget increases were generous, other commitments made it unlikely that all 6,000 new grants would be awarded. NIH officials told Congress that the agency would be forced to support research projects not on scientific merit but rather on cost, a policy change that was deeply troubling to many in the scientific community.

If Congress was critical about the way the NIH spent its research dollars, it was even more critical about whom the agency spent them on. In midsummer, Rep. Henry Waxman (Dem., Calif.) held a hearing of the House Subcommittee on Health and the Environment on a report by the General Accounting Office (GAO) showing that women were being sorely neglected in NIH research programs. The GAO report pointed out that despite government rules requiring clinical trials to involve equal numbers of men and women, women were frequently underrepresented and in some studies were omitted altogether. For example, in a landmark study involving 22,000 subjects, which showed that an aspirin a day could reduce the risk of coronary disease, not one woman was included. Rep. Patricia Schroeder (Dem., Colo.), who had requested the GAO report, pointed out that the NIH had more veterinarians on its staff than gynecologists. Acting Director William Raub admitted that his agency could do a better job and announced that he was creating a new Office for Women's Health Research, which would be responsible for making sure women no longer were neglected in biomedical research projects.

Although Raub was able to move quickly on the women's health issue, his status as temporary "acting" director limited his effectiveness as a champion for his agency. Finding a permanent replacement for former director James Wyngaarden turned out to be far more difficult than anybody had imagined. Names of prospective candidates kept circulating in Washington rumor mills, but no nomination was forthcoming from the White House. Finally, in

September Health and Human Services (HHS) Secretary Louis Sullivan told reporters that cardiologist Bernadine Healy, chairman of the Cleveland (Ohio) Clinic Foundation's research institute, would be named to fill the post. Still, the official nomination did not emerge from the White House personnel office until after the new year had begun.

Money from industry. In addition to funding problems, the new NIH director would face several other tough issues that were debated throughout 1990. A particularly contentious one was whether researchers could accept money from industry for the results of research projects paid for by the federal government. The NIH had spent months drawing up guidelines to deal with these issues of conflict of interest, but on the last day of 1989 Sullivan decided the NIH's effort was inadequate, and he sent the agency back to the drawing board.

A key criticism of the proposed guidelines was that they would virtually eliminate contacts between university scientists and industry, contacts that the government had for years been saying were crucial to accelerating the transfer of technology from the research lab to the marketplace. Although the NIH had drafted a new, less restrictive set of rules by midsummer, these proposals became mired in the HHS bureaucracy, and by year's end there was still no official word on what the new guidelines would be like.

Scientific misconduct. Another thorny issue awaiting the NIH's new director was the one of scientific misconduct. Two new offices within the HHS Public Health Service—the Office of Scientific Integrity (OSI) and the Office of Scientific Integrity Review—were supposed to speed the review of cases where scientists were accused of misdeeds related to their research. Most misconduct cases, however, continued to move at a glacial pace. One well-known case involving Robert Gallo, the National Cancer Institute scientist credited with codiscovering the virus that causes AIDS, lumbered almost, but not quite, to a conclusion. The Public Health Service investigation of Gallo determined that he was not guilty of charges that he had misappropriated a virus sent him by a French team of researchers when both were trying to find the cause of AIDS. Nonetheless, the investigators continued to look into possible irregularities in scientific papers published by Gallo after the virus was identified.

One researcher, convinced that the NIH's investigation methods were damaging his scientific career, took the OSI to court. James Abbs, a neurologist at the University of Wisconsin, asked a federal court in Wisconsin to prevent the OSI from continuing to investigate him, claiming that the OSI's procedures violate accepted legal standards. Although the judge in the case determined that the procedures

were legally acceptable—if somewhat misguided—she declared them illegal because they had not been properly implemented. Her decision sent the OSI and dozens of misconduct cases it was investigating into legal limbo.

Congress also kept a watchful eye on the misconduct issue. Rep. John Dingell (Dem., Mich.), chairman of the House Energy and Commerce Committee's Oversight and Investigations Subcommittee, continued to hold hearings into one of the most celebrated misconduct cases, that of Nobel Prize-winning scientist David Baltimore and his colleagues at the Massachusetts Institute of Technology (MIT) and Tufts University, Medford, Mass. Committee staffers also continued to gather information on the doings of Gallo and his colleagues. In an embarrassing revelation for Gallo, the committee uncovered evidence that a Gallo lieutenant, Syed Zaki Salahuddin, had a financial interest in a company that had received thousands of dollars of business from Gallo's federal laboratory.

Gene therapy and "Big Science." Not all the attention Congress lavished on the NIH was critical. Nearly everyone applauded when NIH scientists W. French Anderson, R. Michael Blaese, and Steven Rosenberg began the first set of experiments on human gene therapy. The first patient was a young girl with a rare immune disorder who began receiving infusions of her own cells that had been genetically altered to restore her immune system. Initial results appeared to show that the technique was working, and the three therapy pioneers were seeking permission to start other experiments aimed at treating cancer (see Year in Review: MEDICAL SCIENCES: *General Medicine*).

Congress also gave approval to a Big Science project that had become quite controversial within the scientific community. The Human Genome Initiative, a joint activity of the Department of Energy (DOE) and the NIH, received $135.7 million to continue with its plans to construct a genetic map of all 23 pairs of human chromosomes, the ultimate goal being the sequencing of the three billion base pairs of DNA (deoxyribonucleic acid) that contain the genetic code for life. Proponents argued that the project would accelerate research in genetic diseases in an unprecedented way. Detractors worried that a Big Science project would take money away from individual investigators already feeling a budget squeeze.

The DOE was particularly sensitive to the Big Science/Small Science issue. As the principal federal agency for supporting high-energy-physics research, the department was committed to building the SSC, the largest and most powerful accelerator in the world. Physicists said that the SSC was essential if U.S. scientists were to go further in their attempts to

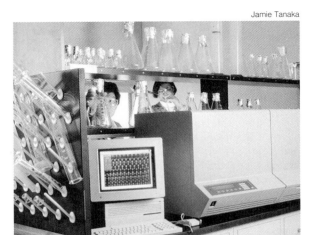

A DNA sequencer chemically "reads" genetic code for the Human Genome Initiative, a "Big Science" project designed to construct a genetic map of all 23 pairs of human chromosomes.

probe the fundamental nature of matter, but legislators and researchers in other scientific disciplines blanched at the nearly $8 billion price tag for the project. Congress agreed to provide $243 million for the project in 1991, but that was significantly less than the $318 million the administration had sought, and SSC supporters could expect to encounter more opposition when the construction began and budgets jumped accordingly.

Another Big Science project that the DOE was trying to keep on track was the $1 billion Burning Plasma Experiment, once known as the Compact Ignition Tokamak. This project would keep the U.S. in competition with Europe in the race to develop a way of controlling thermonuclear fusion so that the energy released could be used for power generation. While Europe was moving ahead with its fusion project, the Joint European Torus, nearly every part of the U.S. fusion program suffered cuts in the 1991 budget.

DOE officials also complained that large increases in other parts of its research budget were being eaten up by so-called pork-barrel projects—special awards to universities or scientific institutes in the home districts of powerful members of Congress. By one estimate there was nearly $115 million worth of such "pork" in the DOE appropriations.

Space programs. Perhaps the most famous Big Science project had one of its roughest years ever, and some began saying that it was not a science project at all. The National Aeronautics and Space Administration's (NASA's) proposed space station *Freedom*, which was estimated to cost $37 billion, came under attack from all sides. In a letter to Norman Augustine, chief of the aerospace giant Martin Marietta Corp.

and chairman of a special White House committee to review U.S. space policy, former NASA administrator Thomas Paine wrote that "the current space station program is no longer endorsed by most scientists." Materials scientists argued that life-science activities aboard the station would disturb their experiments. Life scientists argued that the space station would not give them enough power to do their work. Astronauts warned that the station's construction would require far too many "space walks," and engineers declared that the design plans were cumbersome and possibly fatally flawed.

Although Congress gave NASA $1.9 billion for 1991 to continue work on the space station, it ordered the agency to do a complete overhaul of the design. The space station should be built in a modular fashion, Congress ordered, so that each phase of its construction could stand alone if budget or engineering difficulties precluded realization of the final goal of a permanently occupied station. Just how this edict would be received by the program's international partners remained to be determined.

If NASA was wincing at the criticism over the space station, it was devastated by the problems of the $1.6 billion Hubble Space Telescope. Delayed seven years beyond its scheduled launch date, the space telescope finally made it into space in April 1990. The first pictures transmitted back to Earth seemed to promise the amazing clarity that the telescope's designers had promised. Then, however, there was trouble. Images that should have been brought into sharp focus by adjustments inside the telescope remained fuzzy. A thorough review proved that one of the worst scenarios imaginable had occurred: the telescope's primary light-gathering mirror had a flaw in it. During manufacture a critical test of the mirror's accuracy was ignored when a second test provided more comforting results. The flaw could not be corrected without replacement of the mirror, and that was impossible. Although there was still a lot of science that could be done with the space telescope, astronomers were devastated. While it might be possible to equip the telescope with the astronomical equivalent of spectacles, such a fix would not be possible until a shuttle flight could be spared for the project, and that was unlikely for several years.

It was not all gloom and doom at NASA. Despite some balky moments, the Magellan mission to Venus began sending back incredibly accurate radar images of the planet's surface. Galileo, the combined Jupiter probe and orbiter, took close-up pictures of the Earth as it whizzed by on a complex trajectory that enabled it to use gravity assists from two planets to achieve the velocity necessary for conveying it to the outer planets. The joint U.S.-European Ulysses satellite also started its journey to Jupiter, where it would loop back toward the Sun to study the solar polar region.

Scientific triumphs aside, NASA faced an uncertain future. The White House panel chaired by Augustine suggested that the country needed "fundamental changes in our civil space program." The report recommended that space science be the primary focus of NASA's efforts and that science missions receive the highest priority in future budgets. The panel—like Congress—urged taking a phased approach to the space station. It also recommended canceling plans for a fifth shuttle orbiter and using the money saved to design a new launch vehicle that would reduce the cost of putting payloads in orbit. While NASA's critics were pleased by the proposed changes, they worried that NASA managers would only pay lip service to the need for change and continue on as before.

National Science Foundation. Another federal agency with questions ahead of it was the National Science Foundation (NSF). After six years as its head, Erich Bloch stepped down, and the White House nominated University of Chicago physicist Walter Massey as his replacement. Bloch, an engineer who spent most of his career at IBM Corp., had pushed the agency toward supporting projects oriented toward technology. Although he convinced the administration of Pres. Ronald Reagan and then the Bush administration of the importance of doubling the NSF's budget, critics contended that he did so by supporting programs that would help the country's economy rather than those that would support basic scientific research. He strongly promoted the Science and Technology Centers program, an effort to give grants of up to $5 million to multidisciplinary team projects that were committed to exploring contacts with industry.

Bloch's no-nonsense style won him praise from Congress but did not win the budget increases that the administration requested, with one exception: science education. Congress gave the NSF's education efforts a 46% increase over what the agency had requested. Congress, however, was none too pleased with Bloch when he reorganized the NSF science and engineering education directorate, forcing out its director, Bassam Shakashiri, who had been outspoken in his pleadings on behalf of science education. Luther Williams was named to head the new directorate for education and human resources.

Pressure for stretching resources strongly influenced a decision that brought political heat on the NSF. In August the science agency made a $60 million commitment to a consortium led by Florida State University to be the home of the National High Magnetic Field Laboratory. The competition for the laboratory had been narrowed to two finalists, Florida State and MIT. Although an advisory committee to NSF gave MIT the edge on scientific merit, the state of Florida promised to put up $58 million if Florida State won the new lab. MIT cried foul, and Massachusetts legislators included language in the NSF's appropriation bill that asked the National Academy of Sciences to review the NSF's merit review procedures. The NSF defended its decision,

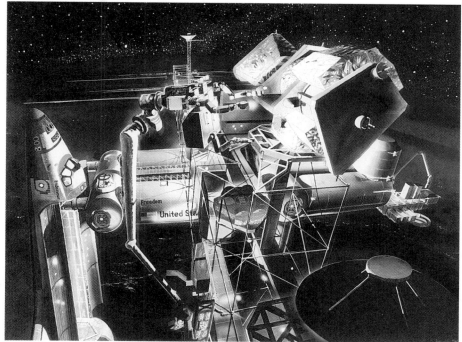

The Flight Telerobotic Servicer, a smart space robot directed by an astronaut in a space shuttle (left), inspects a large superconducting magnet on the proposed space station Freedom, in an artist's rendition. The international, permanently manned Freedom was the subject of much controversy during the past year.

NASA

Children at the Exploratorium museum in San Francisco watch a cow eye being dissected. The exhibit was funded by the National Science Foundation, which had won increased grants for its education programs.

saying that numerous factors, including but not limited to scientific merit, go into its decisions to make major awards.

The NSF also played a key role in one of the Bush administration's major scientific programs: the global change initiative. The administration proposed, and Congress appropriated money for, a fund of approximately $1 billion to be spread among nine federal agencies and used to study how the environment was being altered by human activities. The centerpiece of the program was a collection of high-tech NASA satellites, collectively known as the Earth Observation System. Coordinating the multiagency effort was one of the Federal Coordinating Committees for Science, Engineering, and Technology (FCCSET). This congressionally mandated mechanism for managing large science projects, largely unused in previous administrations, had been given new life by D. Allan Bromley, President Bush's science adviser. Bromley put FCCSET committees to work in organizing other interagency science initiatives, such as high-performance computing, biotechnology, and critical technologies.

Other developments. Another federal agency that stood to benefit from the White House's interest in global climate change was the National Oceanic and Atmospheric Administration (NOAA), a part of the Department of Commerce. NOAA, which operated the National Weather Service, would be responsible for assembling the avalanche of data from satellites, ground stations, and ocean buoys monitoring global climate. The other science agency in the Commerce Department, the National Institute of Standards and Technology (formerly called the National Bureau of Standards), received a whopping 36.3% increase in its budget (to $183.5 million). Most of the increase was to go to the agency's industrial technology services.

Enthusiasm for the academic side of the global change problem was not mirrored by enthusiasm for political action. A White House-sponsored international meeting on global climate change ended in diplomatic disarray when delegates balked at signing on to a 12-page "Charter of Cooperation" prepared by the White House without any European input. The U.S. also disappointed other nations by refusing to stabilize its emissions of carbon dioxide, one of the gases that cause the greenhouse effect, which has been linked to global warming.

One major piece of environmental legislation that did win approval was a revised version of the Clean Air Act. The new version imposed broad new controls on emissions from automobiles; restricted the release of sulfur dioxide from burning fossil fuels; accelerated restrictions on the release of chlorofluorocarbons, which destroy the Earth's ozone layer; and revived the National Acid Precipitation Assessment Program, which monitors pollutants that cause acid rain.

On the military side of the federal science budget, there were some big changes. Congress refused to approve the large increases requested for advanced technology development for the Strategic Defense Initiative, but it did approve a 23.4% increase in spending on basic science, boosting that appropriation to $1.1 billion, the highest level since 1986. Like the DOE, however, the Department of Defense had to cope with "pork"; of the $162.1 million added to the Pentagon's basic science budget above the administration's request, $60 million went to specific universities and research centers. The Defense Department had also become the de facto driver of U.S. technology policy in recent years. Military planners felt compelled to step in as critical technologies for weapons systems were abandoned to foreign industry. The defense appropriations bill contained $5 million for a Critical Technology Institute that would operate out of the White House Office of Science and Technology Policy.

—Joseph Palca

Scientists of the Year

Honors and awards

The following article discusses recent awards and prizes in science and technology. In the first section the Nobel Prizes for 1990 are described in detail. The second section is a selective list of other honors.

Nobel Prize for Chemistry

The 1990 Nobel Prize for Chemistry was awarded to Elias J. Corey of Harvard University, the man who systematized the process whereby organic chemists use simple component molecules to construct complex, biologically active compounds. By 1990 Corey and his graduate students had synthesized some 100 molecules previously found only in nature; many of those molecules became widely used in medicine and industry.

One class of drugs for which Corey was well known is the synthetic prostaglandins—hormonelike compounds used to treat infertility and to induce labor in childbirth. Another substance first made by Corey is ginkgolide B, an active chemical originally identified in the ginkgo tree, which is used to treat asthma and circulatory problems. "It is thanks to Corey's contributions that many of these important pharmaceuticals are commercially available," the Nobel committee said.

Before Corey's method became standard practice, most organic chemists used an ad hoc approach to synthesis. To make a complex natural molecule, they first would identify within its structure some smaller, simpler molecule that could be made easily or that was already readily available. They would then try to manipulate it so as to generate the more complex target molecule. Although that approach met with some success, it involved considerable trial and error and meant that synthesis had to be considered on a case-by-case basis.

Corey began thinking about systematizing organic synthesis in an effort to find a more logical way of teaching the subject to his students. In his first papers on the subject, published in the late 1960s, he described a broad, methodical approach that he called retrosynthetic analysis. In following his method, chemists start with the target molecule and work backward, carefully analyzing its structure and dissecting the molecule piece by piece. By systematically breaking key chemical bonds that join the major components of the target molecule, chemists ultimately arrive at a set of simple precursors. These then can be reassembled into the target molecule in the least possible number of steps using the sim-

plest possible reactions. By employing this method, chemists were able to achieve syntheses that were faster, cheaper, and more efficient.

Corey's approach has enabled chemists to select the best path among the myriad possible routes to a particular target compound. It has also allowed them to apply the lessons learned in the synthesis of one molecule to the syntheses of related molecules within a class of compounds—they can use some of the same intermediate steps in the manufacture of related molecules, thus saving considerable time and trial and error. In its citation the Nobel committee said of Corey, "It is probable that no other chemist has developed such a comprehensive and varied assortment of methods which, often showing the simplicity of genius, have become commonplace in the synthesizing laboratory."

Not surprisingly, Corey's method, because of the logical and systematic nature of its approach, lends itself well to use by computer programs. Although this aspect of chemical synthesis is still in its infancy, computer programs that use retrosynthetic analysis to identify possible component molecules for a target molecule do exist. These programs can then help chemists select the simplest path for making the target.

Corey was born on July 12, 1928, in Methuen, Mass. He gained his bachelor's degree in 1948 and his doctorate in 1950, both from the Massachusetts Institute of Technology. In 1951 he joined the faculty of the University of Illinois, and in 1955 he was made a full professor. He moved to Harvard four

Elias J. Corey

Harvard University News Office; photo, Jane Reed

years later and has been a professor of chemistry there ever since. During his professional career he has received numerous honorary degrees and awards for his work in synthetic organic chemistry. Among these are honorary degrees from Harvard University; the University of Chicago; Hofstra University, Hempstead, N.Y.; and Colby College, Waterville, Maine. Corey also served as a consultant to Pfizer Inc. and to Union Carbide Corp.

Nobel Prize for Physics

In 1964 two scientists at the California Institute of Technology, Murray Gell-Mann and George Zweig, independently hypothesized that the most fundamental building blocks of matter were not protons, neutrons, and electrons, as was thought at the time, but still smaller particles that Gell-Mann whimsically named quarks. That theory won Gell-Mann the 1969 Nobel Prize for Physics. In 1990 the prize was awarded to the three scientists who, in a series of experiments conducted from 1967 to 1973, provided the first empirical evidence for the existence of quarks. Those scientists were Jerome Friedman and Henry Kendall, both of the Massachusetts Institute of Technology (MIT), and Richard Taylor, a Canadian professor working at Stanford University. In its announcement the Royal Swedish Academy of Sciences compared the laureates' achievement to Ernest Rutherford's discovery of the atomic nucleus in 1911, establishing the three physicists in a relatively recent but highly illustrious history of physical discovery.

For centuries atoms were commonly regarded as the basic constituents of matter. The discovery of the electron in 1897 and Rutherford's discovery of the atomic nucleus 14 years later finally established that an atom is actually a composite system comprising a cloud of electrons surrounding a tiny, heavy core. In the early 1930s it was determined that the nucleus itself is composed of smaller particles—namely, protons and neutrons. The prizewinning series of experiments conducted by Friedman, Kendall, and Taylor in the late 1960s and early 1970s confirmed the hypothesis that protons and neutrons are made up of even more basic units—quarks.

The three physicists conducted their prizewinning work, known as the SLAC-MIT experiment, at the Stanford Linear Accelerator Center. There they used a 3.2-km (2-mi)-long particle accelerator to produce a beam of high-energy electrons, which they directed at target protons and neutrons. The manner in which the electrons scattered from the targets indicated that the protons and neutrons were not the solid, uniformly dense bodies that would be expected if they were truly fundamental particles with no structure of their own. Instead, the experiment indicated that the protons and neutrons were composed of still smaller pointlike particles.

These smaller entities were not immediately identified as quarks, however. Ironically, the three physicists had not really expected to find that protons and neutrons were composite. When they began their experiment, they tended to agree with the opinion held by most physicists of the day—that quark theory provided a useful way of classifying the seemingly countless particles that were continually being discovered but did not actually describe physical reality. Quarks were considered theoretical modeling tools, not real particles. However, as the SLAC-MIT team continued to check their results and compare them with findings from other laboratories, it became clear that the properties of the mysterious pointlike entities they were finding in protons and neutrons corresponded to the properties of quarks predicted by Gell-Mann.

Jerome Friedman

Henry Kendall

Richard Taylor

MIT; photo, Donna Coveney

MIT; photo, Donna Coveney

Stanford Linear Accelerator Center/U.S. Department of Energy

Gell-Mann and a colleague, Yuval Ne'eman of Israel, laid the groundwork for quark theory in the early 1960s when they proposed a scheme for classifying certain strongly interacting particles into a simple, orderly arrangement of families. Called the Eightfold Way (after Buddha's Eightfold Path to Enlightenment), the scheme described all particles in the same family as variant states of the same basic particle. In 1964 Gell-Mann introduced the concept of fundamental particles named quarks as a physical basis for the scheme. He adopted the fanciful term from a passage in James Joyce's novel *Finnegans Wake*. (U.S. physicist George Zweig developed a similar theory independently that same year but called his fundamental particles "aces.")

The laureates' discovery was crucial to the formulation of the currently accepted theoretical description of matter and its interactions, known as the standard model of matter, which evolved from Gell-Mann's and Ne'eman's scheme. The standard model provides a system of classification for the hundreds of different particles known to exist. It holds that all these particles are composed of combinations of six kinds of quarks with another class of subatomic particles called leptons, of which there are also six kinds. These elementary particles of matter are believed to interact with one another through the exchange of three kinds of "force particles" called bosons. Bosons, unlike quarks and leptons, are not material building blocks; rather, they transmit the forces of the universe.

According to prevailing theory, quarks have mass, half-integral spin (a type of intrinsic angular momentum corresponding to a rotation around an axis through the particle), and a fractional electric charge. They always seem to occur in combination with other quarks, never alone. For years physicists have attempted to knock a quark out of a larger particle in order to observe it in a free state, but they have not yet succeeded in doing so.

Five of the six quarks predicted by the standard model have already been discovered. They have been given the names "up," "down," "strange," "charm," and "bottom." The sixth, "top," has not yet been observed, though physicists have been seeking evidence of its existence for years. Despite the top quark's continued elusiveness, most physicists believe that the sixth quark does exist because it so neatly completes the scheme outlined in the standard model.

There are those in the physics community, however, who challenge the standard model itself. During recent years, in an attempt to keep up with growing knowledge in the field of particle physics, scientists have been forced to continually revise the standard model. As it currently stands, the model is distressingly unwieldy and leaves certain basic questions unanswered. As a result, some physicists sus-

pect that the search for the ultimate building blocks of matter is not yet ended—there may be particles that are still more fundamental than quarks. If this is the case, such particles may be detected with the aid of the controversial accelerator known as the Superconducting Super Collider, to be built near Waxahachie, Texas, and slated for completion by the end of the century. Friedman and fellow laureate Kendall were collaborating on the design of a particle detector to be installed in the Superconducting Super Collider.

Friedman was born in Chicago on March 28, 1930. He attended the University of Chicago, where he received his bachelor's degree in 1950, his master's degree in 1953, and his doctorate in physics in 1956. After graduation he remained at the university for a year as a research associate in physics, and then, from 1957 to 1960, he held the same position at Stanford University. It was at Stanford that he met the two men with whom he would share a Nobel Prize nearly three decades later.

In 1960 Friedman joined the faculty of MIT as an assistant professor, and in 1967 he became a full professor there. He served as director of MIT's Laboratory for Nuclear Science from 1980 until 1983, when he became head of the physics department.

Kendall was born in Boston on Dec. 9, 1926. He received his bachelor's degree from Amherst (Mass.) College in 1950 and his doctorate in nuclear physics from MIT in 1955. He received an honorary doctorate from Amherst in 1975.

Kendall served as a U.S. National Science Foundation fellow at MIT from 1954 until 1956, when he took a position as research associate at Stanford University's High Energy Laboratory. He became a lecturer in physics at Stanford the following year and then, in 1958, an assistant professor. In 1961 he joined the faculty of MIT as an assistant professor, and he became a full professor there in 1967. Kendall was the founder and served as chairman of the Union of Concerned Scientists. During the 1980s he was an outspoken critic of the U.S. Strategic Defense Initiative, popularly called the Star Wars defense system.

Taylor was born in Medicine Hat, Alta., on Nov. 2, 1929. He attended the University of Alberta, where he received his bachelor's degree in 1950 and his master's degree in 1952. He then moved to the U.S. to attend Stanford University, where he received his doctorate in physics in 1962. He also gained an honorary doctorate from the University of Paris.

Taylor worked for a year as a physicist at the University of California's Lawrence Berkeley Laboratory. From 1962 to 1968 he was a staff member at the Stanford Linear Accelerator Center. He became an associate professor at Stanford in 1968 and a full professor there in 1970.

Nobel Prize for Physiology or Medicine

In the decades before the 1950s, surgeons who attempted to transplant human organs had met with failure. The opponent that thwarted their efforts was the patient's own immune system, which reacts to a transplanted organ as though it were a harmful invader and sets the body's defensive mechanisms in motion to destroy the transplant. While this reaction continues to limit the success of transplantation, it no longer renders it impossible. In 1990 two medical researchers received the Nobel Prize for Physiology or Medicine for proving that fact.

The laureates, Joseph E. Murray and E. Donnall Thomas, were cited for independent work, begun in the 1950s, in developing lifesaving organ- and tissue-transplant techniques. Murray performed the first successful transplant of a human organ (a kidney) in 1954; Thomas, in 1956, was first to transplant bone marrow successfully from one human being to another. Their pioneering efforts paved the way for the treatment of a variety of conditions, such as kidney failure and leukemia, that would otherwise have been fatal.

For researchers in the 1950s, achieving successful transplants meant overcoming the then poorly understood immunologic response of graft rejection. In nearly all cases in which the donor is other than an identical twin, the recipient's immune system treats the tissue or organ as a foreign invader and mounts a destructive attack. The problem of graft rejection had led many in the medical community to conclude that lifesaving organ transplants were impossible. Even Sir Peter Medawar, winner of the 1960 Nobel Prize for his work in immunology, had concluded that some biological force "forever will inhibit transplantation from one individual to another."

While performing skin grafts on wounded soldiers during World War II, Murray observed that the grafts were compatible only between identical twins and concluded that such might be the case for transplanted internal organs as well. He pursued this line of reasoning at Peter Bent Brigham Hospital in Boston after the war. The clinicians with whom he worked were experimenting with kidney transplantation as an alternative to the use of artificial kidney machines, which could keep kidney-failure patients alive for no more than a few weeks. They transplanted a kidney from a cadaver into the patient. Inevitably the kidney was rejected by the patient's immune system within hours or, at the most, days.

Murray conducted his own research in dogs, transplanting kidneys from one animal into another, until in 1954 he was presented with the opportunity to try his techniques in humans. That year the hospital admitted a patient with renal failure whose genetically identical twin brother volunteered to donate a

Joseph E. Murray

kidney. Murray proceeded with the transplant, and the patient survived for several years. According to the Nobel committee, because of Murray's success "the field was then open for transplantation of other organs, such as liver, pancreas and heart."

Murray continued to search for ways of preventing a patient's immune system from rejecting genetically nonidentical transplants. Primarily he experimented with ways of suppressing the patient's immune system in order to allow the transplanted organ to establish itself in its new host. Initially he tried whole-body irradiation—exposing the patient's entire body to a high dose of X-rays—in order to kill the components of the immune system responsible for transplant rejection. Though effective, this technique compromised the patient's entire immune system, leaving the patient highly vulnerable to infection.

Later Murray began using newly developed immunosuppressive drugs, such as azathioprine, which were less hazardous to the patient. (As a result of his success with the drug, azathioprine was routinely administered to transplant patients from the mid-1960s until 1980, when the less-toxic cyclosporin was developed.) Applying the surgical and immunosuppressive treatments that he had developed, Murray in 1962 performed the first successful kidney transplant using a kidney from a donor unrelated to the patient. Ultimately he became the first person to successfully transplant a kidney from a cadaver into a human patient. By the 1990s his techniques had become standard medical practice.

Bone-marrow transplantation, for which Murray's fellow laureate, E. Donnall Thomas, won his share of the prize, is a doubly difficult procedure. In addition to the usual hurdle of graft rejection that exists in any transplant, there is the danger of a second, reverse immune attack from the transplanted cells. In a sort of autoimmune reaction known as graft-versus-host disease, the immune-system cells from the transplanted marrow mount their own immune attack against the host's tissue—an attack that can be fatal to the host.

Thomas persevered despite such daunting complications, focusing on the treatment of leukemia, a cancer of the blood-forming tissues that had previously been inevitably fatal. At the onset of leukemia the victim's bone marrow produces an abnormally large number of immature white blood cells that eventually replace the normal white blood cells, leaving the victim highly susceptible to infection. Thomas began his research in the early 1950s by experimenting with dogs, destroying the dog's own marrow and replacing it with marrow from another dog. His first success in treating humans occurred in 1956, when he transplanted marrow from a leukemic patient's identical twin. The transplant worked insofar as it was not rejected, although the recipient eventually died from leukemia. Subsequently, Thomas learned how to match closely the tissues of donor and patient, thereby expanding the number of patients who could be treated with marrow transplants. In later

E. Donnall Thomas

work he discovered that the immunosuppressive drug methotrexate could diminish the graft-versus-host reaction.

The refinements Thomas developed enabled him in 1970 to perform the first successful marrow transplant using marrow from a relative who was not an identical twin. As of early 1991, that patient was still alive. Thomas and other researchers later succeeded with donors unrelated to the patient.

By 1991, as a result of Thomas' pioneering work, as many as half of adult leukemia patients and up to 80% of children with leukemia could be expected to survive. Physicians have extended Thomas' bone marrow transplant techniques to treat not only leukemia but also a variety of other cancers and inherited diseases, including aplastic anemia and the genetic disease thalassemia (a severe form of anemia).

Murray was born in Milford, Mass., on April 1, 1919. He received a bachelor of arts degree in 1940 from Holy Cross College, Worcester, Mass., and a medical degree in 1943 from Harvard Medical School. He also holds two honorary doctorates, from Holy Cross College and Rockford (Ill.) College. Murray completed his surgical residency at Peter Bent Brigham Hospital (later Brigham and Women's Hospital) in Boston. From 1964 to 1986 he served as chief plastic surgeon at Brigham, and from 1972 until his retirement in 1985 he was chief plastic surgeon at Children's Hospital Medical Center in Boston. He also became a professor of surgery at Harvard Medical School in 1970.

Thomas was born on March 15, 1920, in Mart, Texas. He received his bachelor's degree in 1941 and his master's degree in 1943, both from the University of Texas at Austin. In 1946 he gained his medical degree from Harvard Medical School, and from 1946 to 1952 he completed his residency at Peter Bent Brigham Hospital. In 1953 Thomas became a hematologist at Peter Bent Brigham Hospital, and for the next two years he worked as a research associate at the Cancer Research Foundation of the Children's Medical Center in Boston. From 1956 to 1963 he served both as physician in chief at Mary Imogene Bassett Hospital in Cooperstown, N.Y., and as associate clinical professor at Columbia University's College of Physicians and Surgeons in New York City. He has also held teaching positions at Harvard Medical School and at Albany (N.Y.) Medical College.

Thomas joined the University of Washington as head of the oncology division in 1963 and served as director of clinical research at the university's Fred Hutchinson Cancer Research Center until 1989. Under his direction that facility became the world's largest center for bone marrow transplantation.

—Carolyn D. Newton

AWARD	WINNER	AFFILIATION
ARCHITECTURE		
Architectural Firm Award	Kohn Pedersen Fox Associates	New York, N.Y.
Gold Medal of the American Institute of Architects	E. Fay Jones	Fayetteville, Ark.
Gold Medal of the American Institute of Architects	Charles W. Moore	University of Texas, Austin
Pritzker Architecture Prize	Aldo Rossi	Milan, Italy
ASTRONOMY		
Arctowski Medal	Peter A. Sturrock	Stanford University, Calif.
Dirk Brouwer Award	Donald Lynden-Bell	University of Cambridge, England
Gerard P. Kuiper Prize	Victor S. Safronov	Institute of the Physics of the Earth, Moscow, U.S.S.R.
Harold C. Urey Prize	David J. Tholen	University of Hawaii, Honolulu
Maxwell Medal and Prize	George Efstathiou	University of Cambridge, England
Newcomb Cleveland Prize	Margaret J. Geller	Harvard University and Harvard-Smithsonian Center for Astrophysics, Cambridge, Mass.
	John P. Huchra	Harvard University and Harvard-Smithsonian Center for Astrophysics, Cambridge, Mass.
CHEMISTRY		
Alan T. Waterman Award	Mark E. Davis	Virginia Polytechnic Institute and State University, Blacksburg
Anachem Award	Janet Osteryoung	State University of New York, Buffalo
Analytical Chemistry Award	Royce W. Murray	University of North Carolina, Chapel Hill
Bingham Medal	Guy C. Berry	Carnegie Mellon University, Pittsburgh, Pa.
Chemical Sciences Award	F. Albert Cotton	Texas A & M University, College Station
Creative Work in Fluorine Chemistry Award	Richard D. Chambers	University of Durham, England
David and Lucile Packard Award	Trina Schroer	Johns Hopkins University, Baltimore, Md.
Distinguished Service in the Advancement of Inorganic Chemistry Award	James P. Collman	Stanford University, Calif.
Enrico Fermi Award	George A. Cowan	Los Alamos National Laboratory and Santa Fe Institute, N.M.
E.V. Murphree Award	Richard Alkire	University of Illinois, Urbana
Frank H. Field and Joe L. Franklin Award	R. Graham Cooks	Purdue University, West Lafayette, Ind.
Garvan Medal	Cynthia Friend	Harvard University, Cambridge, Mass.
George Westinghouse Award	Y.A. Liu	Virginia Polytechnic Institute and State University, Blacksburg
Gold Medal of the American Institute of Chemists	Harry Gray	California Institute of Technology, Pasadena

AWARD	WINNER	AFFILIATION
Industrial Application of Science Award	Carl Djerassi	Stanford University, Calif.
Inorganic Chemistry Award	Robert Bruce King	University of Georgia, Athens
King Faisal International Prize	F. Albert Cotton	Texas A & M University, College Station
King Faisal International Prize	Mostafa A. El-Sayed	University of California, Los Angeles
King Faisal International Prize	Raymond U. Lemieux (Emeritus)	University of Alberta, Edmonton
Organometallic Chemistry Award	Charles P. Casey	University of Wisconsin, Madison
Paracelsus Prize	Ronald Breslow	Columbia University, New York, N.Y.
Pauling Award	James P. Collman	Stanford University, Calif.
Perkin Medal	John E. Franz	Monsanto Co.
Priestley Medal	Harry B. Gray	California Institute of Technology, Pasadena
Pure Chemistry Award	Nathan S. Lewis	California Institute of Technology, Pasadena
Welch Award	William von Eggers Doering (Emeritus)	Harvard University, Cambridge, Mass.
Welch Award	John D. Roberts (Emeritus)	California Institute of Technology, Pasadena
Willard Gibbs Medal	Richard N. Zare	Stanford University, Calif.
Wolf Prize	Richard R. Ernst	Swiss Federal Institute of Technology, Zürich
Wolf Prize	Alexander Pines	University of California, Berkeley

EARTH SCIENCES

Arthur L. Day Medal	William S. Fyfe	University of Western Ontario, London
Arthur L. Day Prize and Lectureship	Ho-kwang Mao	Carnegie Institution of Washington, D.C.
Balzan Prize	J. Freeman Gilbert	Scripps Institution of Oceanography, San Diego, Calif.
Ben H. Parker Memorial Medal	Grover E. Murray (Retired)	Texas Tech University, Lubbock
Carl-Gustaf Rossby Research Medal	Kikuro Miyakoda	National Oceanic and Atmospheric Administration
Charles L. Mitchell Award	Donald R. Devore	National Oceanic and Atmospheric Administration
Clarence Leroy Meisinger Award	Da-lin Zhang	McGill University, Montreal, Quebec
Cleveland Abbe Award	Robert H. Simpson	Simpson Weather Associates, Washington, D.C.
Francis W. Reichelderfer	Joel D. Martin	Ellsworth Air Force Base, South Dakota
George P. Woollard Award	Jack E. Oliver	Cornell University, Ithaca, N.Y.
G.K. Warren Prize	John R.L. Allen	Reading University, England
Henry G. Houghton Award	Susan Solomon	National Oceanic and Atmospheric Administration
James B. Macelwane Award	Richard D. Knabb	Florida State University, Tallahassee
James B. Macelwane Medal	Thomas A. Herring	Massachusetts Institute of Technology, Cambridge
James B. Macelwane Medal	Roderic L. Jones	University of Cambridge, England
James B. Macelwane Medal	Thorne Lay	University of California, Santa Cruz

429

AWARD	WINNER	AFFILIATION
Japan Prize	Jason Morgan	Princeton University, N.J.
	Dan McKenzie	University of Cambridge, England
	Xavier Le Pichon	Collège de France, Paris
John Adam Fleming Medal	Kenneth M. Creer	University of Edinburgh, Scotland
John Adam Fleming Medal	James W. Dungey (Retired)	Imperial College, London
Jule G. Charney Award	Moustafa T. Chahine	California Institute of Technology, Pasadena
Jule G. Charney Award	M. Patrick McCormick	Langley Research Center, Hampton, Va.
Mary Clark Thompson Medal	Harry B. Whittington (Emeritus)	University of Cambridge, England
Maurice Ewing Medal	Charles D. Keeling	Scripps Institution of Oceanography, San Diego, Calif.
Maurice Ewing Medal	Carl I. Wunsch	Massachusetts Institute of Technology, Cambridge
Penrose Medal	Norman D. Newell	American Museum of Natural History, New York
Robertson Memorial Lecture	Klaus Hasselmann	Max-Planck Institute, Germany
Sverdrup Gold Medal Award	Klaus Wyrtki	University of Hawaii, Honolulu
Waldo E. Smith Medal	Naoshi Fukushima (Emeritus)	University of Tokyo
Walter H. Bucher Medal	Seiya Uyeda	University of Tokyo
William Bowie Medal	Don L. Anderson	California Institute of Technology, Pasadena
William Bowie Medal	Eugene N. Parker	University of Chicago, Ill.

ELECTRONICS AND INFORMATION SCIENCES

Computers in Chemistry Award	John A. Pople	Carnegie Mellon University, Pittsburgh, Pa.
Delmer S. Fahrney Medal	Larry L. Smarr	University of Illinois, Urbana
Japan Prize	Marvin Minsky	Massachusetts Institute of Technology, Cambridge

ENERGY

Ernest Orlando Lawrence Memorial Award	James R. Norris	Argonne National Laboratory, Ill.
Nuclear Chemistry Award	John Alexander	State University of New York, Stony Brook

ENVIRONMENT

Discovery Award	F. Sherwood Rowland	University of California, Irvine
Goldman Environmental Award	Bob Brown	Australia
	Lois Marie Gibbs	U.S.
	Janet Gibson	Belize
	Harrison Ngau	Malaysia
	Janos Vargha	Hungary
	Michael Werikhe	Kenya
Marcus Wallenberg Prize	Donald H. Marx	U.S. Forest Service
Tyler Prize for Environmental Achievement	Thomas Eisner	Cornell University, Ithaca, N.Y.
	Jerrold Meinwald	Cornell University, Ithaca, N.Y.

AWARD	WINNER	AFFILIATION
FOOD AND AGRICULTURE		
Alexander von Humboldt Foundation Award	William L. Ogren	U.S. Department of Agriculture
Australia Prize	Allen Kerr	White Agricultural Research Institute, Adelaide, Australia
Australia Prize	Eugene Nester	University of Washington, Seattle
Australia Prize	Jeff Schell	Max-Planck Institute, Germany
Bio-Serv Award in Experimental Animal Nutrition	Anton Beynen	State University, Utrecht, The Netherlands
Borden Award in Nutrition	Raymond Blakley	St. Jude Children's Research Hospital, Memphis, Tenn.
Conrad A. Elvehjem Award for Public Service in Nutrition	George M. Briggs (Deceased)	University of California, Berkeley
Cyrus Hall McCormick Jerome Increase Case Gold Medal Award	Gordon L. Nelson	Ohio State University, Columbus
Food Engineering Award	Roger W. Dickerson, Jr.	U.S. Department of Agriculture
Glenn Downing Award	Gerald C. Zoerb	University of Saskatchewan, Saskatoon
Horace S. Isbell Award	John C. Martin	Bristol-Myers Squibb, Wallingford, Conn.
John Clark Award	William E. Muir	University of Manitoba, Winnipeg
Joseph B. Goldberger Award in Clinical Nutrition	Elaine Bossak Feldman	Augusta, Ga.
Kenneth A. Spencer Award	Robert H. Burris	University of Wisconsin, Madison
Kishida International Award	Gilbert L. Corey	University of Idaho, Moscow
Lederle Award in Human Nutrition	Penny Kris-Etherton	Pennsylvania State University, University Park
Mead Johnson Award for Research in Nutrition	Bruce Hollis	Medical University of South Carolina, Charleston
Melville L. Wolfrom Award	James N. BeMiller	Purdue University, West Lafayette, Ind.
Osborne and Mendel Award	Michael Holick	Boston, Mass.
LIFE SCIENCES		
A.G. Huntsman Silver Medal	Lawrence Pomeroy	University of Georgia, Athens
Alfred Bader Award	Robert H. Abeles	Brandeis University, Waltham, Mass.
Benjamin Dann Walsh Tribute	E.O. Wilson	Harvard University, Cambridge, Mass.
Bower Award and Prize in Science	Paul C. Lauterbur	University of Illinois, Urbana
Charles A. Dana Award	David A. Micklos	Cold Spring Harbor Laboratory, Long Island, N.Y.
Distinguished Achievement in Neuroscience Award	Bertil Hille	University of Washington, Seattle
	Erwin Neher	Max-Planck Institute, Germany
	Jean-Pierre Changeux	Pasteur Institute, Paris
Edman Award	Geoffrey Begg	Royal Melbourne Hospital, Victoria, Australia
	Birgitte Wittman-Liebold	Max-Planck Institute, Germany

AWARD	WINNER	AFFILIATION
Franklin Medal	Hugh E. Huxley	Brandeis University, Waltham, Mass.
Gairdner Foundation International Award	Oliver Smithies	University of North Carolina, Chapel Hill
Gairdner Foundation International Award	Edwin Southern	University of Oxford, England
Hillebrand Prize	Miral Dizdaroglu	National Institute of Standards and Technology, Gaithersburg, Md.
Humboldt Research Award	Robert Snyder	Rutgers University, New Brunswick, N.J.
John P. McGovern Award Lecture	Shosaku Numa	Kyoto University, Japan
J. Roger Porter Award	Cletus P. Kurtzman	U.S. Department of Agriculture
Kyoto Prize for Advanced Technology	Sydney Brenner	Medical Research Council, Cambridge, England
Life Sciences Award	Max D. Cooper	University of Alabama, Birmingham
Molecular Biology Award	Elizabeth H. Blackburn	University of California, Berkeley
Ralph F. Hirschmann Award	Elkan R. Blout	Harvard School of Public Health, Boston, Mass.
R.H. Wright Award	Vincent G. Dethier	University of Massachusetts, Amherst
Roy L. Whistler Award	Johannis P. Kamerling	Utrecht University, The Netherlands
Silver Medal of the Acoustical Society of America	Wesley L. Nyborg	University of Vermont, Burlington
Superior Science Award	T. Kent Kirk	Forest Products Laboratory, Madison, Wis.
Wolf Prize	Maclyn McCarty (Emeritus)	Rockefeller University, New York, N.Y.
W.T. Doherty Recognition Award	William B. Smith	Texas Christian University, Fort Worth
	A. Dean Sherry	University of Texas, Dallas

MATERIALS SCIENCES

Award in the Chemistry of Materials	C. Grant Willson	IBM Corp.
Franklin Medal	David Turnbull	Harvard University, Cambridge, Mass.
Patterson Award	Michael M. Woolfson	University of York, England

MATHEMATICS

Dannie Heineman Prize for Mathematical Physics	Yakov Sinai	L.D. Landau Institute for Theoretical Physics, Moscow, U.S.S.R.
Fields Medal	Vladimir G. Drinfeld	Institute for Low Temperature Physics and Engineering, Kharkov, U.S.S.R.
Fields Medal	Vaughan F.R. Jones	University of California, Berkeley
Fields Medal	Shigefumi Mori	Kyoto University, Japan
Fields Medal	Edward Witten	Institute for Advanced Study, Princeton, N.J.
Frank Nelson Cole Prize in Algebra	Shigefumi Mori	Japan
Japan Prize	Jacques-Louis Lions	Collège de France, Paris
Leroy P. Steele Career Prize	Raoul Bott	Harvard University, Cambridge, Mass.

AWARD	WINNER	AFFILIATION
Leroy P. Steele Prize	Bertram Kostant	Massachusetts Institute of Technology, Cambridge
Leroy P. Steele Prize	R.D. Richtmyer	University of Colorado, Boulder
Norbert Wiener Prize in Applied Mathematics	Michael Aizenman	New York University, N.Y.
Norbert Wiener Prize in Applied Mathematics	Jerrold E. Marsden	University of California, Berkeley
Oswald Veblen Prize in Geometry	Andrew J. Casson	University of California, Berkeley
Oswald Veblen Prize in Geometry	Clifford H. Taubes	Harvard University, Cambridge, Mass.
Ruth Lyttle Satter Prize	Dusa McDuff	State University of New York, Stony Brook

MEDICAL SCIENCES

AWARD	WINNER	AFFILIATION
Benjamin Franklin Medal for Distinguished Achievement in the Sciences	Britton Chance (Emeritus)	University of Pennsylvania, Philadelphia
Benjamin Rush Award	Ralph Crawshaw	Portland, Oregon
Charles A. Dana Award	John W. Farquhar	Stanford University, Calif.
Charles A. Dana Award	Norbert Hirschhorn	John Snow Inc. and Johns Hopkins University School of Public Health and Hygiene, Baltimore, Md.
Distinguished Service Award of the American Medical Association	John H. Burkhart	Knoxville, Tenn.
Distinguished Service Award of the American Medical Association	W. Montague Cobb	Washington, D.C.
E.B. Hershberg Award	George deStevens	Drew University, Madison, N.J.
Enrico Fermi Award	Robley D. Evans (Emeritus)	Massachusetts Institute of Technology, Cambridge
Gairdner Foundation International Award	Francis Collins	University of Michigan, Ann Arbor
Gairdner Foundation International Award	Victor Ling	Ontario Cancer Institute, Toronto
Gairdner Foundation International Award	John Riordan	Hospital for Sick Children, Toronto, Ont.
Gairdner Foundation International Award	E. Donnall Thomas (Emeritus)	Fred Hutchinson Cancer Research Center, Seattle, Wash.
Gairdner Foundation International Award	Lap-Chee Tsui	Hospital for Sick Children, Toronto, Ont.
G.H.A. Clowes Memorial Award	Erkki Ruoslahti	La Jolla Cancer Research Foundation, Calif.
Grand Gold Medal	Earl Owen	Sydney Microsurgery Centre, Australia
Sir Hiram Maxim Award	Gordon W. Duff	Yale University, New Haven, Conn.
	Scott K. Duram	Yale University, New Haven, Conn.
Sir Hiram Maxim Award	Alfredo A. Jalowayski	University of California, San Diego
Sir Hiram Maxim Award	Andre Lwoff	Pasteur Institute, Paris
Sir Hiram Maxim Award	Heather D. Mayor	Baylor University, Waco, Texas
Sir Hiram Maxim Award	Dov Ophir	Kaplan Hospital, Rehovot, Israel
Sir Hiram Maxim Award	William R. Thomas	Baxter Travenol Laboratories, Cambridge, Mass.

AWARD	WINNER	AFFILIATION
Japan Prize	John Julian Wild	Medico-Technological Research Institute, Minneapolis, Minn.
Louis Jeantet Prize for Medicine	Pierre Chambon	University of Strasbourg, France
Louis Jeantet Prize for Medicine	Nicole le Douarin	Nogent-sur-Marne, France
Louis Jeantet Prize for Medicine	Frank Grosveld	National Institute for Medical Research, London
Louis Jeantet Prize for Medicine	Hugh Pelham	Medical Research Council Laboratory of Molecular Biology, Cambridge, England
Louis Jeantet Prize for Medicine	Harald von Boehmer	Basel, Switz.
	Gottfried Schatz	Basel, Switz.
Nancy and Daniel Weisman Award	Joseph P. Coyle	Johns Hopkins University, Baltimore, Md.
Nancy and Daniel Weisman Award	Charles Epstein	University of California, San Francisco
Nancy and Daniel Weisman Award	Robert Guthrie (Emeritus)	State University of New York, Buffalo
Philadelphia Award	Hilary Koprowski	Wistar Institute, Philadelphia, Pa.
Public Service Award	Frederick K. Goodwin	U.S. Public Health Service
Public Welfare Medal	C. Everett Koop	Safe Kids, Washington, D.C.
Sandoz Prize for Immunology	Max Cooper	University of Alabama, Birmington
	Jacques Miller	Walter and Eliza Hall Institute of Medical Research, Melbourne, Australia
Scientific Achievement Award	Henry N. Wagner, Jr.	Baltimore, Md.
Scientific Freedom and Responsibility Award	Adrian R. Morrison	University of Pennsylvania, Philadelphia
Troland Research Award	Robert Desimone	National Institutes of Health, Bethesda, Md.
William D. Coolidge Award	Peter R. Almond	University of Louisville, Ky.
William Beaumont Award	Antonio Damasio	University of Iowa, Iowa City

PHYSICS

AWARD	WINNER	AFFILIATION
Albert A. Michelson Medal	H. Jeffrey Kimble	California Institute of Technology, Pasadena
Award for Initiatives in Research	James G. Fujimoto	Massachusetts Institute of Technology, Cambridge
Award for Initiatives in Research	Wayne H. Knox	AT&T Bell Laboratories
Boltzmann Medal	Leo P. Kadanoff	University of Chicago, Ill.
Copley Medal	Abdus Salam	International Centre for Theoretical Physics, Trieste, Italy
Davisson-Germer Prize	David J. Wineland	National Institute of Standards and Technology, Gaithersburg, Md.
Dirac Medal	Sidney Coleman	Harvard University, Cambridge, Mass.
Dirac Medal	Ludwig D. Fadeev	Steklov Mathematical Institute, Leningrad, U.S.S.R.
Doistau-Blutet Award	Paul André Chamouard, Michel Olivier, and André Tkatchenko	National Saturne Laboratory, Saclay, France
Doistau-Blutet Award	Jean-Bernard Zuber	National Saturne Laboratory, Saclay, France
Elliott Cresson Medal	Marlan O. Scully	University of New Mexico, Albuquerque

AWARD	WINNER	AFFILIATION
Fritz London Prize for Low-Temperature Physics	Robert C. Dynes	AT&T Bell Laboratories
	Pierre C. Hohenberg	AT&T Bell Laboratories
	Anatoly I. Larkin	Landau Institute for Theoretical Physics, Moscow, U.S.S.R.
Gold Medal of the Acoustical Society of America	Eugen J. Skudrzyk (Deceased)	Pennsylvania State University, University Park
Harrie Massey Prize	Richard Dalitz	University of Oxford, England
Hilliard Roderick Prize	Wolfgang K.H. Panofsky (Emeritus)	Stanford Linear Accelerator Center, Calif.
J.J. Sakurai Prize	Toichiro Kinoshita	Cornell University, Ithaca, N.Y.
John Price Wetherill Medal	Akito Arima	University of Tokyo
Max Born Award	Dietrich Marcuse	AT&T Bell Laboratories
Pioneers of Underwater Acoustics Medal	Ivan Tolstoy	Knockvennie, Scotland
R. Bruce Lindsay Award	Thomas J. Hofler	Naval Postgraduate School, Monterey, Calif.
Rescue Award	Per Bak	Brookhaven National Laboratory, Upton, N.Y.
Robert R. Wilson Prize	Kjell Johnsen	CERN
Rutherford Medal and Prize	Roger Phillips	Rutherford Appleton Laboratory, Chilton, England
Tom W. Bonner Prize	Vernon W. Hughes	Yale University, New Haven, Conn.
Tubitak Science Award	A. Nihat Berker	Massachusetts Institute of Technology, Cambridge
Walter Clement Sabine Award	Richard V. Waterhouse	American University, Washington, D.C.
W.K.H. Panofsky Prize	Michael S. Witherell	University of California, Santa Barbara
Wolf Prize	Pierre-Gilles de Gennes	Collège de France, Paris
Wolf Prize	Maurice Goldhaber (Retired)	Brookhaven National Laboratory, Upton, N.Y.
Wolf Prize	Valentine Telegdi	Swiss Federal Institute of Technology, Zürich
Wolf Prize	David J. Thouless	University of Washington, Seattle

TRANSPORTATION

AWARD	WINNER	AFFILIATION
Adm. Luis de Florenz Flight Safety Award	Peter Gallimore	Boeing Co.
	Lester Lautman (Retired)	Boeing Co.
	Richard Sears (Retired)	Boeing Co.
Aeronautical Engineering Award	Robert T. Jones (Retired)	NASA
Graviner Sword	Anatoly Grischenko (Deceased)	Gromov Flight Research Institute, U.S.S.R.
Howard R. Hughes Memorial Award	Jack G. Real (Retired)	McDonnell Douglas Helicopter Co.
Space Systems Award	W. Ray Hook	Langley Research Center, Hampton, Va.

AWARD	WINNER	AFFILIATION
SCIENCE WRITING		
American Institute of Physics Science-Writing Award	Bruce C. Murray	California Institute of Technology, Pasadena
Andrew Gemant Award	Jeremy Bernstein	Stevens Institute of Technology, Hoboken, N.J.
Farrington Daniels Award	Anders Ahnesjo	Karolinska Institute and University of Stockholm, Sweden
Irving and Jean Stone Prize	Steven Vogel	Duke University, Durham, N.C.
James T. Grady—James H. Stack Award	Betty Debnam	*Washington Post*
Scientific Reviewing Award	James N. Spuhler (Emeritus)	University of New Mexico, Albuquerque
Sylvia Sorkin Greenfield Award	E. Mark Haacke	Case Western Reserve University, Cleveland, Ohio
	Steven H. Izen	Case Western Reserve University, Cleveland, Ohio
	Zhi-Pei Liang	University of Illinois, Urbana
OTHER AWARDS		
American Association for the Advancement of Science—Westinghouse Award for Public Understanding of Science and Technology	William L. Rathje	University of Arizona, Tucson
Charles A. Dana Award	David P. Billington	Princeton University, N.J.
National Medal of Science	Baruj Benacerraf	Dana-Farber Cancer Institute, Boston, Mass.
	Elkan R. Blout	Harvard School of Public Health, Boston, Mass.
	Herbert W. Boyer	University of California, Berkeley
	George F. Carrier	Harvard University, Cambridge, Mass.
	Allan M. Cormack	Tufts University, Medford, Mass.
	Mildred S. Dresselhaus	Massachusetts Institute of Technology, Cambridge
	Karl Folkers	University of Texas, Austin
	Nick Holonyak, Jr.	University of Illinois, Urbana
	Leonid Hurwicz	University of Minnesota, Minneapolis
	Stephen C. Kleene	University of Wisconsin, Madison
	Daniel E. Koshland, Jr.	University of California, Berkeley
	Edward B. Lewis	California Institute of Technology, Pasadena
	John McCarthy	Stanford University, Calif.
	Edwin M. McMillan	University of California, Berkeley
	David G. Nathan	Children's Hospital, Boston, Mass.
	Robert V. Pound	Harvard University, Cambridge, Mass.
	R.D. Revelle	Scripps Institution of Oceanography, University of California, San Diego
	John D. Roberts	California Institute of Technology, Pasadena

AWARD	WINNER	AFFILIATION
	Patrick Suppes	Stanford University, Calif.
	E. Donnall Thomas (Emeritus)	Fred Hutchinson Cancer Research Center, Seattle, Wash.
National Medal of Technology	John V. Atanasoff	Iowa State University, Ames
	Marvin Camras	Illinois Institute of Technology, Chicago
	E.I. du Pont de Nemours & Company	Wilmington, Del.
	Donald Frey	Institute for Illinois
	Fred W. Garry	General Electric Co.
	Wilson Greatbatch, Ltd.	Clarence, N.Y.
	Jack St. Clair Kilby	Texas Instruments Inc.
	John S. Mayo	AT&T Bell Laboratories
	Gordon Moore	Intel Corp.
	David B. Pall	Pall Corp.
	Chauncey Starr	Electric Power Research Institute
Scientific Freedom and Responsibility Award	Matthew S. Meselson	Harvard University, Cambridge, Mass.
Westinghouse Science Talent Search	1. Ashley M. Reiter	North Carolina School of Science and Mathematics, Durham
	2. Denis A. Lazarev	Elmwood Park Memorial High School, Elmwood Park, N.J.
	3. William Ching	Riverdale Country School, New York, N.Y.
	4. Dean R. Chung	Mountain Lakes High School, Mountain Lakes, N.J.
	5. Ciamac Moallemi	Benjamin N. Cardozo High School, New York, N.Y.
	6. Tessa L. Walters	San Gabriel High School, San Gabriel, Calif.
	7. Debby Ann Lin	Stuyvesant High School, New York, N.Y.
	8. Yves J. Jeanty	Stuyvesant High School, New York, N.Y.
	9. Jim Way Cheung	Bronx High School of Science, New York, N.Y.
	10. Rageshree Ramachandran	Rio Americano High School, Sacramento, Calif.

Obituaries

Adler, Isidore (Dec. 25, 1916—March 26, 1990), U.S. physical chemist, conducted pioneering studies on the chemical composition of the dark side of the Moon and, as a senior scientist with the Goddard Space Flight Center of the National Aeronautics and Space Administration (NASA), prepared lunar-data-analysis experiments for the Apollo 15 and 16 missions. Adler earned undergraduate degrees from Brooklyn College and New York University before receiving a Ph.D. (1952) from the Polytechnic Institute of New York. During World War II he served as an air force meteorologist, and from 1952 to 1964 he was an X-ray spectroscopy project leader with the U.S. Geological Survey. After joining NASA, Adler also studied condensation processes at high temperatures and radiation-damage phenomena. In 1974 he became professor of chemistry and biochemistry at the University of Maryland. There he also helped codirect "The World of Chemistry," a 26-part television series designed to instill an appreciation of chemistry; the series was scheduled to be shown in the fall of 1990 to teach college-level chemistry. Adler received the John Lindsay Memorial Award from the Goddard center and the NASA Exceptional Scientific Award. He retired in 1986.

Anderson, Carl David (Sept. 3, 1905—Jan. 11, 1991), U.S. physicist, shared the 1936 Nobel Prize for Physics for his discovery of the positron, a positively charged subatomic particle having the same mass and magnitude of charge as the electron and constituting the antiparticle of a negative electron. After earning a B.S. (1927) and Ph.D. (1930) from the California Institute of Technology (Caltech), Anderson began conducting experiments there and verified the existence (1932) of positrons (also known as positive electrons) while studying cloud-chamber photographs of cosmic rays. The following year he produced positrons by gamma irradiation. In 1936 he participated in the discovery of the muon, a subatomic particle similar to the electron but 207 times heavier; at first he thought he had found the meson, postulated by Hideki Yukawa, that was thought to hold the nucleus together, but the muon only infrequently reacted with nuclei. Anderson, who spent his entire career at Caltech, was named professor emeritus in 1976.

Aston, John G. (Dec. 30, 1902—Aug. 6, 1990), British-born scientist, founded (1933) the Low-Temperature Laboratory at Pennsylvania State University, and under his direction the lab, which was renamed the Cryogenics Laboratory, became the first (1960) in the U.S. to achieve temperatures close to absolute zero ($-273.15°$ C; $-459.67°$ F). This feat helped in the study of materials at very low temperatures, when a substance would have no molecular motion and no heat. After studying at the University of California at Berkeley and working briefly at Northwestern University, Evanston, Ill., he joined the faculty at Pennsylvania State University in 1929 as a professor of organic chemistry. There he conducted his pioneering work in cryogenics and produced liquid hydrogen and helium for his experiments in nuclear cooling. Aston retired in 1966.

Bagnold, Ralph Alger (April 3, 1896—May 28, 1990), British scientist, was an expert on the physics of sand dunes and the mechanics of sediment transport; his research proved to be equally applicable to the desert campaigns of World War II and to the study of topographical features on Mars. Bagnold, who served in the Royal Engineers during World War I, received an engineering degree (1919) from Gonville and Caius College, Cambridge, and then transferred (1920) to the Royal Corps of Signals. While stationed in Egypt he led amateur expeditions into the Libyan desert (1926–32) in Model T Fords, invented a compass for desert navigation, and started his first book, *Libyan Sands* (1935). After retiring from the Army (1935), he did serious research at the Imperial College in London and wrote an authoritative text, *Physics of Blown Sand and Desert Dunes* (1941). Bagnold was recalled to military service in 1939 and, as leader (1940–41) of the Long Range Desert Group, used his knowledge of sand movements and desert transport to help defeat the Italian Army in North Africa. After the war he resumed his research and served as a consultant to various oil companies and to the U.S. government. Bagnold was made an Officer of the Order of the British Empire in 1941 and was elected a fellow of the Royal Society in 1944. His other published works include *Flow of Cohesionless Grains in Fluids* (1956).

Bardeen, John (May 23, 1908—Jan. 30, 1991), U.S. physicist, was a scientific genius who shared two Nobel Prizes for Physics; the first, in 1956, was in recognition of his work with Walter Brattain and William Shockley for the development (1947) of the point-contact transistor, and the second, in 1972, was for formulating (1957) the theory of superconductivity with Leon Cooper and John Schrieffer. After earning a B.S. (1928) and M.S. (1929) from the University of Wisconsin, Bardeen went to Princeton University, where he received (1936) a Ph.D. in mathematical physics. He taught at various universities before serving (1941–45) as a physicist at the U.S. Naval Ordnance Laboratory during World War II. After the war Bardeen joined (1945) the American Telephone and Telegraph Co.'s Bell Laboratories in Murray Hill, N.J., where he, Brattain, and Shockley conducted research on the properties of semiconductors. On Dec. 23, 1947, they unveiled the transistor, which ushered in the electronics revolution. The device replaced the bulkier vacuum tube and provided the technology for miniaturizing electronic equipment needed for construction of computers. In 1950 Bardeen resumed research (begun in the 1930s) on superconductivity, and his Nobel Prize-winning investigations provided a theoretical explanation of the disappearance of electrical resistance in materials at temperatures close to absolute zero ($-273.15°$ C; $-459.67°$ F). From 1951 to 1975 he was professor of physics and electrical engineering at the University of Illinois. Some of his other awards included the Franklin Medal (1975) and the Presidential Medal of Freedom (1977).

John Bardeen
UI News Bureau;
photo, Bill Wiegand

Bell, John Stewart (July 28, 1928—Oct. 1, 1990), British physicist, made outstanding contributions to the understanding of quantum theory. He obtained a Ph.D. from the University of Birmingham in 1956 and four years later joined the staff of CERN, the European Organization for Nuclear Research, where he remained until his death. In his Ph.D. thesis he proved a fundamental theorem in quantum-field theory, the CPT (charge conjugation-parity-time reversal) theorem, which guarantees equal masses and lifetimes for particles and antiparticles. He later performed experiments that disproved earlier ideas that a "hidden variable" exists within elementary particles, determining their apparently random behavior. Bell also worked on electron cooling of particle beams and published many papers on electromagnetic theory, nuclear theory, quantum theory, and elementary particle theory. He received the Dirac Medal of the Institute of Physics in 1988 and the Heinemann Prize in 1989.

Bernstein, Richard Barry (Oct. 31, 1923—July 8, 1990), U.S. physical chemist, was a professor at the University of Michigan when in 1955 he pioneered a new field of chemical research, known as femtochemistry, the study of intermolecular reactions that occur in only about one-quadrillionth of a second, or a femtosecond. Bernstein conducted his most impor-

tant work on the collision of molecules. He was able to construct apparatuses to observe the chemical chain of events when molecules are accelerated in beams and are made to approach each other, collide, exchange energy, break their electronic bonds, form new ones, and then separate into new products. This work helped in the study of such chemical processes as explosions and engine-fuel combustion. Bernstein earned an undergraduate degree (1943) and a Ph.D. in chemistry (1948) from Columbia University, New York City. During World War II he helped separate uranium isotopes needed to produce the uranium-235 used for the first atomic bombs, produced under the aegis of the Manhattan Project. He taught at the University of Texas, the University of Wisconsin, the Illinois Institute of Technology, and the University of California at Los Angeles. At the latter institution he collaborated with Ahmed H. Zewail of the California Institute of Technology on research in femtochemistry. Bernstein also published numerous papers and books in his area of expertise, including *Molecular Reaction Dynamics* (1974; with R.D. Levine), *Atom-Molecule Collision Theory* (1979), and *Chemical Dynamics via Molecular Beam and Laser Techniques* (1982). He was the recipient of numerous awards, including the 1988 Robert A. Welch Award in Chemistry, the 1989 Willard Gibbs Medal of the American Chemical Society, and the 1989 National Medal of Science. He suffered a heart attack while attending a conference on laser chemistry in the U.S.S.R. and was flown for treatment to Helsinki, Fin., where a second heart attack claimed his life.

Bettelheim, Bruno (Aug. 28, 1903—March 13, 1990), Austrian-born psychologist, as director (1944–73) of the University of Chicago's Sonia Shankman Orthogenic School, became internationally renowned for his revolutionary treatment of emotionally disturbed children, many of them afflicted with autism, a neurobiological disorder characterized by excessive withdrawal and self-preoccupation. Bettelheim, who was trained as a psychologist at the University of Vienna, developed an interest in treating autistic children by providing them with a special nurturing environment. In 1932 he took an autistic child into his home, but the experiment ended in 1938 when the Nazis annexed Austria. Bettelheim spent nearly two years in concentration camps at Dachau and Buchenwald before being released in 1939 after Eleanor Roosevelt and Gov. Herbert Lehman of New York interceded on his behalf. His experiences in the camps sharpened his powers of observation and analysis and provided the principles that guided his school. Bettelheim created what he termed a "therapeutic milieu," a warm, structured environment that respected the individual yet provided clear limits—the opposite of the demoralizing and dehumanizing regime of the camps. Though some of his theories were provocative, including his belief at one time that the behavior of "schizophrenogenic mothers" caused autism in children, he later amended some of his views and set them forth in such books as *Love Is Not Enough* (1950), *Truants from Life* (1954), *The Informed Heart* (1960), *The Empty Fortress* (1967), and *A Good Enough Parent: A Book on Child-Rearing* (1987). *The Uses of Enchantment*, which stressed the importance of fairy tales in child development, won a National Book Award. Apparently deeply depressed over his health and family life, Bettelheim committed suicide by asphyxiation. He continued to be controversial after his death, when some former students at the Orthogenic School claimed that he had been abusive.

Bowlby, (Edward) John (Mostyn) (Feb. 26, 1907—Sept. 2, 1990), British psychiatrist, advanced the importance of the mother-child bond and developed the "attachment theory," which held that childhood separations and losses influenced a person's entire life. He was educated at Dartmouth Royal Naval College and Trinity College, Cambridge. In 1929 he went to London to study medicine at University College Medical School. In 1933 he qualified as a physician and joined the staff of Maudsley Hospital, London, in adult psychiatry; four years later he completed his training as a psychoanalyst. While working at the London Child Guidance Clinic (1937–40), Bowlby came to believe that children raised in institutions might be unable to love because early in life they had not had the chance to form close ties to a mother or a mother substitute. Following work during World War II as an army psychiatrist, in 1946 he joined the Tavistock Clinic and Tavistock Institute of Human Relations, London, where he served as director of its Department for Children and Parents (1946–69) and was a consultant psychiatrist until 1990. In 1950 he was appointed by the World Health Organization as a consultant in mental health, and he expanded his research to children in other countries who had been orphaned or separated from their families and placed in institutions. His first major book, *Maternal Care and Child Health* (1951), was simplified and first republished (1953) in paperback as *Child Care and the Growth of Love*. Bowlby's most influential work was his trilogy, *Attachment and Loss—Attachment* (1969), *Separation: Anxiety and Anger* (1973), and *Loss: Sadness and Depression* (1980). In these volumes he suggested that a young child's need for his or her mother's love and presence was as basic as the need for food. His convictions led to his final work, *Charles Darwin: A New Biography*, in which he traced Darwin's persistent ill health to his mother's death when he was eight and his inability to grieve her death. Bowlby was made a Commander of the Order of the British Empire in 1972.

Bunshaft, Gordon (May 9, 1909—Aug. 6, 1990), U.S. architect, helped usher in the modernist era in corporate architecture in the U.S. with his International Style designs of glass, metal, and stone, most notably the Lever House on Park Avenue in New York City (1952; declared a landmark in 1983). After earning a master's degree in architecture from the Massachusetts Institute of Technology in 1933, Bunshaft joined the architectural firm of Skidmore & Owings (later Skidmore, Owings, & Merrill) in New York in 1937; he became a full partner in 1949 and remained with the firm until he retired in 1979. The blue- and green-glass-clad Lever House, the first commercial building in New York to boast a glass curtain wall, was followed by other sleek skyscrapers. Some other examples of his refined style include such New York City structures as the Pepsi-Cola Building (1960; now Olivetti Building), One Chase Manhattan Plaza (1961), the W.R. Grace Building (1973), and the 9 West 57th Street Building (1974); the latter two employed a sloping facade to satisfy zoning regulations. His other major buildings include the Beinecke Rare Book and Manuscript Library (Yale University; 1963), Banque Lambert (Brussels; 1965), the Lyndon Baines Johnson Library and Research Building, University of

Gordon Bunshaft
Courtesy, Skidmore, Owings & Merrill

Texas at Austin (1971), the Hirshhorn Museum and Sculpture Garden (Washington, D.C.; 1974), and one of his last, the spectacular Haj Terminal and Support Complex at the Jidda International Airport (Saudi Arabia; 1981). Some of Bunshaft's buildings were also specifically designed to accommodate in their courtyards contemporary sculptures by such artists as Henry Moore and Isamu Noguchi. For his many contributions Bunshaft was the recipient of the prestigious Pritzker Prize in 1988, architecture's equivalent of the Nobel Prize.

Castle, William Bosworth (Oct. 21, 1897—Aug. 9, 1990), U.S. hematologist, discovered that pernicious anemia is caused by a deficiency in the body's digestive system and that the anemia can be corrected by a dietary treatment. He found that a deficiency exists in the gastric secretion of those suffering from pernicious anemia. His discovery paved the way for the identification of vitamin B_{12}, the substance that can facilitate the rendering of pernicious anemia, a sometimes fatal condition, virtually harmless. Castle began his investigations after studying a liver treatment developed by George R. Minot, a Nobel Prize-winning physician with whom he worked for 25 years at the Thorndike Memorial Laboratory of the Boston City Hospital. Castle, who earned his M.D. (1921) from Harvard University, spent nearly 50 years there. He conducted his experiments on pernicious anemia at Harvard during the 1920s and early '30s and also contributed knowledge of such blood disorders as sickle-cell anemia and such deficiency diseases as beriberi and pellagra. Included in his many awards were the William Procter Jr. International Award for distinguished service in science in 1935, the Walter Reed Medal of the American Society of Tropical Medicine in 1939, the Mead Johnson Company Award in 1950 for research on the vitamin B complex, and the Meritorious Service Award of the Veterans Administration in 1972.

Cherenkov, Pavel Alekseyevich (July 28 [July 15, old style], 1904—Jan. 6, 1990), Soviet physicist, shared the 1958 Nobel Prize for Physics with Igor Y. Tamm and Ilya M. Frank (*q.v.*) for the discovery (by Cherenkov) and theoretical interpretation (by Tamm and Frank) of Cherenkov radiation (light emitted by charged particles as they pass through a transparent medium at a speed higher than that of light in that medium). After graduating (1928) from the University of Voronezh, Cherenkov became a research student at the Institute of Physics of the U.S.S.R. Academy of Sciences. In 1934, during his dissertation research, he observed that electrons produced a faint blue glow when passing through a transparent liquid at high velocity. This discovery led to the development of the Cherenkov counter, or Cherenkov detector, which was later used extensively in experimental nuclear and particle physics. Cherenkov continued his research into high-energy particle physics as a professor at the Moscow Physical Engineering Institute. He was also involved in the study of cosmic rays and the development of electron accelerators. He became a corresponding member of the Academy of Sciences in 1964 and a full member in 1970.

Edgerton, Harold Eugene ("Doc") (April 6, 1903—Jan. 4, 1990), U.S. electrical engineer and photographer, revolutionized photography with the invention in 1931 of a repeatable short-duration electronic flash, which captured stop-action images that were beyond the perceptive capacity of the human eye. While completing graduate studies at the Massachusetts Institute of Technology (MIT), Edgerton in 1926 began experimenting with high-speed photography. His pioneering research in stroboscopic photography enabled him to construct a lamp that produced a brilliant light with a duration of as little as a millionth of a second. His photographs of rapidly moving objects, including those of a bullet piercing a playing card, of a falling drop of milk, of athletes in stop-action motion, and of shattering light bulbs, brought a new dimension to photography. During World War II he perfected special flash equipment to use on Allied aerial night reconnaissance missions, and he also built a large stroboscopic unit to photograph night operations of Axis troops. After the war he cofounded E.G.&G., a company specializing in electronic technology, and with his partners designed a camera to photograph U.S. nuclear test explosions. Besides teaching for more than 50 years at MIT, Edgerton also designed sonar and underwater photographic equipment, which he used in his collaborations with French oceanographer Jacques-Yves Cousteau. Edgerton also helped locate the sunken Civil War ironclad warship USS *Monitor* and the sunken British Army ship HMS *Britannia* but was unable to locate or photograph the reputed Loch Ness monster in Scotland. His striking photographs were displayed in museums and galleries throughout the world, and a collection of them appeared in *Stopping Time* (1987). He also published four books on photography.

Harold Edgerton
The MIT Museum

Frank, Ilya Mikhaylovich (Oct. 23 [Oct. 10, old style], 1908—June 22, 1990), Soviet physicist, shared the 1958 Nobel Prize for Physics with Pavel A. Cherenkov (*q.v.*) and Igor Y. Tamm for the discovery (by Cherenkov) and theoretical interpretation (by Frank and Tamm) of Cherenkov radiation (light given off by high-speed charged particles as they travel through a transparent medium at a speed faster than that of light in the same medium). Frank, a specialist in physical optics and nuclear physics, graduated (1930) from Moscow State University and began his career at the State Optics Institute (1931–34). From 1934 he worked at the Physics Institute of the U.S.S.R. Academy of Sciences. In 1937 Frank and Tamm published a theoretical interpretation of Cherenkov radiation based on classical electrodynamics. They also collaborated with Cherenkov on electron radiation research, for which the three men shared the Stalin Prize in 1946. Frank was a professor of physics (1944–90) at Moscow State University and director (1957–90) of the Neutron Physics Laboratory of the Joint Institute for Nuclear Research. Much of his later work focused on the study of gamma rays and neutron propagation. Frank became a corresponding member of the Academy of Sciences in 1946 and an academician in 1968.

Hofstadter, Robert (Feb. 5, 1915—Nov. 17, 1990), U.S. physicist, shared the 1961 Nobel Prize for Physics with Rudolf Mössbauer for his research on the proton and neutron, the particles that constitute the nuclei of atoms. While conducting his pioneering research at Stanford University (1950–85), he discovered that protons and neutrons have a definite size and form and are not mere point particles; he was able to determine the precise size and shape of the proton and neutron and provide the first "reasonably consistent" picture of the structure of the atomic nucleus. Hofstadter, who earned (1938) a Ph.D. from Princeton University, conducted his first important research there as an assistant professor (1946–50). In what he considered a major breakthrough, he invented (1948) a scintillation counter, using sodium iodide activated with thallium, which could detect subatomic particles even smaller than protons and neutrons. During World War II as a physicist at the National Bureau of Standards, he was instrumental in developing the proximity fuse, which was used to detonate warheads. After moving to Stanford in 1950, he also directed the university's high-energy physics laboratory from 1967 to 1974. After his retirement in 1985 Hofstadter continued to delve into scientific areas that sparked his interest. He pursued research into coronary angiography, a method for exploring heart functions with radioactive substances rather than catheters, and contributed to the construction of a gamma ray observatory that was scheduled to be sent aloft in a space shuttle in 1991.

Johnson, Clarence Leonard ("KELLY") (Feb. 27, 1910, —Dec. 21, 1990), U.S. aeronautical engineer, was the creative genius behind the pioneering designs for Lockheed Corp.'s secret "Skunk Works," which built the first U.S. jet fighter to go into production, the P-80 (later F-80) Shooting Star, in 1943. Johnson earned an M.A. in 1933 in aeronau-

tical engineering from the University of Michigan and joined Lockheed the same year. As head of the Skunk Works for 30 years, he helped design more than 40 planes, including the P-38 Lightning of World War II fame; the F-80, the first U.S. tactical jet; the F-104 Starfighter, which travels at twice the speed of sound; the high-altitude U-2, the first plane to sustain flight above 18,300 m (60,000 ft); and the YF-12 and SR-71 Blackbird, the fastest and highest-flying planes in the world, with speeds exceeding 3,220 km/h (2,000 mph) and flying heights in excess of 25,925 m (85,000 ft). Johnson used titanium alloy instead of standard aluminum on the SR-71, which allowed high-speed flying despite intense temperatures. During his illustrious career Johnson garnered nearly every important aeronautical award. He was the recipient of three presidential citations, including the Medal of Freedom in 1964, two Collier Trophies, two Sylvanus Albert Reed awards, the Wright Brothers Memorial Trophy, the Daniel Guggenheim Medal, and the 1990 National Air and Space Museum trophy. After retiring from Lockheed in 1975 as senior vice president, he remained a director until 1980 and was senior adviser until his death.

Menninger, Karl Augustus (July 22, 1893—July 18, 1990), U.S. psychiatrist, was a towering figure in the field of psychoanalysis and was instrumental in dispelling long-held beliefs that the mentally ill or emotionally disturbed should be institutionalized rather than receiving psychiatric treatment. After graduating from Harvard Medical School in 1917, he became what was then known as a nerve specialist and was one of the first physicians in the United States to receive psychoanalytic training. Menninger believed that a humane environment was essential for patients and, with his father, founded (1920) the now famous Menninger Clinic in Topeka, Kan., which was followed by the opening of a sanitarium in 1925 and the establishment of a foundation in 1941. He believed that psychiatric treatment, in the proper circumstances, aided virtually every disturbed individual. During the 1940s, '50s, and '60s, psychiatrists were educated in psychoanalysis at the foundation, and this training helped shape psychiatry in the U.S. Menninger was a champion of neglected and abused children, American Indians, wildlife, and prisoners. In his book *The Crime of Punishment* (1968), he argued that criminals were not rehabilitated by being incarcerated and that most crime was a result of mental or emotional sickness and should be treated. Menninger deplored the use of capital punishment. He believed that society was responsible for some forms of mental illness and held that adult problems sometimes stemmed from lack of parental love. He maintained that "it is much easier, more logical, and more efficacious to help a child grow up with love and courage than it is to instill hope in a despondent soul." Menninger was also a prolific author, publishing such books as *The Human Mind* (1930), *Man Against Himself* (1938), *Love Against Hate* (1942), and *Whatever Became of Sin?* (1973). He founded (1945) and directed (1946–69) the Menninger School of Psychiatry. He was awarded the Presidential Medal of Freedom in 1981.

Mestral, Georges de (June 19, 1907—Feb. 8, 1990), Swiss inventor, developed Velcro, the grasping nylon fastener that revolutionized everything from children's shoes to artificial hearts to astronauts' space suits. De Mestral, who studied engineering at the Federal Institute of Technology at Lausanne, Switz., was reportedly inspired on a walk in the woods near Geneva in 1941 when he observed the way burrs clung to his clothing and his dog's hair. By 1948 he had developed two compatible materials (one covered with tiny hooks and the other with tiny loops) that would cling tenaciously when pressed together and yet could be easily separated and readjusted. In 1957 de Mestral began manufacturing Velcro at a small factory in Aubonne, Switz., but he eventually sold the international licensing rights and collected royalties. His less publicized work included research into fiber optics and the marketing of a commercially successful asparagus peeler.

Mirowski, Michel (1924—March 26, 1990), U.S. physician, was the coinventor of the automatic implantable cardioverter-defibrillator, a device first used in 1980 to control potentially fatal irregular heartbeats. The battery-operated invention was designed to be surgically implanted in the abdomen and attached to the heart by three electrodes. The defibrillator both sensed erratic heartbeats and shocked the heart back to a normal rhythm; it reduced the mortality rate for patients with irregular heartbeats from 40 to 2%. Mirowski, born in Poland, earned his M.D. from the University of Lyon, France, in 1953. He pursued graduate studies at hospitals in the U.S., Mexico, and Israel, where in 1963 he became chief of cardiology at the Asaf-Harofe governmental hospital in Zerifin. He later served in the U.S. as professor of medicine at Johns Hopkins University School of Medicine and director of the coronary care unit at Sinai Hospital in Baltimore, Md. As a member of the hospital staff from 1968, he was at the helm of a group of physicians who spent 10 years designing the defibrillator. Mirowski also published more than 260 scientific articles. He was the recipient of the Symbol of Excellence from the Texas Heart Institute in 1981 and the Eugene Drake Award from the American Heart Association in 1990.

Noyce, Robert Norton (Dec. 12, 1927—June 3, 1990), U.S. engineer, helped usher in the modern technological age as the coinventor (1959) of the integrated circuit, a system of interconnecting transistors on a single silicon microchip. This device heralded the arrival of miniaturization and the advent of microcomputers, digital watches, pocket calculators, home computers, robots, microwave ovens, and advanced missile guidance systems. While at Grinnell (Iowa) College, Noyce studied the newly developed transistor. He later earned (1953) a Ph.D. at the Massachusetts Institute of Technology and briefly worked for Philco Corp. before joining Nobel laureate William Shockley at his Semiconductor Laboratory in Mountain View, Calif. Noyce became disenchanted with Shockley's management style, and he and seven others, referred to by Shockley as "the traitorous eight," launched their own firm, Fairchild Semiconductor. Soon more than 45 other electronics companies sprang up in this area of California, which became known as Silicon Valley. In 1968 Noyce and Gordon Moore set out on their own and founded Intel Corp., which became a leading manufacturer of semiconductors. During their first year they concentrated on research in the little-explored field of computer memory. Within two years they had devised the 1103 memory chip of silicon and polysilicon, which replaced the less efficient ceramic cores used to store data in computers. Their microchip boosted sales to $25 million and the following year to $66 million. In 1971 Intel introduced the microprocessor, which permitted a single silicon chip to possess circuitry for both information storage and information processing. The firm became the leading manufacturer of microprocessor chips. In 1988 Noyce agreed to head Sematech Inc., a research consortium equally financed by industry and the U.S. government and formed to keep abreast of Japan in semiconductor-manufacturing technology. His monumental contributions were recognized in 1979 when he was awarded the National Medal of Science and in 1987 when he received the National Medal of Technology. Noyce was inducted into the National Inventors Hall of Fame in 1983.

Phillips, Samuel Cochran (Feb. 19, 1921—Jan. 31, 1990), U.S. general and space program executive, as director (1964–69) of the Apollo space program was a hands-on administrator with responsibilities for coordinating the many divisions of the program, which climaxed in the July 1969 Apollo 11 manned lunar landing. After earning a degree in electrical engineering from the University of Wyoming, Phillips became a lieutenant in the Army. He later transferred to the Army Air Corps and was a combat pilot in the U.K. during World War II. In 1950 Phillips earned an M.S. in engineering from the University of Michigan. He returned to Britain in 1956 to become chief of logistics for the 7th Air Division of the Strategic Air Command, and later he was assigned to manage the development of the Minuteman intercontinental ballistic missile program. His success in the latter position attracted the attention of leaders of the National Aeronautics and Space Administration (NASA). The Air Force lent Phillips to NASA, and he took charge of the Apollo program. During his tenure he was praised for the competent manner in which he handled the tragic 1967 launching-pad fire aboard Apollo 1, in which three astronauts were killed. During the Apollo 11 flight Phillips announced plans to return to the Air Force as commander of the Air Force Space Program and Missile System Organization. He then served as director of the National Security Agency, and in 1973 he was named commander of the Air Force Strategic Air Command. Phillips retired in 1975, but he was called back to duty in 1986 when his expertise was needed following the *Challenger* space shuttle explosion.

Roberts, Walter Orr (Aug. 20, 1915—March 12, 1990), U.S. astronomer, was instrumental in establishing the contemporary science of climatology as the founder (1960) of the National Center for Atmospheric Research at the University of Colorado. Roberts was one of the first scientists to ponder the implications of modern technology on climate. Some of his investigations included the relationship of the Sun to the Earth's changing climate, global warming, and nuclear winter. In 1940, together with his wife, Roberts assembled the first solar coronograph in the Western Hemisphere. The telescope, equipped with a circular disk that covered the Sun, permitted him to observe its gaseous outer halo, the corona. During his observations Roberts found that strong coronal flares were followed several days later by radio fade-outs; this information was vital to U.S. military communications during World War II. His one-man station was reorganized in 1946 and became Harvard's High Altitude Observatory, now affiliated with the University of Colorado. There during the 1950s the world's largest coronograph was constructed. Later he directed the program on food, climate, and the world's future for the Aspen Institute for Humanistic Studies. In 1984 he co-wrote *The Cold and the Dark*, an opus on nuclear winter. Roberts won many awards, including the 1989 United Nations Environmental Leadership Medal, and also was active in promoting (1988) a computer dialogue on global warming, entitled Greenhouse/Glasnost, between U.S. and Soviet scientists.

Rothschild, Nathaniel Mayer Victor Rothschild, 3RD BARON (Oct. 31, 1910—March 20, 1990), British biophysicist, civil servant, and counterespionage expert, diverged from the family banking business to bring enormous energy and a sense of purpose to a variety of influential positions in science, academia, government, and industry. He attended Harrow School and Trinity College, Cambridge, where he won a fellowship in 1935. In 1937 he succeeded his uncle as third baron. During World War II Lord Rothschild worked for MI-5 (the United Kingdom's domestic intelligence agency) in counterintelligence, antisabotage, and bomb disposal. After the war he returned to Cambridge to pursue research into the biochemical mechanisms of spermatozoa and fertilization. He became a fellow of the Royal Society in 1953 and published two significant books in biology, *Fertilization* (1956) and *A Classification of Living Animals* (1961). As chairman of the Agricultural Research Council (1948–58) and assistant director of zoological research (1950–70), Lord Rothschild brought much-needed attention and money to scientific research at Cambridge. In 1971 he was chosen by U.K. Prime Minister Edward Heath to head the new Central Policy Review Staff (a Cabinet-level think tank), where he became even more closely involved in the government funding of scientific research. In the private sector he served as vice chairman (1961–63), chairman (1963–65), and coordinator (1965–70) of research for the Royal Dutch/Shell Group; director of financial holdings at N.M. Rothschild & Sons, Ltd. (1975–90), and other companies; and founding chairman of Biotechnology Investments Ltd. (1981–89). Late in his life he published two autobiographical volumes, *Meditations of a Broomstick* (1977) and *Random Variables* (1984). After the disclosure in 1979 that Sir Anthony Blunt had been recruited as a Soviet spy while at Cambridge, Lord Rothschild, who had been among Blunt's friends there, came under suspicion as the long-sought "fifth man" in the spy ring. This accusation was resurrected in 1986, when he was mentioned in connection with the controversial book *Spycatcher*. After several months of investigation by the attorney general's office, Lord Rothschild was exonerated on all charges.

Skinner, B(urrhus) F(rederic) (March 20, 1904—Aug. 18, 1990), U.S. psychologist, was an influential pioneer in the study of behaviorism, the branch of psychology asserting that human behavior can be shaped and controlled almost exclusively by the effects of stimulus and positive and negative reinforcement. After earning his B.A. in 1926 from Hamilton College, Clinton, N.Y., Skinner dabbled in writing but became fascinated with the study of behaviorism. He then earned an M.A. (1930) and a Ph.D. (1931) in psychology from Harvard University, where he conducted research until 1936, when he joined the faculty of the University of Minnesota. There he wrote *The Behavior of Organisms* (1938) and conducted animal experiments. As a professor of psychology at Indiana University (1945–48), he gained renown for his Air-Crib invention. The large, soundproof, germ-free, air-conditioned box was designed to serve as an optimum environment and a baby tender for a child's first two years of life. Later (1948) Skinner returned to Harvard, and he remained there until his retirement from teaching in 1974. To elicit conditioned responses during his animal experiments, he created his celebrated Skinner box, a soundproof enclosure equipped with a food dispenser that, for example, a rat could operate by pressing a lever and a pigeon could operate by pecking a key. He later proposed that children could be taught to read by using a programmed teaching machine that would reinforce correct responses. As a behaviorist, Skinner studied the individual interacting with the environment and discarded any mental explanations for behavior. He created a stir with the publication of *Walden Two* (1948), which depicted life in a behaviorally engineered community where various restrictions were placed on individuals in order to achieve a utopian society. He advocated using such techniques in the treatment of the mentally ill and in the upbringing of children. Perhaps Skinner's most important contribution to behaviorism was the study of operant behavior. While most behaviorists studied responses through stimuli, he studied behavior through the active contributor acting (or operating) on his environment. He advocated behavior modification through positive reinforcement (anything that strengthens the behavior that produces it) and negative reinforcement (anything that strengthens the behavior that reduces it). A prolific author, Skinner detailed his theories in such volumes as *Science and Human Behavior* (1953), *The Technology of Teaching* (1968), *Beyond Freedom and Dignity* (1971), *Notebooks* (1980), and his last work, *Recent Issues in the Analysis of Behavior* (1989). His *Particulars of My Life* (1976) and *The Shaping of a Behaviorist* (1979) were autobiographical.

Throckmorton, Peter (July 30, 1928—June 5, 1990), U.S. marine archaeologist, discovered and scientifically excavated two of the oldest sunken ships on record and was instrumental in establishing marine archaeology as a science. Throckmorton's fascination with shipwrecks began when he was a child. After serving in the Army (1948–51), he studied at the University of Hawaii (1951–54), the University of the Americas, Mexico City (1954), and the Institute of Ethnology, Paris (1954–55). He then served for five years as a free-lance photographer for a documentary filmmaker before embarking on his first scientific examination of a shipwreck. In 1960, with museum and private funding, Throckmorton located a shipwreck in the Mediterranean Sea off Cape Gelidonya in Turkey. The vessel was then the oldest-known wreck in the world, having sunk around 1200 BC. Instead of selling its valuable contents, he insisted on studying and preserving them as archaeological treasures. In 1975 Throckmorton headed a group that explored the Aegean Sea near the Greek island of Hydra; he found a sunken cargo ship that dated from the Bronze Age. The contents of these two shipwrecks yielded numerous extraor-

dinary objects. Throckmorton's initiative led to the creation of the Institute of Nautical Archaeology at Texas A & M University and to the establishment of a museum of shipwreck archaeology in the Crusader castle at Bodrum, Turkey. He served as research associate (1960–69) at the University of Pennsylvania Museum, and he wrote a number of books, including *The Lost Ships* (1964; coauthor), *Shipwrecks and Archaeology: The Unharvested Sea* (1970), and *The Sea Remembers* (1987).

Wang, An (Feb. 7, 1920—March 24, 1990), Chinese-born engineering executive, invented (1948) a magnetic core memory for computers while working at Harvard's Computer Laboratory and in 1951 founded Wang Laboratories, which became one of the most successful high-technology companies in the U.S. Wang earned (1940) a B.S. degree in China at the prestigious Jiaotung (Chiao-t'ung) University before immigrating to the U.S., where he attended Harvard University and earned (1948) a Ph.D. in applied physics and engineering. His doughnut-shaped ring of iron, which served as the core for computer memory, revolutionized the industry until the advent of the microchip. During the 1960s his company gained stature with the introduction of the desktop

An Wang
UPI/Bettmann

calculator and office computers, and Wang Laboratories later played a vital part in the "Massachusetts Miracle" that revived the state's aging factory towns. Wang, who made numerous original inventions of basic components for word-processing systems, held 40 patents and was inducted into the National Inventors Hall of Fame in 1988. In 1984, a year before the entire computer industry fell into a slump, he was ranked as the fifth-richest American, with a worth of $1.6 billion. In 1986 Wang stepped down as president of his company and named his son Frederick as his successor. However, product delays and stiff minicomputer competition with IBM Corp. led to steep losses and a restructuring in 1989. That year Wang named a new company president.

Contributors to the Science Year in Review

D. James Baker *Earth sciences: Oceanography.* President, Joint Oceanographic Institutions Inc., Washington, D.C.

David M. Boore *Earth sciences: Geophysics.* Geophysicist, U.S. Geological Survey, Menlo Park, Calif.

Harold Borko *Electronics and information sciences: Information systems and services.* Professor, Graduate School of Library and Information Science, University of California, Los Angeles.

John M. Bowen *Medical sciences: Veterinary medicine.* Associate Dean for Research and Graduate Affairs and Professor of Pharmacology and Toxicology, College of Veterinary Medicine, University of Georgia, Athens.

Keith J. Bowman *Materials sciences: Metallurgy.* Assistant Professor of Materials Engineering, Purdue University, West Lafayette, Ind.

George G. Brown *Life sciences: Zoology.* Professor of Zoology and Genetics, Iowa State University, Ames.

George R. Brubaker *Chemistry: Inorganic chemistry.* Supervisory Chemist, U.S. Food and Drug Administration, Chicago District Laboratory, Chicago.

Paul J. Campbell *Mathematics.* Professor of Mathematics and Computer Science, Beloit College, Beloit, Wis.

Douglas E. Comer *Electronics and information sciences: Computers and computer science.* Professor of Computer Science, Purdue University, West Lafayette, Ind.

Dave Dooling *Space exploration.* D² Associates, Freelance Science Writing and Aerospace Consulting, Huntsville, Ala.

Carl B. Dover *Physics: Nuclear physics.* Senior Scientist, Brookhaven National Laboratory, Upton, N.Y.

F.C. Durant III *Electronics and information sciences: Satellite systems.* Aerospace Historian and Consultant, Chevy Chase, Md.

Richard L. Gordon *Energy.* Professor of Mineral Economics, MICASU University Endowed Fellow, and Director of the Center for Energy and Mineral Policy Research, Pennsylvania State University, University Park.

David Guise *Architecture and civil engineering.* Professor of Architecture, City College of New York, and private practice of architecture, New York, N.Y.

Robert Haselkorn *Life sciences: Molecular biology.* F.L. Pritzker Distinguished Service Professor, Department of Molecular Genetics and Cell Biology, University of Chicago, Ill.

Lawrence W. Jones *Physics: High-energy physics.* Professor of Physics, University of Michigan, Ann Arbor.

John Patrick Jordan *Food and agriculture: Agriculture.* Administrator, Cooperative State Research Service, U.S. Department of Agriculture, Washington, D.C.

Lou Joseph *Medical sciences: Dentistry.* Supervisor, Medical/Science Media, Hill and Knowlton, Inc., Chicago.

Allan P. Katz *Materials sciences: Ceramics.* Technical Manager for Structural Ceramics, Wright Laboratory, Wright-Patterson Air Force Base, Ohio.

George B. Kauffman *Chemistry: Applied chemistry.* Professor of Chemistry, California State University, Fresno.

David B. Kitts *Earth sciences: Geology and geochemistry.* Professor Emeritus of the History of Science, University of Oklahoma, Norman.

Mina W. Lamb *Food and agriculture: Nutrition.* Professor Emeritus, Department of Food and Nutrition, Texas Tech University, Lubbock.

Steven G. Louie *Physics: Condensed-matter physics.* Professor of Physics, University of California, Berkeley.

Melvin H. Marx *Psychology* (in part). Professor of Psychology, Florida Institute of Psychology, Melbourne, and

Professor Emeritus of Psychology, University of Missouri, Columbia.

John E. McMurry *Chemistry: Organic chemistry.* Professor of Chemistry, Cornell University, Ithaca, N.Y.

Franz J. Monssen *Electronics and information sciences: Electronics.* Instructor, Department of Electronic and Computer Engineering Technology, Queensborough Community College, New York, N.Y.

Colin V. Newman *Psychology* (in part). Executive Secretary, British Psychological Society, Leicester, England.

Carolyn D. Newton *Scientists of the Year: Nobel prizes.* Free-lance Writer and Editor, Seattle, Wash.

Joseph Palca *U.S. science policy.* Senior Writer, *Science* magazine, Washington, D.C.

Roger A. Pielke *Earth sciences: Atmospheric sciences.* Professor of Atmospheric Science, Colorado State University, Fort Collins.

W.M. Protheroe *Astronomy.* Professor of Astronomy, Ohio State University, Columbus.

John Rhea *Defense research.* Free-lance Science Writer, Woodstock, Va.

Phillip F. Schewe *Physics: General developments.* Chief Science Writer, American Institute of Physics, New York, N.Y.

Ernest L. Schusky *Anthropology.* Professor of Anthropology, Southern Illinois University, Edwardsville.

Robert R. Shannon *Optical engineering.* Professor and Director, Optical Sciences Center, University of Arizona, Tucson.

Lawrence J. Shimkets *Life sciences: Microbiology.* Associate Professor of Microbiology, University of Georgia, Athens.

Joanne Silberner *Medical sciences: General medicine.* Senior Editor, Health, *U.S. News and World Report,* Washington, D.C.

Albert J. Smith *Life sciences: Botany.* Professor of Biology, Wheaton College, Wheaton, Ill.

Frank A. Smith *Transportation.* Executive Consultant, Eno Foundation for Transportation, Westport, Conn.

Leslie Smith *Earth sciences: Hydrology.* Professor of Geological Sciences, University of British Columbia, Vancouver.

Robert E. Stoffels *Electronics and information sciences: Communications systems.* Editor, *Telephone Engineer & Management* magazine, Chicago, Ill.

Philip R. Watson *Chemistry: Physical chemistry.* Professor of Chemistry, Oregon State University, Corvallis.

Kenneth E.F. Watt *Environment.* Professor of Zoology, University of California, Davis.

James D. Wilde *Archaeology.* Director, Office of Public Archaeology, Brigham Young University, Provo, Utah.

Contributors to the Encyclopædia Britannica Science Update

Bruce Peter Luyendyk *Oceans.* Professor of Marine Geophysics and Director of the Institute for Crustal Studies, University of California, Santa Barbara.

Richard A. Robinson *Geochronology* (in part). Gulf-Hedberg Professor of Geology, University of Kansas, Lawrence.

Brian Frederick Windley *Geochronology* (in part). Professor of Geology, University of Leicester, England.

A

Science

Classic

Michael Faraday

Selections from *Experimental Researches in Electricity*

One of the greatest scientists of the 19th century, Michael Faraday (1791–1867) was the first to produce an electric current from a magnetic field, invented the first electric motor and dynamo, demonstrated the relationship between electricity and chemical bonding, and discovered the effect of magnetism on light. Reprinted below are the first two sections of *Experimental Researches in Electricity,* which he began writing in 1831.

First Series

1. The power which electricity of tension possesses of causing an opposite electrical state in its vicinity has been expressed by the general term Induction; which, as it has been received into scientific language, may also, with propriety, be used in the same general sense to express the power which electrical currents may possess of inducing any particular state upon matter in their immediate neighbourhood, otherwise indifferent. It is with this meaning that I purpose using it in the present paper.

2. Certain effects of the induction of electrical currents have already been recognised and described: as those of magnetization; Ampère's experiments of bringing a copper disc near to a flat spiral; his repetition with electromagnets of Arago's extraordinary experiments, and perhaps a few others. Still it appeared unlikely that these could be all the effects which induction by currents could produce; especially as, upon dispensing with iron, almost the whole of them disappear, whilst yet an infinity of bodies, exhibiting definite phenomena of induction with electricity of tension, still remain to be acted upon by the induction of electricity in motion.

3. Further: Whether Ampère's beautiful theory were adopted, or any other, or whatever reservation

Michael Faraday
By courtesy of the National
Portrait Gallery

were mentally made, still it appeared very extraordinary, that as every electric current was accompanied by a corresponding intensity of magnetic action at right angles to the current, good conductors of electricity, when placed within the sphere of this action, should not have any current induced through them, or some sensible effect produced equivalent in force to such a current.

4. These considerations, with their consequence, the hope of obtaining electricity from ordinary mag-

netism, have stimulated me at various times to investigate experimentally the inductive effect of electric currents. I lately arrived at positive results; and not only had my hopes fulfilled, but obtained a key which appeared to me to open out a full explanation of Arago's magnetic phenomena, and also to discover a new state, which may probably have great influence in some of the most important effects of electric currents.

5. These results I purpose describing, not as they were obtained, but in such a manner as to give the most concise view of the whole.

On the Induction of Electric Currents

6. About twenty-six feet of copper wire one twentieth of an inch in diameter were wound round a cylinder of wood as a helix, the different spires of which were prevented from touching by a thin interposed twine. This helix was covered with calico, and then a second wire applied in the same manner. In this way twelve helices were superposed, each containing an average length of wire of twenty-seven feet, and all in the same direction. The first, third, fifth, seventh, ninth, and eleventh of these helices were connected at their extremities end to end, so as to form one helix; the others were connected in a similar manner; and thus two principal helices were produced, closely interposed, having the same direction, not touching anywhere, and each containing one hundred and fifty-five feet in length of wire.

7. One of these helices was connected with a galvanometer, the other with a voltaic battery of ten pairs of plates four inches square, with double coppers and well charged; yet not the slightest sensible deflection of the galvanometer-needle could be observed.

8. A similar compound helix, consisting of six lengths of copper and six of soft iron wire, was constructed. The resulting iron helix contained two hundred and fourteen feet of wire, the resulting copper helix two hundred and eight feet; but whether the current from the trough was passed through the copper or the iron helix, no effect upon the other could be perceived at the galvanometer.

9. In these and many similar experiments no difference in action of any kind appeared between iron and other metals.

10. Two hundred and three feet of copper wire in one length were coiled round a large block of wood; other two hundred and three feet of similar wire were interposed as a spiral between the turns of the first coil, and metallic contact everywhere prevented by twine. One of these helices was connected with a galvanometer, and the other with a battery of one hundred pairs of plates four inches square, with double coppers, and well charged. When the contact was made, there was a sudden and very slight effect at the galvanometer, and there was also a similar slight effect when the contact with the battery was broken. But whilst the voltaic current was continuing to pass through the one helix, no galvanometrical appearances nor any effect like induction upon the other helix could be perceived, although the active power of the battery was proved to be great, by its heating the whole of its own helix, and by the brilliancy of the discharge when made through charcoal.

11. Repetition of the experiments with a battery of one hundred and twenty pairs of plates produced no other effects; but it was ascertained, both at this and the former time, that the slight deflection of the needle occurring at the moment of completing the connexion, was always in one direction, and that the equally slight deflection produced when the contact was broken, was in the other direction; and also, that these effects occurred when the first helices were used (6, 8).

12. The results which I had by this time obtained with magnets led me to believe that the battery current through one wire, did, in reality, induce a similar current through the other wire, but that it continued for an instant only, and partook more of the nature of the electrical wave passed through from the shock of a common Leyden jar than of the current from a voltaic battery, and therefore might magnetise a steel needle, although it scarcely affected the galvanometer.

13. This expectation was confirmed; for on substituting a small hollow helix, formed round a glass tube, for the galvanometer, introducing a steel needle, making contact as before between the battery and the inducing wire (7, 10), and then removing the needle before the battery contact was broken, it was found magnetised.

14. When the battery contact was first made, then an unmagnetised needle introduced into the small indicating helix (13), and lastly the battery contact broken, the needle was found magnetised to an equal degree apparently as before; but the poles were of the contrary kind.

15. The same effects took place on using the large compound helices first described (6, 8).

16. When the unmagnetised needle was put into the indicating helix, before contact of the inducing wire with the battery, and remained there until the contact was broken, it exhibited little or no magnetism; the first effect having been nearly neutralised by the second (13, 14). The force of the induced current upon making contact was found always to exceed that of the induced current at breaking of contact; and if therefore the contact was made and broken many times in succession, whilst the needle remained in the indicating helix, it at last came out not unmagnetised, but a needle magnetised as if

the induced current upon making contact had acted alone on it. This effect may be due to the accumulation (as it is called) at the poles of the unconnected pile, rendering the current upon first making contact more powerful than what it is afterwards, at the moment of breaking contact.

17. If the circuit between the helix or wire under induction and the galvanometer or indicating spiral was not rendered complete *before* the connexion between the battery and the inducing wire was completed or broken, then no effects were perceived at the galvanometer. Thus, if the battery communications were first made, and then the wire under induction connected with the indicating helix, no magnetising power was there exhibited. But still retaining the latter communications, when those with the battery were broken, a magnet was formed in the helix, but of the second kind (14), i.e., with poles indicating a current in the same direction to that belonging to the battery current, or to that always induced by that current at its cessation.

18. In the preceding experiments the wires were placed near to each other, and the contact of the inducing one with the battery made when the inductive effect was required; but as the particular action might be supposed to be exerted only at the moments of making and breaking contact, the induction was produced in another way. Several feet of copper wire were stretched in wide zigzag forms, representing the letter W, on one surface of a broad board; a second wire was stretched in precisely similar forms on a second board, so that when brought near the first, the wires should everywhere touch, except that a sheet of thick paper was interposed. One of these wires was connected with the galvanometer, and the other with a voltaic battery. The first wire was then moved towards the second, and as it approached, the needle was deflected. Being then removed, the needle was deflected in the opposite direction. By first making the wires approach and then recede, simultaneously with the vibrations of the needle, the latter soon became very extensive; but when the wires ceased to move from or towards each other, the galvanometer-needle soon came to its usual position.

19. As the wires approximated, the induced current was in the *contrary* direction to the inducing current. As the wires receded, the induced current was in the *same* direction as the inducing current. When the wires remained stationary, there was no induced current (54).

20. When a small voltaic arrangement was introduced into the circuit between the galvanometer (10) and its helix or wire, so as to cause a permanent deflection of 30° or 40°, and then the battery of one hundred pairs of plates connected with the inducing wire, there was an instantaneous action as before (11); but the galvanometer-needle immediately

resumed and retained its place unaltered, notwithstanding the continued contact of the inducing wire with the trough: such was the case in whichever way the contacts were made (33).

21. Hence it would appear that collateral currents, either in the same or in opposite directions, exert no permanent inducing power on each other, affecting their quantity or tension.

22. I could obtain no evidence by the tongue, by spark, or by heating fine wire or charcoal, of the electricity passing through the wire under induction; neither could I obtain any chemical effects, though the contacts with metallic and other solutions were made and broken alternately with those of the battery, so that the second effect of induction should not oppose or neutralise the first (13, 16).

23. This deficiency of effect is not because the induced current of electricity cannot pass fluids, but probably because of its brief duration and feeble intensity; for on introducing two large copper plates into the circuit on the induced side (20), the plates being immersed in brine, but prevented from touching each other by an interposed cloth, the effect at the indicating galvanometer, or helix, occurred as before. The induced electricity could also pass through a voltaic trough (20). When, however, the quantity of interposed fluid was reduced to a drop, the galvanometer gave no indication.

24. Attempts to obtain similar effects by the use of wires conveying ordinary electricity were doubtful in the results. A compound helix similar to that already described, containing eight elementary helices (6), was used. Four of the helices had their similar ends bound together by wire, and the two general terminations thus produced connected with the small magnetising helix containing an unmagnetised needle (13). The other four helices were similarly arranged, but their ends connected with a Leyden jar. On passing the discharge, the needle was found to be a magnet; but it appeared probable that a part of the electricity of the jar had passed off to the small helix, and so magnetised the needle. There was indeed no reason to expect that the electricity of a jar possessing as it does great tension, would not diffuse itself through all the metallic matter interposed between the coatings.

25. Still it does not follow that the discharge of ordinary electricity through a wire does not produce analogous phenomena to those arising from voltaic electricity; but as it appears impossible to separate the effects produced at the moment when the discharge begins to pass, from the equal and contrary effects produced when it ceases to pass (16), inasmuch as with ordinary electricity these periods are simultaneous, so there can be scarcely any hope that in this form of the experiment they can be perceived.

26. Hence it is evident that currents of voltaic

electricity present phenomena of induction somewhat analogous to those produced by electricity of tension, although, as will be seen hereafter, many differences exist between them. The result is the production of other currents, (but which are only momentary), parallel, or tending to parallelism, with the inducing current. By reference to the poles of the needle formed in the indicating helix (13, 14) and to the deflections of the galvanometer-needle (11), it was found in all cases that the induced current, produced by the first action of the inducing current, was in the contrary direction to the latter, but that the current produced by the cessation of the inducing current was in the same direction (19). For the purpose of avoiding periphrasis, I propose to call this action of the current from the voltaic battery, *volta-electric induction*. The properties of the second wire, after induction has developed the first current, and whilst the electricity from the battery continues to flow through its inducing neighbour (10, 18), constitute a peculiar electric condition, the consideration of which will be resumed hereafter. All these results have been obtained with a voltaic apparatus consisting of a single pair of plates.

On the Evolution of Electricity from Magnetism

27. A welded ring was made of soft round bar-iron, the metal being seven-eights of an inch in thickness, and the ring six inches in external diameter. Three helices were put round one part of this ring, each containing about twenty-four feet of copper wire one-twentieth of an inch thick; they were insulated from the iron and each other, and superposed in the manner before described (6), occupying about nine inches in length upon the ring. They could be

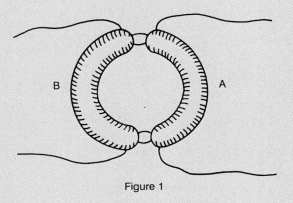

Figure 1

used separately or conjointly; the group may be distinguished by the letter A (Figure 1). On the other part of the ring about sixty feet of similar copper wire in two pieces were applied in the same manner, forming a helix B, which had the same common direction with the helices of A, but being separated from it at each extremity by about half an inch of the uncovered iron.

28. The helix B was connected by copper wires with a galvanometer three feet from the ring. The helices of A were connected end to end so as to form one common helix, the extremities of which were connected with a battery of ten pairs of plates four inches square. The galvanometer was immediately affected, and to a degree far beyond what has been described when with a battery of tenfold power helices *without iron* were used (10); but though the contact was continued, the effect was not permanent, for the needle soon came to rest in its natural position, as if quite indifferent to the attached electromagnetic arrangement. Upon breaking the contact with the battery, the needle was again powerfully deflected, but in the contrary direction to that induced in the first instance.

29. Upon arranging the apparatus so that B should be out of use, the galvanometer be connected with one of the three wires of A (27), and the other two made into a helix through which the current from the trough (28) was passed, similar but rather more powerful effects were produced.

30. When the battery contact was made in one direction, the galvanometer-needle was deflected on the one side; if made in the other direction, the deflection was on the other side. The deflection on breaking the battery contact was always the reverse of that produced by completing it. The deflection on making a battery contact always indicated an induced current in the opposite direction to that from the battery; but on breaking the contact the deflection indicated an induced current in the same direction as that of the battery. No making or breaking of the contact at B side, or in any part of the galvanometer circuit, produced any effect at the galvanometer. No continuance of the battery current caused any deflection of the galvanometer-needle. As the above results are common to all these experiments, and to similar one with ordinary magnets to be hereafter detailed, they need not be again particularly described.

31. Upon using the power of one hundred pairs of plates (10) with this ring, the impulse at the galvanometer, when contact was completed or broken, was so great as to make the needle spin round rapidly four or five times, before the air and terrestrial magnetism could reduce its motion to mere oscillation.

32. By using charcoal at the ends of the B helix, a minute *spark* could be perceived when the contact of the battery with A was completed. This spark

could not be due to any diversion of a part of the current of the battery through the iron to the helix B; for when the battery contact was continued, the galvanometer still resumed its perfectly indifferent state (28). The spark was rarely seen on breaking contact. A small platina[1] wire could not be ignited by this induced current; but there seems every reason to believe that the effect would be obtained by using a stronger original current or a more powerful arrangement of helices.

33. A feeble voltaic current was sent through the helix B and the galvanometer, so as to deflect the needle of the latter 30° or 40°, and then the battery of one hundred pairs of plates connected with A; but after the first effect was over, the galvanometer-

35. When the iron cylinder was replaced by an equal cylinder of copper, no effect beyond that of the helices alone was produced. The iron cylinder arrangement was not so powerful as the ring arrangement already described (27).

36. Similar effects were then produced by *ordinary magnets:* thus the hollow helix just described (34) had all its elementary helices connected with the galvanometer by two copper wires, each five feet in length; the soft iron cylinder was introduced into its axis; a couple of bar magnets, each twenty-four inches long, were arranged with their opposite poles at one end in contact, so as to resemble a horseshoe magnet, and then contact made between the other poles and the ends of the iron cylinder, so

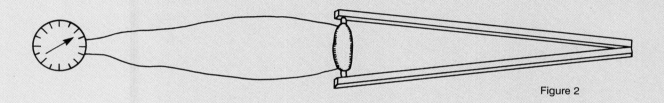

Figure 2

needle resumed exactly the position due to the feeble current transmitted by its own wire. This took place in whichever way the battery contacts were made, and shows that here again (20) no permanent influence of the currents upon each other, as to their quantity and tension, exists.

34. Another arrangement was then employed connecting the former experiments on volta-electric induction (6–26) with the present. A combination of helices like that already described (6) was constructed upon a hollow cylinder of pasteboard: there were eight lengths of copper wire, containing altogether 220 feet; four of these helices were connected end to end, and then with the galvanometer (7); the other intervening four were also connected end to end, and the battery of one hundred pairs discharged through them. In this form the effect on the galvanometer was hardly sensible (11), though magnets could be made by the induced current (13). But when a soft iron cylinder seven-eighths of an inch thick, and twelve inches long, was introduced into the pasteboard tube, surrounded by the helices, then the induced current affected the galvanometer powerfully and with all the phenomena just described (30). It possessed also the power of making magnets with more energy, apparently, than when no iron cylinder was present.

as to convert it for the time into a magnet (Figure 2): by breaking the magnetic contacts, or reversing them, the magnetism of the iron cylinder could be destroyed or reversed at pleasure.

37. Upon making magnetic contact, the needle was deflected; continuing the contact, the needle

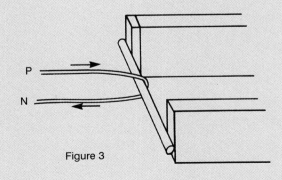

Figure 3

became indifferent, and resumed its first position; on breaking the contact, it was again deflected, but in the opposite direction to the first effect, and then it again became indifferent. When the magnetic contacts were reversed the deflections were reversed.

38. When the magnetic contact was made, the deflection was such as to indicate an induced current of electricity in the opposite direction to that fitted to form a magnet, having the same polarity as that really produced by contact with the bar magnets. Thus when the marked and unmarked poles were placed as in Figure 3, the current in the helix was in the direction represented, P being supposed to be the end of the wire going to the positive pole of the battery, or that end towards which the zinc plates face, and N the negative wire. Such a current would have converted the cylinder into a magnet of the opposite kind to that formed by contact with the poles A and B; and such a current moves in the opposite direction to the currents which in M. Ampère's beautiful theory are considered as constituting a magnet in the position figured.[2]

39. But as it might be supposed that in all the preceding experiments of this section, it was by some peculiar effect taking place during the formation of the magnet, and not by its mere virtual approximation, that the momentary induced current was excited, the following experiment was made. All the similar ends of the compound hollow helix (34) were bound together by copper wire, forming two general terminations, and these were connected with the galvanometer. The soft iron cylinder (34) was removed, and a cylindrical magnet, three-quarters of an inch in diameter and eight inches and a half in length, used instead. One end of this magnet was introduced into the axis of the helix (Figure 4), and then, the galvanometer-needle being stationary, the magnet was suddenly thrust in; immediately the needle was deflected in the same direction as if the

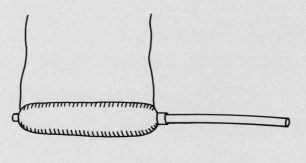

Figure 4

magnet had been formed by either of the two preceding processes (34, 36). Being left in, the needle resumed its first position, and then the magnet being withdrawn the needle was deflected in the opposite direction. These effects were not great; but by introducing and withdrawing the magnet, so that the impulse each time should be added to those previously communicated to the needle, the latter could be made to vibrate through an arc of 180° or more.

40. In this experiment the magnet must not be passed entirely through the helix, for then a second action occurs. When the magnet is introduced, the needle at the galvanometer is deflected in a certain direction; but being in, whether it be pushed quite through or withdrawn, the needle is deflected in a direction the reverse of that previously produced. When the magnet is passed in and through at one continuous motion, the needle moves one way, is then suddenly stopped, and finally moves the other way.

41. If such a hollow helix as that described (34) be laid east and west (or in any other constant position), and a magnet be retained east and west, its marked pole always being one way; then whichever end of the helix the magnet goes in at, and consequently whichever pole of the magnet enters first, still the needle is deflected the same way: on the other hand, whichever direction is followed in withdrawing the magnet, the deflection is constant, but contrary to that due to its entrance.

42. These effects are simple consequences of the *law* hereafter to be described.

43. When the eight elementary helices were made one long helix, the effect was not so great as in the arrangement described. When only one of the eight helices was used, the effect was also much diminished. All care was taken to guard against any direct action of the inducing magnet upon the galvanometer, and it was found that by moving the magnet in the same direction, and to the same degree on the outside of the helix, no effect on the needle was produced.

44. The Royal Society are in possession of a large compound magnet formerly belonging to Dr. Gowin Knight, which, by permission of the President and Council, I was allowed to use in the prosecution of these experiments: it is at present in the charge of Mr. Christie, at his house at Woolwich, where, by Mr. Christie's kindness, I was at liberty to work; and I have to acknowledge my obligations to him for his assistance in all the experiments and observations made with it. This magnet is composed of about 450 bar magnets, each fifteen inches long, one inch wide, and half an inch thick, arranged in a box so as to present at one of its extremities two external poles (Figure 5). These poles projected horizontally six inches from the box, were each twelve inches

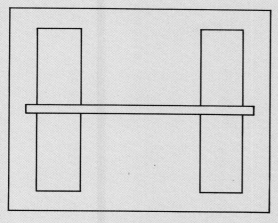

Figure 5

high and three inches wide. They were nine inches apart; and when a soft iron cylinder, three-quarters of an inch in diameter and twelve inches long, was put across from one to the other, it required a force of nearly one hundred pounds to break the contact. The pole to the left in the figure is the marked pole.[3]

45. The indicating galvanometer, in all experiments made with this magnet, was about eight feet from it, not directly in front of the poles, but about 16° or 17° on one side. It was found that on making or breaking the connexion of the poles by soft iron, the instrument was slightly affected; but all error of observation arising from this cause was easily and carefully avoided.

46. The electrical effects exhibited by this magnet were very striking. When a soft iron cylinder thirteen inches long was put through the compound hollow helix, with its ends arranged as two general terminations (39), these connected with the galvanometer, and the iron cylinder brought in contact with the two poles of the magnet (Figure 5), so powerful a rush of electricity took place that the needle whirled round many times in succession.[4]

47. Notwithstanding this great power, if the contact was continued, the needle resumed its natural position, being entirely uninfluenced by the position of the helix (30). But on breaking the magnetic contact, the needle was whirled round in the opposite direction with a force equal to the former.

48. A piece of copper plate wrapped *once* round the iron cylinder like a socket, but with interposed paper to prevent contact, had its edges connected with the wires of the galvanometer. When the iron was brought in contact with the poles the galvanometer was strongly affected.

49. Dismissing the helices and sockets, the galvanometer wire was passed over, and consequently only half round the iron cylinder (Figure 6); but even then a strong effect upon the needle was exhibited, when the magnetic contact was made or broken.

50. As the helix with its iron cylinder was brought towards the magnetic poles, but *without making contact*, still powerful effects were produced. When the helix, without the iron cylinder, and consequently containing no metal but copper, was approached to, or placed between the poles (44), the needle was thrown 80°, 90°, or more, from its natural position. The inductive force was of course greater, the nearer the helix, either with or without its iron cylinder, was brought to the poles; but otherwise the same effects were produced, whether the helix, &c. was or was not brought into contact with the magnet, i.e., no permanent effect on the galvanometer was produced; and the effects of approximation and removal were the reverse of each other (30).

51. When a bolt of copper corresponding to the iron cylinder was introduced, no greater effect was produced by the helix than without it. But when a thick iron wire was substituted, the magneto-electric induction was rendered sensibly greater.

52. The direction of the electric current produced in all these experiments with the helix, was the same as that already described (38) as obtained with the weaker bar magnets.

53. A spiral containing fourteen feet of copper wire, being connected with the galvanometer, and approximated directly towards the marked pole in the line of its axis, affected the instrument strongly; the current induced in it was in the reverse direction to the current theoretically considered by M. Ampère as existing in the magnet (38), or as the current in

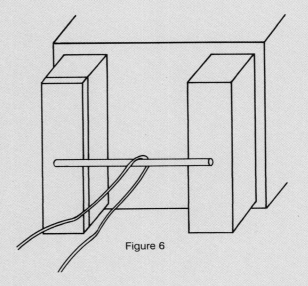

Figure 6

an electro-magnet of similar polarity. As the spiral was withdrawn, the induced current was reversed.

54. A similar spiral had the current of eighty pairs of 4-inch plates sent through it so as to form an electro-magnet, and then the other spiral connected with the galvanometer (53) approximated to it; the needle vibrated, indicating a current in the galvanometer spiral the reverse of that in the battery spiral (18, 26). On withdrawing the latter spiral, the needle passed in the opposite direction.

55. Single wires, approximated in certain directions towards the magnetic pole, had currents induced in them. On their removal, the currents were inverted. In such experiments the wires should not be removed in directions different to those in which they were approximated; for then occasionally complicated and irregular effects are produced, the causes of which will be very evident in the fourth part of this paper.

56. All attempts to obtain chemical effects by the induced current of electricity failed, though the precautions before described (22), and all others that could be thought of, were employed. Neither was any sensation on the tongue, or any convulsive effect upon the limbs of a frog, produced. Nor could charcoal or fine wire be ignited. But upon repeating the experiments more at leisure at the Royal Institution, with an armed loadstone belonging to Professor Daniell and capable of lifting about thirty pounds, a frog was very *powerfully convulsed* each time magnetic contact was made. At first the convulsions could not be obtained on breaking magnetic contact; but conceiving the deficiency of effect was because of the comparative slowness of separation, the latter act was effected by a blow, and then the frog was convulsed strongly. The more instantaneous the union or disunion is effected, the more powerful the convulsion. I thought also I could perceive the *sensation* upon the tongue and the *flash* before the eyes; but I could obtain no evidence of chemical decomposition.

57. The various experiments of this section prove, I think, most completely the production of electricity from ordinary magnetism. That its intensity should be very feeble and quantity small, cannot be considered wonderful, when it is remembered that like thermo-electricity it is evolved entirely within the substance of metals retaining all their conducting power. But an agent which is conducted along metallic wires in the manner described; which whilst so passing possesses the peculiar magnetic actions and force of a current of electricity; which can agitate and convulse the limbs of a frog; and which, finally, can produce a spark by its discharge through charcoal (32), can only be electricity. As all the effects can be produced by ferruginous electro-magnets (34), there is no doubt that arrangements like the magnets of Pro-

fessors Moll, Henry, Ten Eyke, and others, in which as many as two thousand pounds have been lifted, may be used for these experiments; in which case not only a brighter spark may be obtained, but wires also ignited, and, as the current can pass liquids (23), chemical action be produced. These effects are still more likely to be obtained when the magneto-electric arrangements to be explained in the fourth section are excited by the powers of such apparatus.

58. The similarity of action, almost amounting to identity, between common magnets and either electro-magnets or volta-electric currents, is strikingly in accordance with and confirmatory of M. Ampère's theory, and furnishes powerful reasons for believing that the action is the same in both cases; but, as a distinction in language is still necessary, I propose to call the agency thus exerted by ordinary magnets, *magneto-electric* or *magnelectric* induction (26).

59. The only difference which powerfully strikes the attention as existing between volta-electric and magneto-electric induction, is the suddenness of the former, and the sensible time required by the latter; but even in this early state of investigation there are circumstances which seem to indicate that upon further inquiry this difference will, as a philosophical distinction, disappear.

---

[1]*Platina:* early form for *platinum,* used often in this work.

[2]The relative position of an electric current and a magnet is by most persons found very difficult to remember, and three or four helps to the memory have been devised by M. Ampère and others. I venture to suggest the following as a very simple and effectual assistance in these and similar latitudes. Let the experimenter think he is looking down upon a dipping-needle, or upon the pole of the earth, and then let him think upon the direction of the motion of the hands of a watch, or of a screw moving direct; currents in that direction round a needle would make it into such a magnet as the dipping-needle, or would themselves constitute an electro-magnet of similar qualities; or if brought near a magnet would tend to make it take that direction; or would themselves be moved into that position by a magnet so placed; or in M. Ampère's theory are considered as moving in that direction in the magnet. These two points of the position of the dipping-needle and the motion of the watch hands being remembered, any other relation of the current and magnet can be at once deduced from it.

[3]To avoid any confusion as to the poles of the magnet, I shall designate the pole pointing to the north as the marked pole; I may occasionally speak of the north, and south ends of the needle, but do not mean thereby north and south poles. That is by many considered the true north pole of a needle which points to the south; but in this country it is often called the south pole.

[4]A soft iron bar in the form of a lifter to a horseshoe magnet, when applied with a coil of this kind round the middle of it, becomes, by juxtaposition with a magnet, a ready source of a brief but determinate current of electricity.

Institutions

of

Science

THE CENTERS

FOR DISEASE CONTROL

By Horace G. Ogden

Founded during World War II as a small unit to protect
military bases against malaria, the Centers for Disease Control has grown into
the chief institution in the United States dedicated to the prevention
of disease and the promotion of better health.

The duty officer at the Centers for Disease Control (CDC) in Atlanta, Georgia, picks up his telephone late one evening. A health official from a Middle Western state has a disease outbreak on his hands that has some puzzling aspects. Can the CDC help?

The CDC can, and does. By the following day two CDC epidemiologists are on the scene, working with state and local personnel to assess the nature of the outbreak, identify its source, and keep it from spreading. Responding to such "fire calls" is standard operating procedure for what is often called the world's premier public health agency. Legionnaire's disease, toxic shock syndrome, and many less visible but similarly crucial threats to health have been addressed and ultimately controlled through a partnership of federal, state, and local public health workers augmented by many other individuals and organizations in the private sector.

Deployment of "disease detectives" to fight epidemics is probably the most glamorous of the CDC's functions. It represents, however, only a small part of its program as the principal federal agency engaged in disease prevention. Its activities range across a broad spectrum of preventive services: immunization against the deadly diseases of childhood; control of sexually transmitted diseases, including AIDS; reduction of environmental health hazards and the toll of injuries; chronic disease control and health promotion through programs on smoking cessation, exercise, nutrition, cancer, and diabetes control; reduction of hazards in the workplace; upgrading of the nation's public health laboratories; conduct and support of training programs for public health workers; and many more. Since health and disease do not recognize boundary lines, the CDC also has a large and growing international involvement.

History and evolution

The CDC is headquartered in Atlanta and is the only major component of the U.S. Public Health Service based outside the Washington, D.C., metropolitan area. Its location can be traced back to its origin as a small unit established during World War II with the highly specialized mission of protecting military bases in the southeastern region of the country against the potential danger of malaria epidemics.

At the war's end this Malaria Control in War Areas (MCWA) unit, instead of being disbanded, was assigned a broader national mission and renamed the Communicable Disease Center. The newly formed agency, also known as the CDC, was envisioned by a farsighted assistant surgeon general of the U.S. Public Health Service named Joseph Mountin as a "center of expertise," a national resource of specialized knowledge and skills. Its mission was to assist the states, which bore and still bear the primary responsibility for public health, in dealing with communicable disease problems. It would make available nationally the kind of specialized resources no single state could appropriately afford on its own.

Over the years the forms of such assistance have diversified. The Epidemic Intelligence Service (EIS) was formed in 1951 to meet a need for physicians and other health professionals skilled in the rapidly developing

HORACE G. OGDEN, former director of the Bureau of Health Education at the Centers for Disease Control, now retired, is a consultant in the field of public health.

(Opposite) Photograph by David Dobbs, STV/Sanders & Thomas

459

The Malaria Control in War Areas unit in Atlanta, Georgia, seen above in 1945, was the first component of the Centers for Disease Control.

The CDC played a leading role in the 1960s in eradicating smallpox in Guinea (below) and Nigeria (right).

discipline of epidemiology. Graduates of the EIS course have become an elite corps of public health workers, many of whom have developed their own programs as state epidemiologists, while others have assumed leadership positions in a variety of local, national, and international public health activities. Other CDC personnel worked with their state and local counterparts in carrying out such programs as venereal disease control and childhood immunization. Short- and long-term training programs, conducted at the CDC or in the field, helped provide the skilled personnel to upgrade the performance of public health laboratories.

In the 1960s CDC-based EIS officers and public health administrators played a leading role in one of humankind's greatest accomplishments, the worldwide eradication of smallpox. First in 20 countries of West Africa, where CDC teams and their national counterparts achieved eradication in less than three years, and later in India, Bangladesh, and other strongholds of infection, the ancient killer was tracked to its local sources and encircled by rings of immunization, a strategy developed and refined by CDC epidemiologists. The world's last naturally occurring case of smallpox was identified in Somalia in 1977.

Meanwhile, the CDC's domestic responsibilities were broadening far beyond the field of infectious diseases. Between 1970 and 1975 programs in nutrition, smoking and health, public health education, occupational health and safety, and dental public health were either transferred to the CDC or newly created there.

Thus, by the late 1970s the CDC had indeed become the most important government agency for dealing with disease prevention. While retaining its primacy in the infectious disease field, it acquired significant responsibilities concerning problems of the work site and community environment and other factors relevant not only to the prevention of disease but to the improvement of the quality of life.

Physical plant

Headquarters for today's Centers for Disease Control, the name that the agency acquired in 1980, is located on Clifton Road near Atlanta, adjacent to the campus of Emory University. It is built on land deeded to the federal government by Emory's trustees for this specific purpose.

The Clifton Road complex of offices and laboratories houses about 2,000 of the 3,200 CDC employees in the Atlanta area. The others work in seven locations in the city and its suburbs. In addition, another 2,000 CDC employees are located outside Atlanta—in specialized regional laboratories, on assignment to state and local health departments, on special projects outside the U.S., and in the Washington, D.C., area.

Clifton Road first opened its doors in 1960 as a modest set of offices, laboratories, and training facilities. It has expanded and diversified with the growth of the CDC mission. The latest and most spectacular addition, dedicated on Oct. 28, 1988, is a $23 million laboratory facility for the study of viral and rickettsial diseases. This new facility is in many ways unique. Two laboratories are equipped with state-of-the-art technology to provide maximum feasible safety for the study of a number of deadly viruses, including the Marburg, Ebola, Lassa fever, Junin, Machupo, and Congo-Crimean hemorrhagic fever. Each of these organisms, which occur mostly in tropical regions, is known to cause hemorrhagic fever and carries a high fatality rate. Other labs in the new facility deal with disease problems more familiar in the U.S.: viruses that cause AIDS and rabies; retroviruses linked to cancer causation; and rickettsiae that cause typhus and Rocky Mountain spotted fever.

In 1989 the American Cancer Society relocated its national headquarters in a new building directly across Clifton Road from the CDC. With these two national agencies, one private and one governmental, plus the rapid growth of the Emory Medical School and its newly created School

Trucks were used to help inform people about smallpox in Bangladesh in the 1970s (above and above left). The truck at the left is being repainted to increase the reward from 50 to 250 daccas for the first notification of a smallpox case.

461

Photos, David Dobbs, STV/Sanders & Thomas

(Right) A new CDC laboratory for the study of viral and rickettsial diseases was opened near Atlanta in 1988. (Below) Two CDC scientists work in the laboratory to "fingerprint" an unknown virus.

of Public Health, the case can be made convincingly that the northeastern Atlanta metropolitan area is the national focus for disease prevention and public health.

Structure and placement

The Centers for Disease Control, its current official title, is the third name to use the CDC initials—first the Communicable Disease Center, then the Center (singular) for Disease Control, and now the Centers. Each of these changes reflected changes in its scope and mission.

The CDC is one of the seven operating agencies that make up the U.S. Public Health Service (PHS), which in turn is an arm of the U.S. Department of Health and Human Services. Agencies parallel to the CDC on the organization chart include, among others, the National Institutes of Health (NIH), the Food and Drug Administration (FDA), and the Alcohol, Drug Abuse, and Mental Health Administration (ADAMHA). Within the PHS family the CDC's special province is disease prevention and the promotion of better health.

Internally the CDC consists of six major centers with self-explanatory titles: the Center for Chronic Disease Prevention and Health Promotion; the Center for Environmental Health and Injury Control; the Center for Infectious Diseases; the Center for Prevention Services; the National Center for Health Statistics; and the National Institute for Occupational Safety and Health. Major program offices are maintained for epidemiology, international health, and training and laboratory programs.

The 1980s: a decade of challenge

To understand the CDC's programs in the early 1990s, it is necessary to look back briefly at the decade just past. In 1979 a process was initiated to chart the future of public health in the United States. The first stage culminated with the publication and widespread dissemination of

462

the surgeon general's report on health and disease prevention. Its title, *Healthy People*, had dual significance. It proclaimed that people in the U.S. as a whole were enjoying longer lives and better health than ever before. It also sounded a challenge that much remained to be done.

As a next step a group of highly qualified experts in public health, medicine, and many related fields moved the process of setting objectives a critical distance forward. Using *Healthy People* as a guide, they developed, debated, and refined a set of more than 200 objectives for the nation. The target date for each objective, with a few exceptions, was 1990. Each was highly specific and quantified. Each was based on the best available data and predicated on what appeared to be reasonable assumptions of available resources.

The book that resulted from this process was published in 1980 under the title *Promoting Health/Preventing Disease: Objectives for the Nation.* It provided the field of public health with a yardstick against which to measure progress. More precisely, it offered a set of 226 separate yardsticks so that progress could be compared and priorities adjusted along the many lines of endeavor involved in improving the health of the people.

As the 1980s got under way, therefore, public health in the U.S. had, for the first time, a clear charter and an imposing list of expected accomplishments. However, the challenge foreseen for the decade, already formidable enough, was soon to take on a totally unforeseen added dimension of surpassing urgency, for not one of the 226 carefully selected and quantified targets dealt with what was to become the decade's greatest public health challenge. This remarkable fact was caused by a circumstance unique in the annals of public health: the sudden appearance of a swiftly spreading and highly fatal epidemic disease hitherto absolutely unknown.

The disease came to be known as AIDS (acquired immune deficiency syndrome). Its cause has been identified as a virus designated as the human immunodeficiency virus (HIV).

The onslaught of AIDS

The AIDS epidemic was first recognized in the spring of 1981, when the CDC received and published in its *Morbidity and Mortality Weekly Report* (MMWR) reports of Los Angeles physicians that five previously healthy homosexual men had been diagnosed with *Pneumocystis carinii,* a highly unusual form of pneumonia. Within a few weeks 26 cases of Kaposi's sarcoma, a rare cancer, were reported in homosexual men in New York and California.

Alerted by these occurrences of the unusual and statistically improbable, the CDC in June 1981 organized an investigative task force. The same diseases were soon identified among intravenous (IV) drug users in 1981 and among hemophilia patients and recipients of blood transfusions in early 1982.

The AIDS-HIV story presents a dramatic example of the importance and value of epidemiology in public health practice. Within the first 18 months after the disease's first reported appearance and a full year before

463

More than 100 million copies of Understanding AIDS, a brochure containing the basic facts about the lethal disease, were distributed by the CDC throughout the United States. This campaign marked the first time that the CDC was given a mandate to speak directly to the American people.

its viral cause was positively identified, epidemiological studies had led to public health actions that clearly reduced the spread of the disease. Prevention guidelines and recommendations published by the CDC in March 1983 remain valid today. At a time when the U.S. was reporting only a few cases each day, the epidemiology of AIDS was so well understood that the principal risk groups had been accurately identified and high-risk behaviors defined; a virus was believed to be the likely agent; routes of transmission were delineated; and it was known that there existed a large pool of persons without symptoms who were capable of transmitting the presumed virus.

Perhaps more important still, these conclusions at the early stage made it possible to recommend changes in behavior that would enable individuals to protect themselves and, as a result, could ultimately check the spread of the epidemic. These included the adoption of safer sex practices, restriction in the number of sexual contacts, refusal to share needles for intravenous drug use, and precautions in regard to the supply of donated blood including voluntary self-exclusion as donors by those at risk.

Measured against any yardstick of reasonable expectation, progress against AIDS in less than 10 years has been remarkable. Nevertheless, early in the decade of the 1990s, AIDS remains the greatest immediate challenge to public health. Although the rate of increase in numbers of reported cases has declined, it is clear that the epidemic will get much worse before it begins to get better. Even by the most optimistic estimates, a safe and effective vaccine is years away.

Behavior changes achieved through intensive educational efforts, especially in the male homosexual community, are already sparing many potential victims. However, heterosexual transmission continues to spread as more individuals become infected with the HIV virus. The risk of infection by blood transfusion has been minimized through tight controls on the blood supply, but transmission via illicit IV drug users continues virtually unabated.

The impact of AIDS on public health in the U.S. has been overwhelming. Its urgency has commanded an unprecedented commitment of resources. In terms of the CDC budget alone—by no means the only one affected—expenditures for AIDS-HIV prevention increased from $2 million in fiscal year 1982 to $382 million in fiscal 1989. As recently as fiscal 1986, AIDS accounted for about 12% of the CDC budget, as contrasted with 37% in fiscal 1989.

Most of these funds are "new" in the sense that they have not been specifically diverted from other CDC programs; in fact, the non-AIDS-related portion of the CDC's budget has increased at a modest rate during this period. Dollars do not tell the whole story, however. Public health resources in the U.S., and indeed in the world, are finite, not only in money but in expertise and infrastructure. For example, absorption of scientific talent by the AIDS crisis, though manifestly justified, has necessarily come at the expense of other important public health objectives toward which it would otherwise have been directed.

AIDS has thrust public health into the limelight to an extent never before approached. Health officials at all levels have, with occasional exceptions, worked in comparative obscurity on relatively noncontroversial tasks. Suddenly they have found themselves in an explosive atmosphere, dealing day by day with highly sensitive social, ethical, and political issues. Public attitudes toward the AIDS epidemic have swung violently back and forth from apathy to near hysteria. Each new scientific development has seemed to precipitate a new crisis. One highly placed federal health official has lamented that fielding questions about AIDS occupies all his working hours, so that "I have to do my regular job on nights and weekends."

Early in the course of the epidemic, then Surgeon General C. Everett Koop declared that education and information were the only weapons available to combat the disease. Acting on this recognition, the CDC has spearheaded extensive programs designed to reach the groups at highest risk. The message is also being directed to young people through a program of school health education at all grade levels, the largest such effort in history.

The messages are clear. AIDS is a major public health problem. As a sexually transmitted, blood-borne disease, it is preventable. Individuals can protect themselves in very specific ways. Achieving public approval and support of these educational programs has not been easy, nor has it been universally accomplished. Where good programs are under way, though, it is already evident that behaviors are changing, and only through behavior change can the AIDS epidemic be brought under control.

Health workers take to the streets to spread information about AIDS as part of a community-based program sponsored by the CDC.

Centers for Disease Control

A child receives oral vaccine against polio. One of the CDC's objectives for the year 2000 is to reduce to zero the number of cases of polio generated in the United States.

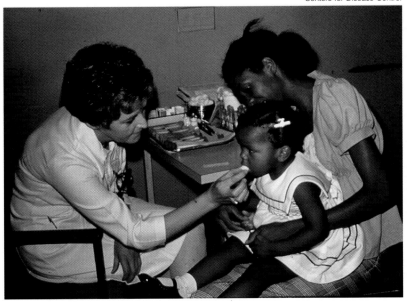

Accomplishments of the 1980s

The national preoccupation with the AIDS epidemic has tended to obscure important advances in the state of the nation's health achieved during the 1980s. The final tally for the decade has yet to be reckoned. It is evident, however, that in some areas the accomplishments have equaled or surpassed the expectations expressed in the 1990 objectives. In others there have been substantial shortfalls. In addition, there remain a number of objectives for which the available methods of data collection and analysis are not yet adequate to provide a reasonable assessment.

As early as 1984 the infant death rate had declined by 24% from its 1979 level, childhood mortality by 23%, adolescent and youth mortality by 13%, and mortality among adults by 16%. In fact, by mid-decade the objective for decline in child mortality had already been exceeded, and the mortality goals for the other three age groups were being approached.

When one turns to specific objectives, it is evident that striking discrepancies exist. Childhood immunization represents one of the success stories of the 1980s. In 1987, 98% of U.S. children starting school were vaccinated against measles, rubella (German measles), and mumps; 97% were vaccinated against diphtheria, pertussis (whooping cough), tetanus, and polio. All of these percentages surpassed the original 1990 objective of 95%.

Moreover, these advances in immunization were paying off. In 1988 no cases of diphtheria and only two cases of tetanus were reported in children under 15 years of age. Record low numbers of rubella were reported. No measles were reported in 94% of the nation's counties in 1988.

However, there is a less encouraging side to the immunization story. Vaccination levels for younger children, under two years of age, remain below the 1990 objective of 90% for all the immunizable diseases of

466

childhood. The national levels in this age group, which range from 75 to 85% among the seven diseases, mask pockets of population where immunization coverage is 60% or even lower.

In the chronic disease field, encouraging progress was made throughout the 1980s in the reduction of cigarette smoking, almost universally recognized as the greatest single cause of preventable premature death in the U.S. The 1990 objective related to the prevalence of smoking among adults 18 years of age and older had appeared extremely optimistic. It called for a reduction from 33.5% in 1979 to 25% by 1990. By 1985 the proportion had already reached 30.5%. The decline was especially rapid among males; in the 20 years between 1965 and 1985 the percentage of adult males who smoked declined from 52 to 33%, a remarkable accomplishment achieved despite the billions of dollars the tobacco industry spent to promote the product. Other accomplishments of the 1980s included the reduction of the motor vehicle fatality rate from 24 to 19 per 100,000 people; reduction of the number of workplace accident deaths and work-related disabling injuries; and lowering of the amount of lead burden in the environment to about one-third the level of the 1970s, thereby protecting millions of children against the physical and mental consequences of heavy lead exposure.

Targets for the 1990s

Building on the objective-setting process of the previous decade, the CDC and the Public Health Service, along with hundreds of other health organizations, began in 1987 to formulate goals and objectives for the year 2000. Released in September 1990, the year 2000 objectives comprise nearly 300 measurable goals grouped in 22 priority areas. The CDC has been assigned the major responsibility in 12 of the 22 priority categories. The following are a few of the high-priority activities currently under way and projected for major emphasis.

1. *AIDS-HIV infection.* By the year 2000 the rising incidence of AIDS should be reversed and stabilized at an annual incidence level of 98,000 new cases per year, the number currently predicted for 1993. Prevalence of HIV infection among women giving birth should be reduced to no more than one per 1,000. Among homosexual men aged 18 to 25 and among IV drug users, the prevalence should be no more than 10%.

To help in the achievement of these objectives, the CDC will continue and augment its nationwide surveillance programs of AIDS-HIV in partnership with state and local health authorities. It will continue its ongoing epidemiological studies to further identify risk factors and define with greater precision the modes of transmission of the infection. New diagnostic tests will be pursued and evaluated, and its Center for Infectious Diseases will continue research on an animal model for vaccine development.

In the continuing effort to encourage behavior change to reduce transmission of the disease, the CDC's National AIDS Information/Education Program will use a variety of media, giving special attention to reaching population groups at highest risk. The year 2000 objectives call for an

467

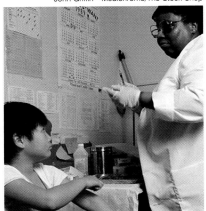

In 1990 a child in New York City is inoculated against measles. The CDC had hoped that measles would be eradicated in the United States by the early 1980s, but transmission of the disease among unvaccinated preschool children and the fact that the vaccine is not 100% effective prevented this goal from being met.

increase in the use of condoms to at least twice the present rate and urge that at least 95% of teenagers and adults be well informed abut HIV and its prevention. The CDC will continue to support the development and introduction of improved AIDS-HIV curricula in the nation's schools. It will also seek to ensure that at least 95% of health care workers receive appropriate training about HIV infection, high-risk behaviors, and control measures.

2. *Chronic disease prevention and health promotion.* The CDC, through its Office on Smoking and Health, expects to play a leading role in accelerating the downward trend in cigarette smoking. The specific target for the year 2000 is that smokers in that year number no more than 15% of adults aged 20 and above, compared with the 1987 rate of 29.1–31.7% for men and 26.8% for women. For this ambitious goal to be achieved, which would constitute a major step toward the "smokeless society" envisioned for the 21st century, special attention must be given to those population groups—notably blue-collar workers, blacks, and Hispanics—that in 1991 showed significantly higher smoking levels than the total population. Another vital target population is teenagers, whose initiation rate for smoking should be reduced to no more than 15%.

The CDC has proposed a major new disease-prevention initiative in the field of breast and cervical cancer. These diseases continue to cause pain, suffering, and premature death for thousands of women in the U.S. despite the fact that means are available to detect breast and cervical cancer in their early stages, when treatment is most effective and survival most likely. In 1990 alone an estimated 43,000 women in the U.S. will have died of breast cancer and 5,000 of cervical cancer. A large proportion of these deaths could have been prevented by the timely use of well-established screening techniques: mammography and the Pap smear.

Specifically, in a new program initiated in 1990, the CDC will support several state health agencies in the development of new or strengthened breast- and cervical-cancer-prevention programs. It will promote improved public and professional education on the importance of early detection and referral and will work to improve surveillance systems for breast and cervical cancer and quality assurance in screening programs. As with antismoking activities, major emphasis will be given to reaching minority groups.

3. *Immunization.* Three major thrusts are envisioned for immunization in the years immediately ahead. These are to address the unfinished business of protecting U.S. children against the immunizable diseases; to strengthen efforts to immunize adults, especially older people, against influenza and pneumonia, and better protect high-risk groups against hepatitis B, for which an effective vaccine now exists; and to provide technical support to worldwide child-immunization activities.

The year 2000 objectives call for the reduction to zero in the number of U.S.-generated cases of six diseases—diphtheria, tetanus, measles, polio, rubella, and congenital rubella syndrome. For most of these, success is almost at hand. However, for measles, a disease for which the complete interruption of domestic transmission had been confidently predicted in

468

An adult receives a shot to protect against influenza. A goal of the CDC is to strengthen the existing efforts to immunize adults against influenza and pneumonia.

the early 1980s, attainment of this goal represents a major challenge. More than 3,000 cases are still being reported each year. They stem in part from transmission among unvaccinated preschool children and in part because the vaccine is not 100% effective and the disease is extremely infectious. The first of these problems was being addressed by ensuring that measles immunizations are more readily accessible and their importance better known by the population groups least well served in the past. To deal with the second, a major change has been made in vaccine recommendations, calling for two doses instead of one.

Adult immunization has never been as well accepted as childhood immunization in the U.S., yet influenza and pneumonia remain a serious threat to the elderly and to many sufferers of chronic diseases. Effective vaccines exist for both, as well as for hepatitis B, which takes an unnecessary toll in certain risk groups, including newborn babies.

Internationally the World Health Assembly has adopted a resolution calling for the eradication of polio from the world by the year 2000. The CDC plans to continue to augment its technical support to the World Health Organization in pursuit of this ambitious goal and other child-immunization objectives, aimed at reducing the toll of 2.8 million needless deaths per year among children who could be saved by universal child immunization.

4. *Safety and health in the workplace.* The CDC's National Institute of Occupational Safety and Health (NIOSH) and the Occupational Safety and Health Administration (OSHA) of the U.S. Department of Labor have complementary responsibilities in protecting the nation's work force. OSHA is a regulatory agency; it is responsible for setting standards, inspecting for compliance, and punishing offenders. NIOSH is a scientific institute, conducting and supporting research in occupational health, recommending standards to OSHA, disseminating information generated by its studies, and training professionals in occupational safety and health.

469

U.S. DEPT. OF HEALTH AND HUMAN SERVICES
PUBLIC HEALTH SERVICE
CENTERS FOR DISEASE CONTROL
NATIONAL INSTITUTE FOR OCCUPATIONAL SAFETY AND HEALTH
DIVISION OF RESPIRATORY DISEASE STUDIES

Coal miners lined up in front of a trailer are taking part in a long-term CDC study of the incidence of pneumoconiosis, a lung disease caused by the habitual inhalation of irritant mineral or metallic particles, among U.S. coal workers.

Despite important progress in some areas, 8,000 workers die each year as a consequence of their employment, and hundreds of thousands are disabled by injury or occupational disease. Major subjects of concern in the immediate future are indoor air quality, the effects of various occupational exposures on reproduction, and work-related damage to the musculoskeletal system. NIOSH planned to continue its scientific assessment of risk, develop strategies for dealing with identified hazards, and build the national infrastructure for coping with occupational injury and disease.

5. *Environmental health and injury control.* Injuries, both intentional (homicides and suicides) and unintentional (motor vehicle collisions, falls, drownings, etc.), kill more Americans aged one to 44 years than do all diseases combined. The leading cause of death and disability of children and young adults, they cost the U.S. an estimated $75 billion–$100 billion a year. In 1990 one in every three Americans was injured—many with permanently disabling consequences. More than 140,000 Americans died from injuries.

The CDC is searching for the causes of injuries and doing research to improve their treatment and prevention. Currently under study are fall-related injuries among the elderly, alcohol-related injuries, family violence, youth suicides, and homicides and injuries among minorities.

The CDC supports research in many fields of injury control: acute care, biomechanics, epidemiology, rehabilitation, and prevention. Grants to study injury prevention and control have been given to academic institutions, professional associations, and state and local public health agencies. In addition, five Injury Prevention Research Centers at major universities across the U.S., supported by the CDC, conduct inter-disciplinary research, train graduate and undergraduate students and practitioners, and are in the process of developing a discrete academic discipline in injury control.

The CDC's environmental scientists are on call to assess the health damages of natural disasters, such as the Mt. St. Helen's volcanic eruption, and such problems as the Three Mile Island nuclear episode. Continuous surveillance of environmental health hazards and the development of laboratory technology to measure background levels of toxicity in people are among its other responsibilities. Measurements as sophisticated as parts per quadrillion have become possible, and significant, in assessing toxicity.

Toward the 21st century

The year 1990 can be seen as a landmark. Building on experiences of the previous decade, the CDC and other organizations have laid out a new charter for public health practice. If the knowledge and technology already at hand are correctly applied, nearly all the problems concerning health in the U.S. can be dramatically reduced and the duration and quality of life enhanced. The CDC—working with state and local health departments, its partner federal agencies, academic institutions, and a broad range of private organizations—will continue to help strengthen the public health system and to ensure that it effectively addresses the needs of the American people in preventing disease and promoting health.

Centers for Disease Control

Researchers from the CDC inspect the ash from a heap created by a municipal trash-burning facility in Pennsylvania. Such ash, when blown through the air, can pollute the atmosphere. Soon after the testing was completed, the facility was shut down.

Science's "Intellectual Hotel":
THE INSTITUTE FOR ADVANCED STUDY

by Naomi Pasachoff

It offers no courses, has no undergraduate or graduate
students, and carries a permanent faculty of fewer than
30. Yet the Institute for Advanced Study has remained a
powerfully influential center of research and scholarship
for more than half a century.

If you are driving from New York City or Washington, D.C., say, to see someone at the Institute for Advanced Study in Princeton, New Jersey, you would be wise to get exact directions in advance. Stopping for advice at a business in the area may not be of much help. You would probably do better asking a physicist in Tokyo or Tel Aviv than flagging down a pedestrian in Princeton.

Despite the fact that many locals have never heard of the place or, if they have, incorrectly assume that it is tucked away somewhere on the campus of Princeton University, the Institute for Advanced Study (IAS) has had an enormous influence on the development of science in the 60 years of its existence. Its small academic membership has encompassed some of the world's best known and most productive scientists, including winners of the Nobel Prize and other significant honors.

More than an institution of science

Although an institute publication defines its purpose as "the encouragement, support, and patronage of learning—of science, in the broad, undifferentiated sense of the word," the IAS is not, strictly speaking, exclusively an institution of science. Today's institute comprises four schools: Historical Studies, Mathematics, Natural Sciences, and Social Science. The oldest—the School of Mathematics, formally founded in 1933—originally subsumed not only mathematics but also physics. Thus, Albert Einstein, probably the best known physicist of all time and certainly the name most often associated with the IAS, was the first professor in its School of Mathematics.

Most of the article focuses on the School of Natural Sciences, which separated from the School of Mathematics only in 1966. Although scholars in each of the other three schools pursue research in many fields, many of which are unrelated to the natural sciences, one can nonetheless often detect an interest in science in the programs of those schools.

Today's School of Mathematics still reflects a strong interest in physics. For example, five people in the school in 1990–91 were engaged in "mathematical physics," and in 1991–92 the school planned to sponsor a program in the field of physics known as fluid dynamics. The Schools of Social Science and Historical Studies are likewise no strangers to the natural sciences. In the fall of 1990 a three-year program at the School of Social Science began an exploration of the history, sociology, and philosophy not only of the social sciences but of the natural sciences as well. The school routinely runs a yearlong seminar to which the work of about half of that year's members relates; in 1992–93 the seminar's focus was to be "science."

Bridging the Schools of Historical Studies and Natural Sciences for 40 years, from 1950 until his death in 1990 at the age of 91, was eminent science historian Otto E. Neugebauer, "member with long-term appointment" in both schools. Neugebauer's specialties included ancient mathematics, astronomy, and chronology, as well as Hindu and medieval astronomy. Income from an endowment fund set up in Neugebauer's name in 1977 continues to foster links between the natural and the

NAOMI PASACHOFF *is a Research Associate in the Department of Astronomy, Williams College, Williamstown, Massachusetts, and a coauthor of several science textbooks.*

(Overleaf) Illustration by Ron Villani

historical sciences; for example, by means of fellowships for individuals engaged in research in scientific biography or history.

Each of the institute's schools consists of a small permanent faculty. In 1991 there were six permanent faculty members in each of the Schools of Mathematics, Natural Sciences, and Historical Studies, three in Social Science, and one professor-at-large. In addition, each school chooses a number of promising young postdoctoral scholars and older, more established ones to serve as "members" or "visitors" for a period that may range from several months to many years. Just as the availability of academic positions is publicized in scholarly journals and at professional meetings, so is the availability of memberships at the institute.

Neugebauer fellows represent one type of member of the institute. The faculty of each school independently selects its own members after carefully scrutinizing applicants' documents and letters of recommendation. Whether an applicant's proposed plan of research will fit in with the interests of one or more of a school's permanent faculty is often a consideration. The primary criterion, however, is how well the applicant demonstrates that a period of residence at the institute will culminate in significant independent work. About 160 members are chosen each year from over 1,000 applications. Typically, more than a third of each year's members come from countries other than the United States.

In addition to faculty-chosen members, there are two director's visitors, selected by the director of the IAS. For 1990–91 physicist director Marvin Goldberger issued invitations to Chinese dissident astrophysicist Fang Lizhi and Soviet theoretical physicist Vladimir Gribov. Fang had been asked by Goldberger to spend six months at the institute even before he took refuge in the U.S. embassy in Beijing (Peking) in the aftermath of the Tiananmen (T'ien-an-men) Square massacre of June 1989.

Funding to support the members comes from different sources. About half of the members in any given year are paid from funds available to their IAS schools and additional funds of the institute. The rest may be supported by their home institutions, by grants from the United States or other governments, by private foundations, and by other donors.

How does a stay at the institute differ from a sabbatical or a stint of postdoctoral work at a university or research institute? For one thing, the number of members, visitors, and faculty in a given year—under 200— is more similar to the number of faculty members of a small college than to that of a university. Unlike a college, however, the IAS has no undergraduates. Also, whereas faculty members of different disciplines often work closely together at a small college, there is little overlap in disciplines at the IAS. Some of the mathematicians interact with physicists, to be sure, but it is the rare Natural Sciences member who will get to know a Historical Studies member well enough for the two to lunch together regularly.

The institute is also different from most universities in that it has no graduate students. Although the institute has the right to confer doctoral degrees, it has never done so. There are no courses, though there are numerous opportunities to attend lectures and seminars. In general, although members are expected to summarize their year's work for the director, each is responsible for designing and implementing his or her own course of work.

Whereas the IAS has intentionally limited itself to work in only a few fields, as opposed to major universities, it pursues more varied work than most research institutes. While scientific work at universities and research institutes is often done in laboratories, there are none to be found at the institute.

Although careful to preserve the distinctions that set it apart from universities and research institutions, the IAS in fact has the best of both worlds because of its close proximity to Princeton University, which is minutes away by foot or vehicle. The institute's libraries, for example, need not duplicate but only complement the holdings of the university's. The opportunities for involvement in each other's seminars, for IAS faculty eager for a stint in the classroom at Princeton, and for formal and informal collaboration between the two communities has helped, in Goldberger's words, "to make the whole greater than the sum of the parts." Princeton is one of the world's great educational centers not only because of the university's distinction but also because of the institute's contributions to science and scholarship.

A resort for the research-minded

Toward the end of J. Robert Oppenheimer's 19-year term as IAS director, he described the institute figuratively as "an intellectual hotel." He meant that a scientist at a small institution with little access to the work of colleagues, or at any institution where teaching and administrative tasks were draining too much energy from research, could be renewed by a period at the institute, surrounded by active scientists and with no responsibilities but to do science.

In fact, however, both the physical setting and the services available to faculty, members, and visitors do make it resemble a resort hotel or an inn where business people go off for working sessions. The institute was built on a former farm, and its extensive grounds—325 hectares (800 acres)—are beautiful. One can hike in the woods, play tennis or bocce on courts reserved for the institute community, and, for a small annual fee, make use of Princeton University's sports facilities. The institute's dining hall is a lovely building designed by architect Robert Geddes, and the reputation of its chef has spread far beyond the local community. Subsidized furnished apartments across the street from the academic facilities are available for housing institute members and visitors.

As for working facilities, each member or visitor has a private office. The scientists at the School of Natural Sciences tend to be centralized in small red brick buildings with unromantic titles—Building E (the astrophysicists) or Building D (the particle physicists)—although some have their offices in Fuld Hall, which is the main building and administrative center, or elsewhere.

Each school has its own computers, while the School of Natural Sciences also has both a computer manager and a senior computer scientist

476

in addition to several computer staff. Most scientists have complex computer workstations on their desks; the others have terminals linked to central computers. The school's computer common rooms in D and E buildings and other locations have additional workstations and terminals. Those scientists who need supercomputers outside the IAS for their work access them through computer networks.

Library facilities available to the scientists range from specialty journal libraries to the joint library of the Schools of Mathematics and Natural Sciences in Fuld Hall, with its more than 30,000 volumes and important journal collection, to the vast holdings of Princeton University's libraries. For historians of science the institute has not only microfilm copies of Einstein's papers but also the Rosenwald rare-book collection on the history of science.

There appears to be no question, then, that the select group of people working in the institute environment are well taken care of, physically and intellectually. How well have these enviable conditions yielded contributions to the world of science in the past? Are they continuing to do so in the present?

Aerial view of the Institute for Advanced Study (top left) shows the main cluster of buildings and part of its extensive grounds. Fuld Hall (also pictured above) dominates the architecture. To its left lie Buildings C and E, while Building D, the library building, and the low, flat-roofed dining hall and lecture hall can be seen above and behind Fuld Hall. Furnished apartments (bottom left) in a housing complex designed by architect Marcel Breuer are available for institute members and visitors and their families.

For the 1990–91 term, IAS director Marvin Goldberger (top) issued two invitations for director's visitors, one going to Chinese dissident astrophysicist Fang Lizhi (center). The Rosenwald rare-book collection on the history of science (above) forms part of the institute's library holdings.

Highlights of the institute's history

The Institute for Advanced Study is also called the Louis Bamberger and Mrs. Felix Fuld Foundation. In 1929 Bamberger's, a New Jersey department store, was the fourth largest retail store in the U.S. Just weeks before the stock market crash of that year, the store's owners, Louis Bamberger and his sister Caroline Bamberger Fuld, sold the business. Since their original intent was to use their time and energy to establish a medical school in Newark, they were put in touch with Abraham Flexner, an educational reformer and longtime critic of American medical education. It was Flexner who conceived of the need for a postdoctoral research and teaching institution in the U.S. Flexner also realized that Princeton—isolated from the big cities but still easily accessible—was a better location for such an institution than Newark. In addition, Princeton University already had a world-class mathematics department and a fine library.

As Bamberger, Fuld, and Flexner refined the plan for the institute, storm clouds were thickening over Europe. News of the emergence of an institution devoted to research and teaching at such a time was heartening to the 1,600 or so refugee scholars fleeing European fascism for a haven in the U.S. The best known of these was Einstein, who became the institute's first faculty member in 1933.

There is no doubt that Einstein, who served as professor at the IAS to 1946 and professor emeritus from 1946 until his death in 1955, made his most significant contributions to science well before arriving at the institute. He had published his special theory of relativity in 1905 and his general theory in 1916. Since 1919 the world had hailed him as one of the greatest geniuses of all time. In that year astronomers performed an experiment during a total solar eclipse that confirmed Einstein's prediction of the bending of light rays by the Sun's mass.

In the years that followed, Einstein was troubled by work that built on his theory that light traveled not in waves but in particles called quanta. Einstein never doubted that each quantum of light was a packet of energy, but subsequent additions to quantum theory by Niels Bohr, Werner Heisenberg, and other leading scientists did not sit well with him. The new theories suggested that the very act of observing particles changes them fundamentally, which Einstein could not accept. A few years after arriving at the institute, he published with two of his colleagues there a short paper aimed at disproving quantum theory as an absolute description of reality. Reactions in the scientific community ranged from sorrow over the loss of Einstein as a leader to anger over his defection from the avant-garde.

Eleven years before going to the institute, Einstein had published his first paper on a "unified field theory," in search of a goal that he viewed as his task for the rest of his life but that eludes scientists still. A unified field theory is an attempt to extend the general theory of relativity, which describes gravity, by finding a single mathematical framework that would relate the gravitational and electromagnetic forces. Until his dying day Einstein pursued a unified field theory with numerous assistants and collaborators.

478

Among those pictured at the 1939 ground-breaking ceremony at Fuld Hall are Albert Einstein (third from left), the institute's first faculty member; C. Lavinia Bamberger (second from left), sister of Caroline Bamberger Fuld; and Abraham Flexner (fourth from right), the founder of the IAS and its first director.

Goldberger in part blames the conditions that greeted Einstein at the IAS for the decline in his scientific output while there. In Goldberger's assessment, had Einstein gone to one of the other institutions that had made competing offers to him, "some place where he would not be treated like a god and someone would have spoken sharply to him about the things he was doing," Einstein might have been better off.

There is no doubt, however, that Einstein's presence there made Princeton a world center for physics. He exerted a gravitational pull himself, attracting scientists of promise to the institute. Though in his will Einstein forbade the institute from making a memorial to him, he cast his aura over the place for all time. Einstein's presence is still to be reckoned with at the IAS, for those who eat in its dining hall do so under the gaze of Einstein's bust by renowned sculptor Jacob Epstein.

A scientist with nearly the same name recognition as Einstein, who was also among the first faculty members of the institute, was John von Neumann. In contrast to Einstein's work at the institute, however, von Neumann's left an indelible mark on how science is done. Under his direction one of the world's first digital computers was built at the IAS.

In 1944 von Neumann visited the Philadelphia site where the U.S. Army was building ENIAC, the Electronic Numerical Integrator and Calculator. The more he learned about the project, the more problems he saw. What bothered him most was that reprogramming the computer involved resetting switches and replugging cables, one by one, by hand.

Von Neumann's solution was to build a stored-program computer, one that could be programmed by changing its instructions through electrical charges and impulses, rather than by reconfiguring switches and cables. The institute's Electronic Computer Project, funded partly by institute sources, partly by governmental agencies, and partly by RCA, began in 1946 in the basement of Fuld Hall. A year later the project moved into its own building across campus. It was operational by the summer of 1950.

Sculptor Jacob Epstein's bust of Einstein, which stands in the IAS dining hall, reminds staff and guests of the lasting aura of greatness that Einstein cast on the institute during his more than two decades there.

479

(Below) Courtesy, The Institute for Advanced Study, photo, Alan Richards; (below left) © 1990 Jay M. Pasachoff

John von Neumann poses with the stored-program digital computer that was built under his direction at the IAS in the late 1940s. The modern digital computers found in homes and offices worldwide bear the imprint of his ideas on design and programming.

Roads having the names Einstein Drive (above) and Von Neumann Drive service the housing complex reserved for IAS members and visitors.

Von Neumann's computer, now on display at the Smithsonian Institution, Washington, D.C., set the standard for today's commercial electronic digital computers found in homes and offices everywhere. Von Neumann served as professor at the institute from 1933 until his death in 1957. Members and visitors who live in institute housing have as their address either Einstein Drive or Von Neumann Drive.

Not many American scientists have had their professional lives dramatized on public television in several installments. One who had this distinction, albeit posthumously, was institute director J. Robert Oppenheimer, former director of the Los Alamos Science Laboratory. Under Oppenheimer's direction the U.S. developed the atomic bomb during World War II. Before going to Los Alamos, Oppenheimer was a distinguished theoretical physicist and university professor. Among his achievements are the calculations that demonstrate that black holes, the final stages of some extremely massive stars, are physically possible.

Oppenheimer was determined not to be an administrator only, and he was the first institute director who simultaneously served as a member of the faculty (there have been two others since). When he redecorated the director's office, replacing the prints of life at Oxford hung by his predecessor, literary scholar Frank Aydelotte, with blackboards—which were always covered with equations—it seemed that his time at the IAS might lead to further physical insights. Fate would not have it so, however. About one-third of the way through his tenure at the institute (1947–66), Oppenheimer lost his security clearance and underwent the indignities visited upon many during the McCarthy era. The trustees rallied the faculty in his support and issued a statement to retain him, but Oppenheimer was a beaten man.

Although many scientists feel that Oppenheimer never fulfilled his potential, he left his stamp on the institute in more ways than one. He made the IAS an important center of particle physics by inviting numer-

480

(Below) Courtesy, The Institute for Advanced Study; (below right) UPI/Bettmann

ous young promising scientists. Among them were T.D. Lee, as a member (1957–58) and professor (1960–62), and C.N. Yang, also as a member (1949–54) and professor (1955–65). Yang and Lee were awarded the Nobel Prize for Physics in 1957, while they were both at the institute, for earlier work that overthrew the so-called law of conservation of parity. Also while affiliated with the institute, Yang co-originated Yang-Mills field theories, now the basis for the successful theoretical description of particle physics known as the standard model. Overlapping with Lee and Yang at the institute were Freeman Dyson, some of whose work is described below, and eminent particle theorist (and later scientific biographer) Abraham Pais, who was a member (1946–50) and then professor (1950–63).

A world center of astrophysics

Despite his own work in astrophysics, Oppenheimer was less partial to astrophysicists than to particle physicists. A few years after his departure, however, in 1971, the institute brought a young astrophysicist, John Bahcall, into the faculty of its recently formed School of Natural Sciences.

The appointment of Bahcall has put the IAS on the map in astrophysics. For example, the weekly astronomy lunches at the institute, which Bahcall initiated shortly after his arrival, are regularly attended by some 50 astronomers and astrophysicists, from the IAS and nearby institutions. Today two of the six faculty in the School of Natural Sciences are astrophysicists, and about 20 postdoctoral scientists work full time in astrophysics and observational cosmology. (There are no telescopes at the institute, so observers travel elsewhere to make their observations, as is also true for other major institutions.)

Bahcall is a scientist of extraordinary energy, managing to be among the more political members of the astronomical community while designing and overseeing cutting-edge research in two separate fields of

Physicist J. Robert Oppenheimer (above) was the first IAS director to serve simultaneously as a faculty member. The more conventional wall decorations of the office that he inherited gave way to blackboards perpetually covered with equations. During his long directorship Oppenheimer brought to the institute such prominent scientists as T.D. Lee (top left) and C.N. Yang (top right), who shared the 1957 Nobel Prize for Physics.

481

The weekly astronomy lunches at the IAS, initiated by John Bahcall soon after he joined the faculty in 1971, is one sign of the institute's current prominence in the field of astrophysics. The gatherings are regularly attended by some 50 astronomers and astrophysicists from the IAS and such nearby institutions as Princeton University, Rutgers University, and AT&T Bell Laboratories.

astrophysics. He served as president of the American Astronomical Society in 1990–91 and was chosen by the National Academy of Sciences to head the 1990 decennial Astronomy and Astrophysics Survey Committee (AASC). Every 10 years, under the auspices of the academy, an AASC is set up to produce a book-length report summarizing the status of the profession and, more importantly, to list priorities for new projects over the next 10 years. The "Bahcall Report" should prove as important to the profession as its predecessors, the Field Report of 1980 (after George Field of the Harvard-Smithsonian Center for Astrophysics) and the Greenstein Report of 1970 (after Jesse Greenstein of the California Institute of Technology, IAS member during 1968–69).

For two decades Bahcall has been active as a lobbyist in Washington on behalf of various astronomical projects. He helped push through the Hubble Space Telescope (HST) and has continued to be politically active in demonstrating that, though crippled by a manufacturing error in the shape of its main mirror, the telescope can still yield high-quality science.

As principal investigator of the Quasar Absorption Line Survey project of the HST, Bahcall has assembled at the institute a distinguished team to work on the data the instrument will provide. By studying ultraviolet absorption lines in the spectra of quasars, the group hopes to learn about the properties of the intergalactic medium and the strength and origin of the ultraviolet background radiation. Although the HST's capability for focusing ultraviolet light is not as good as it should be, the instrument remains by far the best ultraviolet telescope aloft, allowing detailed studies of the strong ultraviolet lines from nearby quasars and interstellar clouds. Such work ultimately may yield information about the age of the universe, its rate of expansion, and its future.

Bahcall's main work over the last 25 years, however, has been as a theoretician attempting to resolve a continuing discrepancy between theory and observation called the solar neutrino problem. In 1989 his book *Neutrino Astrophysics* summarized the subject to date and laid the

482

groundwork for understanding new data. According to standard theories, various nuclear reactions produce neutrinos, particles that have no electric charge and, according to conventional wisdom, no rest mass. Billions of neutrinos from fusion reactions deep inside the Sun—solar neutrinos—hit the Earth every second, but all but a handful pass right through. Bahcall has been a major force spearheading experiments aimed at detecting solar neutrinos as a way of testing whether current theories about nuclear reactions and stellar interiors are accurate.

One long-running experiment involves the fact that very occasionally a neutrino will interact with the nucleus of an atom of chlorine, thereby changing the chlorine into a radioactive isotope of the gas argon that can be detected. This experiment, buried deep underground in the Homestake Gold Mine in Lead, South Dakota, consists of a large tank filled with the cleaning fluid perchloroethylene (C_2Cl_4). According to theory, the tank should register about one neutrino-chlorine interaction each day, but for more than 20 years the experiment has measured only about a third the expected number. Moreover, despite the shielding afforded by the tank's deep burial, some of this low number might still be the result of stray cosmic rays, rather than neutrinos, entering the tank.

A second-generation experiment championed by Bahcall went into operation in early 1990. It involves the use of the metallic element gallium, which is sensitive to neutrinos of lower energy than is chlorine. An interaction with a neutrino turns gallium atoms into germanium atoms, which are then detected. However, a preliminary report from the Soviet-American research team operating the gallium detector (four tanks filled with 30 tons of gallium set up underground) near the Soviet town of Baksan indicated that not a single solar neutrino had been seen. A second gallium detector also began operating in the Gran Sasso Tunnel in Italy as a joint German, French, Italian, and Israeli project.

Bahcall and Nobel laureate Hans Bethe of Cornell University, Ithaca, New York, published a paper that suggests a solution to the completely missing neutrinos of the gallium experiment. Neutrinos come in three known varieties: the electron neutrino, the muon neutrino, and the tau neutrino. Nuclear reactions in the Sun's interior emit electron neutrinos. In the mid-1980s Soviet scientists S.P. Mikheyev and A.Yu. Smirnov, elaborating on an idea by American scientist Lincoln Wolfenstein, had proposed that these neutrinos defy detection by changing into the other types before reaching the Earth. If so, the gallium experiment and the chlorine experiment are not yielding expected results because they were designed to detect only electron neutrinos. From the observed low level of neutrinos, Bahcall and Bethe determined what may be some of the otherwise unknown parameters of the theory.

The implications of the neutrino problem are far-reaching, touching on both astrophysics and basic particle physics. Does the problem lie in astrophysicists' conception of conditions in the Sun's core or in particle physicists' understanding of neutrinos? If Bahcall, Bethe, and the Soviet scientists are right, conventional theories of neutrinos are wrong: if a neutrino can change type, it must have at least a tiny mass. If this is

483

John Bahcall, Piet Hut, and Donald Schneider (left to right) hold an informal scientific discussion on the grounds of the IAS. Schneider, a long-term member in the School of Natural Sciences, has been involved with Bahcall's work on the Hubble Space Telescope. Hut's recent accomplishments include the development of software that allows computers to model astrophysical phenomena.

the case, so many neutrinos exist that together they might have enough mass to account for the unseen but gravitationally felt "dark matter" that scientists think constitutes about 90% of the universe.

Bahcall himself seems to do the work of many mortals, but recently he brought to the faculty of the School of Natural Sciences a second astrophysicist who does very different work. Piet Hut, professor at the school since 1985, had come into the public eye a year earlier as one of the proposers of Nemesis, the so-called Death Star. According to Hut and his collaborators, mass extinctions on Earth, which seem to occur every 26 million years or so, might be caused by the passage of an undetected companion star to the Sun. As this star traveled a 26 million-year orbit around the Sun, its gravity would attract some comets from their orbits, causing them to collide with the Earth. The resulting dust and smoke injected into the atmosphere would cause a period of darkness and cold on the Earth's surface that would culminate in the death of some species.

Although no Death Star has been detected in the intervening years, Hut has continued to pursue important work focusing on the interconnection between computer science and astrophysics, which von Neumann and his collaborators pioneered at the IAS more than three decades ago. Hut's work in the U.S. and elsewhere to develop sophisticated astrophysical software is enabling computers to simulate the evolution of dense star systems. From the institute Hut also uses supercomputers through remote links to make statistical calculations about the evolution of globular clusters—spherically symmetrical collections of stars sharing a common origin—and of galaxies.

Renewed preeminence in particle physics

Nearly all the historically great names in particle physics spent some time at the institute, including Niels Bohr, P.A.M. Dirac, Wolfgang Pauli, Max von Laue, and I.I. Rabi. Each of them was a Nobel Prize recipient, as were later particle physicists in residence at the IAS.

Freeman Dyson, senior faculty member of the School of Natural Sciences, was brought in by Oppenheimer as an outstanding particle physicist, one who in the 1940s helped unify quantum electrodynamics. His career, however, has not followed the straight and narrow. Although officially a mathematical physicist, Dyson defies such easy classification. A prolific contributor to astrophysics and theoretical mathematics, he nevertheless has not shied away from writing popular books. One, *Infinite in All Directions: An Exploration of Science and Belief* (1988), won the Phi Beta Kappa Award for science; a second, *Weapons and Hope* (1985), was serialized in *The New Yorker*. Dyson also has not been afraid to spend time on what others might dismiss as wild schemes, such as the idea that roadside pollution might be curbed by squads of turtles whose DNA had been reprogrammed to give them diamond-tipped teeth, enabling them to chew through all sorts of garbage. In the realm of scientific politics, he is not afraid to take controversial stands; for example, championing the need for governmental support of small, individual science projects rather than of "big science" projects at the expense of such smaller ones.

When asked about his current work, the ever modest Dyson first insists that, now that he is past 65, no one expects much of him anymore and that he mostly lectures on the work of others. When pressed, he admits to enjoying his collaboration with a colleague at the City College of New York on a "nice problem in number theory." As for past work of which he is most proud, he points to a paper entitled "The Three-Fold Way," a recasting of part of quantum mechanics in a new way, which he claims not more than three or four others have read and which therefore has not been very influential, but which he loves for its beauty. If forced to choose between truth and beauty, Dyson says he would always choose the latter.

Bearer of the distinguished title New Jersey Albert Einstein professor, Stephen Adler, some 16 years Dyson's junior, has been at the institute for nearly his entire career. Although perhaps a quarter of his work has been collaborative, Adler is, self-confessedly and by choice, more of an independent researcher. Readers of field theory textbooks are familiar with his work, done at the institute, on the development of the theory of "anomalies" (the breaking of symmetries by quantum mechanical effects), which has had a wide impact on modern theoretical physics. In recent years he has worked on aspects of quantum mechanics, mathematical and computational physics, and approaches to grand unified theories (GUTs), which attempt to unify three of nature's seemingly fundamental forces: the strong and weak forces inside the nucleus and the electromagnetic force.

In the late 1980s the institute made two new appointments that, in the eyes of the world physics community, made the particle physics group at the IAS the rival of its predecessor under Oppenheimer. Its successful wooing of Edward Witten, who joined the faculty in 1987, was the key to the current emphasis in the particle physics program. A picture of Witten at a computer would not be representative of how he works, since he is likely to do his best thinking while wandering around. Witten is one of the chief proponents of string theory, which, according to its adherents, may ultimately yield what has been popularly dubbed a "theory of everything" for its being able to account for all four forces of nature, including gravity in addition to the three forces that GUTs attempt to unify. Such a theory would show that these forces are but different manifestations of a single, more fundamental force. According to Witten, string theory potentially can explain everything from the very small—the atom's inner mechanisms—to the very large—the structure of the universe.

String theory challenges long-held conceptions of elementary particles. It professes that the universe has 10 dimensions, not four (three spatial dimensions—length, breadth, and depth—plus time), and that elementary particles are not points but tiny, vibrating, one-dimensional strings, as much smaller than the atom as an atom is smaller than the solar system. String advocates believe that when the universe began with the big bang, there were nine spatial dimensions. Only three dimensions participated in the universe's subsequent expansion, however, the other six remaining tightly curled up. Over the last several years, string theorists

Contributing to the institute's renewed leadership in the fields of particle physics and quantum theory are (top to bottom) Freeman Dyson, Stephen Adler, and Edward Witten, all permanent faculty members of the School of Natural Sciences.

485

have been trying to reduce the theory to a four-dimensional form so that experiments on Earth can confirm or overturn the theory.

It is hard to convey the excitement Witten feels about the potential of string theory. He fairly bubbles with enthusiasm in quoting a colleague who has dubbed it "the physics of the twenty-first century fallen by chance into our own century." In summarizing why scientists' present understanding is only the tip of the iceberg, Witten explains that, whereas the geometric ideas that Einstein built on were known in the 19th century, theorists do not yet have a full grasp on the basic ideas underlying string theory and thus can understand only a very few of its implications.

That string theory crosses the line between theoretical physics and math was confirmed when Witten was awarded a prestigious Fields Medal in 1990. Since there is no Nobel Prize for mathematics, the Fields Medal is universally considered the Nobel's equivalent in that field. But Witten emphasizes his belief that the work that led to his award will prove ultimately to be only a minuscule aspect of the full explanation of "everything" that string theory will provide. With Witten on the premises, the IAS currently has about 10 members working on string theory and field theory and another 10 working in particle physics and mathematical physics.

Witten has also collaborated with the most recent addition to the faculty of the School of Natural Sciences, Frank Wilczek, who became professor in 1989 at the age of 38. Many members of the scientific community find it fitting that Wilczek and his family are the current owners and occupants of Einstein's house, within walking distance of the institute. A wunderkind of contemporary physics, Wilczek was awarded not only a B.S. in mathematics from the University of Chicago before turning 20 but also a doctorate in physics from Princeton at age 22. In his late 20s he received a MacArthur Foundation Fellowship; he also was recently elected to the U.S. National Academy of Sciences at an unusually young age.

Working with his thesis adviser, David Gross, at Princeton, Wilczek discovered and applied the so-called principle of asymptotic freedom. According to the principle, the interactions between quarks—the constituents of protons and neutrons—become weak, in a calculable manner, at short distances or at high energy. Wilczek used the principle to elucidate the theory of quantum chromodynamics (QCD), thus establishing the theory of the strong force responsible for holding atomic nuclei together. Wilczek's work in this area helped accomplish what had been perhaps the main goal of particle physics since the 1930s. In recognition of their work, Gross and Wilczek in 1984 were awarded the American Physical Society's most distinguished prize for particle physics.

Wilczek has also been a pioneer in applying particle physics to cosmology. The asymptotic freedom property of particle interactions enables physicists to predict with some confidence the properties of matter at the extreme conditions of density and pressure that characterize the moments close to the big bang. Wilczek has clarified the mechanisms by which the perfectly symmetrical conditions in the early universe may

IAS faculty member Frank Wilczek stands on the porch of Einstein's old two-story frame house in Princeton, which the Wilczek family now owns and occupies.

have led to the present asymmetry between matter and antimatter. In other influential work he proposed the existence of a weakly interacting subatomic particle he called the axion. Many physicists believe that, if axions were produced in the big bang, they could provide an important and even dominant component of the mass of the universe.

In 1982 Wilczek introduced the concept of fractional quantum statistics. For decades scientists had thought that all particles fell into two classes, fermions and bosons. Wilczek pointed out a much broader range of possibilities for effectively two-dimensional systems and gave the name anyons to particles falling into this more general framework. Since then the existence of anyons in real material systems has become established. A theory pioneered by Wilczek, postulating that the existence of anyons is responsible for high-temperature superconductivity, has won wide support from other theorists and has garnered some experimental support as well.

Building for the future

More than 60 years have passed since the idea for the Institute for Advanced Study began to gel in Abraham Flexner's mind. What will the next decades bring?

The efforts of the outgoing director, Marvin Goldberger, will yield a change in the physical setup of the institute during the early 1990s. For many years the Electronic Computer Project building, where von Neumann's digital computer was built, was home to about a third of the institute's mathematicians. The situation was not optimal, since these members were isolated from the rest of their colleagues. A new 2,140-square meter (23,000-square foot) building, designed by architect Cesar Pelli, will become the headquarters of the entire School of Mathematics. An auditorium included in the new building will serve as the forum for the institute's film series, concerts, and lectures.

A model shows the new building, designed by Cesar Pelli, that will house the entire School of Mathematics after its completion in the 1990s. An included auditorium will be used for the institute's film series, concerts, and lectures.

Will the IAS open up new fields of research? In 1989–90 one of the director's visitors was Joel E. Cohen, theoretical biologist from Rockefeller University, New York City (and also a past recipient of a MacArthur Fellowship). If theoretical biology or another scholarly field is to take root at the institute, however, the faculty as a whole would have to back it. The institute would have to find additional financial resources to support it so that the viability of current fields would not be threatened. (During Goldberger's tenure, funding was found for a new subdivision of physicists in the School of Natural Sciences. Joseph Atick, a member with a long-term appointment, is heading a small group working in the area of theoretical biophysics and neural systems.)

Most significantly the institute will have a new director, mathematician Phillip A. Griffiths, who began his tenure in the summer of 1991. Each of the previous six directors to date (an educational reformer, a literary scholar and small-college president, two physicists, an economist, and a historian of science) has left a personal imprint on the IAS, but none has seriously challenged the assumptions on which the institute was founded. In accepting the position, Griffiths spoke of the IAS as "the quintessential institution for the creation of fundamental new knowledge." In private correspondence he indicated his belief that such creation "can be best accomplished in the absence of the short term pressures such as grant writing and teaching that are increasingly the situation in even our best universities." What Griffiths' personal contribution to the institute will be, however, only time will tell.

FOR ADDITIONAL READING

"Institute for Advanced Study: Past and Future," interview with Marvin L. Goldberger, *Physics Today* (June 1989, pp. 65–67).
Ed Regis, *Who Got Einstein's Office?: Eccentricity and Genius at the Institute for Advanced Study* (Addison-Wesley, 1987).

488

Index

This is a three-year cumulative index. Index entries for review articles in this and previous editions of the *Yearbook of Science and the Future* are set in boldface type, *e.g.,* **Archaeology.** Feature articles appear under the article title and are identified as such. Entries to other subjects are set in lightface type, *e.g.,* radiation. Additional information on any of these subjects is identified with a subheading and indented under the entry heading. Subheadings in quotes refer to feature articles on that topic. The numbers following headings and subheadings indicate the year (boldface) of the edition and the page number (lightface) on which the information appears. The abbreviation "*il.*" indicates an illustration.

Archaeology 92–279; **91**–281; **90**–288
  honors **90**–438
  "Lessons from the Master Builders" **91**–56
  palynology **90**–103, *ils.* 104, 105

All entry headings are alphabetized word by word. Hyphenated words and words separated by dashes or slashes are treated as two words. When one word differs from another only by the presence of additional characters at the end, the shorter precedes the longer. In inverted names, the words following the comma are considered only after the preceding part of the name has been alphabetized. Names beginning with "Mc" and "Mac" are alphabetized as "Mac"; "St." is alphabetized as "Saint." Examples:

  Lake
  Lake, Simon
  Lake Placid
  Lakeland

Acknowledgments

48   Courtesy, E.S. Cheng, NASA Goddard Space Flight Center

107   Adapted from *Killer Bees: The Africanized Honey Bee in the Americas,* by Mark L. Winston, Harvard University Press, Cambridge, Mass., planned publication date 1992. Used with permission

114   Adapted from "The Protein Folding Problem," by Frederick M. Richards. Copyright © December 1990 by Scientific American, Inc. All rights reserved

118   Adapted from "Catalytic Antibodies," by Richard A. Lerner and Alfonso Tramontano. Copyright © March 1988 by Scientific American, Inc. All rights reserved

119   Adapted from "RNA as an Enzyme," by Thomas R. Cech. Copyright © 1986 by Scientific American, Inc. All rights reserved

181   Originally appearing in *America's Neighborhood Bats,* by Merlin D. Tuttle, University of Texas Press, 1988

196   Brian Walton

204   (Top) Tom Maechtle

389   From "Atomic-Resolution Electrochemistry with the Atomic Force Microscope: Copper Deposition on Gold," S. Manne, P.K. Hansma, J. Massie, V.B. Elings, and A.A. Gewirth, *Science,* vol. 251, no 4990, cover, January 11, 1991, © 1990 AAAS

400   From "Atomic Emission from a Gold Scanning-Tunneling-Microscope Tip," H.J. Mamin, P.H. Guethner, and D. Rugar, *Physical Review Letters,* vol. 65, no. 19, pp. 2418–2421, © 1990 The American Physical Society